Elementary Numerical Analysis

International Series In Pure And Applied Mathematics

WILLIAM TED MARTIN AND E. H. SPANIER, *Consulting Editors*

Ahlfors   *Complex Analysis*
Buck   *Advanced Calculus*
Busacker and Saaty   *Finite Graphs and Networks*
Cheney   *Introduction to Approximation Theory*
Chester   *Techniques in Partial Differential Equations*
Coddington and Levinson   *Theory of Ordinary Differential Equations*
Cohn   *Conformal Mapping on Riemann Surfaces*
Conte and de Boor   *Elementary Numerical Analysis: An Algorithmic Approach*
Dennemeyer   *Introduction to Partial Differential Equations and Boundary Value Problems*
Dettman   *Mathematical Methods in Physics and Engineering*
Epstein   *Partial Differential Equations*
Golomb and Shanks   *Elements of Ordinary Differential Equations*
Graves   *The Theory of Functions of Real Variables*
Greenspan   *Introduction to Partial Differential Equations*
Griffin   *Elementary Theory of Numbers*
Hamming   *Numerical Methods for Scientists and Engineers*
Hildebrand   *Introduction to Numerical Analysis*
Householder   *The Numerical Treatment of a Single Nonlinear Equation*
Kalman, Falb, and Arbib   *Topics in Mathematical Systems Theory*
Lass   *Vector and Tensor Analysis*
LePage   *Complex Variables and the Laplace Transform for Engineers*
McCarty   *Topology: An Introduction with Applications to Topological Groups*
Monk   *Introduction to Set Theory*
Moore   *Elements of Linear Algebra and Matrix Theory*
Mostow and Sampson   *Linear Algebra*
Moursund and Duris   *Elementary Theory and Application of Numerical Analysis*
Nef   *Linear Algebra*
Pipes and Harvill   *Applied Mathematics for Engineers and Physicists*
Ralston   *A First Course in Numerical Analysis*
Ritger and Rose   *Differential Equations with Applications*
Ritt   *Fourier Series*
Rosser   *Logic for Mathematicians*
Rudin   *Principles of Mathematical Analysis*
Saaty and Bram   *Nonlinear Mathematics*
Sagan   *Introduction to the Calculus of Variations*
Simmons   *Differential Equations with Applications and Historical Notes*
Simmons   *Introduction to Topology and Modern Analysis*
Sneddon   *Elements of Partial Equations*
Sneddon   *Fourier Transforms*
Struble   *Nonlinear Differential Equations*
Weinstock   *Calculus of Variations*
Weiss   *Algebraic Number Theory*
Zemanian   *Distribution Theory and Transform Analysis*

Elementary Numerical Analysis

an algorithmic approach

S. D. Conte
Purdue University

Carl de Boor
Purdue University

SECOND EDITION

McGraw-Hill Book Company

New York St. Louis San Francisco Düsseldorf Johannesburg Kuala Lumpur London Mexico Montreal New Delhi Panama Rio de Janeiro Singapore Sydney Toronto

Elementary Numerical Analysis

an algorithmic approach

Library of Congress Catalog Card Number 73–174612

07–012446–4

4567890DODO79876543

*This book was set in Times Roman, and printed and
bound by R. R. Donnelley & Sons Company.　The drawings
were done by Danmark & Michaels, Inc.　The editors
were Lee W. Peterson and Michael Gardner.
Peter Guilmette supervised production.*

Contents

Preface   vii

Introduction   ix

1. Number Systems and Errors   **1**

   1.1 The Representation of Integers   1

   1.2 The Representation of Fractions   4

   1.3 Floating-point Arithmetic   7

   1.4 Error Propagation; Significance Errors and Instability   10

   1.5 Computational Methods for Error Estimation   15

   1.6 Some Comments on Convergence of Sequences   17

   1.7 Some Mathematical Preliminaries   21

2. The Solution of Nonlinear Equations   **27**

   2.1 A Survey of Iterative Methods   28

   2.2 FORTRAN Programs for Some Iterative Methods   35

   2.3 Fixed-point Iteration   44

   2.4 Convergence Acceleration for Fixed-point Iteration   50

   2.5 Quadratic Convergence and Newton's Method   57

   2.6 Polynomial Equations: Real Roots   66

   2.7 Complex Roots and Muller's Method   74

   2.8 Simultaneous Nonlinear Equations   84

3. Matrices and Systems of Linear Equations   **91**

   3.1 Properties of Matrices   91

   3.2 The Solution of Linear Systems by Elimination   110

   3.3 The Pivoting Strategy   123

   3.4 The Triangular Factorization and Calculation of the Inverse   127

   *3.5 Compact Schemes   137

   3.6 Error and Residual of an Approximate Solution; Norms   142

   3.7 The Condition Number and Iterative Improvement   150

   3.8 Iterative Methods   157

   3.9 Eigenvalues and the Convergence of Fixed-point Iteration   170

   3.10 Determinants   180

   3.11 The Eigenvalue Problem   184

4. Interpolation and Approximation   **191**

   4.1 The Interpolating Polynomial: Lagrange Form   191

   4.2 The Interpolating Polynomial: Newton Form   195

   4.3 The Divided-difference Table   201

   4.4 The Error of the Interpolating Polynomial   210

   4.5 Interpolation in a Function Table Based on Equally Spaced Points   213

   4.6 The Divided Difference as a Function of Its Arguments and Osculatory Interpolation   221

   4.7 The Case for Piecewise-polynomial Interpolation   230

  **4.8* Piecewise-cubic Interpolation   233

   4.9 Data Fitting   241

  **4.10* Orthogonal Polynomials   246

  **4.11* Least-squares Approximation by Polynomials   255

  **4.12* Chebyshev Economization   265

5. Differentiation and Integration   **274**

   5.1 Numerical Differentiation   275

   5.2 Numerical Integration: Some Basic Rules   284

   5.3 Numerical Integration: Composite Rules   290

   5.4 Numerical Integration: Gaussian Rules   299

   5.5 Extrapolation to the Limit; Romberg Integration   307

6. The Solution of Differential Equations   **319**

   6.1 Mathematical Preliminaries   320

   6.2 Simple Difference Equations   322

   6.3 Numerical Integration by Taylor Series   327

   6.4 Error Estimates and Convergence of Euler's Method   332

   6.5 Runge-Kutta Methods   336

   6.6 Multistep Formulas   340

   6.7 Predictor-Corrector Methods   346

   6.8 The Adams-Moulton Method   350

   6.9 Stability of Numerical Methods   357

   6.10 Round-off-error Propagation   361

   6.11 Systems of Differential Equations   365

7. Boundary-value Problems in Ordinary Differential Equations   **373**

   7.1 Finite-difference Methods: Second-order Equations   374

   7.2 Finite-difference Methods: Fourth-order Equations   379

   7.3 Shooting Methods   382

   References   388

   Index   391

Preface

This is the second edition of a book on elementary numerical analysis which is geared specifically to the needs and background of students in engineering and science at the undergraduate level. The book is based on an undergraduate course taught at Purdue University since 1963. On the whole, the student who has had the basic college calculus sequence should have no difficulty following the material. Familiarity with matrices will facilitate understanding of the chapter on systems of linear equations, and some knowledge of differential equations will be of assistance in the last two chapters. It should be possible to cover most of the material in the first six chapters in a three-hour one-semester course. The sections marked with asterisks, which usually consider more advanced material, can be omitted with no loss in continuity.

This new edition contains some major changes. Most of Chapter 2 and all of Chapters 3, 4, and 5 have been rewritten. The chapter on linear systems of equations, now Chapter 3, has been enlarged considerably to include a more detailed derivation and algorithmic description of elimination, the use of vector and matrix norms in the computation of errors and condition, and the power method for the discussion of eigenvalues. The chapter on interpolation and approximation now uses divided differences as the main tool in the discussion of polynomial interpolation, and also considers osculatory interpolation, splines, and other piecewise-polynomial functions, orthogonal polynomials, and polynomial least-squares approximations. The chapter on numerical integration and differentiation has been somewhat shortened; more play has been given to Gauss quadrature, and a more cautious attitude toward extrapolation to the limit has been adopted.

It is assumed that a computer is available to the student and that a large number of the algorithms presented will be programmed for the solution of problems. To help in this effort, FORTRAN IV programs for most of the algorithms have been provided. These programs usually appear in examples, together with actual machine results obtained on an IBM 7094, a CDC 6500, or an IBM 360. However, no attempt is made to teach programming. It is assumed that the student already knows how to write programs in a higher-level algorithmic language such as FORTRAN or that he is simultaneously learning such a language.

It is a pleasure to acknowledge our debt to Dr. R. W. Hamming, Professor R. E. Lynch, and Professor W. C. Rheinboldt for constructive criticism of the manuscript.

S. D. Conte
Carl de Boor

Introduction

This book is concerned with the practical solution of problems on computers. In the process of problem solving, it is possible to distinguish several more or less distinct phases. The first phase is *formulation*. In formulating a mathematical model of a physical situation, the scientist should take into account beforehand the fact that he expects to solve his problem on a computer. He will therefore provide for specific objectives, proper input data, adequate checks, and for the type and amount of output.

Once a problem has been formulated, numerical methods, together with a preliminary error analysis, must be devised for solving the problem. A numerical method which can be used to solve a problem will be called an *algorithm*. An algorithm is a complete and unambiguous set of procedures leading to the solution of a mathematical problem. The selection or construction of appropriate algorithms properly falls within the scope of *numerical analysis*. Having decided on a specific algorithm or set of algorithms for solving the problem, the numerical analyst should consider all the sources of error that may affect the results. He must consider how much accuracy is required, estimate the magnitude of the round-off and discretization errors, determine an appropriate step size or the number of iterations required, provide for adequate checks on the accuracy, and make allowance for corrective action in cases of nonconvergence.

The third phase of problem solving is *programming*. The programmer must transform the suggested algorithm into a set of unambiguous step-by-step instructions to the computer. The first step in this procedure is called *flow charting*. A flow chart is simply a set of procedures, usually in logical block form, which the computer will follow. It may be given in graphical or procedural statement form. The complexity of the flow will depend upon the complexity of the problem and the amount of detail included. However, it should be possible for someone other than the programmer to follow the flow of information from the chart. The flow chart is an effective aid to the programmer, who must translate its major functions into machine code, and, at the same time, it is an effective means of communication to others who wish to understand what the program does. In this book we sometimes use flow charts in graphical form, but more often in procedural statement form.

When graphical flow charts are used, standard conventions are followed, whereas all procedural statement charts use a self-explanatory ALGOL-like statement language. Having produced a flow chart, the programmer must transform the indicated procedures into a set of machine instructions. This may be done directly in machine language, in an assembly language, or in a procedure-oriented language. In this book the FORTRAN IV language is used exclusively, primarily because FORTRAN translators are readily available on almost all computers.

A procedure-oriented language such as FORTRAN or ALGOL is sometimes called an *algorithmic* language. It allows us to express a mathematical algorithm in a form more suitable for communication with computers. A FORTRAN procedure that implements a mathematical algorithm will, in general, be much more precise than the mathematical algorithm. If, for example, the mathematical algorithm specifies an iterative procedure for finding the solution of an equation, the FORTRAN program must specify (1) the accuracy that is required, (2) the number of iterations to be performed, and (3) what to do in case of nonconvergence. Most of the algorithms in this book are given in the normal mathematical form and in the more precise form of a FORTRAN procedure.

In many installations, each of these phases of problem solving is performed by a separate person. In others, a single person may be responsible for all three functions. It is clear that there are many interactions among these three phases. As the program develops, more information becomes available, and this information may suggest changes in the formulation, in the algorithms being used, and in the program itself.

Elementary Numerical Analysis

1
Number Systems and Errors

In this chapter we consider methods for representing numbers on computers and the errors introduced by these representations. In addition, we shall examine the sources of various types of computational errors and their subsequent propagation.

1.1 THE REPRESENTATION OF INTEGERS

In everyday life we use numbers based on the decimal system. Thus the number 257, for example, is expressible as

$$257 = 2 \cdot 100 + 5 \cdot 10 + 7 \cdot 1$$
$$= 2 \cdot 10^2 + 5 \cdot 10^1 + 7 \cdot 10^0$$

We call 10 the *base* of this system. Any decimal integer is expressible as a polynomial in the base 10 with integral coefficients between 0 and 9. We use the notation

$$N = (a_n a_{n-1} \cdots a_0)_{10}$$
$$= a_n 10^n + a_{n-1} 10^{n-1} + \cdots + a_0 10^0 \tag{1.1}$$

to denote any positive integer in the base 10. There is no intrinsic reason to use 10 as a base. Other civilizations have used other bases such as 12, 20, or 60. Modern computers read pulses sent by electrical components. The state of an electrical impulse is either *on* or *off*. It is therefore convenient to represent numbers in computers in the *binary* system. Here the base is 2, and the integer coefficients may take the values 0 or 1.

A nonnegative integer N will be represented in the binary system as

$$N = (a_n a_{n-1} \cdots a_1 a_0)_2$$
$$= a_n 2^n + a_{n-1} 2^{n-1} + \cdots + a_1 2^1 + a_0 2^0 \tag{1.2}$$

where the coefficients a_k are either 0 or 1. Note that N is again represented as a polynomial, but now in the base 2. All computers used in scientific work operate internally in the binary system. Users of computers, however, prefer to work in the more familiar decimal system. It is therefore necessary to have some means of converting from decimal to binary when information is submitted to the computer, and from binary to decimal for output purposes.

Conversion of a binary number to decimal form may be accomplished directly from the definition (1.2). As examples we have

$$(11)_2 = 1 \cdot 2^1 + 1 \cdot 2^0 = 3$$
$$(1101)_2 = 1 \cdot 2^3 + 1 \cdot 2^2 + 0 \cdot 2^1 + 1 \cdot 2^0 = 13$$

The conversion of integers from a base β to the base 10 can also be accomplished by the following algorithm, which is derived in Chap. 2.

Algorithm I.I Given the coefficients $a_n, \ldots, a_0$ of the polynomial

$$p(x) = a_n x^n + a_{n-1} x^{n-1} + \cdots + a_1 x + a_0 \tag{1.3}$$

and a number β. Compute recursively the numbers $b_n, b_{n-1}, \ldots, b_0$:

$$b_n = a_n$$
$$b_{n-1} = a_{n-1} + b_n \beta$$
$$b_{n-2} = a_{n-2} + b_{n-1} \beta$$
$$b_{n-3} = a_{n-3} + b_{n-2} \beta$$
$$\cdots \cdots \cdots \cdots \cdots$$
$$b_0 = a_0 + b_1 \beta$$

Then $b_0 = p(\beta)$.

Since, by the definition (1.2), the binary integer $(a_n a_{n-1} \cdots a_0)_2$ represents the value of the polynomial (1.3) at $x = 2$, we can use Algorithm 1.1, with $\beta = 2$, to find the decimal equivalents of binary integers.

Thus the decimal equivalent of $(1101)_2$ computed using Algorithm 1.1 is

$$b_3 = 1$$
$$b_2 = 1 + 1 \cdot 2 = 3$$
$$b_1 = 0 + 3 \cdot 2 = 6$$
$$b_0 = 1 + 6 \cdot 2 = 13$$

and the decimal equivalent of $(10000)_2$ is

$$b_4 = 1$$
$$b_3 = 0 + 1 \cdot 2 = 2$$
$$b_2 = 0 + 2 \cdot 2 = 4$$
$$b_1 = 0 + 4 \cdot 2 = 8$$
$$b_0 = 0 + 8 \cdot 2 = 16$$

Converting a decimal integer N into its binary equivalent can also be accomplished by Algorithm 1.1 if one is willing to use *binary* arithmetic. For if $N = (a_n a_{n-1} \cdots a_0)_{10}$, then by the definition (1.1), $N = p(10)$, where $p(x)$ is the polynomial (1.3). Hence we can calculate the binary representation for N by translating the coefficients $a_n, \ldots, a_0$ into binary integers and then using Algorithm 1.1 to evaluate $p(x)$ at $x = 10 = (1010)_2$ in binary arithmetic. If, for example, $N = 187$, then

$$187 = (187)_{10} = 1 \cdot 10^2 + 8 \cdot 10^1 + 7 \cdot 10^0$$
$$= (1)_2 (1010)_2{}^2 + (1000)_2 (1010)_2{}^1 + (111)_2 (1010)_2{}^0$$

and using Algorithm 1.1 and binary arithmetic,

$$b_2 = (1)_2$$
$$b_1 = (1000)_2 + (1)_2 (1010)_2 = (1000)_2 + (1010)_2 = (10010)_2$$
$$b_0 = (111)_2 + (10010)_2 (1010)_2 = (111)_2 + (10110100)_2 = (10111011)_2$$

Therefore $187 = (10111011)_2$.

Binary numbers and binary arithmetic, though ideally suited for today's computers, are somewhat tiresome for people because of the number of digits necessary to represent even moderately sized numbers. Thus eight binary digits are necessary to represent the three-decimal-digit number 187. The *octal* number system, using the base 8, presents a kind of compromise between the computer-preferred binary and the people-preferred decimal system. It is easy to convert from octal to binary and back since three binary digits make one octal digit. To convert from octal to binary, one merely replaces all octal digits by their binary equivalent; thus

$$(347)_8 = (011 \quad 100 \quad 111)_2 = (11100111)_2$$

Conversely, to convert from binary to octal, one partitions the binary digits in groups of three (starting from the right) and then replaces each three-group by its octal digit; thus

$$(10111011)_2 = (010 \quad 111 \quad 011)_2 = (273)_8$$

If a decimal integer has to be converted to binary by hand, it is usually fastest to convert it first to octal using Algorithm 1.1, and then from octal to binary. To take an earlier example,

$$187 = (187)_{10} = (1)_8(12)_8{}^2 + (10)_8(12)_8{}^1 + (7)_8(12)_8{}^0$$

Hence, using Algorithm 1.1 [with 2 replaced by $10 = (12)_8$, and with *octal* arithmetic],

$$b_2 = (1)_8$$
$$b_1 = (10)_8 + (1)_8(12)_8 = (22)_8$$
$$b_0 = (7)_8 + (22)_8(12)_8 = (7)_8 + (264)_8 = (273)_8$$

Therefore, finally,

$$187 = (273)_8 = (010111011)_2$$

EXERCISES

1.1-1. Convert the following binary numbers to decimal form:

$$(1010)_2 \qquad (100101)_2 \qquad (10000001)_2$$

1.1-2. Convert the following decimal numbers to binary form:

82, 109, 3433

1.1-3. Carry out the conversions in Exercises 1.1-1 and 1.1-2 by converting first to octal form.

1.1-4. Write a FORTRAN subroutine which accepts a number to the base BETIN with the NIN digits contained in the one-dimensional array NUMIN, and returns the NOUT digits of the equivalent in base BETOUT in the one-dimensional array NUMOUT. For simplicity, restrict both BETIN and BETOUT to 2, 4, 8, and 10.

1.2   THE REPRESENTATION OF FRACTIONS

If x is a positive real number, then its *integral* part x_I is the largest integer less than or equal to x, while

$$x_F = x - x_I$$

is its *fractional* part. The fractional part can always be written as a *decimal fraction*:

$$x_F = \sum_{k=1}^{\infty} b_k 10^{-k} \tag{1.4}$$

where each b_k is a nonnegative integer less than 10. If $b_k = 0$ for all k greater than a certain integer, then the fraction is said to *terminate*. Thus

$$\tfrac{1}{4} = 0.25 = 2 \cdot 10^{-1} + 5 \cdot 10^{-2}$$

is a terminating decimal fraction, while

$$\tfrac{1}{3} = 0.333 \cdots = 3 \cdot 10^{-1} + 3 \cdot 10^{-2} + 3 \cdot 10^{-3} + \cdots$$

is not.

If the integral part of x is given as a decimal integer by

$$x_I = (a_n a_{n-1} \cdots a_0)_{10}$$

while the fractional part is given by (1.4), it is customary to write the two representations one after the other, separated by a point, the "decimal point."

$$x = (a_n a_{n-1} \cdots a_0.b_1 b_2 b_3 \cdots)_{10}$$

Completely analogously, one can write the fractional part of x as a *binary* fraction:

$$x_F = \sum_{k=1}^{\infty} b_k 2^{-k}$$

where each b_k is a nonnegative integer less than 2, i.e., either zero or one. If the integral part of x is given by the binary integer

$$x_I = (a_n a_{n-1} \cdots a_0)_2$$

then we write

$$x = (a_n a_{n-1} \cdots a_0.b_1 b_2 b_3 \cdots)_2$$

using a "binary point."

The binary fraction $(.b_1 b_2 b_3 \cdots)_2$ for a given number x_F between zero and one can be calculated as follows: If

$$x_F = \sum_{k=1}^{\infty} b_k 2^{-k}$$

then

$$2x_F = \sum_{k=1}^{\infty} b_k 2^{-k+1} = b_1 + \sum_{k=1}^{\infty} b_{k+1} 2^{-k}$$

Hence b_1 is the integral part of $2x_F$, while

$$(2x_F)_F = 2x_F - b_1 = \sum_{k=1}^{\infty} b_{k+1} 2^{-k}$$

Therefore, repeating this procedure, we find that b_2 is the integral part of $2(2x_F)_F$, b_3 is the integral part of $2(2(2x_F)_F)_F$, etc.

If, for example, $x = 0.625 = x_F$, then

$$2(0.625) = 1.25 \qquad \text{so } b_1 = 1$$
$$2(0.25) = 0.5 \qquad \text{so } b_2 = 0$$
$$2(0.5) = 1.0 \qquad \text{so } b_3 = 1$$

and all further b_k's are zero.   Hence

$$0.625 = (.101)_2$$

This example was rigged to give a terminating binary fraction.   Unhappily, not every terminating decimal fraction gives rise to a terminating binary fraction.   This is due to the fact that the binary fraction for $x_F = 10^{-1} = 0.1$ is not terminating.   We have

$$2(0.1) = 0.2 \qquad \text{so } b_1 = 0$$
$$2(0.2) = 0.4 \qquad \text{so } b_2 = 0$$
$$2(0.4) = 0.8 \qquad \text{so } b_3 = 0$$
$$2(0.8) = 1.6 \qquad \text{so } b_4 = 1$$
$$2(0.6) = 1.2 \qquad \text{so } b_5 = 1$$

and now we are back to a fractional part of 0.2, so that the digits cycle. It follows that

$$0.1 = (.0 \quad 0011 \quad 0011 \cdot \cdot \cdot)_2$$

The procedure just outlined is formalized in the following algorithm.

Algorithm I.2   Given x between 0 and 1 and an integer β greater than 1. Generate recursively $b_1, b_2, b_3, \ldots$ by

$$c_0 = x$$
$$b_1 = (\beta c_0)_I, \qquad c_1 = (\beta c_0)_F$$
$$b_2 = (\beta c_1)_I, \qquad c_2 = (\beta c_1)_F$$
$$\cdot \cdot \cdot \cdot \cdot \cdot \cdot \cdot \cdot \cdot \cdot \cdot \cdot \cdot \cdot \cdot$$

Then

$$x = (.b_1 b_2 b_3 \cdot \cdot \cdot) = \sum_{k=1}^{\infty} b_k \beta^{-k}$$

We have stated this algorithm for a general base β rather than for the specific binary base $\beta = 2$, for two reasons.   If this conversion to binary is carried out with pencil and paper, it is usually faster to convert first to octal, i.e., use $\beta = 8$, and then to convert from octal to binary.   Also, the algorithm can be used to convert a binary (or octal) fraction to decimal, by choosing $\beta = 10$ and using binary (or octal) arithmetic.

To give an example, if $x = (.101)_2$, then, with $\beta = 10 = (1010)_2$ and binary arithmetic, we get from Algorithm 1.2

$$10(.101)_2 = (110.010)_2 \quad \text{so } b_1 = (110)_2 = 6, \quad c_1 = (.01)_2$$
$$10(.01)_2 = (10.10)_2 \quad \text{so } b_2 = (10)_2 = 2, \quad c_2 = (.1)_2$$
$$10(.1)_2 = (101.)_2 \quad \text{so } b_3 = (101)_2 = 5, \quad c_3 = 0$$

Hence subsequent b_k's are zero.   This shows that

$$(.101)_2 = 0.625$$

confirming our earlier calculation.   Note that if x_F is a terminating binary fraction with n digits, then it is also a terminating decimal fraction with n digits, since

$$(.1)_2 = 0.5$$

EXERCISES

1.2-1. Convert the following binary fractions to decimal fractions:

$(.1100011)_2 \quad (.11111111)_2$

1.2-2. Find the first 5 digits of .1 written as an octal fraction, then compute from it the first 15 digits of .1 as a binary fraction.

1.2-3. Convert the following octal fractions to decimal:

$(.614)_8 \quad (.776)_8$

Compare with your answer in Exercise 1.2-1.

1.2-4. Find a binary number which approximates π to within 10^{-3}.

1.2-5. If we want to convert a decimal integer N to binary using Algorithm 1.1, we have to use *binary* arithmetic.   Show how to carry out this conversion using Algorithm 1.2 and *decimal* arithmetic.   (*Hint*: Divide N by the appropriate power of 2, convert the result to binary, then shift the "binary point" appropriately.)

1.2-6. If we want to convert a terminating binary fraction x to a decimal fraction using Algorithm 1.2, we have to use *binary* arithmetic.   Show how to carry out this conversion using Algorithm 1.1 and *decimal* arithmetic.

1.3 FLOATING-POINT ARITHMETIC

Scientific calculations are usually carried out in floating-point arithmetic.

An n-digit floating-point number in base β has the form

$$x = \pm(.d_1 d_2 \cdots d_n)_\beta \beta^e \tag{1.5}$$

where $(.d_1 d_2 \cdots d_n)_\beta$ is a β-fraction called the *mantissa*, and e is an integer called the *exponent*.   Such a floating-point number is said to be *normalized* in case $d_1 \neq 0$, or else $d_1 = d_2 = \cdots = d_n = 0$.

For most computers, $\beta = 2$, although on some, $\beta = 16$, and in hand calculations and on most desk calculators, $\beta = 10$.

The precision or length n of floating-point numbers on any particular computer is usually determined by the word length of the computer and may therefore vary widely (see Fig. 1.1). Computing systems which accept FORTRAN programs are expected to provide floating-point numbers of two different lengths, one roughly double the other. The shorter one, called *single precision*, is ordinarily used unless the other, called *double precision*, is specifically asked for. Calculation in double precision usually doubles the storage requirements and more than doubles running time as compared with single precision.

The exponent e is limited to a range

$$m < e < M \tag{1.6}$$

for certain integers m and M. Usually, $m = -M$, but the limits may vary widely; see Fig. 1.1.

There are two commonly used ways of translating a given real number x into an n β-digit floating-point number $fl(x)$, rounding and chopping. In *rounding*, $fl(x)$ is chosen as the normalized floating-point number nearest x; some special rule, such as symmetric rounding, is used in case of a tie. In *chopping*, $fl(x)$ is chosen as the nearest normalized floating-point number *between* x and 0. If, for example, two-decimal-digit floating-point numbers are used, then

$$fl(\tfrac{2}{3}) = \begin{cases} (0.67)10^0 & \text{rounded} \\ (0.66)10^0 & \text{chopped} \end{cases}$$

and

$$fl(-838) = \begin{cases} -(0.84)10^3 & \text{rounded} \\ -(0.83)10^3 & \text{chopped} \end{cases}$$

On some computers, this definition of $fl(x)$ is modified in case $|x| \geq \beta^M$ (*overflow*) or $0 < |x| \leq \beta^{M-n}$ (*underflow*), where m and M are the bounds on the exponents; either $fl(x)$ is not defined in this case, causing a stop, or else $fl(x)$ is represented by a special number which is not subject to the usual rules of arithmetic when combined with ordinary floating-point numbers.

Computer	β	n	$M = -m$
IBM 7094	2	27	2^7
Burroughs 5000 Series	8	13	2^6
IBM 360	16	6	2^6
CDC 6000 Series	2	48	2^{10}

Fig. 1.1 Floating-point characteristics.

The difference between x and $fl(x)$ is called the *round-off error*. The round-off error depends on the size of x and is therefore best measured relative to x. For if we write

$$fl(x) = x(1 + \delta) \tag{1.7}$$

where $\delta = \delta(x)$ is some number depending on x, then it is possible to *bound δ independently* of x, at least as long as x causes no overflow or underflow. For such an x, it is not difficult to show that

$$|\delta| < \tfrac{1}{2}\beta^{1-n} \qquad \text{in rounding} \tag{1.8}$$

while

$$-\beta^{1-n} < \delta \leq 0 \qquad \text{in chopping} \tag{1.9}$$

See Exercise 1.3-3.

When an arithmetic operation is applied to two floating-point numbers, the result usually fails to be a floating-point number of the same length. If, for example, we deal with two-decimal-digit numbers and

$$x = (0.20)10^1 = 2 \qquad y = (0.77)10^{-6} \qquad z = (0.30)10^1 = 3$$

then

$$x + y = (0.200000077)10^1 \qquad x \cdot y = (0.154)10^{-5}$$

$$\frac{x}{z} = (0.666 \cdot \cdot \cdot)10^0$$

Hence, if ω denotes one of the arithmetic operations (addition, subtraction, multiplication, or division) and ω^* denotes the floating-point operation of the same name provided by the computer, then, however the computer may arrive at the result $x\omega^*y$ for two given floating-point numbers x and y, we can be sure that usually

$$x\omega^*y \neq x\omega y$$

Although the floating-point operation ω^* corresponding to ω may vary in some details from machine to machine, ω^* is usually constructed so that

$$x\omega^*y = fl(x\omega y) \tag{1.10}$$

In words, the floating-point sum (difference, product, or quotient) of two floating-point numbers usually equals the floating-point number which represents the exact sum (difference, product, or quotient) of the two numbers. Hence (unless overflow or underflow occurs) we have

$$x\omega^*y = (x\omega y)(1 + \delta) \tag{1.11}$$

where δ is bounded as in (1.8) or (1.9).

EXERCISES

1.3-1. The following numbers are given in a decimal computer with a four-digit normalized mantissa:

(a) $0.4523 \cdot 10^4$ (b) $0.2115 \cdot 10^{-3}$ (c) $0.2583 \cdot 10^1$

Perform the following operations, and indicate the error in the result, assuming symmetric rounding:

a. $(a) + (b) + (c)$ d. $(a) - (b) - (c)$
b. $(a)/(c)$ e. $(a)(b)/(c)$
c. $(a) - (b)$ f. $(b)/(c) \cdot (a)$

1.3-2. Let $fl(x)$ be given by chopping. Show that $fl(-x) = -fl(x)$, and that $fl(\beta^r x) = \beta^r fl(x)$ (unless overflow or underflow occurs).

1.3-3. Let $fl(x)$ be given by chopping and let $\delta = \delta(x)$ be such that $fl(x) = x(1 + \delta)$. (If $x = 0$, pick $\delta = 0$.) Show that then δ is bounded as in (1.9).

1.3-4. Give examples to show that most of the laws of arithmetic fail to hold for floating-point arithmetic.

1.3-5. Define the FORTRAN FUNCTION R(X,N) [or C(X,N)] so that R [or C] returns the value of X rounded [or chopped] to N places after the decimal point.

1.3-6. Write a FORTRAN FUNCTION FL(X) which returns the value of the n-decimal-digit floating-point number derived from X by rounding. Take n to be 4 and check your calculations in Exercise 1.3-1. [Use ALOG10(ABS(X)) to determine e such that $10^{e-1} \le |x| < 10^e$.]

1.4 ERROR PROPAGATION; SIGNIFICANCE ERRORS AND INSTABILITY

Every floating-point operation in a computational process may give rise to an error which, once generated, may then be amplified or reduced in subsequent operations.

One of the most common (and often avoidable) ways of increasing the importance of an error is commonly called *loss of significant digits*. If x^* is an approximation to x, then we say that x^* approximates x to r significant figures or β-digits provided

$$\frac{|x - x^*|}{|x|} \le \tfrac{1}{2}\beta^{1-r} \tag{1.12}$$

i.e., provided x^* is as good an approximation to x as can in general be had by r-digit floating-point numbers in the base β. For instance, $x^* = 3$ agrees with $x = \pi$ to one significant (decimal) digit, while $x^* = \frac{22}{7} = 3.1428 \cdots$ is correct to three significant digits (as an approximation to π). Suppose now that we are to calculate the number

$$z = x - y$$

and that we have approximations x^* and y^* for x and y, respectively, available, each of which is good to r digits. Then

$$z^* = x^* - y^*$$

is an approximation for z, which is also good to r digits unless x^* and y^* agree to one or more digits. In this latter case, there will be cancellation of digits during the subtraction, and consequently z^* will be accurate to fewer than r digits.

Consider, for example,

$$x^* = (0.76545421)10^1 \qquad y^* = (0.76544200)10^1$$

and assume each to be an approximation to x and y, respectively, correct to seven significant digits. Then, in eight-digit floating-point arithmetic,

$$z^* = x^* - y^* = (0.12210000)10^{-3}$$

is the *exact* difference between x^* and y^*. But as an approximation to $z = x - y$, z^* is good only to three digits, since the fourth significant digit of z^* derived from the eighth digits of x^* and y^*, both possibly in error. Hence, while the *absolute* error in z^* (as an approximation to $z = x - y$) is at most the sum of the absolute errors in x^* and y^*, the *relative* error in z^* is possibly 10,000 times the relative error in x^* or y^*. Loss of significant digits is therefore dangerous only if we wish to keep the relative error small.

Such loss can often be avoided by anticipating its occurrence. Consider, for example, the evaluation of the function

$$f(x) = 1 - \cos x \tag{1.13}$$

in six-decimal-digit arithmetic. Since $\cos x \approx 1$ for x near zero, there will be loss of significant digits for x near zero if we calculate $f(x)$ by first finding $\cos x$ and then subtracting the calculated value from 1. For we cannot calculate $\cos x$ to more than six digits, so that the error in the calculated value may be as large as $5 \cdot 10^{-7}$, hence as large as, or larger than, $f(x)$ for x near zero. If one wishes to compute the value of $f(x)$ near zero to about six significant digits using six-digit arithmetic, one would have to use an alternative formula for $f(x)$, such as

$$f(x) = 1 - \cos x = \frac{1 - \cos^2 x}{1 + \cos x} = \frac{\sin^2 x}{1 + \cos x} \tag{1.14}$$

which can be evaluated quite accurately for small x; else, one could make use of the Taylor expansion (see Sec. 1.7) for $f(x)$,

$$f(x) = \frac{x^2}{2} - \frac{x^4}{24} + \cdots \tag{1.15}$$

which shows, for example, that for $|x| \leq 10^{-3}$, $x^2/2$ agrees with $f(x)$ to at least six significant digits.

Another example is provided by the problem of finding the roots of the quadratic equation

$$ax^2 + bx + c = 0 \tag{1.16}$$

We know from algebra that the roots are given by the quadratic formula

$$x = \frac{-b \pm \sqrt{b^2 - 4ac}}{2a} \tag{1.17}$$

Let us assume that $b^2 - 4ac > 0$, that $b > 0$, and that we wish to find the root of smaller absolute value using (1.17); i.e.,

$$x_1 = \frac{-b + \sqrt{b^2 - 4ac}}{2a} \tag{1.18}$$

If $4ac$ is small compared with b^2, then $\sqrt{b^2 - 4ac}$ will agree with b to several places. Hence, given that $\sqrt{b^2 - 4ac}$ will be calculated correctly only to as many places as are used in the calculations, it follows that the numerator of (1.18), and therefore the calculated root, will be accurate to fewer places than were used during the calculation. To be specific, take the equation

$$x^2 + 111.11x + 1.2121 = 0 \tag{1.19}$$

Using (1.18) and five-decimal-digit floating-point chopped arithmetic, we calculate

$$b^2 = 12{,}345$$
$$b^2 - 4ac = 12{,}340$$
$$\sqrt{b^2 - 4ac} = 111.09$$
$$x_1 = \frac{-b + \sqrt{b^2 - 4ac}}{2a} = -0.01000$$

while in fact,

$$x_1 = -0.010910$$

is the correct root to the number of digits shown. Here too, the loss of significant digits can be avoided by using an alternative formula for the calculation of the absolutely smaller root, viz.,

$$x_1 = \frac{-2c}{b + \sqrt{b^2 - 4ac}} \tag{1.20}$$

Using this formula, and five-decimal-digit arithmetic, we calculate

$$x_1 = -0.010910$$

which is accurate to five digits.

To determine the effect of an individual error on the final answer, one can, in principle, proceed as follows: Let x be the number in which the error occurs, and consider the final answer as it depends on x, that is, as some function $f(x)$. If $f(x)$ is a smooth function, we can use Taylor's series (see Sec. 1.7) to estimate the effect of using the approximation x^* to x:

$$f(x) = f(x^*) + f'(x^*)(x - x^*) + \tfrac{1}{2}f''(x^*)(x - x^*)^2 + \cdots \qquad (1.21)$$

This shows the error $f(x) - f(x^*)$ in $f(x^*)$ to be proportional to the error in x^*, at least when $(x - x^*)$ is sufficiently small, with proportionality factor equal to $f'(x^*)$. If, for example,

$$f(x) = \sqrt{x}$$

then $f'(x) = 1/(2\sqrt{x})$, so that the absolute error in $f(x^*)$ will be less than the absolute error in x^* for x around 1 or larger. As to the relative error, we find

$$\frac{|f(x) - f(x^*)|}{|f(x)|} \approx |f'(x^*)| \left|\frac{x - x^*}{f(x)}\right| \approx \frac{1}{2}\frac{|x - x^*|}{\sqrt{xx^*}} \approx \frac{1}{2}\frac{|x - x^*|}{|x|}$$

so that the relative error in $f(x^*)$ is about half the relative error in x^* regardless of the size of x. We conclude that taking square roots is a "safe" operation from a relative-error point of view.

By contrast, if

$$f(x) = \frac{10}{1 - x^2}$$

then $f'(x) = 20x/(1 - x^2)^2$, so that

$$\frac{|f(x) - f(x^*)|}{|f(x)|} \approx \frac{2|x|^2}{|1 - x^2|} \cdot \frac{|x - x^*|}{|x|}$$

We can therefore expect the relative error in $f(x^*)$ to be considerably larger than the relative error in x^* if $|x|$ is near 1.

Errors from whatever source propagate in different ways. Some of these errors will actually decay, and hence will affect the accuracy very little. Others will grow. Indeed, errors may grow so large as to invalidate the results of a computation completely. If we let $R(\epsilon)$ denote the growth of an error ϵ, and if as the result of n operations the resulting error behaves like

$$R(\epsilon) = cn\epsilon \qquad (1.22)$$

for some constant c which does not depend on n, we say that the growth is *linear*. If, on the other hand, $R(\epsilon)$ behaves like

$$R(\epsilon) = k^n\epsilon \qquad (1.23)$$

for some constant $k > 1$, we say that the rate of growth is *exponential*. Linear growth is normal, usually unavoidable, and not dangerous. Exponential growth may, however, be disastrous and should be avoided at all costs. If a procedure exhibits exponential error growth, we call the procedure *unstable*. The rate of error growth depends upon many factors. It may be inherent in the physical problem being solved. Often, however, it is a function of the algorithm being used.

As an example of an unstable algorithm, we consider the following problem. We are required to find $f_n(x)$ for $n = 0, 1, \ldots$, where $f_n(x)$ is defined by

$$f_n(x) = n! \left[e^x - \left(1 + x + \frac{x^2}{2!} + \cdots + \frac{x^n}{n!} \right) \right] \tag{1.24a}$$

For a given x we can compute $f_n(x)$ directly. However, it can also be shown that $f_n(x)$ satisfies the following recurrence relation:

$$f_{n+1}(x) = (n + 1)f_n(x) - x^{n+1} \qquad n = 0, 1, \ldots \tag{1.24b}$$

Let us set $x = 1$, and assuming a computer with a five-decimal-place mantissa, compute $f_n(1)$. Since $f_0(1) = 2.7183 - 1 = 1.7183$, we obtain the table of values

n	f_n
0	1.7183
1	0.71830
2	0.43660
3	0.30980
4	0.23920
5	0.19600
6	0.17600 (correct value 0.15991)
7	0.23200
8	0.85600
9	6.7040
10	66.040

The underlined digits are in error. After $n = 7$, no significant digits of accuracy remain in f_n. Actually, $f_n(1)$ is a monotone-decreasing function of n, whereas if we use the algorithm (1.24b), f_n begins to increase after $n = 6$. Even if we computed f_0 more accurately, this would merely delay, but not prevent, the growth of error. The algorithm (1.24b) is therefore numerically unstable and cannot be used for large values of n.

Other examples of unstable algorithms will be given in succeeding chapters.

EXERCISES

1.4-1. Find the root of smallest magnitude of the equation

$$x^2 + 0.4002 \cdot 10^0 x + 0.8 \cdot 10^{-4} = 0$$

using formulas (1.18) and (1.20). Work in floating-point arithmetic using a four-(decimal-) place mantissa.

1.4-2. Estimate the error in evaluating $f(x) = (\cos x) \exp (10x^2)$ around $x = 2$ if the absolute error in x is 10^{-6}.

1.4-3. Find a way to calculate

$$(a)\ f(x) = \frac{x - \sin x}{\tan x} \qquad (b)\ f(x) = x - \sqrt{x^2 - \alpha}$$

correctly to the number of digits used when x is near zero for (a), very much larger than α for (b).

1.4-4. Find $f_5(0.2)$ using (1.24b). Begin with $f_0(0.2) = 0.2214$ and work with five significant figures. Then compute $f_5(0.2)$ using (1.24a), carrying as many significant figures as necessary to obtain four-decimal-place accuracy. Compare your results.

1.4-5. Assuming a computer with a four-decimal-place mantissa, add the following numbers first in ascending order (from smallest to largest) and then in descending order. In doing so round off the partial sums. Compare your results with the correct sum $x = 0.107141023 \cdot 10^5$

$0.2653 \cdot 10^0$	$0.7555 \cdot 10^2$	$0.8999 \cdot 10^4$
$0.1580 \cdot 10^0$	$0.6266 \cdot 10^2$	
$0.2581 \cdot 10^1$	$0.7889 \cdot 10^3$	
$0.8288 \cdot 10^1$	$0.7767 \cdot 10^3$	

1.5 COMPUTATIONAL METHODS FOR ERROR ESTIMATION

This chapter is intended to make the student aware of the possible sources of error and to point out some techniques which can be used to avoid these errors. In appraising computer results, such errors must be taken into account. Realistic estimates of the total error are difficult to make in a practical problem, and an adequate mathematical theory is still lacking. An appealing idea is to make use of the computer itself to provide us with such estimates. Various methods of this type have been proposed. We shall discuss briefly five of them. The simplest method makes use of *double precision*. Here one simply solves the same problem twice—once in single precision and once in double precision. From the difference in the results an estimate of the total round-off error can then be obtained (assuming that all other errors are less significant). It can then be assumed that the same accumulation of round-off will occur in other problems solved with the same subroutine. This method is extremely costly in machine time since double-precision arithmetic increases computer time by a factor of 8 on some machines, and in addition, it is not always possible to isolate other errors.

A second method is *interval arithmetic*. Here each number is represented by two machine numbers, the maximum and the minimum values that it might have. Whenever an operation is performed, one computes its maximum and minimum values. Essentially, then, one will obtain two solutions at every step, the true solution necessarily being contained within the range determined by the maximum and minimum values. This method requires more than twice the amount of computer time and about twice the storage of a standard run. Moreover, the usual assumption that the true solution lies about midway within the range is not, in general, valid. Thus the range might be so large that any estimate of the round-off error based upon this would be grossly exaggerated.

A third approach is *significant-digit* arithmetic. As pointed out earlier, whenever two nearly equal machine numbers are subtracted, there is a danger that some significant digits will be lost. In significant-digit arithmetic an attempt is made to keep track of digits so lost. In one version only the significant digits in any number are retained, all others being discarded. At the end of a computation we will thus be assured that all digits retained are significant. The main objection to this method is that some information is lost whenever digits are discarded, and that the results obtained are likely to be much too conservative. Experimentation with this technique is still going on, although the experience to date is not too promising.

A fourth method which gives considerable promise of providing an adequate mathematical theory of round-off-error propagation is based on a *statistical approach*. It begins with the assumption that round-off errors are independent. This assumption is, of course, not valid, because if the same problem is run on the same machine several times, the answers will always be the same. We can, however, adopt a stochastic model of the propagation of round-off errors in which the local errors are treated as if they were random variables. Thus we can assume that the local round-off errors are either uniformly or normally distributed between their extreme values. Using statistical methods, we can then obtain the standard deviation, the variance of distribution, and estimates of the accumulated round-off error. The statistical approach is considered in some detail by Hamming [1] and Henrici [2].† The method does involve substantial analysis and additional computer time, but in the experiments conducted to date it has obtained error estimates which are in remarkable agreement with experimentally available evidence.

A fifth method with considerable promise involves the use of *backward-error analysis*. This method has been used with great success to give insight into the analysis of errors in solving linear systems. It will be developed in greater detail in Chap. 3.

---

† Numbers in brackets refer to items in the references at the end of the book.

1.6 SOME COMMENTS ON CONVERGENCE OF SEQUENCES

Calculus, and more generally analysis, are based on the notion of convergence. Basic concepts such as derivative, integral, and continuity are defined in terms of convergent sequences, and elementary functions such as $\ln x$ or $\sin x$ are defined by convergent series. At the same time, numerical answers to engineering and scientific problems are never needed *exactly*. Rather, an approximation to the answer is required which is accurate "to a certain number of decimal places," or accurate to within a given tolerance ε.

It is therefore not surprising that many numerical methods for finding the answer α of a given problem merely produce (the first few terms of) a sequence $\alpha_1, \alpha_2, \alpha_3, \ldots$ which is shown to converge to the desired answer. To recall the definition:

> *A sequence $\alpha_1, \alpha_2, \ldots$ of (real or complex) numbers converges to α if and only if, for all $\varepsilon > 0$, there exists an integer $n_0(\varepsilon)$ such that for all $n \geq n_0$, $|\alpha - \alpha_n| < \varepsilon$.*

Hence, if we have a numerical method which produces a sequence $\alpha_1, \alpha_2, \ldots$ converging to the desired answer α, then we can calculate α to any desired accuracy merely by calculating α_n for "large enough" n.

From a computational point of view, this definition is unsatisfactory for the following reasons: (1) It is often not possible (without knowing the answer α) to know when n is "large enough." In other words, it is difficult to get hold of the function $n_0(\varepsilon)$ mentioned in the definition of convergence. (2) Even when some knowledge about $n_0(\varepsilon)$ is available, it may turn out that the required n is too large to make the calculation of α_n feasible.

Example The number $\pi/4$ is the value of the infinite series

$$\sum_{i=0}^{\infty} \frac{(-1)^i}{2i + 1} = 1 - \sum_{j=1}^{\infty} \frac{2}{16j^2 - 1}$$

Hence, with

$$\alpha_n = 1 - \sum_{j=1}^{n} \frac{2}{16j^2 - 1} \qquad n = 1, 2, \ldots$$

the sequence $\alpha_1, \alpha_2, \ldots$ is monotone-decreasing to its limit $\pi/4$. Moreover,

$$0 \leq \alpha_n - \pi/4 \leq \frac{1}{4n + 3} \qquad n = 1, 2, \ldots$$

To calculate $\pi/4$ correct to within 10^{-6} using this sequence, we would need $10^6 \leq 4n + 3$, or roughly, $n = 25,000$. On a computer using eight-decimal-digit floating-point arithmetic, round-off in the calculation of $\alpha_{25,000}$ is probably much larger than 10^{-6}. Hence $\pi/4$ could not be computed to within 10^{-6} using this sequence.

To deal with these problems, certain notation is useful. Specifically, we would like to measure how fast sequences converge. As with all measuring, we do this by comparison, in this case with other sequences. We say that *the convergence of* $\alpha_1, \alpha_2, \ldots$ *to* α *is* $O(\beta_n)$, or *at least of order* β_n, provided $\beta_1, \beta_2, \ldots$ is a sequence such that, for some constant K and all sufficiently large n,

$$\frac{|\alpha - \alpha_n|}{|\beta_n|} \leq K$$

If this holds for all $K > 0$, that is, if

$$\lim_{n \to \infty} \frac{\alpha - \alpha_n}{\beta_n} = 0$$

then we say that the *convergence* is $o(\beta_n)$, or *faster than of order* β_n. In the first case, we write

$$\alpha_n = \alpha + O(\beta_n) \tag{1.25}$$

In the second case, we write

$$\alpha_n = \alpha + o(\beta_n) \tag{1.26}$$

Example If $\alpha_n = \alpha + o(1)$, then, by definition,

$$\lim_{n \to \infty} \frac{\alpha - \alpha_n}{1} = 0$$

Hence $\alpha_n = \alpha + o(1)$ is just a fancy way of saying that the sequence $\alpha_1, \alpha_2, \ldots$ converges to α.

Example If $|r| < 1$, then the geometric series $\sum_{i=0}^{\infty} r^i$ sums to $1/(1 - r)$. With $s_n = \sum_{i=0}^{n} r^i$, we have $s_n = (1 - r^{n+1})/(1 - r) = 1/(1 - r) - r^{n+1}/(1 - r)$. Thus

$$s_n = \frac{1}{1 - r} + O(r^n)$$

Further, if $\bar{r} > |r|$, then

$$s_n = \frac{1}{1 - r} + o(\bar{r}^n)$$

Hence, whenever $\alpha_n = \alpha + O(r^n)$ for some $|r| < 1$, we say that the convergence is (at least) geometric, for it is then (at least) of the same order as the convergence of the geometric series.

Although it is better to know that $\alpha_n = \alpha + O(\beta_n)$ than to know nothing, knowledge about the order of convergence becomes quite useful only when we know more precisely that

$$\alpha_n = \alpha + \beta_n + o(\beta_n)$$

This says that for "large enough" n, $\alpha_n \approx \alpha + \beta_n$. To put it differently,

$$\begin{aligned}
\alpha_n &= \alpha + \beta_n + o(\beta_n) \\
&= \alpha + \beta_n + \beta_n o(1) \\
&= \alpha + \beta_n(1 + \varepsilon_n)
\end{aligned}$$

where $\varepsilon_1, \varepsilon_2, \ldots$ is a sequence converging to zero. Although we cannot *prove* that a certain n is "large enough," we can *test the hypothesis* that n is "large enough" by comparing $\alpha_{k+1} - \alpha_k$ with $\beta_{k+1} - \beta_k$. If

$$\frac{|\alpha_{k+1} - \alpha_k|}{|\beta_{k+1} - \beta_k|} \approx 1$$

for k near n, say for $k = n - 2, n - 1, n$, then we accept the hypothesis that n is "large enough" for

$$\alpha_n \approx \alpha + \beta_n$$

to be true, and therefore accept $|\beta_n|$ as a good estimate of the error $|\alpha - \alpha_n|$.

This notation carries over to functions of a real variable. If

$$\lim_{h \to 0} T(h) = A$$

we say that the convergence is $O(f(h))$ provided

$$\frac{|T(h) - A|}{|f(h)|} \leq K$$

for some finite constant K and all small enough h. If this holds for all $K > 0$, that is, if

$$\lim_{h \to 0} \frac{T(h) - A}{f(h)} = 0$$

then we call the convergence $o(f(h))$.

Example For h "near" zero, we have

$$\begin{aligned}
\frac{\sin h}{h} &= 1 - (\tfrac{1}{3}!)h^2 + (\tfrac{1}{5!})h^4 - \cdots = 1 + O(h^2) \\
&= 1 - \tfrac{1}{6}h^2 + o(h^2)
\end{aligned}$$

Hence, for all $\gamma < 2$,

$$\frac{\sin h}{h} = 1 + o(h^\gamma)$$

Example If the function $f(x)$ has a root of order γ at $x = \xi$, then

$$f(\xi + h) = O(h^\gamma) \qquad \text{but} \qquad f(\xi + h) \neq o(h^\gamma)$$

Rules for calculating with the order symbols are collected in the following lemma.

Lemma I.I If $\alpha_n = \alpha + O(f(n))$ and c is some constant, then

$$c\alpha_n = c\alpha + O(f(n))$$

If also $\beta_n = \beta + O(g(n))$, and $g(n) = O(f(n))$, then

$$\alpha_n + \beta_n = \alpha + \beta + O(f(n)) \qquad \text{and} \qquad \alpha_n\beta_n = \alpha\beta + O(f(n)) \qquad (1.27)$$

If, further, $\beta \neq 0$, then also

$$\frac{\alpha_n}{\beta_n} = \frac{\alpha}{\beta} + O(f(n))$$

while if $\alpha = \beta = 0$, then

$$\alpha_n\beta_n = O(f(n)g(n))$$

Finally, all statements remain true if O is replaced by o throughout.

The approximate calculation of a number α via a sequence $\alpha_1, \alpha_2, \ldots$ converging to α always involves an act of faith regardless of whether or not the order of convergence is known. Given that the sequence is known to converge to α, the practicing numerical analyst ascertains that n is "large enough" by making sure that, for small values of i, α_{n-i} differs "little enough" from α_n. If he also knows that the convergence is $\beta_n + o(\beta_n)$, he checks whether or not the sequence behaves accordingly near n. If he also knows that α satisfies certain equations or inequalities—α might be the sought-for solution of an equation—he checks that α_n satisfies these equations or inequalities "well enough." In short, the practicing numerical analyst makes sure that n satisfies all conditions he can think of which are necessary for n to be "large enough." If all these conditions are satisfied, then, lacking sufficient conditions for n to be "large enough," he accepts α_n on faith as a good enough approximation to α. In a way, the numerical analyst uses all means at his disposal to distinguish a "good enough" approximation from a bad one. He can do no more (and should do no less).

It follows that numerical results arrived at in this way should not be mistaken for final answers. Rather, they should be questioned freely if subsequent investigations throw any doubt upon their correctness.

The student should appreciate this as another example of the basic difference between numerical analysis and analysis. Analysis became a precise discipline when it left the restrictions of practical calculations to deal entirely with problems posed in terms of an abstract model of the number system, called the *real numbers*. This abstract model is designed to make a precise and useful definition of limit possible, which opens the way to the abstract or symbolic solution of an impressive array of practical problems, once these problems are translated into the terms of the model. This still leaves the task of translating the abstract or symbolic solutions back into practical solutions.   Numerical analysis assumes this task, and with it the limitations of practical calculations from which analysis managed to escape so elegantly.   Numerical analysis is then of necessity imprecise; its numerical answers are usually tentative and, *at best*, known to be accurate only to within certain bounds.

Numerical analysis is therefore not merely concerned with the *construction* of numerical methods.   Rather, a large portion of numerical analysis consists in the derivation of useful *error bounds*, or *error estimates*, for the numerical answers produced by a numerical algorithm.   Throughout this book, the student will meet this preoccupation with error bounds so typical of numerical analysis.

EXERCISES

1.6-1. The ln 2 may be calculated from the series

$$\ln 2 = 1 - \tfrac{1}{2} + \tfrac{1}{3} - \tfrac{1}{4} + \cdots$$

It is known from analysis that this series converges and that the magnitude of the error in any partial sum is less than the magnitude of the first neglected term.   Estimate the number of terms that would be required to calculate ln 2 to 10 decimal places.

1.6-2. For h near zero it is possible to write

$$\frac{\tan h}{h} = 1 + O(h^\gamma)$$

and

$$\frac{\tan h}{h} = 1 + o(h^\delta)$$

Find the values of γ and δ for which these equalities hold.

1.6-3. Try to calculate, on a computer, the limit of the sequence

$$\alpha_n = (\tan 8^{-n} - \sin 8^{-n}) \cdot 8^{3n} \qquad n = 0, 1, 2, \ldots$$

Theoretically, what is $\alpha = \lim_{n \to \infty} \alpha_n$ and what is the order of convergence of the sequence?

1.7 SOME MATHEMATICAL PRELIMINARIES

It is assumed that the student is familiar with the topics normally covered in the undergraduate analytic geometry and calculus sequence.   These include elementary notions of real and complex number systems; continuity; the concept of limits, sequences, and series; differentiation and integration.   For Chap. 3, some knowledge of determinants is assumed.   For Chaps. 6 and 7, some familiarity with the solution of ordinary differential equations is also assumed, although these chapters may be omitted.

In particular, we shall make frequent use of the following theorems.

Theorem I.I   **Intermediate-value theorem for continuous functions**
Let $f(x)$ be a continuous function on the interval $[a,b]$. If $f(\underline{x}) \le \alpha \le f(\bar{x})$ for some number α and some $\underline{x}, \bar{x} \in [a,b]$, then

$$\alpha = f(\xi) \qquad \text{for some } \xi \in [a,b]$$

This theorem is often used in the following form:

Theorem I.2   Let $f(x)$ be a continuous function on $[a,b]$, let $x_1, \ldots, x_n$ be points in $[a,b]$, and let $g_1, \ldots, g_n$ be real numbers all *of one sign*. Then

$$\sum_{i=1}^{n} f(x_i)g_i = f(\xi) \sum_{i=1}^{n} g_i \qquad \text{for some } \xi \in [a,b]$$

To indicate the proof, assume without loss of generality that $g_i \ge 0$, $i = 1, \ldots, n$. If $f(\underline{x}) = \min_i f(x_i)$ and $f(\bar{x}) = \max_i f(x_i)$, then

$$f(\underline{x}) \sum_{i=1}^{n} g_i = \sum_{i=1}^{n} f(\underline{x})g_i \le \sum_{i=1}^{n} f(x_i)g_i \le \sum_{i=1}^{n} f(\bar{x})g_i = f(\bar{x}) \sum_{i=1}^{n} g_i$$

Hence $\alpha = \sum_i f(x_i)g_i$ is a number between the two values $f(\underline{x}) \sum_i g_i$ and $f(\bar{x}) \sum_i g_i$ of the continuous function $f(x) \sum_i g_i$, and the conclusion follows from Theorem 1.1.

One proves analogously the corresponding statement for *infinite* sums or *integrals*:

Theorem I.3   **Mean-value theorem for integrals**   Let $g(x)$ be a nonnegative or nonpositive integrable function on $[a,b]$. If $f(x)$ is continuous on $[a,b]$, then

$$\int_a^b f(x)g(x)\, dx = f(\xi) \int_a^b g(x)\, dx \qquad \text{for some } \xi \in [a,b] \qquad (1.28)$$

Warning   The assumption that $g(x)$ is of one sign is essential in Theorem 1.3, as the simple example $f(x) = g(x) = x$, $[a,b] = [-1,1]$ shows.

Theorem I.4   Let $f(x)$ be a continuous function on the closed and bounded interval $[a,b]$. Then $f(x)$ "assumes its maximum and minimum values on $[a,b]$"; i.e., there exist points $\underline{x}$ and $\bar{x}$ in $[a,b]$ such that

$$\text{for all } x \in [a,b]: \qquad f(\underline{x}) \le f(x) \le f(\bar{x})$$

Theorem 1.5   Rolle's theorem   Let $f(x)$ be continuous on the (closed and finite) interval $[a,b]$ and differentiable on (a,b). If $f(a) = f(b) = 0$, then

$$f'(\xi) = 0 \qquad \text{for some } \xi \in (a,b)$$

The proof makes essential use of Theorem 1.4.   For by Theorem 1.4, there are points $\underline{x}, \bar{x}$ in $[a,b]$ such that, for all $x \in [a,b]$, $f(\underline{x}) \le f(x) \le f(\bar{x})$. If now neither $\underline{x}$ nor $\bar{x}$ is in (a,b), then $f(x) \equiv 0$, and every $\xi \in (a,b)$ will do. Otherwise, either $\underline{x}$ or $\bar{x}$ is in (a,b), say, $\bar{x} \in (a,b)$.   But then $f'(\bar{x}) = 0$, since

$$0 \le \lim_{h \to 0-} \frac{f(\bar{x}) - f(\bar{x} + h)}{-h} = f'(\bar{x}) = \lim_{h \to 0+} \frac{f(\bar{x} + h) - f(\bar{x})}{h} \le 0$$

$f(\bar{x})$ being the *biggest value* achieved by $f(x)$ on $[a,b]$.

An immediate consequence of Rolle's theorem is the following theorem.

Theorem 1.6   Mean-value theorem for derivatives   If $f(x)$ is continuous on the (closed and finite) interval $[a,b]$ and differentiable on (a,b), then

$$\frac{f(b) - f(a)}{b - a} = f'(\xi) \qquad \text{for some } \xi \in (a,b) \tag{1.29}$$

One gets Theorem 1.6 from Theorem 1.5 by considering in Theorem 1.5 the function

$$F(x) = f(x) - f(a) - \frac{f(b) - f(a)}{b - a}(x - a)$$

instead of $f(x)$. Clearly, $F(x)$ vanishes both at a and at b.

It follows directly from Theorem 1.6 that if $f(x)$ is continuous on $[a,b]$ and differentiable on (a,b), and c is some point in $[a,b]$, then for all $x \in [a,b]$

$$f(x) = f(c) + (x - c)f'(c + \theta(x - c)) \qquad \text{for some } \theta \in (0,1) \tag{1.30}$$

The fundamental theorem of calculus provides the more precise statement: If $f(x)$ is continuously differentiable, then for all $x \in [a,b]$

$$f(x) = f(c) + \int_c^x f'(s) \, ds \tag{1.31}$$

from which (1.30) follows by the mean-value theorem for integrals (1.28), since $f'(x)$ is continuous.   More generally, one has the following theorem.

Theorem 1.7   Taylor's formula with (integral) remainder   If $f(x)$ has $n + 1$ continuous derivatives on $[a,b]$ and c is some point in $[a,b]$, then for all $x \in [a,b]$

$$f(x) = f(c) + f'(c)(x - c) + \frac{f''(c)(x - c)^2}{2!} + \cdots$$

$$+ \frac{f^{(n)}(c)(x - c)^n}{n!} + R_{n+1}(x) \tag{1.32}$$

where

$$R_{n+1}(x) = \frac{1}{n!} \int_c^x (x - s)^n f^{(n+1)}(s) \, ds \qquad (1.33)$$

One gets (1.32) from (1.31) by considering the function

$$F(x) = f(x) + f'(x)(c - x) + \frac{f''(x)(c - x)^2}{2!} + \cdots + \frac{f^{(n)}(x)(c - x)^n}{n!}$$

instead of $f(x)$. For $F'(x) = f^{(n+1)}(x)(c - x)^n/n!$; hence by (1.31),

$$F(x) = F(c) + \frac{1}{n!} \int_c^x (c - s)^n f^{(n+1)}(s) \, ds$$

But since $F(c) = f(c)$, this gives

$$f(c) = F(x) + \frac{1}{n!} \int_x^c (c - s)^n f^{(n+1)}(s) \, ds$$

which is (1.32), after the substitution of x for c and of c for x.

Actually, $f^{(n+1)}(x)$ need not be continuous for (1.32) to hold. However, if in (1.32), $f^{(n+1)}(x)$ is continuous, one gets, using Theorem 1.3, the more familiar but less useful form for the remainder:

$$R_{n+1}(x) = \frac{f^{(n+1)}(\xi)(x - c)^{n+1}}{(n + 1)!} \qquad \text{where } \xi = c + \theta(x - c) \qquad (1.34)$$

By setting $h = x - c$, (1.32) and (1.34) take the form

$$f(c + h) = f(c) + hf'(c) + \frac{h^2}{2!} f''(c) + \cdots + \frac{h^n}{n!} f^{(n)}(c)$$

$$+ \frac{h^{n+1}}{(n + 1)!} f^{(n+1)}(c + \theta h) \qquad \text{for some } \theta \in (0,1) \qquad (1.35)$$

To give some examples, the function $f(x) = e^x$ has the Taylor expansion

$$e^x = 1 + x + \frac{x^2}{2!} + \cdots + \frac{x^n}{n!} + \frac{x^{n+1} e^\xi}{(n + 1)!}$$

$$\text{for some } \xi \text{ between 0 and } x \qquad (1.36)$$

about $c = 0$. The expansion of $f(x) = \ln x = \log_e x$ about $c = 1$ is

$$\ln x = (x - 1) - \frac{(x - 1)^2}{2} + \frac{(x - 1)^3}{3} - \frac{(x - 1)^4}{4} + \cdots$$

$$- \frac{(-1)^n(x - 1)^n}{n} + \frac{(-1)^n(x - 1)^{n+1} \xi^{-(n+1)}}{n + 1}$$

where $0 < x \le 2$, and ξ is between 1 and x.

A similar formula holds for functions of several variables.

Theorem 1.8 If $f(x,y)$ has continuous first and second partial derivatives in a neighborhood D of the point (a,b) in the (x,y) plane, then

$$f(x,y) = f(a,b) + f_x(a,b)(x - a) + f_y(a,b)(y - b) + R_2(x,y) \qquad (1.37)$$

for all (x,y) in D, where

$$R_2(x,y) = \frac{f_{xx}(\xi,\eta)(x - a)^2}{2} + f_{xy}(\xi,\eta)(x - a)(y - b) + \frac{f_{yy}(\xi,\eta)(y - b)^2}{2}$$

for some $(\xi,\eta) \in D$ depending on (x,y), and the subscripts on f denote partial differentiation.

For example, the expansion of $e^{x \sin y}$ about $(a,b) = (0,0)$ is

$$e^{x \sin y} = 1 + 0 \cdot x + 0 \cdot y + R_2(x,y) \qquad (1.38)$$

We also need the following simple theorem.

Theorem 1.9 If $f(x,y)$ has continuous first partial derivatives and $g(x)$ is continuously differentiable, then the function $u(x) = f(x,g(x))$ is continuously differentiable, and

$$\frac{du}{dx} = \frac{\partial f}{\partial x} + \frac{\partial f}{\partial y}\frac{dg}{dx}$$

Finally, in the discussion of eigenvalues of matrices and elsewhere, we need the following theorem.

Theorem 1.10 Fundamental theorem of algebra If $p(x)$ is a polynomial of degree $n \geq 1$, that is,

$$p(x) = a_0 + a_1 x + a_2 x^2 + \cdots + a_n x^n$$

with $a_0, \ldots, a_n$ real or complex numbers and $a_n \neq 0$, then $p(x)$ has at least one zero; i.e., there exists a complex number ξ such that $p(\xi) = 0$.

This rather deep theorem should not be confused with the straightforward statement, "A polynomial of degree n has at most n zeros, counting multiplicity," which we prove in Chap. 2 and use, for example, in the discussion of polynomial interpolation.

EXERCISES

1.7-1. In the mean-value theorem for integrals, Theorem 1.3, let $f(x) = e^x$, $g(x) = x$, $[a,b] = [0,1]$.   Find the point ξ specified by the theorem and verify that this point lies in the interval $(0,1)$.

1.7-2. In the mean-value theorem for derivatives, Theorem 1.6, let $f(x) = x^2$.   Find the point ξ specified by the theorem and verify that this point lies in the interval (a,b).

1.7-3. In the expansion (1.36) for e^x, find n so that the resulting power sum will yield an approximation correct to five decimal places for all x on $[0,1]$.

1.7-4. Use Taylor's formula (1.32) to find a power series expansion about $c = 0$ for $\sin(\pi x/2)$. Find an expression for the remainder, and from this estimate the number of terms that would be needed to guarantee six-decimal-place accuracy for $\sin(\pi x/2)$ for all x on the interval $[-1,1]$.

1.7-5. Find the remainder $R_2(x,y)$ in the example (1.38) and determine its maximum value in the region D defined by $[0 \leq x \leq \pi/2, 0 \leq y \leq \pi/2]$.

1.7-6. Prove that the remainder term in (1.35) can also be written

$$\frac{h^{n+1}}{(n+1)!} f^{(n+1)}(c) + o(h^{n+1})$$

[if $f^{(n+1)}(x)$ is continuous at $x = c$].

1.7-7. Illustrate the statement in Exercise 1.7-6 by calculating, for $f(x) = e^x$, $c = 0$,

$$R_3(h) = e^h - \left(1 + h + \frac{h^2}{2}\right) \quad \text{and} \quad \frac{h^3}{3!} f^{(3)}(0) = \frac{h^3}{3!}$$

for various values of h, for example, for $h = 2^{-k}$, $k = 1, 2, 3, \ldots$, and comparing $R_3(h)$ with $(h^3/3!)f^{(3)}(0)$.

2
The Solution of Nonlinear Equations

One of the most frequently occurring problems in scientific work is to find the roots of equations of the form

$$f(x) = 0 \tag{2.1}$$

The function $f(x)$ may be given explicitly, as, for example, a polynomial in x or as a transcendental function. Frequently, however, $f(x)$ may be known only implicitly; i.e., a rule for evaluating $f(x)$ for any argument may be known, but its explicit form is unknown. Thus $f(x)$ may represent the value which the solution of a differential equation assumes at a specified point, while x may represent an initial condition of the differential equation. In rare cases it may be possible to obtain the exact roots of (2.1), an illustration of this being a factorable polynomial. In general, however, we can hope to obtain only approximate solutions, relying on some computational technique to produce the approximation. Depending on the context, "approximate solution" may then mean either a point x^*, for which (2.1) is "approximately satisfied," i.e., for which $|f(x^*)|$ is "small," or a point x^* which is "close to" a solution of (2.1). In this chapter we consider various iterative methods for finding approximations to simple roots of (2.1). Special attention will be given to polynomial equations because of their importance in analysis.

2.1   A SURVEY OF ITERATIVE METHODS

In this section, we introduce some elementary iterative methods for finding a solution of the equation

$$f(x) = 0 \tag{2.1}$$

and illustrate their use by applying them to the simple polynomial equation

$$x^3 - x - 1 = 0 \tag{2.2}$$

for which $f(x) = x^3 - x - 1$.

For this example, one finds that

$$f(1) = -1 < 0 < 5 = f(2) \tag{2.3}$$

Hence, since $f(x)$ is continuous, $f(x)$ must vanish somewhere in the interval [1,2], by the intermediate-value theorem for continuous functions (see Sec. 1.7). If $f(x)$ were to vanish at two or more points in [1,2], then, by Rolle's theorem (see Sec. 1.7), $f'(x)$ would have to vanish somewhere in [1,2]. Hence, since $f'(x) = 3x^2 - 1$ is positive on [1,2], $f(x)$ has exactly one root in the interval [1,2].   If we call this root ξ, then

$\xi \approx 1.5$ with absolute error ≤ 0.5

To find out more about this root, we evaluate $f(x)$ at the midpoint 1.5 of the interval [1,2] and get

$$f(1.5) = 0.875 > 0 > -1 = f(1)$$

Hence we now know that the root ξ lies in the smaller interval [1,1.5]; i.e.,

$\xi \approx 1.25$ with absolute error ≤ 0.25

Checking again at the midpoint 1.25, we find

$$f(1.25) = -0.296 \cdots < 0 < 0.875 = f(1.5)$$

and know therefore that ξ lies in the yet smaller interval [1.25,1.5]; i.e.,

$\xi \approx 1.375$ with absolute error ≤ 0.125

This procedure of locating a solution of the equation $f(x) = 0$ in a sequence of intervals of decreasing size is known as the *bisection* method.

Algorithm 2.1   Bisection method   Given a function $f(x)$ continuous on the interval $[a_0,b_0]$ and such that $f(a_0)f(b_0) \leq 0$.

For $n = 0, 1, 2, \ldots$, until satisfied, do:

> Set $m = (a_n + b_n)/2$
> If $f(a_n)f(m) \leq 0$, set $a_{n+1} = a_n, b_{n+1} = m$
> Otherwise, set $a_{n+1} = m, b_{n+1} = b_n$
> Then $f(x)$ has a root in the interval $[a_{n+1},b_{n+1}]$

We shall frequently state algorithms in the above concise form.   For students familiar with the ALGOL language, this notation will appear quite

natural.   Further, we have used here the phrase "until satisfied" in order to
stress that this description of the algorithm is *incomplete*.   A user of the
algorithm must specify precise termination criteria.   These will depend in
part on the specific problem to be solved by the algorithm.   Some of the
many possible termination criteria are discussed in the next section.

At each step of the bisection algorithm 2.1, the length of the interval
known to contain a zero of $f(x)$ is reduced by a factor of 2.   Hence each step
produces one more correct binary digit of the root ξ of $f(x) = 0$.   After
20 steps of this algorithm applied to our example and starting as we did with
$a_0 = 1, b_0 = 2$, one gets

$$1.3247175 \cdots = a_{20} \le \xi \le b_{20} = 1.3247184 \cdots$$
$$f(a_{20}) = (-1.857 \cdots)10^{-8} < 0 < (2.209 \cdots)10^{-6} = f(b_{20})$$

Clearly, with enough effort, one can always locate a root to any desired
accuracy with this algorithm.   But compared with other methods to be
discussed, the bisection method converges rather slowly.

One can hope to get to the root faster by using more fully the information about $f(x)$ available at each step.   In our example (2.2), we started with
the information

$$f(1) = -1 < 0 < 5 = f(2)$$

Since $|f(1)|$ is closer to zero than is $|f(2)|$ the root ξ is likely to be closer to 1
than to 2 [at least if $f(x)$ is "nearly" linear].   Hence, rather than check the
midpoint, or average value, 1.5 of 1 and 2, we now check $f(x)$ at the weighted
average

$$w = \frac{|f(2)| \cdot 1 + |f(1)| \cdot 2}{|f(2)| + |f(1)|} \tag{2.4}$$

Note that since $f(1)$ and $f(2)$ have opposite sign, we can write (2.4) more
simply as

$$w = \frac{f(2) \cdot 1 - f(1) \cdot 2}{f(2) - f(1)} \tag{2.5}$$

This gives for our example

$$w = \frac{5 \cdot 1 + 1 \cdot 2}{6} = 1.166666 \cdots$$

and

$$f(w) = -0.578703 \cdots < 0 < 5 = f(2)$$

Hence ξ lies in $[1.166666 \cdots, 2]$.   Repeating the process for this interval,
we get

$$w = \frac{5 \cdot (1.166666 \cdots) + (0.578703 \cdots) \cdot 2}{5.578703 \cdots} = 1.253112 \cdots$$

$$f(w) = -0.285363 \cdots < 0 < 5 = f(2)$$

Consequently, $f(x)$ has a root in the interval $[1.253112 \cdots ,2]$. This algorithm is known as the *regula falsi*, or *false-position*, method.

Algorithm 2.2 Regula falsi Given a function $f(x)$ continuous on the interval $[a_0,b_0]$ and such that $f(a_0)f(b_0) < 0$.

> For $n = 0, 1, 2, \ldots$, until satisfied, do:
>
> Calculate $w = [f(b_n)a_n - f(a_n)b_n]/[f(b_n) - f(a_n)]$
> If $f(a_n)f(w) \leq 0$, set $a_{n+1} = a_n$, $b_{n+1} = w$
> Otherwise, set $a_{n+1} = w$, $b_{n+1} = b_n$

After 16 steps of this algorithm applied to our example and starting as we did with $a_0 = 1$, $b_0 = 2$, one gets

$$1.3247174 \cdots = a_{16} \leq \xi \leq b_{16} = 2$$
$$f(a_{16}) = (-1.95 \cdots) \; 10^{-6} < 0 < 5 = f(b_{16})$$

Hence, although the regula falsi produces a point at which $|f(x)|$ is "small" somewhat faster than does the bisection method, it fails completely to give a "small" interval in which a root is known to lie.

A glance at Fig. 2.1 shows the reason for this.   As one verifies easily, the weighted average

$$w = \frac{f(b_n)a_n - f(a_n)b_n}{f(b_n) - f(a_n)}$$

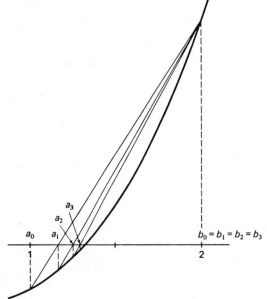

Fig. 2.1 Regula falsi.

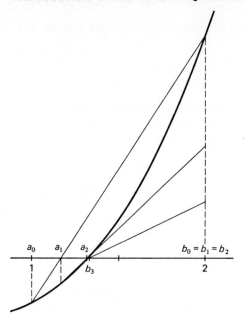

Fig. 2.2 Modified regula falsi.

is the point at which the straight line through the points $\{a_n, f(a_n)\}$ and $\{b_n, f(b_n)\}$ intersects the x axis. Such a straight line is a secant to $f(x)$, and in our example, $f(x)$ is concave upward and increasing (in the interval $[1,2]$ of interest); hence the secant is always above (the graph of) $f(x)$. Consequently, w always lies to the left of the root (in our example). If $f(x)$ were concave downward and increasing, w would always lie to the right of the root.

The regula falsi algorithm can be improved in several ways, two of which we now discuss. The first one, called *modified regula falsi*, replaces secants by straight lines of ever smaller slope until w falls to the opposite side of the root. This is shown graphically in Fig. 2.2.

Algorithm 2.3 Modified regula falsi Given $f(x)$ continuous on $[a_0, b_0]$ and such that $f(a_0)f(b_0) < 0$.

> Set $F = f(a_0)$, $G = f(b_0)$, $w_0 = a_0$
> For $n = 0, 1, 2, \ldots$, until satisfied, do:
>> Calculate $w_{n+1} = (Ga_n - Fb_n)/(G - F)$
>> If $f(a_n)f(w_{n+1}) \leq 0$, set $a_{n+1} = a_n$, $b_{n+1} = w_{n+1}$, $G = f(w_{n+1})$
>>> If also $f(w_n)f(w_{n+1}) > 0$, set $F = F/2$
>> Otherwise, set $a_{n+1} = w_{n+1}$, $F = f(w_{n+1})$, $b_{n+1} = b_n$
>>> If also $f(w_n)f(w_{n+1}) > 0$, set $G = G/2$
>> Then $f(x)$ has a root in the interval $[a_{n+1}, b_{n+1}]$

If the modified regula falsi is applied to our example with $a_0 = 1$, $b_0 = 2$, then after six steps, one gets

$$1.32471795 \cdots = a_6 \leq \xi \leq b_6 = 1.32471796 \cdots$$
$$f(a_6) = (-1.736 \cdots)10^{-8} < 0 < (1.730 \cdots)10^{-8} = f(b_6)$$

which shows an impressive improvement over the bisection method.

A second, very popular modification of the regula falsi, called the *secant* method, retains the use of secants throughout, but *gives up the bracketing of the root*.

Algorithm 2.4 Secant method Given a function $f(x)$ and two points x_{-1}, x_0.

For $n = 0, 1, 2, \ldots$, until satisfied, do:
  Calculate $x_{n+1} = [f(x_n)x_{n-1} - f(x_{n-1})x_n]/[f(x_n) - f(x_{n-1})]$

If the second method is applied to our example with $x_{-1} = 1$, $x_0 = 2$, then after six steps one gets

$$x_6 = 1.3247179 \cdots, \qquad f(x_6) = (3.458 \cdots)10^{-8}$$

Apparently, the secant method locates quite rapidly a point at which $|f(x)|$ is "small," but gives, in general, no feeling for how far away from a root of $f(x)$ this point might be. Also, $f(x_n)$ and $f(x_{n-1})$ need not be of opposite sign, so that the expression

$$x_{n+1} = \frac{f(x_n)x_{n-1} - f(x_{n-1})x_n}{f(x_n) - f(x_{n-1})} \tag{2.6}$$

is prone to round-off-error effects. In an extreme situation, we might even have $f(x_n) = f(x_{n-1})$, making the calculation of x_{n+1} impossible. Although this does not cure the trouble, it is better to calculate x_{n+1} from the equivalent expression

$$x_{n+1} = x_n - f(x_n)\frac{x_n - x_{n-1}}{f(x_n) - f(x_{n-1})} \tag{2.7}$$

in which x_{n+1} is obtained from x_n by adding the "correction term"

$$\frac{-f(x_n)}{[f(x_n) - f(x_{n-1})]/(x_n - x_{n-1})} \tag{2.8}$$

Here $[f(x_n) - f(x_{n-1})]/(x_n - x_{n-1})$ is the slope of the secant to $f(x)$ through $\{x_{n-1}, f(x_{n-1})\}$ and $\{x_n, f(x_n)\}$; hence equal to the slope of $f(x)$ at some point between x_{n-1} and x_n if $f(x)$ is differentiable. Hence, when x_{n-1} and x_n are so close to each other that the calculation of $[f(x_n) - f(x_{n-1})]/(x_n - x_{n-1})$ involves severe loss of significance, then it is better to replace this ratio by the value of $f'(x)$ at some point "near" x_n and x_{n-1}, given that $f'(x)$ can be calculated.

If $f(x)$ is differentiable, then on replacing in (2.7) the slope of the secant by the slope of the tangent at x_n, one gets the iteration formula

$$x_{n+1} = x_n - \frac{f(x_n)}{f'(x_n)} \tag{2.9}$$

of Newton's method.

Algorithm 2.5   Newton's method   Given $f(x)$ continuously differentiable and a point x_0.

For $n = 0, 1, 2, \ldots$, until satisfied, do:

$\quad$⌊ Calculate $x_{n+1} = x_n - f(x_n)/f'(x_n)$

If this algorithm is applied to our example with $x_0 = 1$, then after four steps, one gets

$$x_4 = 1.3247181 \cdots, \qquad f(x_4) = (9.24 \cdots)10^{-7}$$

Finally, we mention fixed-point iteration, of which Newton's method is a special example.   If we set

$$g(x) = x - \frac{f(x)}{f'(x)} \tag{2.10}$$

then the iteration formula (2.9) for Newton's method takes on the simple form

$$x_{n+1} = g(x_n) \tag{2.11}$$

If the sequence $x_1, x_2, \cdots$ so generated converges to some point ξ, and $g(x)$ is continuous, then

$$\xi = \lim_{n \to \infty} x_{n+1} = \lim_{n \to \infty} g(x_n) = g\left(\lim_{n \to \infty} x_n \right) = g(\xi) \tag{2.12}$$

or $\xi = g(\xi)$, that is, ξ is then a fixed point of $g(x)$.   Clearly, if ξ is a fixed point of the iteration function $g(x)$ for Newton's method, then ξ is a solution of the equation $f(x) = 0$.   Now, for a given equation $f(x) = 0$, it is possible to choose various iteration functions $g(x)$, each having the property that a fixed point of $g(x)$ is a root of $f(x)$.   For each such choice, one may then calculate the sequence $x_1, x_2, \cdots$ by

$$x_{n+1} = g(x_n) \qquad n = 0, 1, 2, \cdots$$

and hope that it converges.   If it does, then its limit is a solution of the equation $f(x) = 0$.   We discuss fixed-point iteration in more detail in Secs. 2.3 and 2.4.

Example 2.1   The function $f(x) = x - 0.2 \sin x - 0.5$ has a root between $x_0 = 0.5$ and $x_1 = 1.0$.   It is easily verified that $f(0.5) = -0.09589$ while $f(1.0) = +0.33171$. Locate the root correct to six significant figures using Algorithms 2.1, 2.3, 2.4, and 2.5. The following calculations were performed on an IBM 7094 computer in single-precision floating-point arithmetic.

	Algorithm 2.1		Algorithm 2.3		Algorithm 2.4	Algorithm 2.5
n	x_n	ε_n	x_n	ε_n	x_n	x_n
−1					1.	
0	0.75	$3 \cdot 10^{-1}$	0.75	$3 \cdot 10^{-1}$	0.5	0.5
1	0.625	$2 \cdot 10^{-1}$	0.80606124	$2 \cdot 10^{-1}$	0.61212248	0.61629718
2	0.5625	$6 \cdot 10^{-2}$	0.61534080	$3 \cdot 10^{-3}$	0.61549349	0.61546820
3	0.59375	$3 \cdot 10^{-2}$	0.61701328	$2 \cdot 10^{-3}$	0.61546816	0.61546816
4	0.609375	$2 \cdot 10^{-2}$	0.61701363	$2 \cdot 10^{-3}$		
5	0.6171875	$8 \cdot 10^{-3}$	0.61546816	0		
6	0.61328125	$4 \cdot 10^{-3}$				
...	....	......				
10	0.61547852	$4 \cdot 10^{-4}$				
...	....	......				
19	0.61546850	$5 \cdot 10^{-7}$				

In Algorithms 2.1 and 2.2, x_n is the midpoint between the lower and the upper bounds, a_n and b_n, after n iterations, while the ε_n gives the corresponding bound on the error in x_n provided by the algorithm.   Note the rapid and systematic convergence of Algorithms 2.4 and 2.5.   The bisection method converges very slowly but steadily, while the modified regula falsi method seems to converge "in jumps," although it does obtain the correct zero rather quickly.

EXERCISES

2.1-1. Find an interval containing the real positive root of the function $f(x) = x^2 - 2x - 2$.   Use Algorithms 2.1 and 2.2 to compute this root correct to two significant figures.   Can you estimate how many steps each method would require to produce six significant figures?

2.1-2. For the example given in the text, carry out two steps of the modified regula falsi (Algorithm 2.3).

2.1-3. The polynomial $x^3 - 2x - 1$ has a root between 1 and 2.   Using the secant method (Algorithm 2.4), find this root correct to three significant figures.

2.1-4. In Algorithm 2.1 let M denote the length of the initial interval $[a_0, b_0]$.   Let $\{x_0, x_1, x_2, \ldots\}$ represent the successive midpoints generated by the bisection method. Show that

$$|x_{i+1} - x_i| = \frac{M}{2^{i+2}}$$

Also show that the number I of iterations required to guarantee an approximation to a root to an accuracy ε is given by

$$I > -2 - \frac{\log (\varepsilon/M)}{\log 2}$$

2.1-5. The bisection method can be applied whenever $f(a)f(b) < 0$. If $f(x)$ has more than one root in (a,b), which root does Algorithm 2.1 usually locate?

2.1-6. With $a = 0$, $b = 1$, each of the following functions changes sign in (a,b), that is, $f(a)f(b) < 0$. What point does the bisection Algorithm 2.1 locate? Is this point a zero of $f(x)$?

$$f(x) = (3x - 1)^{-1} \qquad f(x) = \cos 10x \qquad f(x) = \begin{cases} 1 & x \ge 0.3 \\ -1 & x < 0.3 \end{cases}$$

2.2 FORTRAN PROGRAMS FOR SOME ITERATIVE METHODS

When the algorithms introduced in the preceding section are used in calculations, the vague phrase "until satisfied" has to be replaced by precise termination criteria. In this section, we discuss some of the many possible ways of terminating iteration in a reasonable way and give translations of Algorithms 2.1, 2.3, 2.4, and 2.5 into FORTRAN.

FORTRAN SUBROUTINE FOR THE BISECTION ALGORITHM 2.1

```
      SUBROUTINE BISECT(F,A,B,XTOL,IFLAG)
      IFLAG = 0
      N = -1
      FA = F(A)
CHECK FOR SIGN CHANGE
      IF (FA*F(B) .LE. 0.)            GO TO 5
      IFLAG = 2
      WRITE (6,601) A,B
  601 FORMAT (43H F(X) IS OF SAME SIGN AT THE TWO ENDPOINTS
     *           2E15.7)
                                     RETURN
    5 ERROR = ABS(B - A)
    6 ERROR = ERROR/2.
CHECK FOR SUFFICIENTLY SMALL INTERVAL
      IF (ERROR .LE. XTOL)           RETURN
      XM = (A + B)/2.
CHECK FOR UNREASONABLE ERROR REQUIREMENT
      IF (XM + ERROR .EQ. XM)        GO TO 20
      FM = F(XM)
C   TEMPORARY PRINTOUT
      N = N + 1
      WRITE (6,606) N,A,XM,B,FA,FM
  606 FORMAT(I3,9H X-VALUES3E15.7/3X9H F-VALUES2E15.7/)
CHANGE TO NEW INTERVAL
      IF (FA*FM .LE. 0.)             GO TO 9
      A = XM
      FA = FM
                                     GO TO 6
    9 B = XM
                                     GO TO 6
   20 IFLAG = 1
                                     RETURN
      END
```

The following program makes use of this subroutine to find the root of Eq. (2.2), discussed in the preceding section.

```
      EXTERNAL FF
      A = 1.
      B = 2.
      CALL  BISECT(FF,A,B,1.E−6,IFLAG)
      IF (IFLAG .GT. 1)                      STOP
      XI = (A + B)/2.
      ERROR = ABS(A − B)/2.
      WRITE (6,600) XI,ERROR
  600 FORMAT(13H THE  ROOT IS E15.7,12H PLUS/MINUS E15.7)
                                             STOP
      END
      FUNCTION FF(X)
      FF = −1. − X*(1. − X*X)
                                             RETURN
      END
```

We now comment in some detail on the subroutine BISECT above. We have dropped the subscripts used in Algorithm 2.1. At any stage, the variables A and B contain the current lower and upper bound for the root to be found, the initial values being supplied by the calling program. In particular, the midpoint

$$XM = \frac{A + B}{2}$$

is always the current best estimate for the root, its absolute difference from the root always being bounded by

$$ERROR = \frac{|A - B|}{2}$$

Iteration is terminated once

$$ERROR \le XTOL$$

where XTOL is a given absolute error bound. The calling program then uses the current value of A and B to estimate the root. In addition to A, B, and XTOL, the calling program is also expected to supply the FORTRAN name of the function $f(x)$ whose zero is to be located. Since the assumption that $f(A)$ and $f(B)$ are of opposite sign is essential to the algorithm, there is an initial test for this condition. If $f(A)$ and $f(B)$ are not of opposite sign, the routine immediately terminates. The output variable IFLAG is used to signal this unhappy event to the calling program.

The subroutine never evaluates the given function more than once for the same argument, but rather saves those values which might be needed in subsequent steps. This is a reasonable policy since the routine might well be used for functions whose evaluation is quite costly. Finally, the routine has some protection against an unreasonable error requirement: Suppose, for simplicity, that all calculations are carried out in four-decimal-digit floating-point arithmetic and that the bounds A and B have already been improved to the point that

$$A = 131.6 \quad \text{and} \quad B = 131.7$$

so that

$$\text{ERROR} = \frac{B - A}{2} = 0.05$$

Then

$$XM = \frac{A + B}{2} = \frac{263.3}{2} = 131.6, \text{ or } 131.7$$

depending on how rounding to four decimal places is done. In any event,

$$XM = A \quad \text{or} \quad XM = B$$

so that, at the end of this step, neither A nor B has changed. If now the given error tolerance XTOL were less than 0.05, then the routine would never terminate, since $|B - A|/2$ would never decrease below 0.05. To avoid such an infinite loop due to an unreasonable error requirement (unreasonable since it requires the bounds A and B to be closer together than is possible for two floating-point numbers of that precision to be without coinciding), the routine calculates the current value of ERROR as follows. Initially,

$$\text{ERROR} = |B - A|$$

At the beginning of each step, ERROR is then halved, since that is the reduction in error per step of the bisection method. The routine terminates, once ERROR is so small that its floating-point addition to the current value of XM does not change XM.

Next we consider the modified regula falsi algorithm 2.3. In contrast to the bisection method, the modified regula falsi is not guaranteed to produce as small an interval containing the root as is possible with the finite-precision arithmetic used (see Exercise 2.2-1). Hence additional termination criteria must be used for this algorithm.

FORTRAN PROGRAM USING THE MODIFIED REGULA FALSI ALGORITHM 2.3

```
      EXTERNAL FG
      A = 1.
      B = 2.
```

```
      CALL MRGFLS(FG,A,B,1.E−7,1.E−10,30,IFLAG)
      IF (IFLAG .GT. 2)                          STOP
      XI = (A + B)/2.
      ERROR = ABS(B − A)/2.
      FXI = FG(XI)
      WRITE (6,600) XI, ERROR, FX1
  600 FORMAT (13H THE ROOT IS E15.7,12H PLUS/MINUS E15.7/
     *           11H FG(ROOT) = E15.7)
                                                 STOP
      END
      FUNCTION FG(X)
      FG = −1. − X*(1. − X*X)
                                                 RETURN
      END
      SUBROUTINE MRGFLS(F,A,B,XTOL,FTOL,NTOL,IFLAG)
      IFLAG = 0
      FA = F(A)
      SIGNFA = SIGN(1.,FA)
      FB = F(B)
CHECK FOR SIGN CHANGE
      IF (SIGNFA*FB .LE. 0.)                    GO TO 5
      IFLAG = 3
      WRITE (6,601) A,B
  601 FORMAT(43H F(X) IS OF SAME SIGN AT THE TWO ENDPOINTS
     *           2E15.7)
                                                 RETURN
    5 W = A
      FW = FA
      DO 20 N = 1,NTOL
CHECK FOR SUFFICIENTLY SMALL INTERVAL
      IF (ABS(B − A)/2. .LE. XTOL)             RETURN
CHECK FOR SUFFICIENTLY SMALL FUNCTION VALUES
      IF (ABS(FW) .GT. FTOL)                    GO TO 9
      A = W
      B = W
      IFLAG = 1
                                                 RETURN
    9 W = (FA*B − FB*A)/(FA − FB)
      PREVFW = SIGN(1.,FW)
      FW = F(W)
C   TEMPORARY PRINT OUT
      NM1 = N − 1
      WRITE (6,609) NM1,A,W,B,FA,FW,FB
  609 FORMAT(I3, 9H X-VALUES3E16.8/3X9H F-VALUES3E16.8/)
CHANGE TO NEW INTERVAL
      IF (SIGNFA*FW .LT. 0.)                    GO TO 10
      A = W
      FA = FW
      IF (FW*PREVFW .GT. 0.) FB = FB/2.
                                                 GO TO 20
   10 B = W
```

```
        FB = FW
        IF (FW*PREVFW .GT. 0.) FA = FA/2.
    20  CONTINUE
        IFLAG = 2
        WRITE (6,620) NTOL
   620  FORMAT(18H NO CONVERGENCE IN I5,11H ITERATIONS)
                                             RETURN
        END
```

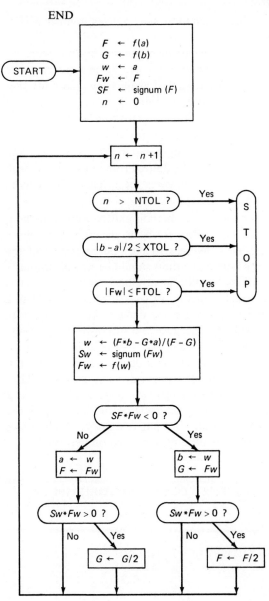

First, the routine terminates if the newly computed function value is no bigger in absolute value than a given tolerance FTOL. This brings in the point of view that an "approximate root" of the equation $f(x) = 0$ is a point x at which $|f(x)|$ is "small." Also, since the routine repeatedly divides by function values, such a termination is necessary in order to avoid, in extreme cases, division by zero.

Second, the routine terminates when more than a given number NTOL of iteration steps have been carried out. In a way, NTOL specifies the amount of computing the user is willing to invest in solving his problem. Use of such a termination criterion also protects the user against unreasonable error requirements and programming errors, and against the possibility that he has not fully understood the problem he is trying to solve. Hence such a termination criterion should be used with any iterative method.

As in the routine for the bisection method, the subroutine MRGFLS returns an integer IFLAG which indicates why iteration was terminated, and the latest value of the bounds A and B for the desired root. Finally, as with the bisection routine, the routine never evaluates the given function more than once for the same argument.

Algorithms 2.4 and 2.5 for the secant method and Newton's method, respectively, do not bracket a root. Rather, both generate a sequence $x_0, x_1, x_2, \ldots$, which, hopefully, converges to the desired root ξ of the given equation $f(x) = 0$. Hence both algorithms should be viewed primarily as finding points at which $f(x)$ is "small" in absolute value; iteration is terminated when the newly computed function value is absolutely less than a given FTOL. We have discussed, in Sec. 1.6, the danger of concluding that a certain sequence has "converged" just because two successive terms in the sequence differ by "very little." Nevertheless, we have used precisely such a termination criterion in both the routines listed below. For one, such a criterion is necessary in the secant method to avoid division by zero. Also, in both methods, the difference between the last two iterates calculated is a rather conservative bound for the error in the most recent iterate once the iterates are "close enough" to the root. To put it naively: If successive iterates do not differ by much, there is little reason to go on iterating.

FORTRAN PROGRAM USING THE SECANT ALGORITHM 2.4

```
EXTERNAL FF
X0 = 1.
X1 = 2.
CALL SECANT(FF,X0,X1,1.E−7,1.E−7,30,IFLAG)
IF (IFLAG .GT. 1)                          STOP
FX1 = FF(X1)
WRITE (6,600) X1,FX1
```

```
    600 FORMAT(13H THE ROOT IS E15.7,11H F(ROOT) = E15.7)
                                        STOP
        END
        SUBROUTINE SECANT(F,X0,X1,XTOL,FTOL,NTOL,IFLAG)
        IFLAG = 0
        F0 = F(X0)
        DELTAX = X1 − X0
        DO 20 N = 1,NTOL
        F1 = F(X1)
C   TEMPORARY PRINT OUT
        WRITE (6,600) N,X0,X1,F0,F1
    600 FORMAT (I5,9H X-VALUES 2E16.8/5X9H F-VALUES 2E16.8/)
        IF (ABS(F1) .LE. FTOL)                GO TO 30
        DELTAF = F0 − F1
        IF (DELTAF .EQ. 0.)                   GO TO 999
        DELTAX = F1/DELTAF*DELTAX
        X0 = X1
        X1 = X1 + DELTAX
        IF (ABS(DELTAX) .LE. XTOL)            RETURN
     20 F0 = F1
    999 IFLAG = 2
                                             RETURN
     30 IFLAG = 1
                                             RETURN
        END
        FUNCTION FF(X)
        FF = −1. − X*(1. − X*X)
                                             RETURN
        END
```

Finally, we note that we have used *absolute* error criteria exclusively. Thus we terminate iteration if

$$|f(x_n)| \leq \text{FTOL} \quad \text{or} \quad |x_n - x_{n-1}| \leq \text{XTOL} \tag{2.13}$$

If the size of the numbers involved is not known in advance, it is better policy to use *relative* error requirements, i.e., to terminate if

$$\frac{|f(x_n)|}{\text{FSIZE}} \leq \text{FTOL} \quad \text{or} \quad |x_n - x_{n-1}| \leq \text{XTOL}*|x_n| \tag{2.14}$$

where FSIZE is an estimate of the magnitude of $f(x)$ in some vicinity of the root established during the iteration.

FORTRAN PROGRAM USING NEWTON'S METHOD, ALGORITHM 2.5

```
        EXTERNAL FF,FFDER
        X0 = 1.
```

```
      CALL NEWTON(FF,FFDER,X0,1.E−7,1.E−7,10,IFLAG)
      IF (IFLAG .GT. 1)                        STOP
      FX0 = FF(X0)
      WRITE (6,600) X0,FX0
  600 FORMAT(13H THE ROOT IS E15.7,11H F(ROOT) = E15.7)
                                               STOP
      END
      SUBROUTINE NEWTON(F,FDERIV,X0,XTOL,FTOL,NTOL,IFLAG)
      IFLAG = 0
      DO 20 N = 1,NTOL
      FX0 = F(X0)
      IF (ABS(FX0) .LT. FTOL)                  RETURN
      DERIV = FDERIV(X0)
C TEMPORARY PRINT OUT
      WRITE (6,600) N,X0,FX0,DERIV
  600 FORMAT(I5,16H X0, FX0, DERIV 3E15.7)
      IF (DERIV .EQ. 0.)                       GO TO 999
      DELTAX = FX0/DERIV
      X0 = X0 − DELTAX
   20 IF (ABS(DELTAX) .LT. XTOL)               RETURN
  999 IFLAG = 2
                                               RETURN
      END
      FUNCTION FF(X)
      FF = −1. − X*(1. − X*X)
      RETURN
      END
      FUNCTION FFDER(X)
      FFDER = 3.*X*X − 1.
      RETURN
      END
```

In this program and the similar program for the secant method, iteration is terminated if the divisor D in a certain fraction is equal to zero. A termination criterion like this is usually necessary to avoid a program stop because of attempted division by zero. Some people prefer a test like

IF(ABS(D) .LT. EPS)   GO TO 999

where EPS is some small positive tolerance, to account for the situation where D would have been zero had it not been for rounding errors. But the aesthetic pleasure one may derive from following this reasoning usually does not pay for the pain of finding an equitable value for EPS.

Example 2.2 Find the real positive root of the equation

$$x^3 − x − 1 = 0$$

The results for Algorithms 2.1, 2.3, 2.4, and 2.5 are given in the following table, which parallels the table in Example 2.1.

| n | Bisection | | Modified regula falsi | | Secant | Newton |
	x_n	ε_n	x_n	ε_n	x_n	x_n
					1.0	
0	1.5	$5 \cdot 10^{-1}$	1.5	$5 \cdot 10^{-1}$	2.0	1.0
1	1.25	$3 \cdot 10^{-1}$	1.5833333	$4 \cdot 10^{-1}$	1.1666667	1.5
2	1.375	$1 \cdot 10^{-1}$	1.6616541	$3 \cdot 10^{-1}$	1.2531120	1.3478261
3	1.3125	$6 \cdot 10^{-2}$	1.3249256	$2 \cdot 10^{-3}$	1.3372064	1.3252004
4	1.34375	$3 \cdot 10^{-2}$	1.3256293	$9 \cdot 10^{-4}$	1.3238501	1.3247182
5	1.328125	$2 \cdot 10^{-2}$	1.3256305	$9 \cdot 10^{-4}$	1.3247079	1.3247180
6	1.3203125	$8 \cdot 10^{-3}$	1.3247180	$4 \cdot 10^{-9}$	1.3247180	
...	....	......				
10	1.3247070	$5 \cdot 10^{-4}$				
...	....	......				
20	1.3247180	$5 \cdot 10^{-7}$				

EXERCISES

2.2-1. Try to find the root $x = 1.3333$ of the equation $(x - 1.3333)^3 = 0$ to five places of accuracy using the modified regula falsi algorithm 2.3 and starting with the interval [1,2]. Why does the method fail in this case to give a "small" interval containing the root?

2.2-2. Because of the use of the product FA*FM in the subroutine BISECT, overflow or underflow may occur during the execution of this subroutine, even though the function values FA and FM are well-defined floating-point numbers. Repair this flaw in the subroutine, using the FORTRAN function SIGN. Also, is it necessary to update the value of FA each time A is changed?

2.2-3. Prove that the function $f(x) = e^x - 1 - x - x^2/2$ has exactly one zero, namely, $\xi = 0$. (*Hint*: Use the remainder in a Taylor expansion for e^x around 0.) Then evaluate the FORTRAN function

$$F(X) = EXP(X) - 1. - X - X*X/2.$$

for various values of the argument X "near" zero to show that this function has many sign changes, hence many zeros, "near" $X = 0$. What can you conclude from these facts, specifically, as regards the bisection method, and more generally, as regards the (theoretical) concept of a "zero of a function"?

2.2-4. Suppose you are to find that root of the equation $\tan x = x$ which is closest to 50, using the secant method and nine-decimal-digit floating-point arithmetic. Would it be "reasonable" to use the termination criterion

$$|f(x_n)| \leq 10^{-8}?$$

2.2-5. Find the smallest positive root of each of the following equations to maximum precision on your computer using Algorithms 2.1, 2.3, 2.4, and 2.5. Compare your results, the number of iterations required, and the accuracy attained.

(a) $e^{-x^2} - \cos x = 0$ (b) $\sinh x - \sin x = 0$

2.2-6. (Binary Search) The problem of table lookup consists in finding for given X, an integer I such that X lies between TABLE (I) and TABLE (I + 1), where TABLE is a given one-dimensional array containing an increasing (or a decreasing) sequence.

Write a FORTRAN subprogram which utilizes the bisection method to carry out this search efficiently. How many times does your routine compare X with an entry of TABLE, if TABLE has n entries?

2.3 FIXED-POINT ITERATION

In Sec. 2.1, we mentioned fixed-point iteration as a possible method for obtaining a root of the equation

$$f(x) = 0 \qquad (2.15)$$

In this method, one derives from (2.15) an equation of the form

$$x = g(x) \qquad (2.16)$$

so that any solution of (2.16), i.e., any *fixed point* of $g(x)$, is a solution of (2.15). This may be accomplished in many ways. If, for example,

$$f(x) = x^2 - x - 2 \qquad (2.17)$$

then among possible choices for $g(x)$ are the following:

(a) $g(x) = x^2 - 2$

(b) $g(x) = \sqrt{2 + x}$

(c) $g(x) = 1 + \dfrac{2}{x}$ $\qquad (2.18)$

(d) $g(x) = x - \dfrac{x^2 - x - 2}{m}$ for some nonzero constant m

Each such $g(x)$ is called an *iteration function* for solving (2.15) [with $f(x)$ given by (2.17)]. Once an iteration function $g(x)$ for solving (2.15) is chosen, one carries out the following algorithm.

Algorithm 2.6 Fixed-point iteration Given an iteration function $g(x)$ and a starting point x_0

> For $n = 0, 1, 2, \ldots$, until satisfied, do:
> $\quad$ Calculate $x_{n+1} = g(x_n)$

For this algorithm to be useful, we must prove:

(i) For the given starting point x_0, we can calculate successively $x_1, x_2, \ldots$.

(ii) The sequence $x_1, x_2, \ldots$ converges to some point ξ.

(iii) The limit ξ is a fixed point of $g(x)$, that is, $\xi = g(\xi)$.

The example of the real-valued function

$$g(x) = -\sqrt{x}$$

shows that (i) is not a trivial requirement. For in this case, $g(x)$ is defined only for $x \geq 0$. Starting with any $x_0 > 0$, we get $x_1 = g(x_0) < 0$; hence we cannot calculate x_2. To settle (i), we make the following assumption.

Assumption 2.1 There is an interval $I = [a,b]$ such that, for all $x \in I$, $g(x)$ is defined and $g(x) \in I$; that is, the function $g(x)$ maps I into itself.

It follows from this assumption, by induction on n, that if $x_0 \in I$, then for all n, $x_n \in I$; hence $x_{n+1} = g(x_n)$ is defined and is in I.

We discussed (iii) already, in Sec. 2.1. For we proved there that (iii) holds if $g(x)$ is continuous. Hence, to settle (iii), we make Assumption 2.2.

Assumption 2.2 The iteration function $g(x)$ is continuous on $I = [a,b]$.

We note that Assumptions 2.1 and 2.2 together imply that $g(x)$ *has a fixed point* in $I = [a,b]$. For if either $g(a) = a$ or $g(b) = b$, this is obviously so. Otherwise, we have $g(a) \neq a$ and $g(b) \neq b$. But by Assumption 2.1, both $g(a)$ and $g(b)$ are in $I = [a,b]$; hence $g(a) > a$ and $g(b) < b$. This implies that the function $h(x) = g(x) - x$ satisfies $h(a) > 0$, $h(b) < 0$. Since $h(x)$ is continuous on I, by Assumption 2.2, $h(x)$ must therefore vanish somewhere in I, by the intermediate-value theorem for continuous functions (see Sec. 1.7). But this says that $g(x)$ has a fixed point in I, and proves the assertion.

For the discussion of (ii) concerning convergence, it is instructive to carry out the iteration graphically. This can be done as follows. Since $x_n = g(x_{n-1})$, the point $\{x_{n-1}, x_n\}$ lies on the graph of $g(x)$. To locate $\{x_n, x_{n+1}\}$ from $\{x_{n-1}, x_n\}$, draw the straight line through $\{x_{n-1}, x_n\}$ parallel to the x axis. This line intersects the line $y = x$ at the point $\{x_n, x_n\}$. Through this point, draw the straight line parallel to the y axis. This line intersects the graph $y = g(x)$ of $g(x)$ at the point $\{x_n, g(x_n)\}$. But since $g(x_n) = x_{n+1}$, this is the desired point $\{x_n, x_{n+1}\}$. In Fig. 2.3, we have carried out the first few steps of fixed-point iteration for four typical cases. Note that ξ is a fixed point of $g(x)$ if and only if $y = g(x)$ and $y = x$ intersect at $\{\xi, \xi\}$.

As Fig. 2.3 shows, fixed-point iteration may well fail to converge, as it does in Fig. 2.3a and d. Whether or not the iteration converges [given that $g(x)$ has a fixed point] seems to depend on the slope of $g(x)$. If the slope of $g(x)$ is too large in absolute value, near a fixed point ξ of $g(x)$, then we cannot hope for convergence to that fixed point. We therefore make Assumption 2.3.

Assumption 2.3 The iteration function is differentiable on $I = [a,b]$. Further, there exists a nonnegative constant $K < 1$ such that

$$\text{for all } x \in I \qquad |g'(x)| \leq K$$

Note that Assumption 2.3 implies Assumption 2.2, since a differentiable function is, in particular, continuous.

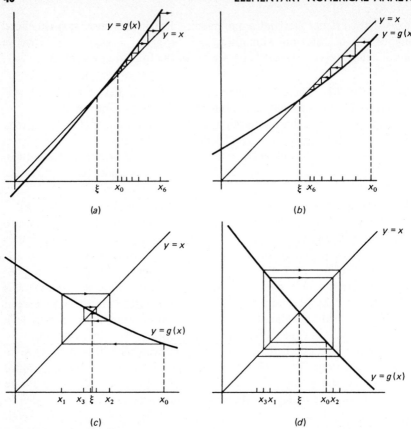

Fig. 2.3 Fixed-point iteration.

Theorem 2.1 Let $g(x)$ be an iteration function satisfying Assumptions 2.1 and 2.3. Then $g(x)$ has exactly one fixed point ξ in I, and starting with any point x_0 in I, the sequence $x_1, x_2, \ldots$ generated by fixed-point iteration of Algorithm 2.6 converges to ξ.

To prove this theorem, recall that we have already proved the existence of a fixed point ξ for $g(x)$ in I. Now let x_0 be any point in I. Then, as we remarked earlier, fixed-point iteration generates a sequence $x_1, x_2, \ldots$ of points all lying in I, by Assumption 2.1. Denote the error in the nth iterate by

$$e_n = \xi - x_n \qquad n = 0, 1, 2, \ldots$$

Then since $\xi = g(\xi)$ and $x_n = g(x_{n-1})$, we have

$$e_n = \xi - x_n = g(\xi) - g(x_{n-1}) = g'(\eta_n)e_{n-1} \qquad (2.19)$$

for some η_n between ξ and x_{n-1} by the mean-value theorem for derivatives (see Sec. 1.7). Hence by Assumption 2.3,

$$|e_n| \leq K|e_{n-1}|$$

It follows by induction on n that

$$|e_n| \leq K|e_{n-1}| \leq K^2|e_{n-2}| \leq \cdots \leq K^n|e_0|$$

Since $0 \leq K < 1$, we have $\lim_{n\to\infty} K^n = 0$; therefore

$$\lim_{n\to\infty} |e_n| = \lim_{n\to\infty} K^n|e_0| = 0$$

regardless of the initial error e_0. But this says that $x_1, x_2, \ldots$ converges to ξ. It also proves that ξ is the only fixed point of $g(x)$ in I. For if, also, ζ is a fixed point of $g(x)$ in I, then with $x_0 = \zeta$, we should have $x_1 = g(x_0) = \zeta$; hence $|e_0| = |e_1| \leq K|e_0|$. Since $K < 1$, this then implies $|e_0| = 0$, or $\zeta = \xi$. This completes the proof.

It is often quite difficult to verify Assumption 2.1. In such a situation, the following weaker statement may at least assure success if the iteration is started "sufficiently close" to the fixed point.

Corollary If $g(x)$ is continuously differentiable in some open interval containing the fixed point ξ, and if $|g'(\xi)| < 1$, then there exists an $\varepsilon > 0$ so that fixed-point iteration with $g(x)$ converges whenever $|x_0 - \xi| \leq \varepsilon$.

Indeed, since $g'(x)$ is continuous near ξ and $|g'(\xi)| < 1$, there exists, for any K with $|g'(\xi)| < K < 1$, an $\varepsilon > 0$ so that $|g'(x)| \leq K$ for every x with $|x - \xi| \leq \varepsilon$. Fix one such K with its corresponding ε. Then, for $I = [\xi - \varepsilon, \xi + \varepsilon]$, Assumption 2.3 is satisfied. As to Assumption 2.1, let x be any point in I, so that $|x - \xi| \leq \varepsilon$. Then, as in the proof of Theorem 2.1,

$$g(x) - \xi = g(x) - g(\xi) = g'(\eta)(x - \xi)$$

for some point η between x and ξ, hence in I. But then

$$|g(x) - \xi| \leq |g'(\eta)| \, |x - \xi| \leq K\varepsilon < \varepsilon$$

showing that $g(x)$ is in I if x is in I. This verifies Assumption 2.1, and the conclusion now follows from Theorem 2.1.

Because of this corollary, a fixed point ξ for $g(x)$, for which $|g'(\xi)| < 1$, is often called *a point of attraction* [for the iteration with $g(x)$].

We consider again the quadratic function $f(x) = x^2 - x - 2$ of (2.17). The zeros of this function are 2 and -1. Suppose we wish to calculate the root $\xi = 2$ by fixed-point iteration. If we use the iteration function given by (2.18a),

$$g(x) = x^2 - 2$$

then for $x > \frac{1}{2}, g'(x) > 1$. It follows that Assumption 2.3 is not satisfied for any interval containing $\xi = 2$; that is, $\xi = 2$ is not a point of attraction. In fact, one can prove for this example that, starting at any point x_0, the sequence $x_1, x_2, \ldots$ generated by this fixed-point iteration will converge to $\xi = 2$ only if, for some n_0, $x_n = 2$ for all $n \geq n_0$, that is, if $\xi = 2$ is hit "accidentally" (see Exercise 2.3-1).

On the other hand, if we choose (2.18b), then

$$g(x) = \sqrt{2 + x} \qquad \text{hence} \qquad g'(x) = \frac{1}{2\sqrt{2 + x}}$$

Now $x \geq 0$ implies $g(x) \geq 0$ and $0 \leq g'(x) \leq 1/\sqrt{8} < 1$, while, for example, $x \leq 7$ implies $g(x) = \sqrt{2 + x} \leq \sqrt{2 + 7} = 3$. Hence, with $I = [0,7]$, both Assumptions 2.1 and 2.3 are satisfied, and any $x_0 \in [0,7]$ leads, therefore, to a convergent sequence. Indeed, if we take $x_0 = 0$, then

$$\begin{aligned}
x_1 &= \sqrt{2} &&= 1.41421 \\
x_2 &= \sqrt{3.41421} &&= 1.84775 \\
x_3 &= \sqrt{3.84775} &&= 1.96157 \\
x_4 &= \sqrt{3.96157} &&= 1.99036 \\
x_5 &= \sqrt{3.99036} &&= 1.99759
\end{aligned}$$

which clearly converges to the root $\xi = 2$.

As a more realistic example, we consider the transcendental equation

$$f(x) = x - 2 \sin x = 0 \tag{2.20}$$

The most natural rearrangement here is

$$x = 2 \sin x$$

so that $g(x) = 2 \sin x$. An examination of the curves $y = g(x)$ and $y = x$ shows that there is a root between $\pi/3$ and $2\pi/3$. Further,

$$\text{if } \frac{\pi}{3} \leq x \leq \frac{2\pi}{3} \qquad \text{then } \sqrt{3} \leq g(x) \leq 2$$

Hence if $\pi/3 \leq a \leq \sqrt{3}$ and $2 \leq b \leq 2\pi/3$, then Assumption 2.1 is satisfied. Finally, $g'(x) = 2 \cos x$ strictly decreases from 1 to -1 as x increases from $\pi/3$ to $2\pi/3$. It follows that Assumption 2.3 is satisfied whenever $\pi/3 < a \leq \sqrt{3}$, $2 \leq b < 2\pi/3$. In conclusion, fixed-point iteration with $g(x) = 2 \sin x$ converges to the unique solution of (2.20) in $[\pi/3,2\pi/3]$ whenever $x_0 \in (\pi/3,2\pi/3)$.

Example 2.3 Using fixed-point iteration, find the positive zero of the function $f(x) = x - 0.2 \sin x - 0.5$ considered in Example 2.1.

Rewriting the equation $f(x) = 0$ in the form

$$x = 0.5 + 0.2 \sin x = g(x)$$

which is suitable for fixed-point iteration, and choosing $x_0 = 0.5$, we verify directly that $|g'(x)| = |0.2 \cos x| < 1$ in the interval $[0,1]$ while $0 \le g(x) \le 0.7$ for $x \in [0,1]$; hence convergence is assured.   We give below a FORTRAN program for this example and the machine results (as computed on an IBM 7094).

FORTRAN PROGRAM FOR EXAMPLE 2.3

```
C       TO SOLVE F(X) = 0 OR G(X) = X
        F(X) = X − .2*SIN(X) − .5
        G(X) = .5 + .2*SIN(X)
        X = .5
        Y = F(X)
        WRITE(6,4)X,Y
        DO 1 I = 1,20
        X1 = G(X)
        Y = F(X1)
        WRITE(6,5)I,X1,Y
        IF(ABS (X1 − X) .LT. 1.E−7)GO TO 2
      1 X = X1
        WRITE(6,6)
      2 STOP
      4 FORMAT(1H03X1HI8X 4HX(I) 12X 8HF(X(I)) //4X1H0I2E17.8)
      5 FORMAT(1H0 I4,2E17.8)
      6 FORMAT(//36H0FAILED TO CONVERGE IN 20 ITERATIONS)
        END
```

COMPUTER RESULTS FOR EXAMPLE 2.3

I	X(I)	F(X(I))
0	0.50000000E 00	−0.95885109E−01
1	0.59588511E 00	−0.16363200E−01
2	0.61224830E 00	−0.26934631E−02
3	0.61494176E 00	−0.44042990E−03
4	0.61538219E 00	−0.71939081E−04
5	0.61545412E 00	−0.11753291E−04
6	0.61546587E 00	−0.19222498E−05
7	0.61546779E 00	−0.32037497E−06
8	0.61546810E 00	−0.55879354E−07
9	0.61546815E 00	−0.14900161E−07

EXERCISES

2.3-1. Verify that the iteration

$$x_{i+1} = x_i^2 - 2$$

will converge to the solution $\xi = 2$ of the equation

$$x^2 - x - 2 = 0$$

only if, for some n_0, all iterates x_n with $n \geq n_0$ are equal to 2, i.e., only "accidentally."

2.3-2. For each of the following equations determine an iteration function (and an interval I) so that the conditions of Theorem 2.1 are satisfied (assume that it is desired to find the smallest positive root):

$$(a)\ x^3 - x - 1 = 0 \qquad (b)\ x - \tan x = 0 \qquad (c)\ e^{-x} - \cos x = 0$$

2.3-3. Write a program based on Algorithm 2.6 and use this program to calculate the smallest roots of the equations given in Exercise 2.3-2.

2.3-4. Determine the largest interval I with the following property: For all $x_0 \in I$, fixed-point iteration with the iteration function

$$g(x) = x(2 - ax)$$

converges, when started with x_0. Are Assumptions 2.1 and 2.3 satisfied for your choice of I? What numbers are possible limits of this iteration? Can you think of a good reason for using this particular iteration? Note that the interval depends on the constant a.

2.3-5. Same as Exercise 2.3-4, but with $g(x) = (x + a/x)/2$.

2.3-6. The function $g(x) = \sqrt{1 + x^2}$ satisfies Assumption 2.1 for $I = (-\infty,\infty)$, and Assumption 2.3 on any finite interval, yet fixed-point iteration with this iteration function does not converge. Why?

2.4 CONVERGENCE ACCELERATION FOR FIXED-POINT ITERATION

In this section, we investigate the rate of convergence of fixed-point iteration and show how information about the rate of convergence can be used at times to accelerate convergence.

We assume that the iteration function $g(x)$ is continuously differentiable and that, starting with some point x_0, the sequence $x_1, x_2, \ldots$ generated by fixed-point iteration converges to some point ξ. This point ξ is then a fixed point of $g(x)$, and we have, by (2.19), that

$$e_{n+1} = \xi - x_{n+1} = g'(\eta_n)e_n \tag{2.21}$$

for some η_n between ξ and x_n, $n = 1, 2, \ldots$. Since $\lim_{n \to \infty} x_n = \xi$, it then follows that $\lim \eta_n = \xi$; hence

$$\lim_{n \to \infty} g'(\eta_n) = g'(\xi)$$

$g'(x)$ being continuous, by assumption. Consequently,

$$e_{n+1} = g'(\xi)e_n + \varepsilon_n e_n \tag{2.22}$$

where $\lim \varepsilon_n = 0$. Hence, if $g'(\xi) \neq 0$, then for large enough n,

$$e_{n+1} \approx g'(\xi)e_n \tag{2.23}$$

or the error e_{n+1} in the $(n + 1)$st iterate depends (more or less) linearly on the error e_n in the nth iterate. We therefore say that $x_0, x_1, x_2, \ldots$ converges *linearly* to ξ.

Now note that we can solve (2.21) for ξ.   For

$$\xi - x_{n+1} = g'(\eta_n)(\xi - x_n)$$

gives

$$\xi(1 - g'(\eta_n)) = x_{n+1} - g'(\eta_n)x_n$$
$$= x_{n+1} - x_n + [1 - g'(\eta_n)]x_n$$

Therefore

$$\xi = x_n + \frac{x_{n+1} - x_n}{1 - g'(\eta_n)} \qquad (2.24)$$

Of course, we do not know the number $g'(\eta_n)$.   But we know that the ratio

$$r_n = \frac{x_{n+1} - x_n}{x_n - x_{n-1}} = \frac{g(x_n) - g(x_{n-1})}{x_n - x_{n-1}} = g'(\zeta_n) \qquad (2.25)$$

for some ζ_n between x_n and x_{n-1}, by the mean-value theorem for derivatives. For large enough n, therefore, we have

$$r_n = g'(\zeta_n) \approx g'(\xi) \approx g'(\eta_n)$$

and then the point

$$\hat{x}_n = x_n + \frac{x_{n+1} - x_n}{1 - r_n} \qquad \text{with } r_n = \frac{x_{n+1} - x_n}{x_n - x_{n-1}} \qquad (2.26)$$

should be a very much better approximation to ξ than is x_n or x_{n+1}.

This can also be seen graphically.   Retracing the argument which led to (2.26), we find from (2.26) that

$$(\hat{x}_n - x_n)(1 - r_n) = x_{n+1} - x_n$$

or

$$\hat{x}_n - x_{n+1} = r_n(\hat{x}_n - x_n)$$

or with $x_{n+1} = g(x_n)$,

$$\hat{x}_n = g(x_n) + r_n(\hat{x}_n - x_n)$$

Hence $\hat{x}_n$ is the fixed point of the straight line

$$s(x) = g(x_n) + r_n(x - x_n)$$

Since $r_n = [g(x_n) - g(x_{n-1})]/(x_n - x_{n-1})$, $s(x)$ is the *secant* on $g(x)$ through the points $\{x_n, g(x_n)\}$ and $\{x_{n-1}, g(x_{n-1})\}$. If now the slope of $g(x)$ varies little between x_{n-1} and ξ, that is, if $g(x)$ is approximately a straight line

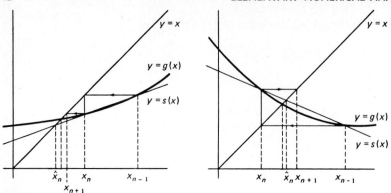

Fig. 2.4 Convergence acceleration for fixed-point iteration.

between x_{n-1} and ξ, then the secant $s(x)$ should be a very good approximation to $g(x)$ in that interval; hence the fixed point $\hat{x}_n$ of the secant should be a very good approximation to the fixed point ξ of $g(x)$; see Fig. 2.4.

Since x_{n+1} is usually closer to ξ than is x_n, it is advantageous to write $\hat{x}_n$ in terms of x_{n+1} plus a (presumably smaller) correction term rather than using (2.26). This gives

$$\hat{x}_n = x_{n+1} + \frac{x_{n+1} - x_n}{r_n^{-1} - 1} \quad \text{with } r_n^{-1} = \frac{x_n - x_{n-1}}{x_{n+1} - x_n} \tag{2.27}$$

involving the divisor $(r_n^{-1} - 1)$ whose magnitude is larger than $(1 - r_n)$ if $|r_n| < 1$.

In practice, we will not be able to prove that any particular x_n is "close enough" to ξ to make $\hat{x}_n$ a better approximation to ξ than is x_n or x_{n+1}. But we can test the hypothesis that x_n is "close enough" by checking the ratios r_{n-1}, r_n. If the ratios are approximately constant, we accept the hypothesis that the slope of $g(x)$ varies little in the interval of interest; hence we believe that the secant $s(x)$ is a good enough approximation to $g(x)$ to make $\hat{x}_n$ a very much better approximation to ξ than is x_n. In particular, we then accept $|\hat{x} - x_n|$ as a good estimate for the error $|e_n|$.

Example 2.4 The equation

$$1.5x - \tan x = 0.1 \tag{2.28}$$

has a root $\xi = 0.20592169510 \cdot \cdots$. We choose the iteration function

$$g(x) = \frac{0.1 + \tan x}{1.5}$$

and starting with $x_0 = 0$, generate the sequence $x_1, x_2, \ldots$ by fixed-point iteration. Some of the x_n are listed in Fig. 2.5. The sequence seems to converge, slowly but

n	x_n	$\hat{x}_n$	r_n	y_n
	0.0			0.0
1	0.0666667	0.2005954	0.6678	0.2005954
2	0.1111771	0.2024021	0.6721	0.2059125
3	0.1410916	0.2039180	0.6774	0.2059217
4	0.1613569	0.2048536	0.6822	
5	0.1751813	0.2053721	0.6859	
...	....	....	......	
10	0.2009941	0.2059055	0.6940	
15	0.2051206	0.2059213	0.6955	
20	0.2057911	0.2059217	0.6957	
25	0.2059004		0.6957	
30	0.2059182		0.6958	

Fig. 2.5

surely, to ξ. We also calculate the sequence of ratios r_n. These too are listed in Fig. 2.5. Specifically, we find

$$r_1 = 0.667 \cdots \qquad r_2 = 0.672 \cdots \qquad r_3 = 0.677 \cdots$$

which we think is "sufficiently" constant to conclude that, for all $n \geq 1$, $\hat{x}_n$ is a better approximation to ξ than is x_n. This is confirmed in Fig. 2.5, where we have also listed the $\hat{x}_n$.

Whether or not any particular $\hat{x}_n$ is a better approximation to ξ than is x_n, one can prove that the sequence $\hat{x}_1, \hat{x}_2, \ldots$ converges faster to ξ than does the original sequence $x_0, x_1, \ldots$; that is,

$$\hat{x}_n = \xi + o(e_n) \tag{2.29}$$

[See Sec. 1.6 for the definition of $o(\ )$.]

This process of deriving from a linearly converging sequence $x_0, x_1, x_2, \ldots$ a faster converging sequence $\hat{x}_1, \hat{x}_2, \ldots$ by (2.27) is usually called *Aitken's Δ^2 process*. Using the abbreviations

$$\Delta x_k = x_{k+1} - x_k \qquad \Delta^2 x_k = \Delta(\Delta x_k) = \Delta x_{k+1} - \Delta x_k$$

(2.27) is generally written

$$\hat{x}_n = x_{n+1} - \frac{(\Delta x_n)^2}{\Delta^2 x_{n-1}} \tag{2.30}$$

therefore the name "Δ^2 process." This process is applicable to any linearly convergent sequence, whether generated by fixed-point iteration or not.

Algorithm 2.7 Aitken's Δ^2 process Given a sequence $x_0, x_1, x_2, \ldots$ converging to ξ, calculate the sequence $\hat{x}_1, \hat{x}_2, \ldots$ by (2.30).

If the sequence $x_0, x_1, x_2, \ldots$ converges linearly to ξ, that is, if

$$\xi - x_{n+1} = K(\xi - x_n) + o(\xi - x_n) \qquad \text{for some } K \neq 0$$

then

$$\hat{x}_n = \xi + o(\xi - x_n)$$

Further, if from a certain k on, the sequence $\Delta x_k / \Delta x_{k-1}, \Delta x_{k+1}/\Delta x_k, \ldots$ of difference ratios is approximately constant, then $\hat{x}_k$ can be assumed to be a better approximation to ξ than is x_k. In particular, $|\hat{x}_k - x_k|$ is then a good estimate for the error $|\xi - x_k|$.

If, in the case of fixed-point iteration, we decide that a certain $\hat{x}_k$ is a very much better approximation to ξ than is x_k, then it is certainly wasteful to continue generating x_{k+1}, x_{k+2}, etc. It seems more reasonable to start fixed-point iteration afresh with $\hat{x}_k$ as the initial guess. This leads to the following algorithm.

Algorithm 2.8 Steffensen iteration Given the iteration function $g(x)$ and a point y_0.

> For $n = 0, 1, 2, \ldots$, until satisfied, do:
> | Set $x_0 = y_n$
> | Calculate $x_1 = g(x_0)$, $x_2 = g(x_1)$
> | Calculate $d = \Delta x_1$, $r^{-1} = \Delta x_0 / d$
> | Calculate $y_{n+1} = x_2 + d/(r^{-1} - 1)$

One step of this algorithm consists of two steps of fixed-point iteration followed by one application of (2.27), using the three iterates available to get the starting value for the next step.

We have listed in Fig. 2.5 the y_n generated by this algorithm applied to Example 2.4. Already y_3 is accurate to all places shown.

In the FORTRAN program below we have combined Steffensen iteration with ordinary fixed-point iteration in the following way: Initially, fixed-point iteration is used to generate iterates $x_0, x_1, x_2, \ldots$. Also, the ratios $r_1^{-1}, r_2^{-1}, \ldots$ are calculated. As soon as these ratios become sufficiently constant, we switch over to Steffensen iteration. The program terminates if

$$n > \text{NTOL} \qquad \text{or} \qquad |g(x_n) - x_n| \leq \text{XTOL}$$

with NTOL a given upper bound on the number of steps to be carried out, and XTOL a given absolute-error requirement.

FORTRAN PROGRAM USING ALGORITHM 2.8

```
      EXTERNAL GG
      Y = 0.
      CALL STEFF(GG,Y,1.E − 7,30,IFLAG)
      IF (IFLAG .GT. 1)                      STOP
      WRITE (6,600) Y
  600 FORMAT(20H THE FIXED POINT IS E15.7)
                                             STOP
      END
      SUBROUTINE STEFF(G,Y,XTOL,NTOL,IFLAG)
      IFLAG = 0
      X1 = G(Y)
      D = X1 − Y
      RINV = 0.
      DO 20 N = 1,NTOL
C   TEMPORARY PRINT OUT
      WRITE (6,618) N,Y,X1
  618 FORMAT(I4,2E15.7)
      Y = G(X1)
      DELX1 = Y − X1
CHECK FOR SUFFICIENTLY SMALL CHANGE
      IF (ABS(DELX1) .LE. XTOL)           RETURN
      PREVRI = RINV
      RINV = D/DELX1
C   TEMPORARY PRINT OUT
      WRITE (6,619) Y,RINV
  619 FORMAT(34XE15.7,E20.5)
CHECK WHETHER CURRENT RATIO INDICATES AT LEAST THAT
C               ABS(GPRIME(X)).LT.1.
      IF (ABS(RINV) .LE. 1.)                 GO TO 19
CHECK FOR APPROXIMATELY CONSTANT RATIOS
      IF (ABS((RINV − PREVRI)/RINV) .GE. .1) GO TO 19
      Y = Y + DELX1/(RINV − 1.)
      X1 = G(Y)
      D = X1 − Y
                                             GO TO 20
   19 X1 = Y
      D = DELX1
   20 CONTINUE
      IFLAG = 3
      WRITE (6,620) NTOL
  620 FORMAT(39H ERROR REQUIREMENT NOT SATISFIED AFTER
     *          I4,11H ITERATIONS)
                                             RETURN
      END
      FUNCTION GG(X)
      GG = (.1 + TAN(X))/1.5
                                             RETURN
      END
```

EXERCISES

2.4-1. Assume that the error of a fixed-point iteration satisfies the recurrence relation

$$e_{n+1} = ke_n$$

for some constant k, $|k| < 1$. Find an expression for the number of iterations N required to reduce the initial error e_0 by a factor $10^{-m}(m > 0)$.

$$\text{Ans.: } N > -\frac{m}{\log |k|}$$

2.4-2. Fixed-point iteration applied to the equation

$$f(x) = 0.5 - x + 0.2 \sin x = 0$$

produced the successive approximations given in the following table:

k	x_k
0	0.5000 0000
1	0.5958 8511
2	0.6122 4830
3	0.6149 4176
4	0.6153 8219
5	0.6154 5412
6	0.6154 6587
7	0.6154 6779
8	0.6154 6810
9	0.6154 6815

      Use the Aitken Algorithm 2.7 to compute an accelerated sequence $\hat{x}_k$ and the ratios r_k (see Fig. 2.5). From the ratios r_k calculate the approximate value of $g'(\xi)$.

2.4-3. Adapt the program in the text on the Steffensen accelerated iteration (Algorithm 2.8) for use in your computing center. For the problem considered in Exercise 2.4-2, an appropriate iteration function is

$$g(x) = 0.5 + 0.2 \sin x$$

Using this iteration function, calculate an accelerated sequence of approximations using Algorithm 2.8 and taking $x_0 = 0.5$.

2.4-4. In Sec. 2.3 we showed that the fixed-point iteration

$$x_{i+1} = \sqrt{2 + x_i}$$

produced the following sequence of approximations to the positive root of $f(x) = x^2 - x - 2$:

$$x_0 = 0 \qquad x_1 = 1.41421 \qquad x_2 = 1.84775$$
$$x_3 = 1.96157 \qquad x_4 = 1.99036 \qquad x_5 = 1.99759$$

Use Aitken's Algorithm 2.7 to accelerate this sequence and note the improvement in the rate of convergence to the root $\xi = 2$.

2.4-5. Consider the iteration function $g(x) = x - x^3$. Find the unique fixed point of $g(x)$. Prove that fixed-point iteration with this iteration function converges to the unique fixed point ξ of $g(x)$ if $x_0 \in (-1,1)$. (*Hint:* Use the fact that if $x_n \leq x_{n+1} \leq x_{n+2} \leq \cdots \leq c$ for some constant c, then the sequence converges.) Is it true that, for some $k < 1$ and all n, $|e_n| \leq k|e_{n-1}|$?

2.5 QUADRATIC CONVERGENCE AND NEWTON'S METHOD

In the preceding section, we proved that the error e_n in the nth iterate x_n of fixed-point iteration satisfies

$$e_{n+1} \approx g'(\xi)e_n \tag{2.31}$$

for large enough n, provided $g(x)$ is continuously differentiable. Apparently, the smaller $g'(\xi)$, the more rapidly e_n goes to zero as $n \to \infty$. The convergence of fixed-point iteration should therefore be most rapid when $g'(\xi) = 0$.

If $g(x)$ is twice-differentiable, we get from Taylor's formula that

$$e_{n+1} = \xi - x_{n+1} = g(\xi) - g(x_n)$$
$$= -g'(\xi)(x_n - \xi) - \tfrac{1}{2}g''(\zeta_n)(x_n - \xi)^2$$

for some ζ_n between ξ and x_n, that is, that

$$e_{n+1} = g'(\xi)e_n - \tfrac{1}{2}g''(\zeta_n)e_n^2 \tag{2.32}$$

Hence, *if $g'(\xi) = 0$ and $g''(x)$ is continuous at ξ, then*

$$e_{n+1} \approx -\tfrac{1}{2}g''(\xi)e_n^2 \qquad \text{for large enough } n \tag{2.33}$$

In this case, e_{n+1} is (more or less) a quadratic function of e_n. We therefore say that, in this case, $x_1, x_2, \ldots$ converges *quadratically* to ξ.

Such an iteration function is obviously very desirable. The popularity of Newton's method can be traced to the fact that its iteration function

$$g(x) = x - \frac{f(x)}{f'(x)} \tag{2.34}$$

is usually of this kind.

Before proving that Newton's method usually converges quadratically (when it converges), we consider a simple example. Finding the positive square root of a positive number A is equivalent to finding the positive solution of the equation $f(x) = x^2 - A = 0$. Then $f'(x) = 2x$, and substituting into (2.34), we obtain the iteration function

$$g(x) = x - \frac{x^2 - A}{2x} = \frac{1}{2}\left(x + \frac{A}{x}\right) \tag{2.35}$$

for finding the square root of A leading to the iteration

$$x_{n+1} = \frac{1}{2}\left(x_n + \frac{A}{x_n}\right) \tag{2.36}$$

In particular, if $A = 2$ and $x_0 = 2$, the result of fixed-point iteration with (2.36) is as follows:

$x_0 = 2.$
$x_1 = 1.5$ $r_1 = 0.16 \cdots$
$x_2 = 1.41666666 \cdots$ $r_2 = 0.029 \cdots$
$x_3 = 1.41421568 \cdots$ $r_3 = 0.00086 \cdots$
$x_4 = 1.41421356 \cdots$ $r_4 = 0.0$
$x_5 = 1.41421356 \cdots$

The sequence of iterates is evidently converging quite rapidly. The corresponding sequence $r_1, r_2, \ldots$ of ratios $r_n = \Delta x_n / \Delta x_{n-1}$ converges to 0. Since, for convergent fixed-point iteration, $\lim_{n \to \infty} r_n = g'(\xi)$, the example illustrates our assertion and shows the very desirable rapid convergence of Newton's method.

Theorem 2.2 Let $f(x)$ be twice continuously differentiable and assume that $f(\xi) = 0$. If $f'(\xi) \neq 0$, then the iteration function

$$g(x) = x - \frac{f(x)}{f'(x)}$$

of Newton's method is continuously differentiable in an open neighborhood of ξ, and $g'(\xi) = 0$. Consequently, by the corollary to Theorem 2.1, there exists $\varepsilon > 0$ such that fixed-point iteration with $g(x)$ converges to ξ for any choice of x_0 such that $|\xi - x_0| \leq \varepsilon$.

For the proof observe that, if $f'(\xi) \neq 0$, then, as $f'(x)$ is continuous, we have $f'(x) \neq 0$ on some interval $J = [a,b]$, with $a < \xi < b$. Hence $g(x)$ is defined and continuous on this interval J and $g(\xi) = \xi$. Further, for x in J,

$$g'(x) = 1 - \frac{f'(x)f'(x) - f(x)f''(x)}{[f'(x)]^2} = \frac{f(x)f''(x)}{[f'(x)]^2}$$

showing $g'(x)$ to be continuous on J and giving $g'(\xi) = 0$.

It is possible to show (see Exercise 2.5-2) that if $f'''(x)$ is continuous near ξ, then $g''(x)$ is continuous. Since we have already shown that $g'(\xi) = 0$ for Newton's method, it follows that Newton's method converges quadratically. This is sometimes expressed rather loosely by saying that the number of correct digits doubles at each step of the iteration. This is certainly true for our example above: x_2 has 3 correct digits, x_3 has 6 correct digits, and x_4 (if calculated with enough places) has 12 correct digits. But it should be noted that we only know

$$e_{n+1} \approx -\tfrac{1}{2}g''(\xi)e_n^2 \qquad \text{for large enough } n$$

If $\frac{1}{2}g''(\xi)$ is large in absolute value, or if n is not "large enough," then we cannot expect an exact doubling of correct digits at each step (see Exercise 2.5-7).

From a computational point of view, the accuracy attainable with Newton's method depends upon the accuracy to which $f(x)/f'(x)$ can be computed. It may happen, for example, that $f'(x)$, though it does not vanish, is very small near the root. In this case, we can expect that any errors in $f(x)$ will be magnified when $f(x)/f'(x)$ is computed. In such cases, it will be difficult to obtain good accuracy.

There are two major disadvantages to Newton's method. First, one has to start "close enough" to a root ξ of $f(x)$ to ensure convergence to ξ. (See Exercise 2.5-6 but also 2.3-4 and 2.3-5.) Since one usually does not know ξ, this might be difficult to do in practice, unless one has already obtained a good estimate $\hat{\xi}$ for ξ by some other method. If, for example, one has calculated an approximation $\hat{\xi}$ to ξ by the bisection method or some other iterative method which is good to two or three places, one might start Newton's method with $x_0 = \hat{\xi}$ and carry out two or three iterations to obtain quickly an accurate approximation to ξ. In this way, Newton's method is often used to *improve* a good estimate of the root obtained by some other means.

A second disadvantage of Newton's method is the necessity to calculate $f'(x)$. In some cases, $f'(x)$ may not be available explicitly, and even when one can evaluate $f'(x)$, this may require considerable computational effort. In the latter case, one can decide to compute $f'(x_n)$ only every k steps, using the most recently calculated value at every step. But in both cases, it is usually better to use the *secant* method instead.

The secant method uses only values of $f(x)$, and only one function evaluation is required per step, while Newton's method requires two evaluations per step. On the other hand, when the secant method converges, it does not converge quite as fast as does Newton's method; although it usually converges much faster than linear. To recall from Sec. 2.1, the secant method generates a sequence $x_1, x_2, \ldots$ by the iteration formula of Algorithm 2.4:

$$x_{n+1} = x_n - \frac{f(x_n)}{[f(x_n) - f(x_{n-1})]/(x_n - x_{n-1})} \qquad n = 0, 1, 2, \ldots$$

$$(2.37)$$

In effect, it employs the secant on $f(x)$ through $\{x_{n-1}, f(x_{n-1})\}$ and $\{x_n, f(x_n)\}$ rather than the tangent on $f(x)$ at $\{x_n, f(x_n)\}$ to find the next x_{n+1}. It therefore shares with Newton's method the disadvantage that the starting points x_{-1}, x_0 must be "close enough" to the root ξ of $f(x)$ to ensure convergence.

To investigate the rate of convergence of the secant method, we assume that the sequence $x_1, x_2, \ldots$ generated by the secant method converges to the root ξ of $f(x)$. We further assume that $f(x)$ is twice continuously differentiable and that $f'(\xi) \neq 0$. Recall from (2.6) that we can write the iteration formula (2.37) also as

$$x_{n+1} = \frac{f(x_n)x_{n-1} - f(x_{n-1})x_n}{f(x_n) - f(x_{n-1})}$$

Hence

$$e_{n+1} = \xi - x_{n+1} = \xi - \frac{f(x_n)x_{n-1} - f(x_{n-1})x_n}{f(x_n) - f(x_{n-1})}$$

$$= \frac{f(x_n)e_{n-1} - f(x_{n-1})e_n}{f(x_n) - f(x_{n-1})} \tag{2.38}$$

We assume that the secant method produces a (convergent infinite) sequence; hence we must have $\xi \neq x_n \neq x_{n-1}$, for all n, since otherwise x_{n+1} would not be defined for some n. Hence we can consider the expression

$$\frac{f(x_n)e_{n-1} - f(x_{n-1})e_n}{x_{n-1} - x_n} = e_n e_{n-1} \frac{f(x_n)/e_n - f(x_{n-1})/e_{n-1}}{x_{n-1} - x_n} \tag{2.39}$$

Since $f(\xi) = 0$ and $e_n = \xi - x_n$ for all n, the factor of $e_n e_{n-1}$ in (2.39) has the form

$$\frac{\dfrac{f(x_n)}{e_n} - \dfrac{f(x_{n-1})}{e_{n-1}}}{x_{n-1} - x_n} = \frac{\dfrac{f(x_n) - f(\xi)}{x_n - \xi} - \dfrac{f(x_{n-1}) - f(\xi)}{x_{n-1} - \xi}}{x_n - x_{n-1}}$$

In Chap. 4, we identify this number as the *second divided difference* of $f(x)$ at the points x_n, ξ, x_{n-1}, and prove (in Theorem 4.2) that this number equals $\frac{1}{2}f''(\eta_n)$ for some point η_n in the smallest interval containing x_{n-1}, ξ, x_n, provided $f''(x)$ is continuous, as we assume. In particular, then, $\lim_{n \to \infty} \eta_n = \xi$. Returning with this information to (2.38), we get that

$$e_{n+1} = \frac{e_n e_{n-1} f''(\eta_n)/2}{[f(x_n) - f(x_{n-1})]/(x_{n-1} - x_n)} = \frac{-e_n e_{n-1} f''(\eta_n)/2}{f'(\zeta_n)}$$

where, by the mean-value theorem for derivatives, ζ_n is a point between x_n and x_{n-1}; hence $\lim_{n \to \infty} \zeta_n = \xi$ also. Consequently,

$$e_{n+1} \approx e_n e_{n-1} \frac{-\frac{1}{2}f''(\xi)}{f'(\xi)} \qquad \text{for all large enough } n \tag{2.40}$$

showing the convergence to be faster than linear, yet not quite quadratic.

The more rapid rate of convergence of Newton's method over the secant method is demonstrated in Example 2.2.

In this chapter we have considered six algorithms for finding zeros of functions. In comparing algorithms for use on computers one should take into account various criteria, the most important of which are assurances of convergence, the rate of convergence, and computational efficiency. No one method can be said to be always superior to another method. The bisection method, for example, while slow in convergence, is certain to converge when properly used, while Newton's method will frequently diverge unless the initial approximation is carefully selected. The term "computational efficiency" used above attempts to take into account the amount of work required to produce a given accuracy. Newton's method, although it generally converges more rapidly than the secant method, is not usually as efficient, because it requires the evaluation of both $f(x)$ and $f'(x)$ for each iteration. In cases where $f'(x)$ is available and easily computable, Newton's method may be more efficient than the secant method, but for a general-purpose routine, the secant method will usually be more efficient and should be preferred.

Algorithms 2.1 to 2.3 all have the advantage that they bracket the root and thus guarantee error bounds on the root. Of these, Algorithm 2.2 (regula falsi) should never be used because it fails to produce a contracting interval containing the root. In general, of these three, the modified regula falsi method (Algorithm 2.3) should be preferred.

Fixed-point iteration is effective when it converges quadratically, as in Newton's method. In general, fixed-point iteration converges only linearly; hence offers no real competition to the secant method or the modified regula falsi. Even with repeated extrapolation, as in the Steffensen iteration algorithm 2.8, convergence is at best only quadratic. Since one step of the Steffensen iteration costs two evaluations of the iteration function $g(x)$, Steffensen iteration is therefore comparable with Newton's method. But since the extrapolation part of one step of Steffensen iteration is the same as one step of the secant method applied to the function $f(x) = x - g(x)$, it would seem more efficient to forgo Steffensen iteration altogether, and just use the secant method on $f(x) = x - g(x)$.

The main purpose of discussing fixed-point iteration at all was to gain a simple model for an iterative procedure which can be analyzed easily. The insight gained will be very useful in the discussion of several equations in several unknowns.

Example 2.5 Of considerable importance in determining the rate of convergence of methods for solving partial differential equations are the zeros of the function

$$f(x) = g(x)\left(g(x) - \frac{\omega}{2}(\cosh xh + \cos \pi h)\right) + \omega - 1$$

where

$$g(x) = \frac{\cosh (\frac{1}{2} - h)x}{\cosh x/2}$$

and h, the mesh size, and ω are parameters. For $h = \frac{1}{20}$ and $h = \frac{1}{50}$, find the real zeros of $f(x)$ for $\omega = 1.5, 1.6, 1.7, 1.8, 1.9$. As an initial approximation take $x_0 = 1.5$.

This example is fairly typical of many problems that arise in practice. Note that convergence is very rapid in all cases except for $h = 0.05$, $\omega = 1.9$, when the iteration does not appear to be converging. For $\omega = 1.9$ an examination of the value of $f(x)$

shows that $f(x)$ is always positive in the interval $[-4.4, 2.9]$ and oscillating around a minimum of $+0.004$. This indicates that $f(x)$ has no zeros in this interval.

FORTRAN PROGRAM FOR EXAMPLE 2.5

```
C       EXAMPLE 2.5, NEWTON METHOD
C       TO SOLVE F(X) = 0
        SINH(X) = (EXP(X) - EXP(-X))/2.
        COSH(X) = (EXP(X) + EXP(-X))/2.
        G(X)     = COSH((.5 - H)*X)/COSH(X/2.)
        F1(X)    = G(X) - (COSH(H*X) + COS(3.14159265*H))*OMEGA/2.
        F(X)     = G(X)*F1(X) + OMEGA - 1.
        GPRIME(X) = ((.5 - H)*SINH((.5 - H)*X)*COSH(X/2.) - .5*COSH
       1((.5 - H)*X)*SINH(X/2.))/COSH(X/2.)**2
        FPRIME(X) = GPRIME(X)*F1(X) + G(X)*(GPRIME(X)
       1 - H*SINH(H*X)*OMEGA/2.)
        H = .05
     10 DO 2 J = 15,19
        OMEGA = .1*FLOAT(J)
        X = 1.5
        Y = F(X)
        WRITE(6,4) H,OMEGA, X,Y
        DO 1 I = 1,20
        X1 = X - F(X)/FPRIME(X)
        Y = F(X1)
        WRITE(6,5)I, X1, Y
        IF(ABS(X1 - X) .LT. 1.E-6)          GO TO 2
      1 X = X1
        WRITE(6,6)
      2 CONTINUE
        IF(H .LT. .04) STOP
        H = .02
        GO TO 10
      4 FORMAT(//// 5H H = F3.2, 9H OMEGA = F3.1/4H0 I 9X 4HX(I)
       112X 7HF(X(I)) /4H0 2(1PE17.7))
      5 FORMAT(3H0 I4, 2E17.7)
      6 FORMAT(//36H0FAILED TO CONVERGE IN 20 ITERATIONS)
        END
```

COMPUTER RESULTS FOR EXAMPLE 2.5

H = .05 OMEGA = 1.5

I	X(I)	F(X(I))
	1.5000000E 00	$-1.3616674E-02$
1	0.9269378E 00	$-0.8695722E-03$
2	0.8827307E 00	$-0.1294166E-04$
3	0.8820524E 00	$-0.7450581E-08$
4	0.8620520E 00	0.

H = .05 OMEGA = 1.6

I	X(I)	F(X(I))
	1.5000000E 00	−8.6763873E−03
1	0.1041317E 01	−0.3084317E−03
2	0.1023192E 01	−0.1326203E−05
3	0.1023113E 01	0.
4	0.1023113E 01	0.

H = 0.5 OMEGA = 1.7

I	X(I)	F(X(I))
	1.5000000E 00	−3.7360936E−03
1	0.1234473E 01	−0.1738966E−04
2	0.1233212E 01	−0.1490116E−07
3	0.1233211E 01	0.
4	0.1233211E 01	0.

H = 0.5 OMEGA = 1.8

I	X(I)	F(X(I))
	1.5000000E 00	1.2041777E−03
1	0.1630533E 01	0.1719594E−04
2	0.1632456E 01	0.
3	0.1632456E 01	0.

H = .05 OMEGA = 1.9 (NONCONVERGENT CASE)

I	X(I)	F(X(I))
	1.5000000E 00	6.1444789E−03
1	0.2902953E 01	0.3864467E−02
2	−0.4627005E 00	0.1091048E−01
3	−0.3827365E 01	0.6150931E−02
4	−0.2108972E 01	0.4155084E−02
5	−0.4172498E 01	0.7496923E−02
6	−0.2387878E 01	0.3761321E−02
7	−0.6990251E 01	0.2407572E−01
8	−0.3656581E 01	0.5569443E−02
9	−0.1929242E 01	0.4586726E−02
10	−0.3575454E 01	0.5315170E−02
11	−0.1828560E 01	0.4888415E−02
12	−0.3354231E 01	0.4700795E−02
13	−0.1473934E 01	0.6259635E−02
14	−0.2879261E 01	0.3838226E−02

(continued on page 64)

H = .05 OMEGA = 1.9 (NONCONVERGENT CASE)
(*continued*)

I	X(I)	F(X(I))
15	0.7164706E 00	0.9926081E−02
16	0.2962257E 01	0.3938481E−02
17	0.3622484E 01	0.1169105E−01
18	0.4207972E 02	0.3183660E−00
19	−0.2235121E 02	0.1742668E−00
20	−0.4438129E 01	0.8668169E−02

H = .02 OMEGA = 1.5

I	X(I)	F(X(I))
	1.5000000E 00	−7.8362375E−03
1	0.7326013E 00	−0.1098283E−02
2	0.5681534E 00	−0.1030564E−03
3	0.5490572E 00	−0.1519918E−05
4	0.5487670E 00	0.
5	0.5487670E 00	0.

H = .02 OMEGA = 1.6

I	X(I)	F(X(I))
	1.5000000E 00	−5.9007481E−03
1	0.7747899E 00	−0.7342920E−03
2	0.6441120E 00	−0.4953146E−04
3	0.6338895E 00	−0.3352761E−06
4	0.6338193E 00	0.
5	0.6338193E 00	0.

H = .02 OMEGA = 1.7

I	X(I)	F(X(I))
	1.5000000E 00	−3.9652735E−03
1	0.8458567E 00	−0.3950298E−03
2	0.7588747E 00	−0.1492351E−04
3	0.7553154E 00	−0.1490116E−07
4	0.7553118E 00	0.
5	0.7553118E 00	0.

H = 0.2 OMEGA = 1.8

I	X(I)	F(X(I))
	1.5000000E 00	−2.0297989E−03
1	0.9908902E 00	−0.1141801E−03
2	0.9573602E 00	−0.1132488E−05
3	0.9570208E 00	0.
4	0.9570208E 00	0.

H = .02 OMEGA = 1.9

I	X(I)	F(X(I))
	1.5000000E 00	−9.4324350E−05
1	0.1450671E 01	0.1788139E−06
2	0.1450764E 01	−0.7450581E−08
3	0.1450760E 01	0.
4	0.1450760E 01	0.

EXERCISES

2.5-1. From the definition of fixed-point iteration with iteration function $g(x)$, we know that the error of the nth iterate satisfies

$$e_n = \xi - x_n = g(\xi) - g(x_{n-1})$$

We showed in the text that if $g'(\xi) = 0$ and $g''(x)$ is continuous at $x = \xi$, the iteration $x = g(x)$ converges quadratically. State conditions under which one can expect an iteration to converge cubically.

2.5-2. Show that, for Newton's method, if $f(x)$ satisfies the conditions of Theorem 2.2 and if in addition $f''(x)$ and $f'''(x)$ are continuous in a neighborhood of the root ξ, then $g''(x)$ is also continuous in this neighborhood. Also show that $g''(\xi) = f''(\xi)/f'(\xi)$.

2.5-3. In each of the following equations select an initial approximation to the smallest positive zero and show that the conditions of Theorem 2.2 for convergence of Newton's method are satisfied.

(a) $4 \cos x - e^x = 0$
(b) $2 \cos x - \cosh x = 0$
(c) $e^{-x^2} - \cos x = 0$

2.5-4. Solve each of the examples in Exercise 2.5-3 by both the secant method and Newton's method and compare your results.

2.5-5. If $x = \xi$ is a root of $f(x)$ of order 2, then $f'(\xi) = 0$ and $f''(\xi) \neq 0$. Show that in this case Newton's method no longer converges quadratically [i.e., show that $g'(\xi) = \frac{1}{2} \neq 0$]. Also show that if $f'(\xi) = 0, f''(\xi) \neq 0$, but all the other conditions of Theorem 2.2 are satisfied, the iteration

$$x_{n+1} = x_n - \frac{2f(x_n)}{f'(x_n)} = g(x_n)$$

does converge quadratically. {*Hint:* For the calculation of $g'(\xi)$, use the fact that

$$\lim_{x \to \xi} \frac{f(x)f''(x)}{[f'(x)]^2} = \lim_{x \to \xi} \frac{f(x)}{[f'(x)]^2} \lim_{x \to \xi} f''(x)$$

and L'Hospital's rule.}

2.5-6. Find the root of the equation

$$x = \tan x$$

which is closest to 100, by Newton's method. (*Note:* Unless x_0 is very carefully chosen, Newton's method produces a divergent sequence.)

2.5-7. Use Newton's method to find the positive root of $f(x) = x^2 - 1$, taking $x_0 = 100{,}000$ as the initial guess, and calculate $e_0, e_1, e_2, \ldots$. Is convergence quadratic or linear initially? Why? (*Hint:* Use Exercise 2.5-5.)

2.6 POLYNOMIAL EQUATIONS: REAL ROOTS

Although polynomial equations can be solved by any of the iterative methods discussed previously, they arise so frequently that they warrant special treatment. In particular, we shall present some efficient algorithms for finding isolated real and complex zeros of polynomials. In this section we discuss the efficient evaluation of polynomials and an adaptation of Newton's method to finding a real zero of a polynomial.

A polynomial of (exact) degree n is usually written in the form

$$p(x) = a_0 + a_1 x + a_2 x^2 + \cdots + a_n x^n \qquad a_n \neq 0 \qquad (2.41)$$

In any iterative method for finding a zero of a polynomial, we shall have to evaluate the polynomial frequently. It is therefore important to do this as efficiently as possible.

It is inefficient to evaluate each of the $n + 1$ terms in (2.41) separately and then to sum. This would take n additions and $n(n + 1)/2$ multiplications. Even if we used the number x^k already computed to calculate x^{k+1} as $x(x^k)$, all k, we still would need n additions and $2n - 1$ multiplications. Rather, observe that each term in (2.41) but the first contains the factor x; that is,

$$p(x) = a_0 + x(a_1 + a_2 x + \cdots + a_{n-1} x^{n-2} + a_n x^{n-1})$$

Again, each term between the parentheses but the first contains x; that is,

$$p(x) = a_0 + x(a_1 + x(a_2 + \cdots + a_{n-1} x^{n-3} + a_n x^{n-2}))$$

Continuing in this manner, we obtain $p(x)$ in *nested form*:

$$p(x) = a_0 + x(a_1 + x(a_2 + \cdots + x(a_{n-1} + x(a_n)) \cdots))$$

whose evaluation for any particular value of x takes n additions and n multiplications. If, for example, $p(x) = 1 + 2x + 3x^2 + 4x^3$ and we wish to find $p(1.5)$, we calculate as follows:

$$p(1.5) = 1 + 1.5\{2 + 1.5[3 + 1.5(4)]\} = 1 + 1.5\{2 + 1.5[9]\}$$
$$= 1 + 1.5\{15.5\} = 24.25$$

This procedure can be formalized as an algorithm as follows.

Algorithm 2.9 Nested multiplication Given the $n + 1$ coefficients $a_0, \ldots, a_n$ of the polynomial (2.41) and the number z.

Set $b_n = a_n$
For $k = n - 1, \ldots, 0$, do:
$\quad$ Set $b_k = a_k + zb_{k+1}$

Then b_0 is the value of $p(x)$ at $x = z$.

The auxiliary quantities $b_n, b_{n-1}, \ldots, b_1$ which appear in this algorithm have a very useful property, which we now derive. Evidently,

$$a_k = \begin{cases} b_k & k = n \\ b_k - b_{k+1}z & k < n \end{cases} k = 0, \ldots, n$$

Hence, if $q(x)$ is the polynomial of degree $n - 1$ given by

$$q(x) = b_1 + b_2x + \cdots + b_nx^{n-1} \tag{2.42}$$

then

$$\begin{aligned} b_0 + q(x)(x - z) &= b_0 + (b_1 + b_2x + \cdots + b_nx^{n-1})x \\ &\quad - (b_1 + b_2x + \cdots + b_nx^{n-1})z \\ &= (b_0 - b_1z) + (b_1 - b_2z)x + \cdots \\ &\quad + (b_{n-1} - b_nz)x^{n-1} + b_nx^n \\ &= a_0 + a_1x + \cdots + a_{n-1}x^{n-1} + a_nx^n \end{aligned}$$

or

$$p(x) = q(x)(x - z) + b_0 \tag{2.43}$$

Hence $b_1, \ldots, b_n$ are the coefficients of the *quotient* polynomial $q(x)$ obtained on dividing $p(x)$ by the linear polynomial $(x - z)$, and b_0 is the remainder. In particular, if we set $x = z$ in (2.43), we get anew that $p(z) = b_0$.

Example 2.6 Converting a binary integer into a decimal integer In Sec. 1.1, we presented Algorithm 1.1 for converting a binary integer into a decimal integer. By convention, the binary integer

$$\alpha = (a_na_{n-1}a_{n-2} \cdots a_0)_2$$

with the a_i either zero or one, represents the number

$$\alpha = a_n2^n + a_{n-1}2^{n-1} + \cdots + a_02^0$$

Its decimal equivalent can therefore be found by evaluating the polynomial

$$p(x) = a_0 + a_1 x + \cdots + a_n x^n$$

at $x = 2$, using the nested multiplication Algorithm 2.9. This shows Algorithm 1.1 to be a special case of Algorithm 2.9. As an application, the binary integer $\alpha = (110011)_2$ is converted to its decimal equivalent, as follows:

$$
\begin{aligned}
b_5 &= a_5 &&= 1 \\
b_4 &= a_4 + 2b_5 &&= 3 \\
b_3 &= a_3 + 2b_4 &&= 6 \\
b_2 &= a_2 + 2b_3 &&= 12 \\
b_1 &= a_1 + 2b_2 &&= 25 \\
\alpha = b_0 &= a_0 + 2b_1 &&= 51
\end{aligned}
$$

Assume now, in particular, that z in (2.43) is a zero of $p(x)$. Since, then, $b_0 = p(z) = 0$, it follows that

$$p(x) = q(x)(x - z)$$

i.e., the b_i are then the coefficients of the *reduced* polynomial $q(x)$. In this case, every zero of $q(x)$ is also a zero of $p(x)$, and every zero of $p(x)$ other than the zero z must be a zero of $q(x)$. This fact has two nice consequences. For one, it allows us to work with the reduced polynomial $q(x)$ of degree $n - 1$ to find other zeros of $p(x)$, once the zero z is found. Also, it implies by induction that if $p(x)$ has the k distinct zeros $z_1, z_2, \ldots, z_k$, then

$$p(x) = r(x)(x - z_1) \cdots (x - z_k)$$

with $r(x)$ a polynomial of degree $n - k$. In particular, then, *a polynomial of degree $\leq n$ can have at most n distinct zeros.*

Our immediate goal is to adapt Newton's method to the problem of finding real zeros of polynomials. To do this, we must be able to evaluate not only $p(x)$ but also $p'(x)$. To find $p'(x)$ at $x = z$, we differentiate (2.43) with respect to x and obtain

$$p'(x) = q(x) + q'(x)(x - z)$$

Hence, on setting $x = z$,

$$p'(z) = q(z)$$

Since $q(x)$ is itself a polynomial whose coefficients we know, we can apply Algorithm 2.9 once more to find $q(z)$, and therefore $p'(z)$. This gives the following algorithm.

Algorithm 2.10 Newton's method for finding real zeros of polynomials Given the $n + 1$ coefficients $a_0, \ldots, a_n$ of the polynomial $p(x)$ in (2.41) and a starting point x_0.

For $m = 0, 1, \ldots$, until satisfied, do:

> Set $z = x_m$, $b_n = a_n$, $c_n = b_n$
> For $k = n - 1, \ldots, 1$, do:
> > Set $b_k = a_k + zb_{k+1}$
> > Set $c_k = b_k + zc_{k+1}$
> Set $b_0 = a_0 + zb_1$
> Set $x_{m+1} = x_m - b_0/c_1$

Example 2.7　Find all the roots of the polynomial equation $p(x) = x^3 + x - 3 = 0$.
This equation has one real root and two complex roots. Since $p(1) = -1$ and $p(2) = 7$, the real root must lie between $x = 1$ and $x = 2$. We choose $x_0 = 1.1$ and apply Algorithm 2.10, carrying out all calculations on a desk calculator and retaining five places after the decimal point.

	$x_0 = 1.1$			$x_1 = 1.1 - (-0.569)/4.63 = 1.22289$	
k	a_k	b_k	c_k	b_k	c_k
3	1	1	1	1	1
2	0	1.1	2.2	1.22289	2.44578
1	1	2.21	4.63	2.49546	5.48638
0	−3	−0.569		0.05167	

	$x_2 = 1.22289 - b_0/c_1 = 1.21347$			$x_3 = 1.21347 - b_0/c_1 = 1.21341$	
k	a_k	b_k	c_k	b_k	c_k
3	1	1	1	1	1
2	0	1.21347	2.42694	1.21341	2.42682
1	1	2.47251	5.41753	2.47236	5.41709
0	−3	0.000317		−0.00001	

Note that b_0 is approaching zero and that the b_k are converging. No further improvement is possible in the solution or in the b_k, considering the precision to which we are working. We therefore accept $x_3 = 1.21341$, which is correct to at least five significant figures, as the desired real root. To find the remaining complex roots, we apply the quadratic formula to the polynomial equation

$$x^2 + b_2 x + b_1 = x^2 + 1.21341x + 2.47236 = 0$$

This yields the results

$$x = \frac{-b_2 \pm (b_2{}^2 - 4b_1)^{1/2}}{2}$$

$$= \frac{-1.21341 \pm 2.90122i}{2} = -0.60671 \pm 1.45061i$$

for the remaining roots. As a comparison, the zeros of this polynomial will be found again in Sec. 2.7, using a complex-root finder.

Example 2.8 Find the real positive root of the polynomial

$$x^5 - 3.7x^4 + 7.4x^3 - 10.8x^2 + 10.8x - 6.8 = 0$$

It is easily verified that the root lies between 1 and 2. We choose $x_0 = 1.5$. The FORTRAN program and machine results are given below. The exact root is 1.7, so that the machine result is correct to eight figures.

FORTRAN PROGRAM FOR EXAMPLE 2.8

```
C        NEWTONS METHOD FOR FINDING A REAL ROOT OF A POLY-
C        NOMIAL P(X) = 0
         DIMENSION A(10)
         DATA (A(I), I = 1,6)/ −6.8, 10.8, −10.8,7.4, −3.7,1./
         READ (5,3) X
         WRITE (6,4)
         DO 2 J = 1,20
         B = A(6)
         C = A(6)
         DO 1 I = 1,4
         K = 6 − I
         B = A(K) + X*B
       1 C = B + X*C
         B = A(1) + X*B
         WRITE (6,5) J,X,B , C
         DELTAX = B/C
         IF(ABS(DELTAX) .LT. 1.E−7 .AND. ABS(B) .LT.
      11.E−7) STOP
       2 X = X − DELTAX
         WRITE (6,6)
         STOP
       3 FORMAT(E20.8)
       4 FORMAT(34H1NEWTONS METHOD FOR FINDING A REAL
        *21H ROOT OF A POLYNOMIAL//4X1HI1OX1HX14X4HB(0)
        *13X4HC(1)/)
       5 FORMAT(I5, 3(1PE17.7))
       6 FORMAT(36H0FAILED TO CONVERGE IN 20 ITERATIONS)
         END
```

COMPUTER RESULTS FOR EXAMPLE 2.8

I	X	B(0)	C(1)
1	1.5000000E 00	−1.0625001E−00	3.7124998E 00
2	1.7861953E 00	7.2393334E−01	9.6004875E 00
3	1.7107894E 00	8.0013633E−02	7.5470622E 00
4	1.7001875E 00	1.3663173E−03	7.2905675E 00
5	1.7000000E 00	4.7683716E−07	7.2861013E 00
6	1.7000000E 00	−1.1920929E−07	7.2860994E 00
7	1.7000000E 00	−5.9604645E−08	7.2860998E 00

Although in the examples above we encountered no real difficulties in obtaining accurate solutions, the student is warned against assuming that polynomial root finding is without pitfalls. We enumerate some of the difficulties which may be encountered.

1. For some polynomials accuracy may be difficult to obtain, even polynomials of low degree. An example of this type was considered in Sec. 1.4, where we saw that use of the quadratic formula for a polynomial of degree 2 led to a substantial loss of accuracy when $p'(x)$ is small in the vicinity of the root. In particular, this will always occur if $p(x)$ has a double root at $x = \xi$, for then both $p(x)$ and $p'(x)$ will vanish at $x = \xi$.

To illustrate the behavior of Newton's method around a double root, we consider the polynomial

$$p(x) = x^3 - 3x^2 + 4$$

which has a double root at $x = 2$. Choosing $x_0 = 1.5$, we obtain, using the IBM 7094, the results in Table 2.1.

The numbers in parentheses indicate the exponents of 10. The underlined digits are known to be incorrect because of loss of significance in

Table 2.1

i	x_i	$p(x_i)$	$p'(x_i)$	$p(x_i)/p'(x_i)$
0	1.5	0.625 E+0	−0.22499999E+1	−0.27777778E+0
1	1.7777777	0.13717422E+0	−0.11851852E+1	−0.11574074E+0
2	1.8935185	0.32807648E−1	−0.60487403E+0	−0.54238810E−1
3	1.9477573	0.80453157E−2	−0.30526827E−0	−0.26354902E−1
4	1.9741122	0.19932091E−2	−0.15331630E−0	−0.13000633E−1
5	1.9871128	0.49611926E−3	−0.76824840E−1	−0.64577974E−2
6	1.9935706	0.12376904E−3	−0.38452353E−1	−0.32187638E−2
7	1.9967893	0.30934811E−4	−0.19232938E−1	−0.16084287E−2
8	1.9983977	0.77188015E−5	−0.96056932E−2	−0.80356526E−3
9	1.9992013	0.19371510E−5	−0.47900614E−2	−0.40441045E−3
10	1.9996057	0.47683716E−6	−0.23651228E−2	−0.20161200E−3
11	1.9998073	0.11920929E−6	−0.11558611E−2	−0.10313461E−3
12	1.9999104	0.59604645E−7	−0.53713301E−3	−0.11096813E−3
13	2.0000214	0.29802322E−7	+0.12850899E−3	+0.23190846E−3
14	1.9997895	0.14901161E−6	−0.12628894E−2	−0.11799259E−3
15	1.9999074	0.59604645E−7	−0.55501277E−3	−0.10739328E−3

computing $p(x_i)$ *and* $p'(x_i)$. From this table we may make the following observations (see Exercise 2.5-5 in this connection):

a. The iterates are converging in spite of the fact that $p'(2) = 0$.

b. The rate of convergence is linear, not quadratic, as is normally the case for Newton's method. An examination of the corrections $p(x_i)/p'(x_i)$ shows that the error is being reduced by a factor of about $\frac{1}{2}$ with each iteration, up to iteration 12.

c. After iteration 13 we can expect no further improvement in the solution. This is because there are no correct figures left in $p(x_i)$, and at the same time $p'(x_i)$ is of the order of 10^{-3}. Thus the quotient $p(x_i)/p'(x_i)$ will produce an incorrect result in the fifth decimal place, making it impossible to improve the solution.

2. In some cases an improper choice of the initial approximation will cause convergence to a zero other than the one desired.

3. For some polynomials an improper choice of x_0 may lead to a divergent sequence. In Example 2.2, for instance, if we take $x_0 = 0$, we obtain the successive approximations $x_1 = -1$, $x_2 = -\frac{1}{2}$, $x_3 = -3$, $x_4 = -2.04$, $x_5 = -1.40$, which certainly do not appear to be converging to the zero obtained before. An examination of the graph of the polynomial $p(x) = x^3 - x - 1$ (see Fig. 2.6) will help to explain this behavior. The successive iterates may oscillate indefinitely about the point $x = -\frac{1}{3}\sqrt{3}$ at which $p(x)$ has a maximum value.

4. Some polynomials, especially those of high degree, are very unstable, in the sense that small changes in the coefficients will lead to large changes in the zeros (see Example 2.8a below).

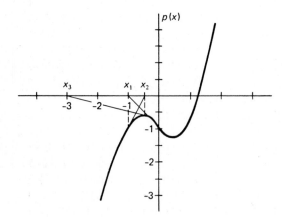

Fig. 2.6

5. If successive zeros are found by continuously reducing the degree of the polynomial, we can expect a loss of accuracy in the later zeros because the coefficients in the reduced polynomials will contain errors from incomplete convergence and from round-off. To minimize such loss of accuracy, the zeros should be obtained in increasing order of magnitude (see Example 2.8a). Also, the accuracy of a root found from a reduced polynomial can be improved by iterating with the original polynomial.

Example 2.8a To illustrate some of the dangers in polynomial zero finding, we consider the two polynomials

$$x^7 - 28x^6 + 322x^5 - 1,960x^4 + 6,769x^3 - 13,132x^2 + 13,068x - 5,040$$
$$(2.44a)$$

and

$$x^5 - 15.5x^4 + 77.5x^3 - 155x^2 + 124x - 32 \qquad (2.44b)$$

We have used Newton's method (on a CDC 6500) to find all the zeros of these polynomials, working with the reduced polynomial at each stage, with roughly 10 percent error in the initial guess, and with the termination criterion $|x_i - x_{i-1}| < 10^{-7}|x_i|$.

The zeros of the first polynomial, (2.44a), are 1, 2, 3, 4, 5, 6, and 7. Column A in the table below contains the approximations found, starting with the initial guesses 0.9, 1.9, 2.9, 3.9, 4.9, 5.9, and 6.9. The number of iterations required is listed after each zero.

The zeros in column B are those obtained when the coefficient of x^2 in (2.44a) is replaced by $-13,133$, i.e., after a change of one unit in the fifth place of one coefficient is made. Only five zeros are found, and some of these differ from the corresponding zeros in column A in the second place. In order to confirm that these changes are not just due to round-off, and to ascertain the fate of the two missing zeros, we also used Muller's method (to be discussed in the next section) which produced the seven zeros listed in column C. These are accurate to all places shown. Note that zeros 5 and 6 have been changed into a complex conjugate pair. Thus a change of 1/100 of 1 percent in one of the coefficients has led to a change of 10 percent in some of the zeros. When the coefficients of a polynomial have been obtained experimentally, errors of this magnitude are easily encountered in the coefficients. We must, therefore, view with great caution zeros of polynomials of high degree found in this manner, especially when there is some doubt about the accuracy of the coefficients.

The zeros of the second polynomial, (2.44b), are 0.5, 1, 2, 4, and 8. Starting with the initial guesses 0.45, 0.9, 1.8, 3.6, and 7.2, we computed the zeros in *ascending* order as shown in column D. Finally, in column E, we have listed the results of computing these zeros in *descending* order, i.e., starting with the initial guess 7.2 to get the zero 8, then using the reduced polynomial and the initial guess 3.6 to obtain the zero 4, etc. Although the first zero found is accurate to nine places, subsequent zeros are found only to six places. Moreover, the number of iterations required is greater. This illustrates the point that it is best to compute the zeros of smallest absolute value first.

COMPUTER RESULTS FOR EXAMPLE 2.8a

A	B		C	D	E
1.00000000 5	1.00139755 5	1.0013976		0.50000000 4	8.00000000 7
2.00000000 5	1.96892082 4	1.9689208		1.00000008 4	3.99999862 6
3.00000000 5	3.31832477 7	3.3183233		2.00000007 4	2.00000552 6
4.00000000 5	3.50505891 7	3.5050604		4.00000005 4	0.99999079 5
5.00000000 4		5.5731849	$+0.2641298i$	7.99999999 2	0.50000485 2
6.00000014 4		5.5731849	$-0.2641298i$		
6.99999993 2	7.05992816 40	7.0599281			

EXERCISES

2.6-1. Using Algorithm 2.10 and a desk calculator, find the real root of

$$x^3 + 2x - 1 = 0$$

correct to seven significant figures. Determine the remaining roots from the reduced polynomial, using the quadratic formula. How accurate are these solutions?

2.6-2. Write a computer program for finding a real root of a polynomial of any degree, based on Algorithm 2.10.

2.6-3. Using the program developed in Exercise 2.6-2, find the real positive roots of the following polynomials:

(a) $x^5 - 3x^3 + x^2 - 1 = 0$ (b) $x^3 + 3x - 1 = 0$

2.6-4. The polynomial $x^4 + 2.8x^3 - 0.38x^2 - 6.3x - 4.2$ has four real zeros. Find them, using Algorithm 2.10.

2.6-5. The polynomial

$$p(x) = x^8 - 170x^6 + 7{,}392x^4 - 39{,}712x^2 + 51{,}200$$

has the zeros ± 10, ± 8, ± 2, $\pm \sqrt{2}$. Find these roots on a computer in ascending order of magnitude, choosing initial approximations within 10 percent of the exact solutions. Then change the coefficient of x^2 to $-39{,}710$, and solve the problem once again. Observe the change in the solutions.

2.7 COMPLEX ROOTS AND MULLER'S METHOD

The methods discussed up to this point allow us to find an isolated zero of a function once an approximation to that zero is known. These methods are not very satisfactory when all the zeros of a function are required or when good initial approximations are not available. For polynomial functions there are methods which yield an approximation to all the zeros simultaneously, after which the iterative methods of this chapter can be applied to obtain more accurate solutions. Among such methods may be mentioned the quotient-difference algorithm [2] and the method of Graeffe [5].

A method of recent vintage, expounded by Muller [6], has been used on computers with remarkable success. This method may be used to find any prescribed number of zeros, real or complex, of an arbitrary function. The method is iterative, converges almost quadratically in the vicinity of a root, does not require the evaluation of the derivative of the function, and obtains both real and complex roots even when these roots are not simple.

Moreover, the method is global in the sense that the user need not supply an initial approximation. In this section we describe briefly how the method is derived, omitting any discussion of convergence, and we discuss its use in finding both real and complex roots. We will especially emphasize the problem of finding complex zeros of polynomials with real coefficients since this problem is of great concern in many branches of engineering.

Muller's method is an extension of the secant method. To recall, in the secant method we determine, from the approximations x_i, x_{i-1} to a root of $f(x) = 0$, the next approximation x_{i+1} as the zero of the linear polynomial $p(x)$ which goes through the two points $\{x_i, f(x_i)\}$ and $\{x_{i-1}, f(x_{i-1})\}$. In Muller's method, the next approximation, x_{i+1}, is found as a zero of the *parabola* which goes through the three points $\{x_i, f(x_i)\}$, $\{x_{i-1}, f(x_{i-1})\}$, and $\{x_{i-2}, f(x_{i-2})\}$.

Let x_i, x_{i-1}, x_{i-2} be three distinct approximations to a root of $f(x) = 0$. We use the abbreviations

$$f_i = f(x_i) \qquad f_{i-1} = f(x_{i-1}) \qquad f_{i-2} = f(x_{i-2})$$

In Chap. 4, we show that, with

$$f[x_i, x_{i-1}] = \frac{f_i - f_{i-1}}{x_i - x_{i-1}}$$

$$f[x_i, x_{i-1}, x_{i-2}] = \frac{f[x_i, x_{i-1}] - f[x_{i-1}, x_{i-2}]}{x_i - x_{i-2}} \qquad (2.45)$$

the function

$$p(x) = f_i + f[x_i, x_{i-1}](x - x_i) + f[x_i, x_{i-1}, x_{i-2}](x - x_i)(x - x_{i-1})$$

is the unique parabola which goes through the three points $\{x_i, f_i\}$, $\{x_{i-1}, f_{i-1}\}$, and $\{x_{i-2}, f_{i-2}\}$. In the more customary way of writing down polynomials, we get that

$$p(x) = a_0 + a_1 x + a_2 x^2$$

with

$$\begin{aligned} a_2 &= f[x_i, x_{i-1}, x_{i-2}] \\ a_1 &= f[x_i, x_{i-1}] - (x_i + x_{i-1})a_2 \\ a_0 &= f_i - x_i(f[x_i, x_{i-1}] - x_{i-1}a_2) \end{aligned} \qquad (2.46)$$

Once the numbers a_0, a_1, a_2 have been calculated from (2.45) and (2.46), the roots of $p(x)$ can be determined from the quadratic formula, written

$$x = \frac{2a_0}{-a_1 \pm (a_1{}^2 - 4a_0a_2)^{1/2}} \qquad (2.47)$$

The sign before the radical in (2.47) is selected so that the denominator is largest in magnitude, and the corresponding root is taken as the next approximation, x_{i+1}. The reason for writing the quadratic formula in this form, as explained in Sec. 1.4, is to obtain maximum accuracy in the formula. The process is then repeated, using x_{i-1}, x_i, x_{i+1} as the three basic approximations. If the roots obtained from (2.47) are real, the situation is pictured graphically in Fig. 2.7. Note, however, that even if the root being sought is real, we may encounter complex approximations because the solutions given by (2.47) may be complex. However, in such cases the complex component will normally be so small in magnitude that it can be neglected. In fact, in the subroutine described later, any complex components encountered when seeking a real root are suppressed.

For reasons of accuracy and convenience, Muller proposed a somewhat different but equivalent sequence of steps for obtaining the next approximation, x_{i+1}. This sequence of steps is described in Algorithm 2.11.

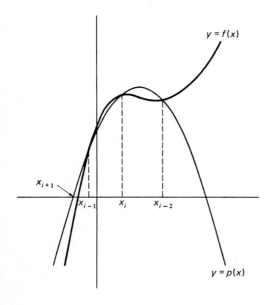

Fig. 2.7

Algorithm 2.11 Muller's method

1. Let x_i, x_{i-1}, x_{i-2} be three approximations to a zero ξ of $f(x)$. Compute f_i, f_{i-1}, f_{i-2}.

2. Compute

$$h_i = x_i - x_{i-1}$$

$$\lambda_i = \frac{h_i}{x_{i-1} - x_{i-2}}$$

3. Compute

$$g_i = (1 + 2\lambda_i)(f_i - f_{i-1}) - \lambda_i^2(f_{i-1} - f_{i-2})$$

4. Compute

$$\lambda_{i+1} = \frac{-2f_i(1 + \lambda_i)}{g_i \pm [g_i^2 - 4f_i(1 + \lambda_i)\lambda_i(f_i - f_{i-1} - \lambda_i(f_{i-1} - f_{i-2}))]^{1/2}}$$

choosing the sign so that the denominator will always have the largest magnitude.

5. Compute

$$x_{i+1} = x_i + h_i\lambda_{i+1}$$
$$h_{i+1} = h_i\lambda_{i+1}$$

6. Compute

$$f_{i+1} = f(x_{i+1}) \text{ and increase } i \text{ by } 1$$

7. Repeat steps 3 to 6 until either of the following criteria is satisfied for prescribed $\varepsilon_1, \varepsilon_2$:

(a) $\dfrac{|x_i - x_{i-1}|}{|x_i|} < \varepsilon_1$

(b) $|f(x_i)| < \varepsilon_2$

A complete subroutine based on this algorithm is given below. The arguments in this subroutine have the following meanings:

$$KN \equiv \text{number of roots previously computed, normally zero.}$$
$$N \equiv \text{number of roots desired.}$$
$$RTS \equiv \text{an array of initial estimates of all desired roots; set to zero if no better estimates are available.}$$
$$MAXIT \equiv \text{maximum number of iterations per root allowed.}$$
$$EP1 \equiv \text{relative error tolerance on } x_i.$$
$$EP2 \equiv \text{error tolerance on } f(x_i).$$
$$FN \equiv FN(Z,FZ) \text{ is a subroutine which, for given } Z, \text{ returns } FZ = f(Z).$$

FNREAL ≡ a logical variable; if TRUE, the subroutine forces all
approximations to all the roots to be real. This makes
it possible to use this routine even if $f(x)$ is defined only
for real x.

```
      SUBROUTINE MULLER(KN,N,RTS,MAXIT,EP1,EP2,FN,FNREAL)
      COMPLEX RTS(1)
      LOGICAL FNREAL
      COMPLEX RT,H,DELFPR,FRTDEF,LAMBDA,DELF,DFPRLM,NUM,
     *DEN,G,SQR,FRT,FRTPRV
C
C     INITIALIZATION
      EPS1=AMAX1(EP1,1.E-12)
      EPS2=AMAX1(EP2,1.E-20)
      IBEG=KN+1
      IEND=KN+N
C
      DO 100 I = IBEG,IEND
      KOUNT=0
COMPUTE FIRST THREE ESTIMATES FOR ROOT AS
C         RTS(I)+.5,  RTS(I) -.5,  RTS(I) .
    1 H=.5
      RT=RTS(I)+H
      ASSIGN 10 TO NN
                                          GO TO 70
   10 DELFPR = FRTDEF
      RT=RTS(I)-H
      ASSIGN 20 TO NN
                                          GO TO 70
   20 FRTPRV=FRTDEF
      DELFPR=FRTPRV-DELFPR
      RT=RTS(I)
      ASSIGN 30 TO NN
                                          GO TO 70
   30 ASSIGN 80 TO NN
      LAMBDA = -.5
COMPUTE NEXT ESTIMATE FOR ROOT
   40 DELF = FRTDEF - FRTPRV
      DFPRLM = DELFPR*LAMBDA
      NUM = -FRTDEF*(1. + LAMBDA)*2.
      G = (1. + LAMBDA*2.)*DELF - LAMBDA*DFPRLM
      SQR = G*G + 2.*NUM*LAMBDA*(DELF - DFPRLM)
      IF (FNREAL .AND. REAL(SQR) .LT. 0.) SQR = 0.
      SQR = CSQRT(SQR)
      DEN = G + SQR
      IF (REAL(G)*REAL(SQR) + AIMAG(G)*AIMAG(SQR) .LT. 0.)
     *DEN = G - SQR
      IF (CABS(DEN) .EQ. 0.) DEN = 1.
      LAMBDA = NUM/DEN
```

```
        FRTPRV = FRTDEF
        DELFPR = DELF
        H = H*LAMBDA
        RT = RT + H
        IF (KOUNT .GT. MAXIT)              GO TO 100
C
    70  KOUNT = KOUNT + 1
        CALL FN(RT,FRT)
        FRTDEF = FRT
        IF (I .LT. 2)                      GO TO 75
        DO 71 J = 2,I
        DEN = RT - RTS(J - 1)
        IF (CABS(DEN) .LT. EPS2)           GO TO 79
    71  FRTDEF = FRTDEF/DEN
    75                                     GO TO NN,(10,20,30,80)
    79  RTS(I) = RT + .001
                                           GO TO 1
CHECK FOR CONVERGENCE
    80  IF (CABS(H) .LT. EPS1*CABS(RT))    GO TO 100
        IF (AMAX1(CABS(FRT),CABS(FRTDEF)) .LT. EPS2)   GO TO 100
C
CHECK FOR DIVERGENCE
        IF (CABS(FRTDEF) .LT. 10.*CABS(FRTPRV))  GO TO 40
        H = H/2.
        LAMBDA = LAMBDA/2.
        RT = RT - H
                                           GO TO 70
   100  RTS(I) = RT
                                           RETURN
        END
```

Muller's method, like the other algorithms described in this chapter, finds one zero at a time. To find more than one zero it uses a procedure known as *deflation*. If, for example, one zero ξ_1 has already been found, the routine calculates the next zero by working with the function

$$f_1(x) = \frac{f(x)}{x - \xi_1} \tag{2.48}$$

If r zeros $\xi_1, \ldots, \xi_r$ have already been found, the next root is obtained by working with the deflated function

$$f_r(x) = \frac{f(x)}{(x - \xi_1)(x - \xi_2) \cdots (x - \xi_r)} \tag{2.49}$$

If no estimates are given, the routine always looks for zeros in order of increasing magnitude since this will usually minimize round-off-error growth. Also, all zeros found using deflated functions are tested for accuracy by substituting into the original function $f(x)$. In applying the Muller subroutine, the user can specify the number of zeros desired. Some functions, for example, may have an infinite number of zeros, of which only the first few may be of interest.

Example 2.9   Bessel's function $J_0(x)$ is given by the infinite series

$$J_0(x) = 1 - \frac{x^2}{2^2 \cdot 1 \cdot 1} + \frac{x^4}{2^4 \cdot 2! \cdot 2!} - \frac{x^6}{2^6 \cdot 3! \cdot 3!} + \cdots$$

It is known that $J_0(x)$ has an infinite number of real zeros. Find the first three positive zeros, using Algorithm 2.11. The machine results given below were obtained on an IBM 7094 using a standard library subroutine for $J_0(x)$ based on the series given above. The values of $J_0(x)$ were computed to maximum accuracy.

The iterations were all started with the approximations $x_0 = -1$, $x_1 = 1$, $x_2 = 0$ and were continued until either of the following error criteria was satisfied:

(a) $\dfrac{|x_{i+1} - x_i|}{|x_{i+1}|} < 10^{-6}$

(b) $|J_0(x_i)| < 10^{-20}$

The converged values are correct to at least six significant figures. Note that the zeros are obtained in ascending order of magnitude.

All the following examples were run on a CDC 6500 computer using Algorithm 2.11. The error criteria for these examples were $\varepsilon_1 = \varepsilon_2 = 10^{-8}$, and all used the same starting values $(0.5, -0.5, 0.0)$ followed by deflation. Although the results are printed to 8 significant figures, one should recall that on a CDC 6500 the floating-point word length is 14 decimal digits. The output consists of the real and imaginary (if applicable) parts of the

COMPUTER RESULTS FOR EXAMPLE 2.9

ROOT 1	ROOT 2	ROOT 3
−0.09999999E 01	−0.09999999E 01	−0.09999999E 01
0.09999999E 01	0.09999999E 01	0.09999999E 01
0.	0.	0.
0.20637107E 01	0.36557332E 01	0.47983123E 01
0.23167706E 01	0.44416171E 01	0.59396663E 01
0.23970029E 01	0.50863190E 01	0.70758440E 01
0.24047983E 01	0.55024961E 01	0.88981197E 01
0.24048255E 01	0.55202182E 01	0.92976399E 01
0.24048255E 01	0.55200780E 01	0.86854592E 01
	0.55200780E 01	0.86529856E 01
		0.86537299E 01
		0.86537278E 01

converged approximations to the roots, and the real and imaginary parts of the value of the function at those roots.

Example 2.10 Find all the zeros of the polynomial $p(x) = x^3 + x - 3$.

ROOT		F(ROOT)	
REAL PART	IMAGINARY PART	REAL PART	IMAGINARY PART
1.2134117E+00	0.	−4.2632564E−14	0.
−6.0670583E−01	1.4506122E+00	2.8421709E−14	4.2632564E−14
−6.0670583E−01	−1.4506122E+10	2.8421709E−14	−2.6290081E−13

Compare these results with those obtained in Example 2.7, where we computed the solutions on a desk calculator. Note that since $p(x)$ has real coefficients, the complex roots occur in complex-conjugate pairs. Note too that no estimates of the complex roots had to be provided. Newton's method, although it can be used to find complex roots, must be supplied with a good estimate of that root, an estimate that is normally very difficult to obtain. Observe that the error in F(ROOT) is considerably smaller than 10^{-8} as required by the error criterion. In fact, in the last iteration, the error must have been reduced from something like 10^{-7} to 10^{-14}, indicating that the method converges almost quadratically.

Example 2.11 Find all the zeros of the polynomial $p(x) = x^3 - x - 1$ considered in Example 2.2.
Note that since this example was calculated in complex arithmetic, the approximation to the one real root $x = 1.3247180$ has a small imaginary component.

ROOT		F(ROOT)	
REAL PART	IMAGINARY PART	REAL PART	IMAGINARY PART
−6.6235898E−01	−5.6227951E−01	0.	3.5527137E−15
−6.6235898E−01	5.6227951E−01	0.	1.4210855E−14
1.3247180E+00	−1.3134765E−14	1.4921397E−13	−5.6014953E−14

Example 2.12 Find all the zeros of the polynomial $f(x) = x^3 - 3x^2 + 4$. This polynomial has a simple zero at $x = -1$ and a double zero at $x = 2$. Note the extremely good accuracy obtained by this method in both modes at a double zero. Most other methods, including Newton's, would have some difficulty producing accurate results at multiple zeros.

REAL MODE

ROOT		F(ROOT)	
REAL PART	IMAGINARY PART	REAL PART	IMAGINARY PART
−1.0000000E+00	0.	2.8421709E−14	0.
2.0000000E+00	0.	0.	0.
2.0000000E+00	0.	2.8421709E−14	0.

COMPLEX MODE

ROOT		F(ROOT)	
REAL PART	IMAGINARY PART	REAL PART	IMAGINARY PART
$-1.0000000E+00$	0.	$2.8421709E-14$	0.
$2.0000000E+00$	$6.7434958E-07$	$-1.2505552E-12$	$-1.1587411E-18$
$2.0000000E+00$	$-1.3139056E-07$	0.	$-9.2370129E-16$

Example 2.13 Find the zeros of the polynomial

$$f(x) = x^5 - 3.7x^4 + 7.4x^3 - 10.8x^2 + 10.8x - 6.8$$

This is Example 2.8 solved earlier by Newton's method. The exact zeros are $1 \pm i$, $\pm \sqrt{2}i$, and 1.7. The results below are correct to eight significant figures, even though there is a small real component to the pure-imaginary zeros $\pm \sqrt{2}i$.

ROOT		F(ROOT)	
REAL PART	IMAGINARY PART	REAL PART	IMAGINARY PART
$1.0000000E+00$	$-1.0000000E+00$	$-2.8421709E-14$	$2.8421709E-14$
$1.0000000E+00$	$1.0000000E+00$	$1.4210855E-13$	$-1.5631940E-13$
$-9.0964472E-12$	$1.4142136E+00$	$-8.5330498E-10$	$-1.2773698E-09$
$8.3306265E-11$	$-1.4142136E+00$	$-8.5339025E-10$	$-1.2785158E-09$
$1.7000000E+00$	$1.3036419E-10$	$6.3431571E-10$	$9.4984654E-10$

Example 2.14 Find the zeros of the polynomial

$$f(x) = x^7 - 28x^6 + 322x^5 - 1{,}960x^4 + 6{,}769x^3 - 13{,}132x^2 + 13{,}068 - 5{,}040$$

This example was treated by Newton's method in Example 2.8a, where we had some difficulty in finding accurate solutions. The zeros are $x = 1, 2, 3, 4, 5, 6, 7$. The results below are remarkably accurate, although the long word length on the CDC 6500 is largely responsible for this. Note that although, in general, Muller's method seeks the zeros in ascending order of magnitude, in this case it did not succeed in doing so.

ROOT		F(ROOT)	
REAL PART	IMAGINARY PART	REAL PART	IMAGINARY PART
$2.0000000E+00$	$-2.6080092E-16$	$-5.8207661E-11$	$3.1296110E-14$
$3.0000000E+00$	$7.4093893E-11$	$-7.8580342E-10$	$3.5565069E-09$
$1.0000000E+00$	$-1.7030067E-16$	0.	$-1.2261648E-13$
$6.0000000E+00$	$1.6284031E-15$	$-1.0710210E-08$	$-1.9540837E-13$
$5.0000000E+00$	$-7.2393906E-13$	$2.4156179E-09$	$-3.4749075E-11$
$4.0000000E+00$	$-2.3682266E-10$	$2.0954758E-09$	$8.5256156E-09$
$7.0000000E+00$	$-8.1000834E-20$	$4.0745363E-10$	$-5.8320601E-17$

Example 2.15 Find the zeros of the polynomial

$$f(x) = x^8 - 170x^6 + 7{,}392x^4 - 39{,}712x^2 + 51{,}200$$

This polynomial has the zeros ± 10, ± 2, ± 8, $\pm \sqrt{2}$. The program was run in the complex mode and produced the zeros correct to eight significant figures. This example shows that this algorithm is capable of handling polynomials of fairly high degree with good results (see Exercise 2.6-5).

ROOT		F(ROOT)	
REAL PART	IMAGINARY PART	REAL PART	IMAGINARY PART
−1.4142136E+00	0.	−2.3282064E−10	0.
1.4142136E+00	0.	−2.3283064E−10	0.
2.0000000E+00	0.	0.	0.
−2.0000000E+00	0.	0.	0.
8.0000000E+00	0.	2.9336661E−08	0.
−8.0000000E+00	0.	2.9336661E−08	0.
1.0000000E+01	0.	2.3352914E−07	0.
−1.0000000E+01	0.	1.8742867E−07	0.

Example 2.16 Find the zeros of the polynomial $x^8 - 1 = 0$.

Finding the Nth roots of unity is an interesting exercise which is frequently used as a severe test for root-finding methods.

It is known that the Nth roots of unity are given by

$$x_k = \cos\frac{2k\pi}{N} + i\sin\frac{2k\pi}{N} \qquad k = 0, 1, \ldots, N - 1$$

For $N = 8$, there are two real roots ± 1 and six complex roots symmetrically located around the unit circle. The results given below, considering the error requirement, $\varepsilon = 10^{-8}$, are again extremely accurate.

ROOT		F(ROOT)	
REAL PART	IMAGINARY PART	REAL PART	IMAGINARY PART
1.0000000E+00	0.	0.	0.
−7.0710678E−01	7.0710678E−01	−6.5682570E−11	2.0663649E−10
−7.0710678E−01	−7.0710678E−01	2.8415670E−09	7.7068592E−09
−8.8408819E−17	1.0000000E+00	0.	7.0727055E−16
−1.5194534E−16	−1.0000000E+00	0.	−1.2155627E−15
7.0710678E−01	7.0710678E−01	−1.4210855E−14	−1.2434498E−14
−1.0000000E+00	−1.2009771E−10	−4.3093777E−09	9.6078167E−10
7.0710678E−01	−7.0710678E−01	3.4821497E−09	−1.6913404E−10

EXERCISES

2.7-1. Use Muller's method to find the zeros, real or complex, of the following polynomials:

    (a) $x^7 - 1$
    (b) $x^4 - 7x^3 + 18x^2 - 20x + 8$
    (c) $x^6 + 2x^5 + x^4 + 3x^3 + 5x^2 + x + 1$

2.7-2. The equation $x - \tan x = 0$ has an infinite number of real roots. Use Muller's method to find the first three positive roots.

2.7-3. Show that x_{i+1} as computed in Algorithm 2.11 is a zero of $p(x) = a_0 + a_1x + a_2x^2$ when a_2, a_1, a_0 are determined from (2.45) and (2.46).

2.8 SIMULTANEOUS NONLINEAR EQUATIONS

In this section we consider the problem of finding roots of simultaneous nonlinear equations.   For simplicity we shall consider only the case of two equations in two unknowns.   For such systems we shall state without proof several algorithms which are generalizations of the algorithms for a single equation.

We take the equations in the form

$$f(x,y) = 0$$
$$g(x,y) = 0 \qquad\qquad (2.50)$$

As a first step in applying fixed-point iteration, we rewrite these equations in the equivalent form

$$x = F(x,y)$$
$$y = G(x,y) \qquad\qquad (2.51)$$

so that any solution of (2.51) is a solution of (2.50), and conversely.   Fixed-point iteration is then defined by Algorithm 2.12.

Algorithm 2.12 Fixed-point iteration for systems Let $\{\xi,\eta\}$ be a solution of (2.50).   Let $\{x_0,y_0\}$ be an approximation to $\{\xi,\eta\}$.   Generate successive approximations from the recursion

$$x_{i+1} = F(x_i,y_i)$$
$$y_{i+1} = G(x_i,y_i) \qquad\qquad (2.52)$$

It is shown in analysis that this iteration will converge under the following sufficient (but not necessary) conditions:

1. F and G and their first partial derivatives are continuous in a neighborhood R of the root $\{\xi,\eta\}$, where R consists of all $\{x,y\}$ with $|x - \xi| \leq \varepsilon$, $|y - \eta| \leq \varepsilon$, for some positive ε.

2. The following inequalities are satisfied:

$$\left.\begin{array}{l} |F_x| + |F_y| \leq K \\ |G_x| + |G_y| \leq K \end{array}\right\} \text{ for all points } \{x,y\} \text{ in } R \text{ and some } K < 1$$

3. The initial approximation $\{x_0,y_0\}$ is chosen in R.

When this iteration does converge, it converges linearly.

As an example we consider the following system:

$$x = 0.1x^2 + 0.1y^2 + 0.8 = F(x,y)$$
$$y = 0.1x + 0.1xy^2 + 0.8 = G(x,y)$$

A solution of this system is easily verified to be $x = 1$, $y = 1$.   It is also easily verified that the inequality conditions for convergence of Algorithm

Table 2.2

i	x_i	y_i
0	0.5	0.5
1	0.85	0.8625
2	0.94664	0.94823
3	0.97953	0.97978
4	0.99182	0.99196

2.12 are satisfied with R all the points $\{x,y\}$ for which $|x - 1| \le 0.5$, $|y - 1| \le 0.5$ since

$$F_x = 0.2x \qquad F_y = 0.2y$$
$$G_x = 0.1 + 0.1y^2 \qquad G_y = 0.2xy$$

By taking $x_0 = 0.5$, $y_0 = 0.5$ and applying Algorithm 2.12, we obtain the successive approximations in Table 2.2. Convergence to the root $x = 1$, $y = 1$ is monotone-increasing, but very slow.

To adapt Newton's method to simultaneous equations, we proceed as follows: Let $\{x_0,y_0\}$ be an approximation to the solution $\{\xi,\eta\}$ of (2.50). Assuming that f and g are sufficiently differentiable, expand $f(x,y)$, $g(x,y)$ about $\{x_0,y_0\}$ using Taylor's series for functions of two variables (see Sec. 1.7)

$$f(x,y) = f(x_0,y_0) + f_x(x_0,y_0)(x - x_0) + f_y(x_0,y_0)(y - y_0) + \cdots$$
$$g(x,y) = g(x_0,y_0) + g_x(x_0,y_0)(x - x_0) + g_y(x_0,y_0)(y - y_0) + \cdots$$

Assuming that $\{x_0,y_0\}$ is sufficiently close to the solution $\{\xi,\eta\}$ so that higher-order terms can be neglected, we equate the expansion through linear terms to zero. This gives us the system

$$f_x(x - x_0) + f_y(y - y_0) = -f$$
$$g_x(x - x_0) + g_y(y - y_0) = -g \tag{2.53}$$

where it is understood that all functions and derivatives in (2.53) are to be evaluated at $\{x_0,y_0\}$. We might then expect that the solution $\{x_1,y_1\}$ of (2.53) will be closer to the solution $\{\xi,\eta\}$ than $\{x_0,y_0\}$. The solution of (2.53) by Cramer's rule yields

$$x_1 - x_0 = \frac{\begin{vmatrix} -f & f_y \\ -g & g_y \end{vmatrix}}{\begin{vmatrix} f_x & f_y \\ g_x & g_y \end{vmatrix}} = \left[\frac{-fg_y + gf_y}{J(f,g)}\right]_{\{x_0,y_0\}} = \Delta x_0$$

$$y_1 - y_0 = \frac{\begin{vmatrix} f_x & -f \\ g_x & -g \end{vmatrix}}{J(f,g)} = \left[\frac{-gf_x + fg_x}{J(f,g)}\right]_{\{x_0,y_0\}} = \Delta y_0$$

provided that $J(f,g) = f_x g_y - g_x f_y \neq 0$ at $\{x_0, y_0\}$. The function $J(f,g)$ is called the *Jacobian* of the functions f and g. The solution $\{x_1, y_1\}$ of this system now provides a new approximation to $\{\xi, \eta\}$. Repetition of this process leads to Newton's method for systems, which we call Algorithm 2.13.

Algorithm 2.13 Newton's method for systems Let $\{x_0, y_0\}$ be an approximation to a root $\{\xi, \eta\}$ of (2.50). Generate successive approximations from the recursion formulas

$$x_{i+1} = x_i - \left[\frac{fg_y - gf_y}{J(f,g)}\right]_i$$

$$y_{i+1} = y_i - \left[\frac{gf_x - fg_x}{J(f,g)}\right]_i \qquad (2.54)$$

where

$$J(f,g) = f_x g_y - g_x f_y$$

and where all functions involved are to be evaluated at $\{x_i, y_i\}$.

When this iteration converges, it converges quadratically. A set of conditions sufficient to ensure convergence is the following:

1. f, g and all their derivatives through second order are continuous and bounded in a region R containing $\{\xi, \eta\}$.
2. The Jacobian $J(f,g)$ does not vanish in R.
3. The initial approximation $\{x_0, y_0\}$ is chosen sufficiently close to the root $\{\xi, \eta\}$.

Newton's method can obviously be applied to a system of n equations in n unknowns. At each step of the iteration we will then have to evaluate n^2 partial derivative functions and n functions. This represents a considerable amount of computational effort. Again, unless a priori information is available about the location of the desired root, there is the definite possibility that the iteration will not converge or that it will converge to another root. The solution of a system of n equations for n large is very difficult, even on computers. In a practical problem, considerable trial and error is frequently necessary, and the use of less sophisticated methods is often resorted to.

As an example we consider the system

$$f(x,y) = x^2 + y^2 - 1 = 0$$
$$g(x,y) = x^2 - y^2 + \tfrac{1}{2} = 0$$

This system has four solutions, one in each of the four quadrants. These solutions are $x = \pm 0.5$, $y = \pm \sqrt{3}/2$. To find the root in the first quadrant by Algorithm 2.13, we compute first the partial derivatives

$$f_x = 2x \qquad f_y = 2y \qquad g_x = 2x \qquad g_y = -2y$$

Then the iteration (2.54) becomes, after some simplification,

$$x_{i+1} = x_i - \frac{g(x_i,y_i) + f(x_i,y_i)}{4x_i}$$

$$y_{i+1} = y_i + \frac{(fx_i,y_i) - g(x_i,y_i)}{-4y_i}$$

The results in Table 2.3 were obtained on an IBM 7094, using the indicated starting values. These results are correct to the figures given. Note that after the first two or three iterations, the number of figures of accuracy doubles with each iteration.

We now describe a final algorithm which requires considerably less labor than Newton's method and which converges more rapidly than linear iteration.

Table 2.3

i	x_i	y_i	$f(x_i,y_i)$	$g(x_i,y_i)$
0	0.1000000E 01	0.3000000E 01	0.9000000E 01	$-0.7500000E$ 01
1	6.2500000E$-$01	1.6250000E 00	2.0312500E 00	$-1.7500000E$ 00
2	5.1249999E$-$01	1.0432692E 00	3.5106692E$-$01	$-3.2575442E-01$
3	5.0015244E$-$01	8.8108162E$-$01	2.6457280E$-$02	$-2.6152365E-02$
4	5.0000002E$-$01	8.6615404E$-$01	2.2284687E$-$04	$-2.2280216E-04$
5	4.9999999E$-$01	8.6602540E$-$01	0.	$-7.4505806E-09$
6	5.0000000E$-$01	8.6602540E$-$01	$-7.4505806E-09$	7.4505806E$-$09
0	0.5000000E 00	0.5000000E 00	$-0.5000000E$ 00	0.5000000E 00
1	5.0000000E$-$01	1.0000000E 00	2.5000000E$-$01	$-2.5000000E-01$
2	5.0000000E$-$01	8.7500000E$-$01	1.5625000E$-$02	$-1.5625000E-02$
3	5.0000000E$-$01	8.6607141E$-$01	7.9706311E$-$05	$-7.9713762E-05$
4	5.0000000E$-$01	8.6602540E$-$01	$-7.4505806E-09$	7.4505806E$-$09
5	5.0000000E$-$01	8.6602540E$-$01	$-7.4505806E-09$	7.4505806E$-$09

Algorithm 2.14   Let $\{x_0, y_0\}$ be an initial approximation to a root $\{\xi, \eta\}$ of (2.50).   Generate succeeding approximations from the recursion

$$x_{i+1} = x_i - \frac{f(x_i, y_i)}{f_x(x_i, y_i)}$$

$$y_{i+1} = y_i - \frac{g(x_{i+1}, y_i)}{g_y(x_{i+1}, y_i)}$$

This iteration resembles closely Newton's method for a single equation and requires only one derivative evaluation for the improvement of each component.   There is one important difference, however.   In the second equation we use the improved value x_{i+1} rather than x_i.   We shall see later, in Chap. 3, that the use of improved values as soon as they become available will generally speed up convergence.

For the example of Table 2.3, the iteration of Algorithm 2.14 becomes

$$x_{i+1} = x_i - \frac{x_i^2 + y_i^2 - 1}{2x_i} = \frac{x_i^2 - y_i^2 + 1}{2x_i}$$

$$y_{i+1} = y_i - \frac{x_{i+1}^2 - y_i^2 + \frac{1}{2}}{-2y_i} = \frac{y_i^2 + x_{i+1}^2 + \frac{1}{2}}{2y_i} \qquad (2.55)$$

If we now attempt to find the solution in the first quadrant, using the initial values given in Table 2.3, we find that the iteration *diverges*.   Indeed, it can happen that the iteration of Algorithm 2.14 will diverge for any choice of initial conditions, whereas Newton's method will generally converge provided that the initial approximations are sufficiently close to the root.

An example illustrating convergence of Algorithm 2.14 is the following:

$$f(x,y) = e^x + xy - 1 = 0$$
$$g(x,y) = \sin xy + x + y - 1 = 0$$

It is easily verified that $x = 0$, $y = 1$ is a solution of this system.   Applying the iteration of Algorithm 2.14, we obtain

$$x_{i+1} = x_i - \frac{e^{x_i} + x_i y_i - 1}{e^{x_i} + y_i}$$

$$y_{i+1} = y_i - \frac{\sin(x_{i+1} y_i) + x_{i+1} + y_i - 1}{x_{i+1} \cos(x_{i+1} y_i) + 1} \qquad (2.56)$$

If we choose as initial approximations $x = 0.1$, $y = 0.5$, we obtain from (2.56) for the next two approximations

$$x_1 = -0.02 \qquad y_1 = 1.34$$
$$x_2 = 0.00009 \qquad y_2 = 0.99979$$

This iteration is obviously converging very rapidly.

Example 2.17 Find to six significant places the solution of the system

$$x + 3 \log x - y^2 = 0$$
$$2x^2 - xy - 5x + 1 = 0$$

using $x_0 = 3.4$, $y_0 = 2.2$ as initial approximations. (This example is taken from Scarborough [4].)

The FORTRAN program and the solution of this problem by Newton's method are given below. Convergence is remarkably rapid, primarily because the initial approximations are very good.

If we take the initial approximations as $x_0 = 1.0$ and $y_0 = -2.0$, convergence is equally rapid, but now to a different solution.

FORTRAN PROGRAM FOR EXAMPLE 2.17

```
C       EXAMPLE 2.17 BY NEWTON METHOD
C       TO SOLVE F(X,Y) = 0 AND G(X,Y) = 0
        F(X,Y) = X + 3.*ALOG10(X) - Y**2
        G(X,Y) = 2.*X**2 - X*Y - 5.*X + 1.
        FX(X,Y) = 1. + 3./(ALOG(10.)*X)
        FY(X,Y) = -2.*Y
        GX(X,Y) = 4.*X - Y - 5.
        GY(X,Y) = -X
        WRITE(6,6)
     10 READ(5,2) X,Y
        A = F(X,Y)
        B = G(X,Y)
        WRITE(6,3)X,Y,A,B
        DO 1 I = 1, 20
        DELTAX = (-F(X,Y)*GY(X,Y)
       *+ G(X,Y)*FY(X,Y))/(FX(X,Y)*GY(X,Y) - FY(X,Y)*GX(X,Y))
        DELTAY = (-G(X,Y)*FX(X,Y)
       *+ F(X,Y)*GX(X,Y))/(FX(X,Y)*GY(X,Y) - FY(X,Y)*GX(X,Y))
        X = X + DELTAX
        Y = Y + DELTAY
        A = F(X,Y)
        B = G(X,Y)
        WRITE(6,4) I,X,Y,A,B
        IF(AMAX1(ABS(DELTAX),ABS(DELTAY),ABS(A),ABS(B)).LT.1.E-7)
       *                    GO TO 10
      1 CONTINUE
        WRITE(6,5)
        GO TO 10
      2 FORMAT(2E20.7)
      3 FORMAT(//4X1HI8X 1HX 16X 1HY 15X 6HF(X,Y) 12X
       16HG(X,Y) /4X1H04(1PE17.7))
      4 FORMAT(I5, 4(1PE17.7))
      5 FORMAT(36H0FAILED TO CONVERGE IN 20 ITERATIONS)
      6 FORMAT(28H EXAMPLE 2.17, NEWTON METHOD)
        END
```

COMPUTER RESULTS FOR EXAMPLE 2.17

I	X	Y	F(X,Y)	G(X,Y)
0	3.4000000E 00	2.2000000E 00	1.5443677E−01	−3.6000001E−01
1	3.4899123E 00	2.2633644E 00	−4.4626594E−03	1.0471106E−02
2	3.4874446E 00	2.2616299E 00	−3.2186508E−06	7.8678131E−06
3	3.4874428E 00	2.2616286E 00	5.9604645E−08	−0.
4	3.4874428E 00	2.2616286E 00	5.9604645E−08	−0.

I	X	Y	F(X,Y)	G(X,Y)
0	1.0000000E 00	−2.0000000E 00	−3.0000000E 00	−0.
1	1.4759726E 00	−1.5240274E 00	−3.3945185E−01	2.2654986E−01
2	1.4573549E 00	−1.4011608E 00	−1.5200734E−02	2.9807091E−03
3	1.4588864E 00	−1.3967715E 00	−1.9967556E−05	−2.0265579E−06
4	1.4588902E 00	−1.3967670E 00	−1.4901161E−08	−1.1920929E−07
5	1.4588902E 00	−1.3967670E 00	0.	−0.

EXERCISES

2.8-1. Obtain two more approximations in Table 2.2. Then use Aitken's Δ^2 process to accelerate convergence.

2.8-2. A solution of the system

$$x^2 + y^2 = 1$$
$$xy = 0$$

is $x = 1$, $y = 0$. Using Algorithm 2.13 with $x_0 = 0.5$, $y_0 = 0.1$, carry out three iterations on a desk calculator. How many iterations would be required for eight-place accuracy?

2.8-3. Write a program to find solutions of the system

$$x^2 + xy^3 = 9$$
$$3x^2y - y^3 = 4$$

using Newton's method. Use the starting values given below, and observe which root the method converges to and the number of iterations required.

$$\{x_0, y_0\} = \{1.2, 2.5\}, \{-2, 2.5\}, \{-1.2, -2.5\}, \{2, -2.5\}$$

2.8-4. The system

$$x - \sinh y = 0$$
$$2y - \cosh x = 0$$

has a solution near $x_0 = 0.6$, $y_0 = 0.6$. Rearrange this system in a form suitable for solution by Algorithm 2.12. Then write a computer program to locate this root correct to seven significant figures, using both Algorithms 2.12 and 2.13.

2.8-5. Starting with $x_0 = 0.5$, $y_0 = 0.5$, carry out five steps of the iteration in (2.55), and verify the statement in the text that the subsequent iteration diverges.

2.8-6. Program the iteration of (2.56), and obtain the solution of the system correct to seven significant figures.

3
Matrices and Systems of Linear Equations

Many of the problems of numerical analysis can be reduced to the problem of solving linear systems of equations. Among the problems which can be so treated are the solution of ordinary or partial differential equations by finite-difference methods, the solution of systems of equations, the eigenvalue problems of mathematical physics, least-squares fitting of data, and polynomial approximation. The use of matrix notation is not only convenient, but extremely powerful, in bringing out fundamental relationships. In Sec. 3.1 we introduce some simple properties of matrices which will be used in later sections. Some of the theorems and properties will be stated without proof.

3.1 PROPERTIES OF MATRICES

A *system of m linear equations in n unknowns* has the general form

$$
\begin{aligned}
a_{11}x_1 + a_{12}x_2 + \cdots + a_{1n}x_n &= b_1 \\
a_{21}x_1 + a_{22}x_2 + \cdots + a_{2n}x_n &= b_2 \\
\cdots\cdots\cdots\cdots\cdots\cdots\cdots \\
a_{m1}x_1 + a_{m2}x_2 + \cdots + a_{mn}x_n &= b_m
\end{aligned}
\tag{3.1}
$$

The *coefficients* a_{ij} $(i = 1, \ldots, m; j = 1, \ldots, n)$ and the *right sides* b_i
$(i = 1, \ldots, m)$ are given numbers. The problem is to find, if possible,
numbers x_j $(j = 1, \ldots, n)$ such that the m equations (3.1) are satisfied
simultaneously. The discussion and understanding of this problem is greatly
facilitated when use is made of the algebraic concepts of *matrix* and *vector*.

DEFINITION OF MATRIX AND VECTOR

A *matrix* is a rectangular array of (usually real) numbers arranged in rows
and columns. The coefficients of (3.1) form a matrix, which we will call A.
It is customary to display such a matrix A as follows:

$$A = \begin{bmatrix} a_{11} & a_{12} & \cdots & a_{1n} \\ a_{21} & a_{22} & \cdots & a_{2n} \\ \cdots & \cdots & \cdots & \cdots \\ a_{m1} & a_{m2} & \cdots & a_{mn} \end{bmatrix} \tag{3.2}$$

At times, we will write more briefly

$$A = (a_{ij}) \tag{3.3}$$

The matrix A in (3.2) has m *rows* and n *columns*, or A *is of order* $m \times n$, for
short. The (i,j) *entry* a_{ij} of A is located at the intersection of the ith row
and the jth column of A. If A is an $n \times n$ matrix, we say that A is a *square
matrix of order n*. If a matrix has only one column, we call it a *column vector*,
and a matrix having only one row is called a *row vector*. We denote column
vectors by a single lowercase letter in bold type, to distinguish them from
other matrices, and call them *vectors*, for short. Thus both the right-side
constants b_i $(i = 1, \ldots, m)$ and the unknowns x_j $(j = 1, \ldots, n)$ form
vectors,

$$\mathbf{b} = \begin{bmatrix} b_1 \\ b_2 \\ b_3 \\ \cdot \\ \cdot \\ \cdot \\ b_m \end{bmatrix} \qquad \mathbf{x} = \begin{bmatrix} x_1 \\ x_2 \\ x_3 \\ \cdot \\ \cdot \\ \cdot \\ x_n \end{bmatrix} \tag{3.4}$$

We say that $\mathbf{b}$ *is an m-vector*, and $\mathbf{x}$ is an n-vector.

EQUALITY

If $A = (a_{ij})$ and $B = (b_{ij})$ are both matrices, then we say that A *equals* B,
or $A = B$, provided A and B have the same order *and* $a_{ij} = b_{ij}$, all i and j.

MATRIX MULTIPLICATION

In the terminology so far introduced, (3.1) states that the matrix A combined in a certain way with the one-column matrix, or vector, $\mathbf{x}$ should equal the one-column matrix, or vector, $\mathbf{b}$. The process of combining matrices involved here is called *matrix multiplication* and is defined, in general, as follows: Let $A = (a_{ij})$ be an $m \times n$ matrix, $B = (b_{ij})$ an $n \times p$ matrix; then *the matrix* $C = (c_{ij})$ *is the* (matrix) *product of* A *with* B (in that order), or $C = AB$, provided C is of order $m \times p$ and

$$c_{ij} = \sum_{k=1}^{n} a_{ik}b_{kj} \qquad \text{for } i = 1, \ldots, m; j = 1, \ldots, p \qquad (3.5)$$

In words, the (i,j) entry of the product $C = AB$ of A with B is calculated by taking the n entries of row i of A and the n entries of column j of B, multiplying corresponding entries, and summing the resulting n products.

Example

$$\text{If } A = \begin{bmatrix} 3 & 0 & 2 \\ 1 & -2 & -0 \\ 0 & 1 & 1 \end{bmatrix} \text{ and } B = \begin{bmatrix} 2 & 1 \\ 0 & 1 \\ 1 & 0 \end{bmatrix}, \text{ then } AB = \begin{bmatrix} 8 & 3 \\ 2 & 3 \\ 1 & 1 \end{bmatrix}$$

The $(2,1)$ entry of AB, for instance, is obtained by combining row 2 of A with column 1 of B:

$$1*2 + 2*0 + 0*1 = 2$$

as indicated by the arrows.

With this definition of matrix product and the definitions (3.2) and (3.4), we can write our system of equations (3.1) simply as

$$A\mathbf{x} = \mathbf{b} \qquad (3.6)$$

At present, it looks as if this simplification was achieved at the cost of several definitions, one of them quite complicated, but the many advantages of matrix notation will become apparent in the course of this chapter.

Matrix multiplication does not at all behave like multiplication of numbers. For example, it is possible to form the product of the matrix A with the matrix B only when the number of columns of A equals the number of rows of B. Hence, even when the product AB is defined, the product of B with A need not be defined. Further, even when both AB and BA are defined, they need not be equal.

Example

$$\text{If } A = \begin{bmatrix} 2 & 1 \\ 1 & 3 \end{bmatrix} \text{ and } B = \begin{bmatrix} 2 & 1 \\ 0 & 1 \end{bmatrix}, \text{ then } AB = \begin{bmatrix} 4 & 3 \\ 2 & 4 \end{bmatrix} \neq \begin{bmatrix} 5 & 5 \\ 1 & 3 \end{bmatrix} = BA$$

On the other hand, *matrix multiplication is associative*: If A, B, C are matrices of order $m \times n$, $n \times p$, $p \times q$, respectively, then

$$(AB)C = A(BC) \tag{3.7}$$

This can be seen as follows: Since A is of order $m \times n$, while B is of order $n \times p$, AB is defined and is of order $m \times p$; hence $(AB)C$ is defined and is of order $m \times q$. In the same way, one verifies that $A(BC)$ is defined and is also of order $m \times q$, so that at least one condition for equality is satisfied. Further,

$$\begin{aligned}
(i,j) \text{ entry of } (AB)C &= \sum_{k=1}^{p} [(i,k) \text{ entry of } AB] * c_{kj} \\
&= \sum_{k=1}^{p} \left[\sum_{r=1}^{n} a_{ir} * b_{rk} \right] * c_{kj} \\
&= \sum_{r=1}^{n} a_{ir} * \left[\sum_{k=1}^{p} b_{rk} * c_{kj} \right] \\
&= \sum_{r=1}^{n} a_{ir} * [(r,j) \text{ entry of } BC] \\
&= (i,j) \text{ entry of } A(BC)
\end{aligned}$$

proving that $(AB)C = A(BC)$. We will make repeated use of the special case when C is a vector (of appropriate order), that is

$$(AB)\mathbf{x} = A(B\mathbf{x})$$

DIAGONAL AND TRIANGULAR MATRICES

If $A = (a_{ij})$ is a square matrix of order n, then we call its entries a_{11}, a_{22}, $\ldots$, a_{nn} the *diagonal* entries of A, and call all other entries *off-diagonal*. All entries a_{ij} of A with $i < j$ are called *superdiagonal*, all entries a_{ij} with $i > j$ are called *subdiagonal* (see Fig. 3.1).

If all off-diagonal entries of the *square* matrix A are zero, we call A a *diagonal matrix*. If all subdiagonal entries of the square matrix A are zero, we call A an *upper* (or right) *triangular matrix*, while if all superdiagonal entries of A are zero, then A is called *lower* (or left) *triangular*. Clearly, a matrix is diagonal if and only if it is both upper and lower triangular.

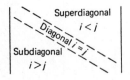

Superdiagonal
$i < j$
Diagonal $i = j$
Subdiagonal
$i > j$

Fig. 3.1

Examples   In the following examples, matrices A and C are diagonal; matrices A, B, C are upper-triangular and matrices A, C, and D are lower-triangular, and matrix E has none of these properties.

$$A = \begin{bmatrix} 1 & 0 & 0 \\ 0 & 1 & 0 \\ 0 & 0 & 1 \end{bmatrix} \quad B = \begin{bmatrix} 0 & 1 & 2 \\ 0 & 3 & 1 \\ 0 & 0 & 4 \end{bmatrix} \quad C = \begin{bmatrix} 0 & 0 & 0 \\ 0 & 0 & 0 \\ 0 & 0 & 0 \end{bmatrix}$$

$$D = \begin{bmatrix} 10 & 0 & 0 \\ 8 & 7 & 0 \\ 1 & 1 & 1 \end{bmatrix} \quad E = \begin{bmatrix} 1 & 0 & 0 \\ 3 & 2 & 6 \\ 0 & 0 & 4 \end{bmatrix}$$

THE IDENTITY MATRIX AND MATRIX INVERSION

If a diagonal matrix of order n has all its diagonal entries equal to 1, then we call it the *identity matrix* of order n and denote it by the special letter I, or I_n if the order is important.   The name identity matrix was chosen for this matrix because

$$I_n A = A \quad \text{for all } n \times p \text{ matrices } A$$
$$B I_n = B \quad \text{for all } m \times n \text{ matrices } B$$

The matrix I acts just like the number 1 in ordinary multiplication.

Division of matrices is, in general, not defined.   However, for square matrices, we define a related concept, *matrix inversion*.   We say that the *square* matrix A of order n is *invertible* provided there is a square matrix B of order n such that

$$AB = I = BA \tag{3.8}$$

The matrix $A = \begin{bmatrix} 1 & 1 \\ 0 & 1 \end{bmatrix}$, for instance, is invertible since

$$\begin{bmatrix} 1 & 1 \\ 0 & 1 \end{bmatrix}\begin{bmatrix} 1 & -1 \\ 0 & 1 \end{bmatrix} = \begin{bmatrix} 1 & 0 \\ 0 & 1 \end{bmatrix} = \begin{bmatrix} 1 & -1 \\ 0 & 1 \end{bmatrix}\begin{bmatrix} 1 & 1 \\ 0 & 1 \end{bmatrix}$$

On the other hand, the matrix $A = \begin{bmatrix} 1 & 2 \\ 2 & 4 \end{bmatrix}$ is not invertible.   For if B were a matrix such that $BA = I$, then it would follow that

$$\begin{bmatrix} b_{11} + 2b_{12} & 2b_{11} + 4b_{12} \\ b_{21} + 2b_{22} & 2b_{21} + 4b_{22} \end{bmatrix} = BA = \begin{bmatrix} 1 & 0 \\ 0 & 1 \end{bmatrix}$$

Hence we should have $b_{11} + 2b_{12} = 1$ and, at the same time, $2(b_{11} + 2b_{12}) = 2b_{11} + 4b_{12} = 0$, which is impossible.

We note that (3.8) can hold for at most one matrix B.   For if

$$AB = I \quad \text{and} \quad CA = I$$

where B and C are square matrices of the same order as A, then

$$C = CI = C(AB) = (CA)B = IB = B$$

showing that B and C must then be equal. Hence, if A is invertible, then there exists exactly one matrix B satisfying (3.8). This matrix is called *the inverse of A* and is denoted by A^{-1}.

It follows at once from (3.8) that if A is invertible, then so is A^{-1}, and its inverse is A; that is,

$$(A^{-1})^{-1} = A \tag{3.9}$$

Further, if both A and B are invertible square matrices of the same order, then their product is invertible and

$$(AB)^{-1} = B^{-1}A^{-1} \tag{3.10}$$

Note the change in order! The proof of (3.10) rests on the associativity of matrix multiplication:

$$(AB)(B^{-1}A^{-1}) = A(BB^{-1})A^{-1} = AA^{-1} = I$$
$$(B^{-1}A^{-1})(AB) = B^{-1}(A^{-1}A)B = B^{-1}B = I$$

Example The matrix $A = \begin{bmatrix} 1 & 1 \\ 0 & 1 \end{bmatrix}$ has inverse $A^{-1} = \begin{bmatrix} 1 & -1 \\ 0 & 1 \end{bmatrix}$, while the matrix $B = \begin{bmatrix} 1 & 0 \\ 1 & 1 \end{bmatrix}$ has inverse $B^{-1} = \begin{bmatrix} 1 & 0 \\ -1 & 1 \end{bmatrix}$. Further, $AB = \begin{bmatrix} 2 & 1 \\ 1 & 1 \end{bmatrix}$. Hence, by (3.10), $(AB)^{-1} = \begin{bmatrix} 1 & -1 \\ -1 & 2 \end{bmatrix} = B^{-1}A^{-1}$. On the other hand, $A^{-1}B^{-1} = \begin{bmatrix} 2 & -1 \\ -1 & 1 \end{bmatrix}$, and

$$(AB)(A^{-1}B^{-1}) = \begin{bmatrix} 2 & 1 \\ 1 & 1 \end{bmatrix} \begin{bmatrix} 2 & -1 \\ -1 & 1 \end{bmatrix} = \begin{bmatrix} 3 & -1 \\ 1 & 0 \end{bmatrix} \neq I$$

so that $A^{-1}B^{-1}$ cannot be the inverse of AB.

MATRIX ADDITION AND SCALAR MULTIPLICATION

It is possible to multiply a matrix by a scalar (=number) and to add two matrices of the same order in a reasonable way. First, if $A = (a_{ij})$ and $B = (b_{ij})$ are matrices and d is a number, we say that B *is the product of d with A*, or $B = dA$, provided B and A have the same order and

$$b_{ij} = da_{ij} \qquad \text{all } i \text{ and } j$$

Further, if $A = (a_{ij})$ and $B = (b_{ij})$ are matrices of the same order and $C = (c_{ij})$ is a matrix, we say that C *is the sum of A and B*, or $C = A + B$, provided C is of the same order as A and B and

$$c_{ij} = a_{ij} + b_{ij} \qquad \text{all } i \text{ and } j$$

Hence multiplication of a matrix by a number and addition of matrices is done entry by entry. The following rules regarding these operations, and also matrix multiplication, are easily verified: Assume that A, B, C are matrices such that all the sums and products mentioned below are defined, and let a, b be some numbers. Then

$$(i)\ A + B = B + A$$
$$(ii)\ (A + B) + C = A + (B + C)$$
$$(iii)\ a(A + B) = aA + aB$$
$$(iv)\ (a + b)A = aA + bA \qquad\qquad (3.11)$$
$$(v)\ (A + B)C = AC + BC$$
$$(vi)\ A(B + C) = AB + AC$$
$$(vii)\ a(AB) = (aA)B = A(aB)$$

(viii) If $a \neq 0$ and A is invertible, then aA is invertible and $(aA)^{-1} = (1/a)A^{-1}$

For the sake of illustration we now give a proof of (vi). With A an $m \times n$ matrix and B and C $n \times p$ matrices, both sides of (vi) are well-defined $m \times p$ matrices. Further,

$$(i,j) \text{ entry of } A(B + C) = \sum_{k=1}^{n} a_{ik} * [(k,j) \text{ entry of } B + C]$$

$$= \sum_{k=1}^{n} a_{ik} * [b_{kj} + c_{kj}]$$

$$= \sum_{k=1}^{n} a_{ik}b_{kj} + \sum_{k=1}^{n} a_{ik}c_{kj}$$

$$= [(i,j) \text{ entry of } AB] + [(i,j) \text{ entry of } AC]$$

$$= (i,j) \text{ entry of } AB + AC$$

Finally, if the $m \times n$ matrix A has all its entries equal to 0, then we call it the *null matrix* of order $m \times n$ and denote it by the special letter O. A null matrix has the obvious property that

$$B + O = B \qquad \text{for all matrices } B \text{ of the same order}$$

LINEAR COMBINATIONS

The definition of sums of matrices and products of numbers with matrices makes it, in particular, possible to sum n-vectors and multiply n-vectors by numbers or scalars. If $\mathbf{x}^{(1)}, \ldots, \mathbf{x}^{(k)}$ are k n-vectors and $b_1, b_2, \ldots, b_k$ are k numbers, then the weighted sum

$$b_1\mathbf{x}^{(1)} + b_2\mathbf{x}^{(2)} + \cdots + b_k\mathbf{x}^{(k)}$$

is also an n-vector, called the *linear combination* of $\mathbf{x}^{(1)}, \ldots, \mathbf{x}^{(k)}$ with *weights*, or coefficients, $b_1, \ldots, b_k$.

Consider now, once more, our system of equations (3.1). For $j = 1, \ldots, n$, let $\mathbf{a}_j$ denote the jth column of the $m \times n$ coefficient matrix A; that is, $\mathbf{a}_j$ is the m-vector whose ith entry is the number a_{ij}, $i = 1, \ldots, m$. Then we can write the m-vector $A\mathbf{x}$ as

$$A\mathbf{x} = x_1\mathbf{a}_1 + x_2\mathbf{a}_2 + \cdots + x_n\mathbf{a}_n$$

i.e., as a linear combination of the n columns of A with weights the entries of $\mathbf{x}$. The problem of solving (3.1) has therefore the equivalent formulation: Find weights $x_1, \ldots, x_n$ so that the linear combination of the n columns of A with these weights adds up to the right-side m-vector $\mathbf{b}$.

Consistent with this notation, we denote the jth column of the identity matrix I by the special symbol

$$\mathbf{i}_j$$

Clearly, $\mathbf{i}_j$ has all its entries equal to zero except for the jth entry, which is 1. It is customary to call $\mathbf{i}_j$ the jth *unit* vector. (As with the identity matrix, we do not bother to indicate explicitly the length or order of $\mathbf{i}_j$, it being understood from the context.) With this notation, we have

$$b_1\mathbf{i}_1 + b_2\mathbf{i}_2 + \cdots + b_n\mathbf{i}_n = \mathbf{b}$$

for every n-vector $\mathbf{b} = (b_i)$. Further, the jth column $\mathbf{a}_j$ of the matrix A can be obtained by multiplying A with $\mathbf{i}_j$; that is,

$$\mathbf{a}_j = A\mathbf{i}_j$$

Hence, if $C = AB$, then

$$C\mathbf{i}_j = (AB)\mathbf{i}_j = A(B\mathbf{i}_j)$$

so that the jth column of the product AB is obtained by multiplying the first factor A with the jth column of the second factor B.

EXISTENCE AND UNIQUENESS OF SOLUTIONS TO (3.1)

In later sections, we will deal exclusively with linear systems having a *square* coefficient matrix. We now justify this by showing that our system (3.1) cannot have exactly one solution for every right side unless the coefficient matrix is square.

Lemma 3.1 If $\mathbf{x} = \mathbf{x}_1$ is a solution of the linear system

$$A\mathbf{x} = \mathbf{b}$$

then any solution $\mathbf{x} = \mathbf{x}_2$ of this system is of the form

$$\mathbf{x}_2 = \mathbf{x}_1 + \mathbf{y}$$

where $\mathbf{x} = \mathbf{y}$ is a solution of the *homogeneous* system

$$A\mathbf{x} = \mathbf{0}$$

Indeed, if both $\mathbf{x}_1$ and $\mathbf{x}_2$ solve $A\mathbf{x} = \mathbf{b}$, then

$$A(\mathbf{x}_2 - \mathbf{x}_1) = A\mathbf{x}_2 - A\mathbf{x}_1 = \mathbf{b} - \mathbf{b} = \mathbf{0}$$

i.e., then their difference $\mathbf{y} = \mathbf{x}_2 - \mathbf{x}_1$ solves the homogeneous system $A\mathbf{x} = \mathbf{0}$.

Example The linear system

$$\begin{aligned} x_1 + 2x_2 &= 3 \\ 2x_1 + 4x_2 &= 6 \end{aligned}$$

has the solution $x_1 = 2$, $x_2 = 1$. The corresponding homogeneous system

$$\begin{aligned} x_1 + 2x_2 &= 0 \\ 2x_1 + 4x_2 &= 0 \end{aligned}$$

has the solution $x_1 = -2a$, $x_2 = a$, where a is an arbitrary scalar. Hence any solution of the original system is of the form $x_1 = 2 - 2a$, $x_2 = 1 + a$ for some number a.

The lemma implies the following theorem.

Theorem 3.1 The linear system $A\mathbf{x} = \mathbf{b}$ has at most one solution (i.e., the solution is unique if it exists) if and only if the corresponding homogeneous system $A\mathbf{x} = \mathbf{0}$ has only the "trivial" solution $\mathbf{x} = \mathbf{0}$.

Next we prove that we cannot hope for a unique solution unless our linear system has at least as many equations as unknowns.

Theorem 3.2 Any homogeneous linear system with fewer equations than unknowns has nontrivial (i.e., nonzero) solutions.

We have to prove that if A is an $m \times n$ matrix with

$$m < n$$

then we can find $\mathbf{y} \neq \mathbf{0}$ such that $A\mathbf{y} = \mathbf{0}$. This we do by induction on n. First, consider the case $n = 2$. In this case, we can have only one equation,

$$a_{11}x_1 + a_{12}x_2 = 0$$

and this equation has the nontrivial solution $x_1 = 0$, $x_2 = 1$, if $a_{12} = 0$; otherwise, it has the nontrivial solution $x_1 = a_{12}$, $x_2 = -a_{11}$. This proves our statement for $n = 2$. Let now $n > 2$, and assume it proved that any homogeneous system with less equations than unknowns and with less than n unknowns has nontrivial solutions; further, let $A\mathbf{x} = \mathbf{0}$ be a homogeneous linear system with m equations and n unknowns where $m < n$. We have to prove that this system has nontrivial solutions. This is certainly so if the nth column of A is zero, i.e., if $\mathbf{a}_n = \mathbf{0}$; for then the nonzero n-vector $\mathbf{x} = \mathbf{i}_n$ is a solution. Otherwise, some entry of $\mathbf{a}_n$ must be different from 0, say,

$$a_{in} \neq 0$$

In this case, we consider the $m \times (n-1)$ matrix B whose jth column is

$$\mathbf{b}_j = \mathbf{a}_j - \frac{a_{ij}}{a_{in}} \mathbf{a}_n \qquad j = 1, \ldots, n-1$$

If we can show that the homogeneous system

$$B\mathbf{x} = \mathbf{0}$$

has nontrivial solutions, then we are done. For if we can find numbers $x_1, \ldots, x_{n-1}$ not all zero such that

$$x_1 \mathbf{b}_1 + x_2 \mathbf{b}_2 + \cdots + x_{n-1} \mathbf{b}_{n-1} = \mathbf{0}$$

then it follows from the definition of the $\mathbf{b}_j$'s that

$$x_1 \mathbf{a}_1 + x_2 \mathbf{a}_2 + \cdots + x_{n-1} \mathbf{a}_{n-1} + \left(-\sum_{j=1}^{n-1} x_j \frac{a_{ij}}{a_{in}} \right) \mathbf{a}_n = \mathbf{0}$$

thus providing a nontrivial solution to $A\mathbf{x} = \mathbf{0}$. Hence it remains only to show that $B\mathbf{x} = \mathbf{0}$ has nontrivial solutions. For this, note that for each j, the ith entry of $\mathbf{b}_j$ is

$$a_{ij} - \frac{a_{ij}}{a_{in}} a_{in} = 0$$

so that the ith equation of $B\mathbf{x} = \mathbf{0}$ looks like

$$0 \cdot x_1 + 0 \cdot x_2 + \cdots + 0 \cdot x_{n-1} = 0$$

and is therefore satisfied by any choice of $x_1, \ldots, x_{n-1}$. It follows that $\mathbf{x} = \mathbf{y}$ solves $B\mathbf{x} = \mathbf{0}$ if and only if $\mathbf{x} = \mathbf{y}$ solves the homogeneous system

$$\hat{B}\mathbf{x} = \mathbf{0}$$

which we get from $B\mathbf{x} = \mathbf{0}$ by merely omitting the ith equation. But now $\hat{B}\mathbf{x} = \mathbf{0}$ is a homogeneous linear system with $m-1$ equations in $n-1$ unknowns, hence with less equations than unknowns and with less than n unknowns. Therefore, by the induction hypothesis, $\hat{B}\mathbf{x} = \mathbf{0}$ has nontrivial solutions, which finishes the proof.

Example Consider the homogeneous linear system $A\mathbf{x} = \mathbf{0}$ given by

$$x_1 + 2x_2 - x_3 = 0$$
$$x_1 - x_2 + x_3 = 0$$

so that $m = 2$, $n = 3$. Following the argument for Theorem 3.2, we construct a non-trivial solution as follows: Since $a_{23} \neq 0$, we pick $i = 2$ and get

$$\mathbf{b}_1 = \mathbf{a}_1 - \frac{a_{21}}{a_{23}} \mathbf{a}_3 = \begin{bmatrix} 1 \\ 1 \end{bmatrix} - (1/1) \begin{bmatrix} -1 \\ 1 \end{bmatrix} = \begin{bmatrix} 2 \\ 0 \end{bmatrix}$$

$$\mathbf{b}_2 = \mathbf{a}_2 - \frac{a_{22}}{a_{23}} \mathbf{a}_3 = \begin{bmatrix} 2 \\ -1 \end{bmatrix} - (-1/1) \begin{bmatrix} -1 \\ 1 \end{bmatrix} = \begin{bmatrix} 1 \\ 0 \end{bmatrix}$$

The smaller homogeneous system $B\mathbf{x} = \mathbf{0}$ is therefore

$$2x_1 + x_2 = 0$$
$$0x_1 + 0x_2 = 0$$

We can ignore the last equation and get, then, the homogeneous system $\hat{B}\mathbf{x} = \mathbf{0}$ which consists of just one equation,

$$2x_1 + x_2 = 0$$

A nontrivial solution for this is $x_1 = 1$, $x_2 = -2$. Hence, with

$$x_3 = -[1(1/1) + (-2)(-1/1)] = -3$$

the 3-vector $\mathbf{x} = (x_j)$ is a nontrivial solution of the original system.

Next we prove that we cannot expect to get a solution to our linear system (3.1) for all possible choices of the right side $\mathbf{b}$ unless we have no more equations than unknowns.

Lemma 3.2 If A is an $m \times n$ matrix and the linear system $A\mathbf{x} = \mathbf{b}$ has a solution for every m-vector $\mathbf{b}$, then there exists an $n \times m$ matrix C such that

$$AC = I_m$$

Such a matrix C can be constructed as follows: By assumption, we can find a solution to the system $A\mathbf{x} = \mathbf{b}$ no matter what $\mathbf{b}$ is. Hence, choosing $\mathbf{b}$ to be the jth column of I, we can find an n-vector $\mathbf{c}_j$ such that

$$A\mathbf{c}_j = \mathbf{i}_j \qquad j = 1, \ldots, m$$

But then, with C the $n \times m$ matrix whose jth column is $\mathbf{c}_j$, $j = 1, \ldots, m$, we get

$$(AC)\mathbf{i}_j = A(C\mathbf{i}_j) = A\mathbf{c}_j = \mathbf{i}_j = I\mathbf{i}_j \qquad j = 1, \ldots, m$$

showing that the jth column of the product AC agrees with the jth column of I, $j = 1, \ldots, m$. But that says that $AC = I$.

Lemma 3.3 If B and C are matrices such that

$$BC = I$$

then the homogeneous system $C\mathbf{x} = \mathbf{0}$ has only the trivial solution $\mathbf{x} = \mathbf{0}$. Indeed, if $C\mathbf{x} = \mathbf{0}$, then

$$\mathbf{x} = I\mathbf{x} = (BC)\mathbf{x} = B(C\mathbf{x}) = B\mathbf{0} = \mathbf{0}$$

Theorem 3.3 If A is an $m \times n$ matrix and the linear system $A\mathbf{x} = \mathbf{b}$ has a solution for every possible m-vector $\mathbf{b}$, then $m \leq n$.

For the proof, we get from Lemma 3.2 that

$$AC = I$$

for some $n \times m$ matrix C. But this implies by Lemma 3.3 that the homogeneous system $C\mathbf{x} = \mathbf{0}$ has only the trivial solution $\mathbf{x} = \mathbf{0}$. Therefore, by Theorem 3.2, C must have at least as many rows as columns, that is, $n \geq m$, which finishes the proof.

We now know that we cannot expect to get exactly one solution to our system (3.1) for every possible right side unless the system has exactly as many equations as unknowns, i.e., unless the coefficient matrix is square. We will therefore consider from now on only linear systems with a square coefficient matrix. For such square matrices, we prove a final theorem.

Theorem 3.4 Let A be an $n \times n$ matrix. Then the following are equivalent:

   (i) The homogeneous system $A\mathbf{x} = \mathbf{0}$ has only the trivial solution $\mathbf{x} = \mathbf{0}$.
  (ii) For every right side $\mathbf{b}$, the system $A\mathbf{x} = \mathbf{b}$ has a solution.
 (iii) A is invertible.

First we prove that (i) implies (ii). Let $\mathbf{b}$ be a given n-vector. We have to prove that $A\mathbf{x} = \mathbf{b}$ has a solution. For this, let D be the $m \times (n + 1)$ matrix whose first n columns agree with those of A, while the $(n + 1)$st column is $\mathbf{b}$. Since D has more columns than rows, we can find, by Theorem 3.2, a nonzero $(n + 1)$-vector $\mathbf{y}$ such that $D\mathbf{y} = \mathbf{0}$, that is, such that

$$y_1\mathbf{a}_1 + y_2\mathbf{a}_2 + \cdots + y_n\mathbf{a}_n + y_{n+1}\mathbf{b} = 0 \qquad (3.12)$$

Clearly, the number y_{n+1} cannot be zero. For if y_{n+1} were zero, then as $\mathbf{y} \neq \mathbf{0}$, at least one of the numbers $y_1, \ldots, y_n$ would have to be nonzero, while at the same time

$$y_1\mathbf{a}_1 + \cdots + y_n\mathbf{a}_n = \mathbf{0}$$

But this says that $A\mathbf{x} = \mathbf{0}$ admits the *nontrivial* solution $x_i = y_i, i = 1, \ldots, n$, which contradicts (i). Hence, since $y_{n+1} \neq 0$, we can solve (3.12) for $\mathbf{b}$ to get that

$$-\frac{y_1}{y_{n+1}}\mathbf{a}_1 - \cdots - \frac{y_n}{y_{n+1}}\mathbf{a}_n = \mathbf{b}$$

But this says that $Ax = b$ has a solution, viz., the solution $x_i = -(y_i/y_{n+1})$, $i = 1, \ldots, n$, which proves (ii).

Next we prove that (ii) implies (iii). Assuming (ii), it follows with Lemma 3.2 that there exists an $n \times n$ matrix C such that

$$AC = I$$

Hence, by Lemma 3.3, the equation $Cx = 0$ has only the trivial solution $x = 0$. This says that the $n \times n$ matrix C satisfies (i); hence, by the argument we just went through, C satisfies (ii); therefore, by Lemma 3.2, there exists an $n \times n$ matrix D such that

$$CD = I$$

But now we are done. For we showed earlier that if

$$AC = I = CD$$

with A, C, D square matrices, then C is invertible and

$$A = D = C^{-1}$$

Hence A is the inverse of an invertible matrix, therefore invertible.

Finally, Lemma 3.3 shows that (iii) implies (i).

Example We showed in an earlier example that the 2×2 matrix

$$A = \begin{bmatrix} 1 & 2 \\ 2 & 4 \end{bmatrix}$$

is not invertible and, in another example, that for this matrix the homogeneous system $Ax = 0$ has nontrivial solutions. By Theorem 3.4, the linear system $Ax = b$ should therefore not be solvable for some 2-vector b. Indeed, with $b = i_1$, we get the system

$$x_1 + 2x_2 = 1$$
$$2x_1 + 4x_2 = 0$$

which has no solution since the second equation demands that

$$2(x_1 + 2x_2) = 0$$

while the first equation demands that

$$2(x_1 + 2x_2) = 2$$

LINEAR INDEPENDENCE AND BASES

Let $a_1, \ldots, a_n$ be n m-vectors, and let A be the $m \times n$ matrix whose jth column is a_j, $j = 1, \ldots, n$. We say that these m-vectors are *linearly independent*

$$\text{if} \quad x_1 a_1 + \cdots + x_n a_n = 0 \quad \text{implies that} \quad x_1 = \cdots = x_n = 0$$

Otherwise, we call the vectors linearly dependent. Clearly, the m-vectors are linearly independent if and only if the homogeneous system $Ax = 0$ has only the trivial solution $x = 0$. Hence we can infer from Theorem 3.2 that any set of more than m m-vectors must be linearly dependent.

Let $a_1, \ldots, a_n$ be linearly independent. If every m-vector b can be written as a linear combination of these n m-vectors, then we call $a_1, \ldots, a_n$ a *basis* (for all m-vectors). Clearly, $a_1, \ldots, a_n$ is a basis if and only if the linear system $Ax = b$ has exactly one solution for every m-vector b, that is, if and only if every m-vector can be written in exactly one way as a linear combination of the m-vectors $a_1, \ldots, a_n$. In particular, a basis (for all m-vectors) consists of exactly m m-vectors (that is, $n = m$), and the corresponding matrix is invertible.

Examples The vectors

$$a_1 = \begin{bmatrix} 1 \\ 0 \\ 0 \end{bmatrix} \qquad a_2 = \begin{bmatrix} 0 \\ 1 \\ 0 \end{bmatrix}$$

are linearly independent; but they do not form a basis since there are only two 3-vectors. Further, every 2-vector can be written as a linear combination of the three 2-vectors

$$a_1 = \begin{bmatrix} 1 \\ 0 \end{bmatrix} \qquad a_2 = \begin{bmatrix} 0 \\ 1 \end{bmatrix} \qquad a_3 = \begin{bmatrix} 1 \\ 1 \end{bmatrix}$$

but these three 2-vectors do not form a basis since they must be linearly dependent. Finally, the three 3-vectors

$$a_1 = \begin{bmatrix} 1 \\ 0 \\ 0 \end{bmatrix} \qquad a_2 = \begin{bmatrix} 1 \\ 1 \\ 0 \end{bmatrix} \qquad a_3 = \begin{bmatrix} 1 \\ 1 \\ 1 \end{bmatrix}$$

do form a basis, since the corresponding matrix is invertible. To see this, it is, by Theorem 3.4, sufficient to prove that the system

$$x_1 + x_2 + x_3 = 0$$
$$x_2 + x_3 = 0$$
$$x_3 = 0$$

has only the trivial solution $x_1 = x_2 = x_3 = 0$. But that is obvious.

THE TRANSPOSED MATRIX

Finally, there is an operation on matrices which has no parallel in ordinary arithmetic, the formation of the transposed matrix. If $A = (a_{ij})$ and $B = (b_{ij})$ are matrices, we say that B *is the transpose of* A, or $B = A^T$, provided B has as many rows as A has columns and as many columns as A has rows and

$$b_{ij} = a_{ji} \qquad \text{all } i \text{ and } j$$

In words, one forms the transpose A^T of A by "reflecting A across the diagonal."

If

$$A^T = A$$

then A is said to be *symmetric*.

The matrices

$$A = \begin{bmatrix} 1 & 3 & 2 \\ 3 & 0 & 4 \\ 2 & 4 & 5 \end{bmatrix} \qquad B = \begin{bmatrix} 3 & -1 \\ 2 & 6 \\ 0 & 8 \end{bmatrix} \qquad C = \begin{bmatrix} 3 & 4 & 7 \end{bmatrix}$$

have the transpose

$$A^T = \begin{bmatrix} 1 & 3 & 2 \\ 3 & 0 & 4 \\ 2 & 4 & 5 \end{bmatrix} \qquad B^T = \begin{bmatrix} 3 & 2 & 0 \\ -1 & 6 & 8 \end{bmatrix} \qquad C^T = \begin{bmatrix} 3 \\ 4 \\ 7 \end{bmatrix}$$

In particular, the transpose $\mathbf{b}^T$ of a column vector $\mathbf{b}$ is a row vector.

One easily verifies the following rules regarding transposition:

1. If A and B are matrices such that AB is defined, then $B^T A^T$ is defined and $(AB)^T = B^T A^T$. Note the change in order!
2. For any matrix A, $(A^T)^T = A$.
3. If the matrix A is invertible, then so is A^T, and $(A^T)^{-1} = (A^{-1})^T$.

To prove Rule 1, let A be an $m \times n$ matrix and B an $n \times p$ matrix so that AB is an $m \times p$ matrix and $(AB)^T$ is a $p \times m$ matrix. Then A^T is $n \times m$, B^T is $p \times n$; therefore the product $B^T A^T$ is well defined and a $p \times m$ matrix. Finally,

$$\begin{aligned}
(i,j) \text{ entry of } (AB)^T &= (j,i) \text{ entry of } AB \\
&= \sum_{k=1}^{n} [(j,k) \text{ entry of } A] * [(k,i) \text{ entry of } B] \\
&= \sum_{k=1}^{n} [(i,k) \text{ entry of } B^T] * [(k,j) \text{ entry of } A^T] \\
&= (i,j) \text{ entry of } B^T A^T
\end{aligned}$$

As to Rule 3, we get from Rule 1 that

$$A^T(A^{-1})^T = (A^{-1}A)^T = I^T = I$$
$$(A^{-1})^T A^T = (AA^{-1})^T = I^T = I$$

which proves Rule 3.

If $\mathbf{a}$ and $\mathbf{b}$ are n-vectors, then $\mathbf{b}^T\mathbf{a}$ is a 1×1 matrix, or number, called the *scalar product of* $\mathbf{a}$ and $\mathbf{b}$.

PERMUTATIONS AND PERMUTATION MATRICES

A *permutation of degree n* is any rearrangement of the first n integers; i.e., it is a sequence of n integers in which each integer between 1 and n appears at least once, hence at most once, therefore exactly once. There are many ways of writing a permutation of degree n. For our purposes, it is sufficient (and in a sense quite rigorous) to think of a permutation as an n-vector $\mathbf{p} = (p_i)$ with $p_i \in \{1, 2, \ldots, n\}$, all i, and $p_i \neq p_j$ for $i \neq j$. There are $n!$ permutations of degree n. A permutation $\mathbf{p}$ is said to be even or odd depending on whether the *number of inversions* in $\mathbf{p}$ is even or odd. Here the number of inversions in a permutation $\mathbf{p} = (p_i)$ is the number of instances an integer precedes a smaller one. For example, in the permutation $\mathbf{p}$ with $\mathbf{p}^T = [7,2,6,3,4,1,5]$,

7 precedes 2, 6, 3, 4, 1, 5	giving 6 inversions
2 precedes 1	giving 1 inversion
6 precedes 3, 4, 1, 5	giving 4 inversions
3 precedes 1	giving 1 inversion
4 precedes 1	giving 1 inversion
	————
Hence $\mathbf{p}$ has altogether	13 inversions

Note that any interchange of two entries in a permutation changes the number of inversions by an odd amount.

A *permutation matrix of order n* is any $n \times n$ matrix P whose columns (rows) are a rearrangement or permutation of the columns (rows) of the identity matrix of order n. Precisely, the $n \times n$ matrix P is a permutation matrix if

$$P\mathbf{i}_j = \mathbf{i}_{p_j} \qquad j = 1, \ldots, n \tag{3.13}$$

for some permutation $\mathbf{p} = (p_i)$ of degree n.

Theorem 3.5 Let P be the permutation matrix satisfying (3.13). Then

(i) P^T is a permutation matrix, satisfying

$$P^T\mathbf{i}_{p_j} = \mathbf{i}_j \qquad j = 1, \ldots, n$$

Hence $P^TP = I$; therefore P is invertible, and $P^{-1} = P^T$.

(ii) If A is an $m \times n$ matrix, then AP is the $m \times n$ matrix whose jth column equals the p_jth column of A, $j = 1, \ldots, n$.

(iii) If A is an $n \times m$ matrix, then P^TA is the $n \times m$ matrix whose ith row equals the p_ith row of A, $i = 1, \ldots, n$.

Example The matrix

$$P = \begin{bmatrix} 0 & 0 & 1 \\ 1 & 0 & 0 \\ 0 & 1 & 0 \end{bmatrix}$$

is the permutation matrix corresponding to the permutation $\mathbf{p}^T = [2 \quad 3 \quad 1]$ since, apparently, $P\mathbf{i}_1 = \mathbf{i}_2$, $P\mathbf{i}_2 = \mathbf{i}_3$, and $P\mathbf{i}_3 = \mathbf{i}_1$. One has

$$P^T = \begin{bmatrix} 0 & 1 & 0 \\ 0 & 0 & 1 \\ 1 & 0 & 0 \end{bmatrix}$$

Hence $P^T\mathbf{i}_1 = \mathbf{i}_3$, $P^T\mathbf{i}_2 = \mathbf{i}_1$, $P^T\mathbf{i}_3 = \mathbf{i}_2$, illustrating (i) of Theorem 3.5. Further, one calculates, for example, that

$$AP = \begin{bmatrix} 1 & 2 & 3 \\ 4 & 5 & 6 \\ 7 & 8 & 9 \end{bmatrix} \begin{bmatrix} 0 & 0 & 1 \\ 1 & 0 & 0 \\ 0 & 1 & 0 \end{bmatrix} = \begin{bmatrix} 2 & 3 & 1 \\ 5 & 6 & 4 \\ 8 & 9 & 7 \end{bmatrix}$$

Hence column 2 of AP is column $3 = p_2$ of A, illustrating (ii) of Theorem 3.5.

THE NUMERICAL SOLUTION OF LINEAR SYSTEMS

We will consider only linear systems

$$A\mathbf{x} = \mathbf{b}$$

which have one and only one solution for every right side **b**. By Theorems 3.2 and 3.3, we must therefore restrict attention to those systems which have exactly as many equations as unknowns, i.e., for which the coefficient matrix A is square. For such systems, Theorem 3.4 tells us that A should be invertible in order that the system have exactly one solution for every right side **b**. We will therefore assume that all linear systems under discussion have an invertible coefficient matrix.

A frequently quoted test for invertibility of a matrix is based on the concept of the *determinant*. The relevant theorem states that the matrix A is invertible if and only if det $(A) \neq 0$. If det $(A) \neq 0$, then it is even possible to express the solution of $A\mathbf{x} = \mathbf{b}$ in terms of determinants, by the so-called Cramer's rule. Nevertheless, determinants are not of *practical* interest for the solution of linear systems since the calculation of one determinant is, in general, of the same order of difficulty as solving the linear system. For this reason, we make no use of determinants in solving linear systems, nor do we attempt to define a determinant here. However, in Sec. 3.10, we do present a method for evaluating determinants (based on a direct method for solving linear systems) for use in another context.

Numerical methods for solving linear systems may be divided into two types, *direct* and *iterative*. Direct methods are those which, in the absence of round-off or other errors, will yield the exact solution in a finite number of elementary arithmetic operations. In practice, because a computer works with a finite word length, direct methods do not lead to exact solutions. Indeed, errors arising from round-off, instability, and loss of significance may lead to extremely poor or even useless results. A large part of numerical analysis is concerned with why and how these errors arise, and with the search for methods which minimize the totality of such errors. The fundamental method used for direct solutions is *Gauss elimination*, but even within this class there are a variety of choices of methods which vary in computational efficiency and accuracy. Some of these methods will be examined in Secs. 3.2 and 3.5.

Iterative methods are those which start with an initial approximation and which, by applying a suitably chosen algorithm, lead to successively better approximations. Even if the process converges, we can only hope to obtain an approximate solution by iterative methods. Iterative methods vary with the algorithm chosen and in their rates of convergence. Some iterative methods may actually diverge; others may converge so slowly that they are computationally useless. The important advantages of iterative methods are the simplicity and uniformity of the operations to be performed, which make them well suited for use on computers, and their relative insensitivity to the growth of round-off errors.

Matrices associated with linear systems are also classified as *dense* or *sparse*. Dense matrices have very few zero elements, and the order of such matrices tends to be relatively small—perhaps of order 100 or less. It is usually most efficient to handle problems involving such matrices by direct methods. Sparse matrices have very few nonzero elements. They usually arise from attempts to solve differential equations by finite-difference methods. The order of such matrices may be very large, and they are ideally suited to solution by iterative methods which take advantage of the sparse nature of the matrix involved. Iterative methods for solving linear systems will be discussed in Sec. 3.8.

EXERCISES

3.1-1. Let

$$A = \begin{bmatrix} 2 & 3 & 1 \\ 1 & -1 & 1 \\ 0 & 2 & 2 \end{bmatrix} \qquad B = \begin{bmatrix} 1 & 2 & 1 \\ -1 & 2 & -1 \\ 2 & 0 & 2 \end{bmatrix} \qquad C = \begin{bmatrix} 1 & 0 & 1 \\ 0 & 1 & 1 \\ 1 & 0 & 2 \end{bmatrix}$$

(a) Compute AB and BA and show that $AB \neq BA$.
(b) Find $(A + B) + C$ and $A + (B + C)$.
(c) Show that $A(BC) = (AB)C$.
(d) Verify that $(AB)^T = B^T A^T$.

3.1-2. Show that the matrix A is not invertible (see Theorem 3.4):

$$A = \begin{bmatrix} 1 & 2 & 1 \\ 2 & -1 & -1 \\ 6 & 2 & 0 \end{bmatrix}$$

3.1-3. For the matrix A given below, find a permutation matrix P such that
  (a) Postmultiplication of A by P interchanges the fourth and the first columns of A
  (b) Premultiplication of A by P interchanges the third row and the first row of A

$$A = \begin{bmatrix} 4 & 1 & 2 & 1 \\ 3 & 2 & 1 & 1 \\ 1 & 2 & 0 & 1 \\ 1 & 1 & 0 & 1 \end{bmatrix}$$

3.1-4. In the matrix A in Exercise 3.1-3 find a sequence of permutation matrices which will transform A into the form

$$A' = \begin{bmatrix} 1 & 0 & 1 & 1 \\ 1 & 0 & 1 & 2 \\ 1 & 1 & 3 & 2 \\ 1 & 2 & 4 & 1 \end{bmatrix}$$

3.1-5. Write the following system in matrix form and identify the matrix A and the vector b.

$$\begin{aligned}
2x_1 + 3x_2 + 4x_3 + x_4 &= 1 \\
x_1 + 2x_2 \qquad\quad + x_4 &= 0 \\
2x_1 + 3x_2 + x_3 - x_4 &= 2 \\
x_1 - 2x_2 - x_3 - x_4 &= 3
\end{aligned}$$

3.1-6. Convince yourself that the notion of invertibility makes sense for *square* matrices only by proving the following: Let A be an $m \times n$ matrix; if B and C are $n \times m$ matrices such that $AB = I_m$ and $CA = I_n$, then $B = C = A^{-1}$; in particular, then $m = n$. [*Hint:* Prove first that $B = C$. Then show that $m = $ trace $(AB) = $ trace $(BA) = n$, where the *trace* of a square matrix is defined as the sum of its diagonal entries.]

3.1-7. Make use of Theorem 3.4 to prove that a permutation matrix is invertible.

3.1-8. Make use of Theorem 3.4 to prove that, if A and B are square matrices such that their product is invertible, then both A and B must be invertible.

3.1-9. Do the vectors

$$\begin{bmatrix} 1 \\ -1 \\ 0 \\ 0 \end{bmatrix} \quad \begin{bmatrix} 0 \\ 1 \\ -1 \\ 0 \end{bmatrix} \quad \begin{bmatrix} 0 \\ 0 \\ 1 \\ -1 \end{bmatrix} \quad \begin{bmatrix} 1 \\ 0 \\ 0 \\ 1 \end{bmatrix}$$

form a basis?

3.1-10. Prove that the three vectors

$$\begin{bmatrix} 1 \\ 1 \\ 0 \end{bmatrix} \quad \begin{bmatrix} 1 \\ -1 \\ 0 \end{bmatrix} \quad \begin{bmatrix} 0 \\ 0 \\ 1 \end{bmatrix}$$

form a linearly independent set. Do they form a basis?

3.1-11. For each of the three operations with matrices, namely, addition of two matrices, multiplication of two matrices, and multiplication of a scalar with a matrix, write a

FORTRAN subroutine which carries out the operation on appropriate input and returns the resulting matrix.

3.1-12. If $p(x) = c_0 + c_1 x + c_2 x^2 + \cdots + c_k x^k$ is a given polynomial and A is a given $n \times n$ matrix, then the matrix $p(A)$ is defined by

$$p(A) = c_0 A^0 + c_1 A^1 + c_2 A^2 + \cdots + c_k A^k$$

Here $A^0 = I$, $A^1 = A$, and for $j > 1$, $A^j = A(A^{j-1})$. Write an efficient FORTRAN subroutine with arguments N, KP1, A, C, PA, where N is the order of the matrix A, and PA is to contain, on return, the matrix $p(A)$, with C a one-dimensional array containing $C(i) = c_{i-1}$, $i = 1, \ldots, KP1$. Do not use any arrays in the subroutine other than the arrays A, C, and PA. (*Hint:* Remember Algorithm 2.9.)

3.1-13. Suppose there exists, for a given matrix A of order n, a polynomial $p(x)$ such that $p(0) \neq 0$, while $p(A)$ is the null matrix. Prove that A must be invertible.

3.1-14. Verify the rules stated in (3.11).

3.2 THE SOLUTION OF LINEAR SYSTEMS BY ELIMINATION

Let A be a given square matrix of order n, $\mathbf{b}$ a given n-vector. We wish to solve the linear system

$$A\mathbf{x} = \mathbf{b} \tag{3.14}$$

for the unknown n-vector $\mathbf{x}$. The solution vector $\mathbf{x}$ can be obtained without difficulty in case A is *upper-triangular* with *all* diagonal entries *nonzero*. For then the system (3.14) has the form

$$
\begin{aligned}
a_{11}x_1 + a_{12}x_2 + \cdots + a_{1,n-1}x_{n-1} &+ a_{1n}x_n &= b_1 \\
a_{22}x_2 + \cdots + a_{2,n-1}x_{n-1} &+ a_{2,n}x_n &= b_2 \\
&\cdots\cdots\cdots\cdots\cdots \\
a_{n-1,n-1}x_{n-1} &+ a_{n-1,n}x_n &= b_{n-1} \\
&a_{n,n}x_n &= b_n
\end{aligned}
\tag{3.15}
$$

In particular, the last equation involves only x_n; hence, since $a_{nn} \neq 0$, we must have

$$x_n = \frac{b_n}{a_{nn}}$$

Since we now know x_n, the second last equation

$$a_{n-1,n-1}x_{n-1} + a_{n-1,n}x_n = b_{n-1}$$

involves only one unknown, namely, x_{n-1}. As $a_{n-1,n-1} \neq 0$, it follows that

$$x_{n-1} = \frac{b_{n-1} - a_{n-1,n}x_n}{a_{n-1,n-1}}$$

With x_n and x_{n-1} now determined, the third last equation

$$a_{n-2,n-2}x_{n-2} + a_{n-2,n-1}x_{n-1} + a_{n-2,n}x_n = b_{n-2}$$

contains only one true unknown, namely, x_{n-2}. Once again, since $a_{n-2,n-2}$ $\neq 0$, we can solve for x_{n-2},

$$x_{n-2} = \frac{b_{n-2} - a_{n-2,n-1}x_{n-1} - a_{n-2,n}x_n}{a_{n-2,n-2}}$$

In general, with $x_{k+1}, x_{k+2}, \ldots, x_n$ already computed, the kth equation can be uniquely solved for x_k, since $a_{kk} \neq 0$, to give

$$x_k = \frac{b_k - \sum\limits_{j=k+1}^{n} a_{kj}x_j}{a_{kk}}$$

This process of determining the solution of (3.15) is called *back-substitution*.

Algorithm 3.1 Back-substitution Given the upper-triangular $n \times n$ matrix A with all diagonal entries not zero, and the n-vector **b**. The entries $x_n, x_{n-1}, \ldots, x_1$ of the solution **x** of $A\mathbf{x} = \mathbf{b}$ can then be obtained (in that order) by

For $k = n, n - 1, \ldots, 1$, do:

$$\text{Calculate } x_k = \frac{b_k - \sum\limits_{j=k+1}^{n} a_{kj}x_j}{a_{kk}}$$

Here two remarks are in order: When $k = n$, then the summation $\sum_{j=k+1}^{n}$ reads $\sum_{j=n+1}^{n}$, which is interpreted as the sum over *no* terms and gives, by convention, the value 0. Also, we note the following consequence, evident from our description of back-substitution.

Theorem 3.6 If A is an upper-triangular matrix and all diagonal entries of A are not zero, then A is invertible.

Indeed, back-substitution shows that the system (3.15) has at most one solution for given **b**; hence, by Theorem 3.4, A must be invertible. We are therefore justified in calling the vector **x** calculated by Algorithm 3.1 *the* solution of (3.15).

Example 3.1 Consider the following linear system:

$$\begin{aligned} 2x_1 + 3x_2 - x_3 &= 5 \\ -2x_2 - x_3 &= -7 \\ -5x_3 &= -15 \end{aligned} \tag{3.16}$$

From the last equation, $x_3 = b_3/a_{33} = \tfrac{15}{5} = 3$. With this, from the second (last) equation, $x_2 = (b_2 - a_{23}x_3)/a_{22} = (-7 + 3)/(-2) = 2$. Hence, from the first equation, $x_1 = (b_1 - a_{12}x_2 - a_{13}x_3)/a_{11} = (5 - 3 \cdot 2 + 3)/2 = 1$.

If now the coefficient matrix A of the system $A\mathbf{x} = \mathbf{b}$ is not upper-triangular, we subject the system first to the method of elimination due to Gauss. This method is probably familiar to the student, from elementary algebra. Its objective is the transformation of the given system into an equivalent system with upper-triangular coefficient matrix. The latter system can then be solved by back-substitution.

We say that the two linear systems $A\mathbf{x} = \mathbf{b}$ and $\tilde{A}\mathbf{x} = \tilde{\mathbf{b}}$ are *equivalent* provided any solution of one is a solution of the other. We cite the following theorem from linear algebra.

Theorem 3.7   Let $A\mathbf{x} = \mathbf{b}$ be a given linear system, and suppose we subject this system to a sequence of operations of the following kind:

   (i)   Multiplication of one equation by a nonzero constant
   (ii) Addition of a multiple of one equation to another equation
   (iii) Interchange of two equations

If this sequence of operations produces the new system $\tilde{A}\mathbf{x} = \tilde{\mathbf{b}}$, then the systems $A\mathbf{x} = \mathbf{b}$ and $\tilde{A}\mathbf{x} = \tilde{\mathbf{b}}$ are equivalent. In particular, then, A is invertible if and only if $\tilde{A}$ is invertible.

Elimination is based on this theorem and the following observation: If $A\mathbf{x} = \mathbf{b}$ is a linear system and if, for some k and j, $a_{kj} \neq 0$, then we can eliminate the unknown x_j from any equation $i \neq k$ by adding $-(a_{ij}/a_{kj})$ times equation k to equation i. The resulting system $\tilde{A}\mathbf{x} = \tilde{\mathbf{b}}$ is equivalent to the original system.

In its simplest form, Gauss elimination derives from a given linear system $A\mathbf{x} = \mathbf{b}$ of order n a sequence of equivalent systems $A^{(k)}\mathbf{x} = \mathbf{b}^{(k)}$, $k = 0, \ldots, n - 1$. Here $A^{(0)}\mathbf{x} = \mathbf{b}^{(0)}$ is just the original system. The $(k - 1)$st system has the following form:

$$a_{11}^{(k-1)}x_1 + a_{12}^{(k-1)}x_2 + \cdots + a_{1,k-1}^{(k-1)}x_{k-1} + a_{1,k}^{(k-1)}x_k + \cdots + a_{1n}^{(k-1)}x_n = b_1^{(k-1)}$$

$$a_{22}^{(k-1)}x_2 + \cdots + a_{2,k-1}^{(k-1)}x_{k-1} + a_{2k}^{(k-1)}x_k + \cdots + a_{2n}^{(k-1)}x_n = b_2^{(k-1)}$$

$$\cdots\cdots\cdots\cdots\cdots\cdots\cdots$$

$$a_{k-1,k-1}^{(k-1)}x_{k-1} + a_{k-1,k}^{(k-1)}x_k + \cdots + a_{k-1,n}^{(k-1)}x_n = b_{k-1}^{(k-1)}$$

$$a_{kk}^{(k-1)}x_k + \cdots + a_{kn}^{(k-1)}x_n = b_k^{(k-1)}$$

$$\cdots\cdots\cdots\cdots\cdots\cdots\cdots$$

$$a_{nk}^{(k-1)}x_k + \cdots + a_{nn}^{(k-1)}x_n = b_n^{(k-1)}$$

In words, the first k equations are already in upper-triangular form, while the last $n - k$ equations involve only the unknowns $x_k, \ldots, x_n$. From this, the kth system $A^{(k)}\mathbf{x} = \mathbf{b}^{(k)}$ is derived during the kth step of Gauss elimination as follows: The first k equations are left unchanged; further, if the coefficient $a_{kk}^{(k-1)}$ of x_k in equation k is not zero, then $-a_{ik}^{(k-1)}/a_{kk}^{(k-1)}$ times equation k is added to equation i, thereby eliminating the unknown x_k from equation i, $i = k + 1, \ldots, n$. The resulting system $A^{(k)}\mathbf{x} = \mathbf{b}^{(k)}$ is clearly equivalent to $A^{(k-1)}\mathbf{x} = \mathbf{b}^{(k-1)}$, hence, by induction, to the original system; further, the kth system has its first $k + 1$ equations in upper-triangular form.

After $n - 1$ steps of this procedure, one arrives at the system $A^{(n-1)}\mathbf{x} = \mathbf{b}^{(n-1)}$, whose coefficient matrix is upper-triangular, so that this system can now be solved quickly by back-substitution.

Example 3.2 Consider the following linear system:

$$\begin{aligned}
(a) \quad & 2x_1 + 3x_2 - x_3 = 5 \\
(b) \quad & 4x_1 + 4x_2 - 3x_3 = 3 \\
(c) \quad & -2x_1 + 3x_2 - x_3 = 1
\end{aligned} \tag{3.17}$$

To eliminate x_1 from equations (b) and (c), we add $-\frac{4}{2} = -2$ times equation (a) to equation (b), getting the new equation

$$0x_1 - 2x_2 - x_3 = -7$$

Also, adding $-(-2)/2 = 1$ times equation (a) to equation (c), we get the new equation (c),

$$0x_1 + 6x_2 - 2x_3 = 6$$

This gives the new system $A^{(1)}\mathbf{x} = \mathbf{b}^{(1)}$:

$$\begin{aligned}
(a) \quad & 2x_1 + 3x_2 - x_3 = 5 \\
(b) \quad & - 2x_2 - x_3 = -7 \\
(c) \quad & 6x_2 - 2x_3 = 6
\end{aligned} \tag{3.18}$$

completing the first step of Gauss elimination for this system. In the second (and for this example, last) step, we eliminate x_2 from equation (c) by adding $-6/(-2) = 3$ times equation (b) to equation (c), getting the new equation (c),

$$0x_2 - 5x_3 = -15$$

hence the new and final system

$$\begin{aligned}
2x_1 + 3x_2 - x_3 &= 5 \\
-2x_2 - x_3 &= -7 \\
-5x_3 &= -15
\end{aligned} \tag{3.19}$$

By Theorem 3.7, this system is equivalent to the original system (3.17) but has an upper-triangular coefficient matrix; hence can be solved quickly by back-substitution, as we did in Example 3.1.

In the simple description of Gauss elimination given earlier, we used the kth equation to eliminate x_k from equations $k + 1, \ldots, n$ during the

kth step of the procedure. This is of course possible only if, at the beginning of the kth step, the coefficient $a_{kk}^{(k-1)}$ of x_k in equation k is not zero. Unfortunately, it is not difficult to devise linear systems for which this condition is not satisfied. If, for example, the linear system $A\mathbf{x} = \mathbf{b}$ is

$$
\begin{align}
(a) \quad & & x_2 + x_3 &= 1 \\
(b) \quad & x_1 & + x_3 &= 1 \\
(c) \quad & x_1 + x_2 & &= 1
\end{align}
\tag{3.20}
$$

then it is impossible to use equation (a) to eliminate x_1 from the other equations. To cope with this difficulty and still end up with a triangular system equivalent to the given one, we have to allow at each step more freedom in the choice of the *pivotal equation* for the step, i.e., the equation which is used to eliminate one unknown from certain of the other equations.

In the system (3.20), for example, we could use equation (b) as the pivotal equation during the first step of elimination, eliminating x_1 from [equation (a) and] equation (c). This gives the new system $A^{(1)}\mathbf{x} = \mathbf{b}^{(1)}$:

$$
\begin{align}
(a) \quad & & x_2 + x_3 &= 1 \\
(b) \quad & x_1 & + x_3 &= 1 \\
(c) \quad & & x_2 - x_3 &= 0
\end{align}
$$

in which equations (a) and (c) involve only the unknowns x_2 and x_3. During the second (and last) step, we then can use equation (a) to eliminate x_2 from equation (c), getting the new system $A^{(2)}\mathbf{x} = \mathbf{b}^{(2)}$.

$$
\begin{align}
x_2 + & x_3 = & 1 \\
x_1 & + x_3 = & 1 \\
& - 2x_3 = & -1
\end{align}
$$

This linear system is not upper-triangular, but it does have the feature essential to back-substitution: for each unknown x_j there is an equation involving only x_j and unknowns with subscripts higher than j, namely, the pivotal equation used to eliminate x_j from other equations. Thus we can solve, in this example, equation (c) for x_3, getting $x_3 = \frac{1}{2}$. Then, substituting this value into equation (a) (the pivotal equation for step 2), we can solve for x_2 to get $x_2 = 1 - \frac{1}{2} = \frac{1}{2}$. Finally, we can substitute these values for x_2 and x_3 into equation (b) (the pivotal equation for step 1) to get

$$x_1 = 1 - 0 - \tfrac{1}{2} = \tfrac{1}{2}.$$

This greater freedom in the choice of the pivotal equation is necessary not only because of the possibility of zero coefficients. Experience has shown that this freedom is also essential in combating rounding-error effects (see Sec. 3.3). Of course, this freedom requires some bookkeeping during elimination and introduces some notational complications in the description of the process which are at times a deterrent to its understanding, but are only a minor nuisance in a computer implementation of the process.

When this process is carried out with the aid of a computer, the n original equations and the various changes made in them have to be recorded in some convenient and systematic way. Typically, one uses an $n \times (n + 1)$ working array or matrix which we will call W and which contains initially the coefficients and right side of the n equations $Ax = b$. Whenever some unknown is eliminated from an equation, the changed coefficients and right side for this equation are calculated and stored in the working array W in place of the previous coefficients and right side. Further, one uses an n-vector which we will call $p = (p_i)$ to keep track of which equations have already been used as pivotal equations (and therefore should not be changed any further) and which equations are still to be modified.

Initially, the ith entry p_i of p contains the integer i, $i = 1, \ldots, n$. Further, the working array W contains the coefficients and right side of $Ax = b$ as follows:

In general:

$$W = (w_{ij}): \begin{bmatrix} a_{11} & a_{12} & a_{13} & \cdots & a_{1n} & b_1 \\ a_{21} & a_{22} & a_{23} & \cdots & a_{2n} & b_2 \\ \cdot & \cdot & \cdot & & \cdot & \cdot \\ a_{n1} & a_{n2} & a_{n3} & \cdots & a_{nn} & b_n \end{bmatrix}$$

For Example 3.2:

$$W: \begin{bmatrix} 2 & 3 & -1 & 5 \\ 4 & 4 & -3 & 3 \\ -2 & 3 & -1 & 1 \end{bmatrix}$$

Step 1 In this step, we eliminate the first unknown, x_1, from all equations but the so-called *pivotal* equation for this step. For this, the coefficient of x_1 in the pivotal equation must be nonzero. Accordingly, we find an integer j between 1 and n such that

$$w_{p_j 1} = (a_{p_j 1}) \neq 0$$

In our Example 3.2, $j = 1$ will do. For the general case, we assume that such a j can be found. Then, for the purpose of record keeping, we exchange the contents of p_1 and p_j so that now equation p_1 is the pivotal equation. Then, for $i = p_2, \ldots, p_n$, we add $-m_{i1}$ times the pivotal equation to equation i, where the *multiplier* m_{i1} is given by

$$m_{i1} = \frac{a_{i1}}{a_{p_j 1}}$$

The resulting new coefficients $a_{ij}^{(1)}$ and right side $b_i^{(1)}$ for equation i are again stored in row i of W. This will change the content of w_{i1} to $a_{i1}^{(1)} = a_{i1} -$

$(a_{i1}/a_{p_11})a_{p_11} = 0$. Since we know this, there is no point in calculating or storing these zeros. Instead, we use the entry w_{i1} of W to record the multiplier m_{i1}. After these operations, the ith row of W contains:

In general:

$$[a_{i1} \quad a_{i2} \quad a_{i3} \quad \cdots \quad a_{in} \quad b_i \;] \qquad \text{if } i = p_1$$

$$[m_{i1} \mid a_{i2}^{(1)} \quad a_{i3}^{(1)} \quad \cdots \quad a_{in}^{(1)} \quad b_i^{(1)}] \qquad \text{otherwise}$$

For Example 3.2:

$$\begin{array}{llll}
[\;\; 2 & 3 & -1 & 5] \qquad i = 1 = p_1 \\
[\;\; 2 \mid -2 & -1 & -7] \qquad i = 2 = p_2 \\
[-1 \mid \;\; 6 & -2 & 6] \qquad i = 3 = p_3
\end{array}$$

Explicitly, the changed entries of W are calculated by

For all $i \neq p_1$:

$$\text{Set } w_{i1} = m_{i1} = \frac{w_{i1}}{w_{p_11}}$$

$$\text{Set } w_{ij} = w_{ij} - m_{i1}w_{p_1j} \qquad j = 2, \ldots, n+1$$

Step 2 In this step we eliminate the second unknown, x_2, from all equations $p_2, \ldots, p_n$ but the pivotal equation for this step. First, we find an integer j between 2 and n such that

$$w_{p_j2} = (a_{p_j2}^{(1)}) \neq 0$$

In our example, $j = 2$ will do. For the general case, we assume that such a j can be found. Then, to keep the record straight, we exchange the content of p_2 and p_j, making equation p_2 the pivotal equation for this step. Next, for $i = p_3, p_4, \ldots, p_n$, we add $-m_{i2}$ times the pivotal equation p_2 to equation i, using the multiplier

$$m_{i2} = \frac{a_{i2}^{(1)}}{a_{p_22}^{(1)}}$$

and record the new coefficients $a_{ij}^{(2)}$ and right side $b_i^{(2)}$ again in row i of W. As before, we use the entry w_{i2} (which would contain zero after these operations) to store the multiplier m_{i2}. After this, the ith row of W contains:

In general:

$$[a_{i1} \quad a_{i2} \quad a_{i3} \quad \cdots \quad a_{in} \quad b_i \;] \qquad \text{if } i = p_1$$

$$[m_{i1} \mid a_{i2}^{(1)} \quad a_{i3}^{(1)} \quad \cdots \quad a_{in}^{(1)} \quad b_i^{(1)}] \qquad \text{if } i = p_2$$

$$[m_{i1} \quad m_{i2} \mid a_{i3}^{(2)} \quad \cdots \quad a_{in}^{(2)} \quad b_i^{(2)}] \qquad \text{otherwise}$$

For Example 3.2:

$$[\ \ 2 \quad\ \ 3 \quad -1 \quad\ \ \ 5]\quad i = 1 = p_1$$
$$[\ \ 2\ |{-2}\ \ \ -1 \quad -7]\quad i = 2 = p_2$$
$$[-1 \quad -3\ |\ -5 \quad -15]\quad i = 3 = p_3$$

Specifically, the changed entries of W are calculated by

For $i \neq p_1, p_2$:

$$\text{Set } w_{i2} = m_{i2} = \frac{w_{i2}}{w_{p_2 2}}\qquad j = 3, \dots, n + 1$$
$$\text{Set } w_{ij} = w_{ij} - m_{i2}w_{p_2 j}$$

After this step, Example 3.2 is now in upper-triangular form. Usually, this will be so after $n - 1$ steps, the general, or kth, step proceeding as follows:

Step k At the beginning of the kth step, the ith row of W contains

$$[a_{i1} \quad a_{i2} \quad \cdots \quad a_{i,k-1} \quad a_{ik} \quad a_{i,k+1} \quad \cdots \quad a_{in} \quad b_i \quad]$$
$$\text{if } i = p_1$$

$$[m_{i1}\ |\ a_{i2}^{(1)} \quad \cdots \quad a_{i,k-1}^{(1)} \quad a_{ik}^{(1)} \quad a_{i,k+1}^{(1)} \quad \cdots \quad a_{in}^{(1)} \quad b_i^{(1)} \quad]$$
$$\text{if } i = p_2$$

$$[\cdots\cdots\cdots\cdots\cdots\cdots\cdots\cdots\cdots\cdots\cdots\cdots\cdot]$$

$$\cdots$$

$$[m_{i1} \quad m_{i2} \quad \cdots\ |\ a_{i,k-1}^{(k-2)} \quad a_{ik}^{(k-2)} \quad a_{i,k+1}^{(k-2)} \quad \cdots \quad a_{in}^{(k-2)} \quad b_i^{(k-2)}]$$
$$\text{if } i = p_{k-1}$$

$$[m_{i1} \quad m_{i2} \quad \cdots \quad m_{i,k-1}\ |\ a_{ik}^{(k-1)} \quad a_{i,k+1}^{(k-1)} \quad \cdots \quad a_{in}^{(k-1)} \quad b_i^{(k-1)}]$$
$$\text{otherwise}$$

$$(3.21)$$

where the a's and b's are the coefficients and right sides of a linear system equivalent to the original system $Ax = b$. In this step, we eliminate the unknown x_k from all equations $p_k, p_{k+1}, \dots, p_n$ but one, the pivotal equation for this step. First, we find an integer j between k and n such that

$$w_{p_j k} = (a_{p_j k}^{(k-1)}) \neq 0$$

Rather than assuming the existence of such a j (as we did in the description of steps 1 and 2), we now take time out to prove that *such a j must exist if A is invertible.* For otherwise our present linear system would contain the $n - k + 1$ equations,

$$0 \cdot x_k + a_{i,k+1}^{(k-1)}x_{k+1} + \cdots + a_{in}^{(k-1)}x_n = b_i^{(k-1)}\qquad i = p_k, \dots, p_n$$
$$(3.22)$$

which involve in effect only the $n - k$ unknowns $x_{k+1}, \ldots, x_n$. By Theorem 3.3, this subsystem (3.22) would therefore not be solvable for some right side; hence our whole present system would not be solvable for some right side, and therefore, by Theorem 3.4, the coefficient matrix of our present system would not be invertible. But since our present system is equivalent to the original system $A\mathbf{x} = \mathbf{b}$, it would then follow that A is not invertible. This proves our assertion.

Hence, if A is invertible, we can find a j between k and n such that $w_{p_jk} \neq 0$. If j is not k, we exchange the content of p_k and p_j. Then, with the coefficient of x_k in equation p_k nonzero, we add, for $i = p_{k+1}, \ldots, p_n$, $-m_{ik}$ times equation p_k to equation i, where $m_{ik} = a_{ik}^{(k-1)}/a_{p_kk}^{(k-1)}$, and store the new coefficients $a_{ij}^{(k)}$ and right side $b_i^{(k)}$ of equation i again in row i of W, and store the multiplier m_{ik} in w_{ik}. The contents of W are now as described in (3.21), with every k replaced by $k + 1$. Explicitly, the changed entries in W are calculated by:

For $i = p_{k+1}, \ldots, p_n$:

$$\text{Set } w_{ik} = m_{ik} = \frac{w_{ik}}{w_{p_kk}}$$

$$\text{Set } w_{ij} = w_{ij} - m_{ik}w_{pkj} \qquad j = k+1, \ldots, n+1$$

After the last, or $(n-1)$st, step, the ith row of W contains

$$[a_{i1} \quad a_{i2} \quad \cdots \quad a_{i,n-1} \quad a_{in} \quad b_i \quad] \qquad i = p_1$$
$$[m_{i1} \mid a_{i2}^{(1)} \quad \cdots \quad a_{i,n-1}^{(1)} \quad a_{in}^{(1)} \quad b_i^{(1)} \quad] \qquad i = p_2$$
$$[\cdots \cdots \cdots \cdots \cdots \cdots \cdots \cdots] \qquad \cdots$$
$$[m_{i1} \quad m_{i2} \quad \cdots \mid a_{i,n-1}^{(n-2)} \quad a_{in}^{(n-2)} \quad b_i^{(n-2)}] \qquad i = p_{n-1}$$
$$[m_{i1} \quad m_{i2} \quad \cdots \quad m_{i,n-1} \mid a_{in}^{(n-1)} \quad b_i^{(n-1)}] \qquad i = p_n$$

Note that the earlier argument also proves that now $a_{p_nn}^{(n-1)} \neq 0$ if A is invertible.

Let the $n \times n$ matrix $U = (u_{ij})$ and the n-vector $\tilde{\mathbf{b}} = (\tilde{b}_i)$ be given by

$$u_{ij} = \begin{cases} w_{p_ij} & j \geq i \\ 0 & j < i \end{cases}$$
$$\tilde{b}_i = w_{p_i,n+1} \qquad i = 1, \ldots, n \tag{3.23}$$

Then $U\mathbf{x} = \tilde{\mathbf{b}}$ is a linear system which is equivalent to the original system $A\mathbf{x} = \mathbf{b}$ but has an upper-triangular coefficient matrix with all diagonal entries nonzero (if A is invertible). Hence the unique solution of $A\mathbf{x} = \mathbf{b}$ can now be obtained by applying the back-substitution algorithm 3.1 to the linear system $U\mathbf{x} = \tilde{\mathbf{b}}$.

Algorithm 3.2 Gauss elimination　Given the $n \times (n + 1)$ matrix W containing the matrix A of order n in its first n columns and the n-vector $\mathbf{b}$ in its last column.

> Initialize the n-vector $\mathbf{p}$ to have $p_i = i$, $i = 1, \ldots , n$
> For $k = 1, \ldots , n - 1$, do:
>
> > Find (the smallest) $j \geq k$ such that $w_{p_j k} \neq 0$
> > If no such j exists, signal that A is not invertible and stop
> > Otherwise, exchange the contents of p_k and p_j and continue
> > For $i = k + 1, \ldots , n$, do:
> >
> > > Set m and $w_{p_i k}$ equal to $\dfrac{w_{p_i k}}{w_{p_k k}}$
> > >
> > > For $j = k + 1, \ldots , n + 1$, do:
> > >
> > > > Set $w_{p_i j} = w_{p_i j} - m w_{p_k j}$

If $w_{p_n n} = 0$, signal that A is not invertible and stop

Otherwise, the original system $A\mathbf{x} = \mathbf{b}$ is known to be equivalent to the system $U\mathbf{x} = \tilde{\mathbf{b}}$, where U and $\tilde{\mathbf{b}}$ are given in terms of the entries of W and $\mathbf{p}$ by (3.23). In particular, U is an upper-triangular matrix with all diagonal entries nonzero; hence Algorithm 3.1 can now be used to calculate the solution $\mathbf{x}$.

It is often possible to reduce the computational work necessary for solving $A\mathbf{x} = \mathbf{b}$ by taking into account special features of the coefficient matrix A, such as symmetry or sparseness. As an example we now discuss briefly the solution of tridiagonal systems.

We say that the matrix $A = (a_{ij})$ of order n is *tridiagonal* if

$$a_{ij} = 0 \quad \text{whenever } |i - j| > 1$$

In words, A is tridiagonal if the only nonzero entries of A lie on the diagonal of A, a_{ii}, $i = 1, \ldots , n$, or the *subdiagonal* of A, $a_{i,i-1}$, $i = 2, \ldots , n$, or the *superdiagonal* of A, $a_{i,i+1}$, $i = 1, \ldots , n - 1$. Thus the following matrices are all tridiagonal.

$$\begin{bmatrix} 3 & 1 & 0 & 0 \\ 1 & 3 & 1 & 0 \\ 0 & 2 & 2 & 1 \\ 0 & 0 & 1 & 6 \end{bmatrix} \quad \begin{bmatrix} 1 & 0 & 0 & 0 \\ 0 & 1 & 0 & 0 \\ 0 & 0 & 1 & 0 \\ 0 & 0 & 1 & 0 \end{bmatrix} \quad \begin{bmatrix} 4 & 7 & 0 & 0 \\ 0 & 8 & 1 & 0 \\ 0 & 1 & 1 & 0 \\ 0 & 0 & 0 & 1 \end{bmatrix}$$

Assume that the coefficient matrix A of the linear system $A\mathbf{x} = \mathbf{b}$ is tridiagonal, and assume further that, for each k, we can use equation k as the pivotal equation during step k. Then, during the kth step of Algorithm 3.2, the variable x_k needs to be eliminated only from equation $k + 1$, $k = 1$, $\ldots$, $n - 1$. Further, during back-substitution, only x_{k+1} needs to be substituted into equation k in order to find x_k, $k = n - 1, \ldots, 1$. Finally, there is no need to store any of the entries of A known to be zero. Rather, only three vectors need to be retained, containing the subdiagonal, the diagonal, and the superdiagonal of A, respectively.

Consider now more specifically the following tridiagonal system of order n:

$$
\begin{aligned}
d_1 x_1 + c_1 x_2 && = b_1 \\
a_2 x_1 + d_2 x_2 + c_2 x_3 && = b_2 \\
a_3 x_2 + d_3 x_3 + c_3 x_4 && = b_3 \\
\end{aligned}
$$

$$
\begin{aligned}
a_{n-1} x_{n-2} + d_{n-1} x_{n-1} + c_{n-1} x_n &= b_{n-1} \\
a_n x_{n-1} \quad + d_n x_n &= b_n
\end{aligned}
$$

Assuming $d_1 \neq 0$, we eliminate x_1 from the second equation, getting the new equation

$$ d_2' x_2 + c_2 x_3 = b_2' $$

with

$$ d_2' = d_2 - \frac{a_2}{d_1} c_1 \qquad b_2' = b_2 - \frac{a_2}{d_1} b_1 $$

Next, assuming $d_2' \neq 0$, we use this equation to eliminate x_2 from the third equation, getting the new equation

$$ d_3' x_3 + c_3 x_4 = b_3' $$

with

$$ d_3' = d_3 - \frac{a_3}{d_2'} c_2 \qquad b_3' = b_3 - \frac{a_3}{d_2'} b_2' $$

Continuing in this manner, we eliminate, during step k, x_k from equation $k + 1$ (assuming that $d_k' \neq 0$), getting the new equation

$$ d_{k+1}' x_{k+1} + c_{k+1} x_{k+2} = b_{k+1}' $$

with

$$ d_{k+1}' = d_{k+1} - \frac{a_{k+1}}{d_k'} c_k \qquad b_{k+1}' = b_{k+1} - \frac{a_{k+1}}{d_k'} b_k' $$

for $k = 1, 2, \ldots, n - 1$.

During back-substitution, we first get

$$x_n = \frac{b'_n}{d'_n}$$

and then, for $k = n - 1, \ldots, 1,$

$$x_k = \frac{b'_k - c_k x_{k+1}}{d'_k}$$

Algorithm 3.3 Elimination for tridiagonal systems Given the co-efficients a_i, d_i, c_i and right side b_i of the tridiagonal system

$$a_i x_{i-1} + d_i x_i + c_i x_{i+1} = b_i \qquad i = 1, \ldots, n \text{ (with } a_1 = c_n = 0)$$

For $k = 2, \ldots, n$, do:

> If $d_{k-1} = 0$, signal failure and stop
>
> Otherwise, set $m = \dfrac{a_k}{d_{k-1}}$ and continue
>
> Set $d_k = d_k - m * c_{k-1}$
> Set $b_k = b_k - m * b_{k-1}$

If $d_n = 0$, signal failure and stop

Otherwise, set $x_n = \dfrac{b_n}{d_n}$ and continue

For $k = n - 1, \ldots, 1$, do:

> Set $x_k = \dfrac{b_k - c_k * x_{k+1}}{d_k}$

Example 3.3 Solve the linear system

$$
\begin{aligned}
2x_1 \quad - \quad x_2 \qquad\qquad &= 1 \\
-x_{i-1} + 2x_i \quad - x_{i+1} &= 0 \qquad i = 2, \ldots, n-1 \\
- \quad x_{n-1} + 2x_n \quad &= 0
\end{aligned}
$$

when $n = 10$.

The following FORTRAN program solves this problem. Note that we have translated Algorithm 3.3 into a subroutine called

TRID (SUB, DIAG, SUP, B, N)

where SUB, DIAG, SUP, B, are N-vectors which are expected to contain the coefficients and right side of the tridiagonal system

$$\text{SUB}(i)x_{i-1} + \text{DIAG}(i)x_i + \text{SUP}(i)x_{i+1} = \text{B}(i) \qquad i = 1, \ldots, \text{N}$$

[with SUB(1) and SUP(N) ignored]. The subroutine alters the contents of DIAG and returns the solution vector in B.

The exact solution of the given system is

$$x_i = \frac{n + 1 - i}{n + 1} \qquad i = 1, \ldots, n$$

Hence the computed solution is in error in the sixth place after the decimal point. This program was run on an IBM 360.

FORTRAN PROGRAM FOR EXAMPLE 3.3

```
      DIMENSION A(10),D(10),C(10),B(10)
      N = 10
      DO 10 I = 1,N
      A(I) = -1.
      D(I) = 2.
      C(I) = -1.
   10 B(I) = 0.
      B(1) = 1.
      CALL TRID(A,D,C,B,N)
      WRITE (6,610) (I,B(I),I = 1,N)
  610 FORMAT(16H1THE SOLUTION IS /(I5,E15.7))
      STOP
      END
      SUBROUTINE TRID(SUB,DIAG,SUP,B,N)
      DIMENSION SUB(30),DIAG(30),SUP(30),B(30)
      IF (N .GT. 1)                        GO TO 10
      B(1) = B(1)/DIAG(1)
                                           RETURN
   10 DO 11 K = 2,N
      RATIO = -SUB(K)/DIAG(K - 1)
      DIAG(K) = DIAG(K) + RATIO*SUP(K - 1)
   11 B(K) = B(K) + RATIO*B(K - 1)
      B(N) = B(N)/DIAG(N)
      K = N
      DO 12 NP1MK = 2,N
      K = K - 1
   12 B(K) = (B(K) - SUP(K)*B(K + 1))/DIAG(K)
                                           RETURN
      END
```

OUTPUT

THE SOLUTION IS

```
 1   0.9090915E  00
 2   0.8181832E  00
 3   0.7272751E  00
 4   0.6363666E  00
 5   0.5454577E  00
 6   0.4545485E  00
 7   0.3636391E  00
 8   0.2727295E  00
 9   0.1818197E  00
10   0.9090990E -01
```

EXERCISES

3.2-1. One measure of the efficiency of an algorithm is the number of arithmetic operations required to obtain the solution.   Show that Algorithm 3.2 applied to a system of
order n requires $n(n - 1)/2$ divisions, $(n^3 - n)/3$ multiplications, and $(n^3 - n)/3$ additions.

3.2-2. Show that the back-substitution algorithm 3.1 requires n divisions, $n(n - 1)/2$
multiplications, and $n(n - 1)/2$ additions.

3.2-3. On some machines, division is more time-consuming than multiplication.   How
would you modify Algorithm 3.2 for such a machine?

3.2-4. Calculate the number of additions and the number of multiplications necessary
to multiply an $n \times n$ matrix with an n-vector.

3.2-5. How many additions, multiplications, and divisions are required in Algorithm 3.2
if only the final upper-triangular matrix U is desired?

3.2-6. Use elimination to show that the following system does not have a solution.

$$x_1 + 2x_2 + \ x_3 = 3$$
$$2x_1 + 3x_2 + \ x_3 = 5$$
$$3x_1 + 5x_2 + 2x_3 = 1$$

3.2-7. Solve the following systems by elimination:

(a) $\begin{aligned} 2x_1 - 3x_2 + x_3 &= 1 \\ 3x_1 + \ x_2 - x_3 &= 2 \\ x_1 - \ x_2 - x_3 &= 1 \end{aligned}$ (b) $\begin{aligned} x_1 - 5x_2 + x_3 &= 2 \\ 2x_1 + 4x_2 + x_3 &= 1 \\ x_1 + \ x_2 + x_3 &= 0 \end{aligned}$

3.2-8. Solve the following system by elimination.   Round off all calculations to three
decimal places.

$$0.20x_1 + 0.32x_2 + 0.12x_3 + 0.30x_4 = 0.94$$
$$0.10x_1 + 0.15x_2 + 0.24x_3 + 0.32x_4 = 0.81$$
$$0.20x_1 + 0.24x_2 + 0.46x_3 + 0.36x_4 = 1.26$$
$$0.60x_1 + 0.40x_2 + 0.32x_3 + 0.20x_4 = 1.52$$

Check your answers by substituting back into the original equations, and estimate their
accuracy.   Exact solution: [1,1,1,1].

3.2-9. Use subroutine TRID to solve the linear system

$$-2(1 + h^2)x_1 + x_2 = 1$$
$$x_{i-1} - 2(1 + h^2)x_i + x_{i+1} = 0 \qquad i = 2, 3, \ldots, n - 1$$
$$x_{n-1} - 2(1 + h^2)x_n = 1$$

when $n = 30$ and $h = 0.1$.

3.3 THE PIVOTING STRATEGY

The elimination algorithm 3.2 presented in the preceding section calculates
efficiently and with certainty the solution of any system $A\mathbf{x} = \mathbf{b}$, if all
calculations are carried out in infinite-precision arithmetic.   If, as is more
usual, finite-precision arithmetic is used, it is not difficult to give examples
for which Algorithm 3.2 produces completely erroneous answers.

In this section, we discuss briefly just one possible source for such a
failure, an incorrect *pivoting strategy*.   In rigorous terms, a pivoting strategy

for Algorithm 3.2 is a permutation $\mathbf{p}$ (see Sec. 3.1) which designates equation p_k as the pivotal equation for step k, $k = 1, 2, \ldots , n - 1$. Hence, in the terms of Algorithm 3.2, the final contents of the n-vector $\mathbf{p}$ constitute the pivoting strategy used during execution of the algorithm.

Example 3.4   The solution of the system

$$0.0003x_1 + 1.566x_2 = 1.569$$
$$0.3454x_1 - 2.436x_2 = 1.018$$

is $x_1 = 10$, $x_2 = 1$. We use four-decimal floating arithmetic to solve this system by elimination, picking the first equation as the pivotal equation during the first (and only) step. We get

$$m_{21} = 0.3454/0.0003 = 1,151.$$

Hence

$$a_{22}^{(1)} = -2.436 - (1,151.)(1.566) = -2.436 - 1,802. = -1,804.$$
$$b_2^{(1)} = 1.018 - (1,151.)(1.569) = 1.018 - 1,806. = -1,805.$$

This gives

$$x_2 = -1,805./-1,804. = 1.001$$

Hence, from the first equation,

$$x_1 = [1.569 - (1.566)(1.001)]/0.0003 = 3.333$$

A "plausible" explanation of this failure goes as follows: The *pivot* entry $a_{11} = 0.0003$ is "very small"; since the computations would break down if a_{11} were zero, it is not surprising that, in the environment of finite-precision arithmetic, the algorithm performs badly for a_{11} "near zero."

Of course, this explanation uses such undefined terms as "very small" and "near zero" and is therefore quite useless. In fact, by multiplying the first equation by an appropriate power of 10, we can make a_{11} as large as we wish *without changing the computed solution*. To see this, consider again the system of Example 3.4, but with the first equation multiplied by 10^m, where m is some integer:

$$0.0003 \cdot 10^m x_1 + 1.566 \cdot 10^m x_2 = 1.569 \cdot 10^m$$
$$0.3454 \quad x_1 - 2.436 \quad x_2 = 1.018$$

Using again the first equation as pivotal equation, and using four-decimal floating arithmetic, we get

$$m_{21} = \frac{0.3454}{0.0003 \cdot 10^m} = 1,151. \cdot 10^{-m}$$

Hence

$$a_{22}^{(1)} = -2.436 - (1,151. \cdot 10^{-m})(1.566 \cdot 10^m) = -1,804.$$
$$b_2^{(1)} = \quad 1.018 - (1,151. \cdot 10^{-m})(1.569 \cdot 10^m) = -1,805.$$

which is the same result as before.   Hence again $x_2 = 1.001$, and finally, $x_1 = (0.001 \cdot 10^m)/(0.0003 \cdot 10^m) = 3.333$.

Actually, the failure in this example is due to the fact that $|a_{11}|$ is small compared with $|a_{12}|$; thus a relatively small error due to round-off in the computed x_2 led to a large variation of the computed x_1 from the correct x_1. This is confirmed if we use equation 2 as pivotal equation, where $|a_{22}/a_{21}| \approx 6$ as compared with $|a_{12}/a_{11}| \approx 5{,}220$.   We get

$$m_{11} = \frac{0.0003}{0.3454} = 0.0008686$$

and the new first equation becomes

$$1.568x_2 = 1.568$$

so that $x_2 = 1$, the correct answer, and finally, from the second equation, $x_1 = 10$.   But even if round-off had conspired to give $x_2 = 1.001$ (as it did in Example 3.4), the second equation would still give

$$x_1 = \frac{1.018 + 2.438}{0.3454} = 10.01$$

a good result.

It is much more difficult (if not impossible) to ascertain for a general linear system how various pivoting strategies affect the accuracy of the computed solution.   A notable and important exception to this statement are the linear systems with positive definite coefficient matrix, that is, systems whose coefficient matrix satisfies

$$A = A^T; \text{ for all } \mathbf{x} \neq \mathbf{0}, \qquad \mathbf{x}^T A \mathbf{x} > 0$$

For such a system, the error in the computed solution due to rounding errors during elimination and back-substitution can be shown [18] to be acceptably small if the trivial pivoting strategy $\mathbf{p}^T = [1, 2, \ldots, n]$ is used.   (See Exercise 3.5-1 for an efficient algorithm for this case.)   But it is not possible at present to give a "best" pivoting strategy for a general linear system, nor is it even clear what such a term might mean.

For the sake of economy, the pivotal equation for each step must be selected on the basis of the current state of the system under consideration at the beginning of the step, i.e., without foreknowledge of the effect of the selection on later steps.

A currently accepted strategy is *scaled partial pivoting*.   In this strategy, one calculates initially the "size" d_i of row i of A, for $i = 1, \ldots, n$.   A convenient measure of this size is (see Sec. 3.6) the number

$$d_i = \max_{1 \leq j \leq n} |a_{ij}|$$

Then, at the beginning of the general, or kth, step of the elimination algorithm 3.2, one picks as pivotal equation that one from the available $n - k$ candidates which has the absolutely largest coefficient of x_k relative to the size of the equation. In the terms of Algorithm 3.2, this means that the integer j is selected as the (usually smallest) integer between k and n for which

$$\frac{|w_{p_j k}|}{d_{p_j}} \geq \frac{|w_{ik}|}{d_i} \qquad \text{for all } i = p_k, \ldots, p_n$$

Clearly, scaled partial pivoting selects the correct pivoting strategy for the system in Example 3.4, and is not thrown off by a rescaling of the equations.

It is possible to modify Algorithm 3.2 so as to leave not only the pivotal equation, but also the unknown to be eliminated open to choice. In this modification, a pivoting strategy consists of two permutations, **p** and **q**, which designate the p_kth equation as the equation to be used during the kth step to eliminate x_{q_k}, $k = 1, \ldots, n - 1$. In *total pivoting*, pivotal equation and unknown are selected by looking for the absolutely largest coefficient of any of the $n - k$ unknowns in any of the $n - k$ candidate equations. Of course, such a strategy is much more expensive than scaled partial pivoting, hence is not often employed, even though it is admittedly superior to partial pivoting.

Example 3.5 We apply the elimination algorithm 3.2 to the system of Example 3.2, using scaled partial pivoting and exact arithmetic to illustrate the mechanics of the process. We list below the "size" vector $\mathbf{d} = (d_i)$, and the successive contents of the working array W and the pivotal strategy vector **p**. Initially,

$$
\begin{array}{cc}
\mathbf{d} & W \\
\begin{bmatrix} 3 \\ 4 \\ 3 \end{bmatrix} &
\begin{bmatrix} 2 & 3 & -1 & 5 \\ 4 & 4 & -3 & 3 \\ -2 & 3 & -1 & 1 \end{bmatrix}
\end{array}
\qquad \mathbf{p}^T = [1, \quad 2, \quad 3]
$$

Step 1 A comparison of the numbers

$$\frac{|w_{i1}|}{d_i}: \qquad \tfrac{2}{3}, \tfrac{4}{4}, \tfrac{2}{3}$$

shows that, with scaled partial pivoting, row 2 becomes the pivotal row for this step; interchange first and second entry of **p** and eliminate.

$$
\begin{bmatrix} 3 \\ 4 \\ 3 \end{bmatrix}
\begin{bmatrix} \tfrac{1}{2} & 1 & \tfrac{1}{2} & \tfrac{7}{2} \\ 4 & 4 & -3 & 3 \\ -\tfrac{1}{2} & 5 & -\tfrac{5}{2} & \tfrac{5}{2} \end{bmatrix}
\qquad \mathbf{p}^T = [2, \quad 1, \quad 3]
$$

Step 2 Comparing the numbers

$$\frac{|w_{i2}|}{d_i}: \qquad \tfrac{1}{3}, \tfrac{5}{3}$$

we find that row 3 becomes the pivotal row for this step; interchange second and third entry of **p** and eliminate.

$$\begin{bmatrix} \frac{1}{2} & \frac{1}{3} & 1 & 3 \\ 4 & 4 & -3 & 3 \\ -\frac{1}{3} & 5 & -\frac{5}{2} & \frac{5}{2} \end{bmatrix} \qquad \mathbf{p}^T = [2, \quad 3, \quad 1]$$

Elimination is now complete. The equivalent upper-triangular system $U\mathbf{x} = \tilde{\mathbf{b}}$ is

$$\begin{array}{ll} 4x_1 + 4x_2 - 3x_3 = 3 & \text{from equation } p_1 = 2 \\ 5x_2 - \frac{5}{2}x_3 = \frac{5}{2} & \text{from equation } p_2 = 3 \\ x_3 = 3 & \text{from equation } p_3 = 1 \end{array}$$

Solution by back-substitution gives $x_3 = 3$; hence $x_2 = (\frac{5}{2} + \frac{5}{2}\cdot 3)/5 = 2$; hence $x_1 = (3 - 4\cdot 2 + 3\cdot 3)/4 = 1$, which agrees with the solution found in Sec. 3.2.

EXERCISES

3.3-1. Describe a modification of Algorithm 3.2 which incorporates total pivoting.

3.3-2. Give an example of a 2×2 linear system for which total pivoting gives more accurate results than scaled partial pivoting in four-decimal floating arithmetic. (*Hint:* Make both a_{11} and a_{21} "small" compared with a_{12} and a_{22}.)

3.3-3. Solve the following linear system, using four-decimal floating arithmetic, once with the first equation as pivotal equation and once with the second equation as pivotal equation, and finally with total pivoting.

$$0.1410\cdot 10^{-2}x_1 + 0.4004\cdot 10^{-1}x_2 = 0.1142\cdot 10^{-1}$$
$$0.2000\cdot 10^{0}x_1 + 0.4912\cdot 10^{1}x_2 = 0.1428\cdot 10^{1}$$

Compare with the exact answer $x_1 = 1.000$, $x_2 = 0.2500$.

3.3-4. Solve the system of Exercise 3.2-8, but using scaled partial pivoting, and compare with the results of Exercise 3.2-8.

3.4 THE TRIANGULAR FACTORIZATION AND CALCULATION OF THE INVERSE

Let $A\mathbf{x} = \mathbf{b}$ be a given linear system of order n with invertible coefficient matrix. Suppose we have solved this system by the elimination algorithm 3.2 followed by back-substitution. If we now also have to solve the system $A\mathbf{x} = \mathbf{c}$ with the same coefficient matrix A, only the right side being different, we do not have to go through the entire elimination process again. Rather, since we have saved, in the working matrix W, all the multipliers used and the entries of the final upper-triangular matrix U, and also have saved the pivoting strategy in the n-vector $\mathbf{p}$, we merely have to repeat the operations on the right side to obtain $\tilde{\mathbf{c}}$ such that $U\mathbf{x} = \tilde{\mathbf{c}}$ is equivalent to $A\mathbf{x} = \mathbf{c}$.

To understand what calculations are necessary to derive $\tilde{\mathbf{c}}$ from $\mathbf{c}$, we consider what changes the right side $\mathbf{b}$ underwent during the elimination process. Let k be an integer between 1 and n, and assume that the ith equation was used as pivotal equation during step k of the elimination process. Then $i = p_k$. Initially, the right side of equation i is just b_i.

If $k > 1$, then after step 1, the right side is

$$b_i^{(1)} = b_i - m_{i1}b_{p_1}$$

If also $k > 2$, then after step 2 the right side is

$$b_i^{(2)} = b_i^{(1)} - m_{i2}b_{p_2}^{(1)}$$
$$= b_i - m_{i1}b_{p_1} - m_{i2}b_{p_2}^{(1)}$$

In general, since $i = p_k$, the right side of equation i is changed from $b_i^{(j-1)}$ to

$$b_i^{(j)} = b_i^{(j-1)} - m_{ij}b_{p_j}^{(j-1)}$$

during step j for $j < k$, and remains unchanged during the kth step and thereafter. Therefore the final right side of equation $i = p_k$ is

$$
\begin{aligned}
b_i^{(k-1)} &= b_i^{(k-2)} - m_{i,k-1}b_{p_{k-1}}^{(k-2)} \\
&= b_i^{(k-3)} - m_{i,k-2}b_{p_{k-2}}^{(k-3)} - m_{i,k-1}b_{p_{k-1}}^{(k-2)} \\
&\cdots\cdots\cdots\cdots\cdots\cdots\cdots\cdots\cdots\cdots\cdots\cdots\cdots \\
&= b_i - m_{i1}b_{p_1} - m_{i2}b_{p_2}^{(1)} - \cdots - m_{i,k-1}b_{p_{k-1}}^{(k-2)}
\end{aligned}
\tag{3.24}
$$

Recall from (3.23) that the right side of the final upper-triangular system $U\mathbf{x} = \tilde{\mathbf{b}}$ is given by

$$\tilde{b}_j = w_{p_j, n+1} = b_{p_j}^{(j-1)} \qquad j = 1, \ldots, n \tag{3.25}$$

where $\mathbf{b}^{(0)} = \mathbf{b}$.

Hence, remembering that $i = p_k$, we conclude from (3.24) that

$$\tilde{b}_k = b_{p_k} - m_{p_k 1}\tilde{b}_1 - m_{p_k 2}\tilde{b}_2 - \cdots - m_{p_k, k-1}\tilde{b}_{k-1}$$
$$k = 1, \ldots, n \quad (3.26)$$

Consequently, the entries of $\tilde{\mathbf{b}}$ can be calculated recursively; we can compute $\tilde{b}_k$ once we know $\tilde{b}_1 = b_{p_1}, \tilde{b}_2, \ldots, \tilde{b}_{k-1}$, and if we know the multipliers $m_{p_k j}$. But recall that the multiplier m_{ij} is stored in entry w_{ij} of the working matrix W. Hence, knowing just the final content of the first n columns of W and the pivoting strategy $\mathbf{p}$, we can calculate the solution $\mathbf{x}$ of $A\mathbf{x} = \mathbf{b}$ as follows:

Algorithm 3.4 Forward- and back-substitution Given the final contents of the first n columns of the working matrix W and of the n-vector $\mathbf{p}$ of Algorithm 3.2 (applied to the system $A\mathbf{x} = \mathbf{b}$); also, given the right side $\mathbf{b}$.

For $k = 1, \ldots, n$, do:

$$\text{Set } \tilde{b}_k = b_{p_k} - \sum_{j=1}^{k-1} w_{p_k j}\tilde{b}_j$$

For $k = n, n-1, \ldots, 1$, do:

$$\text{Set } x_k = \frac{\tilde{b}_k - \sum_{j=k+1}^{n} w_{p_k j}x_j}{w_{p_k k}}$$

The vector $\mathbf{x} = (x_i)$ now contains the solution of $A\mathbf{x} = \mathbf{b}$

Note that, once again, both sums are sometimes empty.

The practical significance of the preceding discussion becomes clear when we count (floating-point) operations in Algorithms 3.2 and 3.4. By Exercise 3.2-2, it takes n divisions, $n(n - 1)/2$ multiplications, and $n(n - 1)/2$ additions to carry out the second loop in Algorithm 3.4. The first loop takes the same number of operations, except that no divisions are required. Hence Algorithm 3.4 takes

n^2 multiplications/divisions and $n(n - 1)$ additions

By Exercise 3.2-4, this is exactly the number of operations required to multiply an $n \times n$ matrix with an n-vector.

By contrast,

$(n^3 - n)/3$ multiplications/divisions and $n^3/3 + n^2/2 - n/6$ additions

are necessary to calculate the first n columns of the final contents of the working matrix W by Algorithm 3.2 (see Exercise 3.2-5). Hence the bulk of the work in solving $A\mathbf{x} = \mathbf{b}$ by elimination is needed to obtain the final content of the working matrix W, namely, $O(\frac{1}{3}n^3)$ additions and the same number of multiplications/divisions, for large n. The subsequent forward- and back-substitution takes *an order of magnitude less* operations, namely, $O(n^2)$ additions and the same number of multiplications, per right side. Hence we can solve $A\mathbf{x} = \mathbf{b}$ for many different right sides (once we know the final content of W) in the time it takes to calculate the final content of W.

A FORTRAN subroutine, called SUBST, which incorporates the substitution algorithm 3.4, follows.

```
      SUBROUTINE SUBST(W,B,X,IPIVOT,N)
      DIMENSION  W(N,N),B(N),X(N),IPIVOT(N)
      IF (N .GT. 1)                          GO TO 10
      X(1) = B(1)/W(1,1)
                                             RETURN
   10 IP = IPIVOT(1)
      X(1) = B(IP)
      DO 15 K = 2,N
      IP = IPIVOT(K)
      KM1 = K - 1
      SUM = 0.
      DO 14 J = 1,KM1
   14 SUM = W(IP,J)*X(J) + SUM
   15 X(K) = B(IP) - SUM
C
      X(N) = X(N)/W(IP,N)
      K = N
```

```
      DO 20 NP1MK = 2,N
      KP1 = K
      K = K − 1
      IP = IPIVOT(K)
      SUM = 0.
      DO 19 J = KP1,N
   19 SUM = W(IP,J)*X(J) + SUM
   20 X(K) = (X(K) − SUM)/W(IP,K)
                                    RETURN
      END
```

It is possible to visualize the elimination process of Algorithm 3.2 as deriving a *factorization* of the coefficient matrix A into three factors, a permutation matrix P associated with the pivoting strategy **p**, a lower-triangular matrix L containing (essentially) the multipliers used, and the final upper-triangular coefficient matrix U. This point of view is helpful for the understanding of the elimination process and the substitution algorithm 3.4 and for the analysis of round-off-error effects in these algorithms.

We begin by observing that Eq. (3.26) can also be written

$$\sum_{j=1}^{k-1} m_{p_k j}\tilde{b}_j + \tilde{b}_k = b_{p_k} \qquad k = 1, \ldots, n \tag{3.27}$$

Hence, if we let $L = (l_{ij})$ be the matrix of order n given by

$$l_{kj} = \begin{cases} w_{p_k j} = (m_{p_k j}) & k > j \\ 1 & k = j \\ 0 & k < j \end{cases} \tag{3.28}$$

then L is unit-lower-triangular, and by (3.27)

$$L\tilde{b} = \check{b} \tag{3.29}$$

where $\check{b} = (\check{b}_j)$ is the n-vector **b** permuted; i.e.,

$$\check{b}_j = b_{p_j} \qquad j = 1, \ldots, n$$

In other words, if P is the permutation matrix of order n given by

$$P\mathbf{i}_j = \mathbf{i}_{p_j} \qquad j = 1, \ldots, n \tag{3.30}$$

then, by Theorem 3.5,

$$\check{b} = P^{-1}\mathbf{b} \tag{3.31}$$

On the other hand, we know from Algorithm 3.2 that, with $U = (u_{ij})$ the matrix given by

$$u_{kj} = \begin{cases} w_{p_k j} & k \le j \\ 0 & k > j \end{cases} \tag{3.32}$$

the solution $\mathbf{x}$ of $A\mathbf{x} = \mathbf{b}$ also satisfies $U\mathbf{x} = \tilde{\mathbf{b}}$. Combining (3.29) and (3.31) with this information, we get that

$$(LU)\mathbf{x} = L(U\mathbf{x}) = L\tilde{\mathbf{b}} = \check{\mathbf{b}} = P^{-1}\mathbf{b} = P^{-1}(A\mathbf{x}) = (P^{-1}A)\mathbf{x} \qquad (3.33)$$

Since (3.33) holds for all $\mathbf{x}$, it follows that

$$LU = P^{-1}A \qquad \text{or} \qquad PLU = A \qquad\qquad (3.34)$$

which is the above-mentioned factorization.

We now recognize Algorithm 3.4 for what it is: In the first loop, we solve the *triangular* system $L\tilde{\mathbf{b}} = P^{-1}\mathbf{b}$ for $\tilde{\mathbf{b}}$, getting the kth unknown $\tilde{b}_k$ from the kth equation, in the order $\tilde{b}_1, \tilde{b}_2, \ldots$, since L is *lower*-triangular; then, with $\tilde{\mathbf{b}}$ computed, we solve the *triangular* system $U\mathbf{x} = \tilde{\mathbf{b}}$ for $\mathbf{x}$ in the second loop, getting the kth unknown x_k again from the kth equation, but now in the order $x_n, x_{n-1}, \ldots$, since U is *upper*-triangular. The first loop requires no divisions because all diagonal entries of L are unity.

Example 3.6 In Example 3.5, we applied the elimination algorithm 3.2 to the linear system of Example 3.2, with the following results:

$$
\begin{array}{ccccc}
A & \mathbf{x} & \mathbf{b} & P & W
\end{array}
$$

$$
\begin{bmatrix} 2 & 3 & -1 \\ 4 & 4 & -3 \\ -2 & 3 & -1 \end{bmatrix}
\begin{bmatrix} x_1 \\ x_2 \\ x_3 \end{bmatrix}
=
\begin{bmatrix} 5 \\ 3 \\ 1 \end{bmatrix}
\qquad \text{Final result:} \qquad
\begin{bmatrix} 2 \\ 3 \\ 1 \end{bmatrix}
\begin{bmatrix} \frac{1}{2} & \frac{1}{5} & 1 & 3 \\ 4 & 4 & -3 & 3 \\ -\frac{1}{2} & 5 & -\frac{5}{2} & \frac{5}{2} \end{bmatrix}
$$

Applying Algorithm 3.4, we get during the first loop,

With $p_1 = 2$: $\tilde{b}_1 = b_2 = 3$
With $p_2 = 3$: $\tilde{b}_2 = b_3 - w_{31}\tilde{b}_1 = 1 + \frac{1}{2}\cdot 3 = \frac{5}{2}$
With $p_3 = 1$: $\tilde{b}_3 = b_1 - w_{11}\tilde{b}_1 - w_{12}\tilde{b}_2 = 5 - \frac{1}{2}\cdot 3 - \frac{1}{5}\cdot\frac{5}{2} = 3$

Hence $\tilde{\mathbf{b}}$ coincides with the right side of $U\mathbf{x} = \tilde{\mathbf{b}}$ as calculated in Example 3.5. The second loop then gives

With $p_3 = 1$: $x_3 = \dfrac{\tilde{b}_3}{w_{13}} = \dfrac{3}{1} = 3$

With $p_2 = 3$: $x_2 = \dfrac{\tilde{b}_2 - w_{33}x_3}{w_{32}} = \dfrac{\frac{5}{2} + \frac{5}{2}\cdot 3}{5} = 2$

With $p_1 = 2$: $x_1 = \dfrac{\tilde{b}_1 - w_{22}x_2 - w_{23}x_3}{w_{21}} = \dfrac{3 - 4\cdot 2 + 3\cdot 3}{4} = 1$

as it should.

Also, for this example,

$$
L = \begin{bmatrix} 1 & 0 & 0 \\ -\frac{1}{2} & 1 & 0 \\ \frac{1}{2} & \frac{1}{5} & 1 \end{bmatrix}
\qquad
U = \begin{bmatrix} 4 & 4 & -3 \\ 0 & 5 & -\frac{5}{2} \\ 0 & 0 & 1 \end{bmatrix}
\qquad \text{hence} \qquad
LU = \begin{bmatrix} 4 & 4 & -3 \\ -2 & 3 & -1 \\ 2 & 3 & -1 \end{bmatrix}
$$

On the other hand, with $P^{-1}\mathbf{i}_{p_j} = \mathbf{i}_j$, all j (see Theorem 3.5), we have

$$P^{-1}A = \begin{bmatrix} 0 & 1 & 0 \\ 0 & 0 & 1 \\ 1 & 0 & 0 \end{bmatrix} \begin{bmatrix} 2 & 3 & -1 \\ 4 & 4 & -3 \\ -2 & 3 & -1 \end{bmatrix} = \begin{bmatrix} 4 & 4 & -3 \\ -2 & 3 & -1 \\ 2 & 3 & -1 \end{bmatrix}$$

showing the validity of (3.34) for this example.

We give below a FORTRAN subroutine called FACTOR, which uses the elimination algorithm 3.2, with the pivoting strategy dictated by scaled partial pivoting, to calculate a triangular factorization (if possible) for a given $N \times N$ matrix A, storing the factorization in an $N \times N$ matrix W, and storing the pivoting strategy in an N-vector IPIVOT, ready for use in the subroutine SUBST given earlier. The user must provide an additional N-vector D as a working space needed to store the "size" of the rows of A. If there is no further need for the matrix A and storage is scarce, then A itself can be used for W in the argument list of the CALL statement; the factorization will then replace the original matrix in the array A.

```
        SUBROUTINE FACTOR(A,W,IPIVOT,D,N,IFLAG)
        DIMENSION A(N,N),W(N,N),IPIVOT(N),D(N)
        IFLAG = 1
C       INITIALIZE W, IPIVOT, D
        DO 10 I = 1,N
        IPIVOT(I) = I
        ROWMAX = 0.
        DO 9 J = 1,N
        W(I,J) = A(I,J)
      9 ROWMAX = AMAX1(ROWMAX,ABS(W(I,J)))
        IF (ROWMAX .EQ. 0.)                GO TO 999
     10 D(I) = ROWMAX
C       GAUSS ELIMINATION WITH SCALED PARTIAL PIVOTING.
        NM1 = N - 1
        IF (NM1 .EQ. 0)                   RETURN
        DO 20 K = 1,NM1
        J = K
        KP1 = K + 1
        IP = IPIVOT(K)
        COLMAX = ABS(W(IP,K))/D(IP)
        DO 11 I = KP1,N
        IP = IPIVOT(I)
        AWIKOV = ABS(W(IP,K))/D(IP)
        IF (AWIKOV .LE. COLMAX)           GO TO 11
        COLMAX = AWIKOV
        J = I
     11 CONTINUE
        IF (COLMAX .EQ. 0.)               GO TO 999
C
        IPK = IPIVOT(J)
```

```
          IPIVOT(J) = IPIVOT(K)
          IPIVOT(K) = IPK
          DO 20 I = KP1,N
          IP = IPIVOT(I)
          W(IP,K) = W(IP,K)/W(IPK,K)
          RATIO = −W(IP,K)
          DO 20 J = KP1,N
    20    W(IP,J) = RATIO*W(IPK,J) + W(IP,J)
          IF (W(IP,N) .EQ. 0.)              GO TO 999
                                           RETURN
   999 IFLAG = 2
                                           RETURN
       END
```

The preceding discussion provides an efficient way to calculate the *inverse* for a given invertible matrix A of order n. As was pointed out in Sec. 3.1, the jth column $A^{-1}\mathbf{i}_j$ of the inverse matrix A^{-1} is the solution of the linear system

$$A\mathbf{x} = \mathbf{i}_j \qquad j = 1, \ldots, n$$

Hence, to calculate A^{-1}, one carries out the elimination algorithm 3.2 for A, then solves each of the n systems $A\mathbf{x} = \mathbf{i}_j, j = 1, \ldots, n$, by Algorithm 3.4. Therefore, once the elimination is carried out, it takes only $n \cdot n^2$ multiplications, and about the same number of additions, to find A^{-1}.

Example 3.7 For the coefficient matrix A of the linear system in Example 3.2, the elimination algorithm produced (see Example 3.5) the final result:

$$\overset{W}{\begin{bmatrix} \frac{1}{2} & \frac{1}{3} & 1 \\ 4 & 4 & -3 \\ -\frac{1}{2} & 5 & -\frac{5}{2} \end{bmatrix}} \qquad \mathbf{p}^T = [2, \quad 3, \quad 1]$$

With $\mathbf{b} = \mathbf{i}_1$, we get from this during the forward loop of Algorithm 3.4

With $p_1 = 2$: $\quad \tilde{b}_1 = b_2 = 0$

With $p_2 = 3$: $\quad \tilde{b}_2 = b_3 - w_{31}\tilde{b}_1 = 0 + \frac{1}{2} \cdot 0 = 0$

With $p_3 = 1$: $\quad \tilde{b}_3 = b_1 - w_{11}\tilde{b}_1 - w_{12}\tilde{b}_2 = 1 - \frac{1}{2} \cdot 0 - \frac{1}{3} \cdot 0 = 1$

or $\tilde{\mathbf{b}}^T = [0 \quad 0 \quad 1]$. The second loop then gives

With $p_3 = 1$: $\quad x_3 = \dfrac{\tilde{b}_3}{w_{13}} = \dfrac{1}{1} = 1$

With $p_2 = 3$: $\quad x_2 = \dfrac{\tilde{b}_2 - w_{33}x_3}{w_{32}} = \dfrac{0 + \frac{5}{2} \cdot 1}{5} = \frac{1}{2}$

With $p_1 = 2$: $\quad x_1 = \dfrac{\tilde{b}_1 - w_{22}x_2 - w_{23}x_3}{w_{21}} = \dfrac{0 - 4 \cdot \frac{1}{2} + 3 \cdot 1}{4} = \frac{1}{4}$

or $(A^{-1}\mathbf{i}_1)^T = [\tfrac{1}{4} \quad \tfrac{1}{2} \quad 1]$. Similarly, with $\mathbf{b} = \mathbf{i}_2$:

$$\bar{b}_1 = 1 \qquad\qquad\qquad x_3 = \frac{-\tfrac{3}{5}}{1} = -\tfrac{3}{5}$$

$$\bar{b}_2 = 0 + \tfrac{1}{2}\cdot 1 = \tfrac{1}{2} \qquad\qquad x_2 = \frac{\tfrac{1}{2} + \tfrac{5}{2}(-\tfrac{3}{5})}{5} = -\tfrac{1}{5}$$

$$\bar{b}_3 = 0 - \tfrac{1}{2}\cdot 1 - \tfrac{1}{5}\cdot\tfrac{1}{2} = -\tfrac{3}{5} \qquad x_1 = \frac{1 - 4(-\tfrac{1}{5}) + 3(-\tfrac{3}{5})}{4} = 0$$

or $(A^{-1}\mathbf{i}_2)^T = [0 \quad -\tfrac{1}{5} \quad -\tfrac{3}{5}]$. Finally, with $\mathbf{b} = \mathbf{i}_3$,

$$\bar{b}_1 = 0 \qquad\qquad\qquad x_3 = \frac{-\tfrac{1}{5}}{1} = -\tfrac{1}{5}$$

$$\bar{b}_2 = 1 + \tfrac{1}{2}\cdot 0 = 1 \qquad\qquad x_2 = \frac{1 + \tfrac{5}{2}(-\tfrac{1}{5})}{5} = \tfrac{1}{10}$$

$$\bar{b}_3 = 0 - \tfrac{1}{2}\cdot 0 - \tfrac{1}{5}\cdot 1 = -\tfrac{1}{5} \qquad x_1 = \frac{0 - 4(\tfrac{1}{10}) + 3(-\tfrac{1}{5})}{4} = -\tfrac{1}{4}$$

or $(A^{-1}\mathbf{i}_3)^T = [-\tfrac{1}{4} \quad \tfrac{1}{10} \quad -\tfrac{1}{5}]$. Hence

$$A^{-1} = \begin{bmatrix} \tfrac{1}{4} & 0 & -\tfrac{1}{4} \\ \tfrac{1}{2} & -\tfrac{1}{5} & \tfrac{1}{10} \\ 1 & -\tfrac{3}{5} & -\tfrac{1}{5} \end{bmatrix}$$

One checks this calculated inverse by forming AA^{-1} and/or $A^{-1}A$. Not surprisingly, both of these products equal the identity matrix for this example, since we used exact arithmetic throughout.

Having given this simple prescription for calculating the inverse of a matrix, we hasten to point out that *there is usually no good reason for ever calculating the inverse*. It does at times happen in certain problems that the entries of A^{-1} have some special physical significance. In the statistical treatment of the fitting of a function to observed data by the method of least squares, for example, the entries of a certain A^{-1} give information about the kinds and magnitudes of errors in the data. But whenever A^{-1} is needed merely to calculate a vector $A^{-1}\mathbf{b}$ (as in solving $A\mathbf{x} = \mathbf{b}$) or a matrix product $A^{-1}B$, A^{-1} should never be calculated explicitly. Rather, the substitution algorithm 3.4 should be used to form these products. The reason for this exhortation is as follows: Calculating the vector $A^{-1}\mathbf{b}$ for given $\mathbf{b}$ amounts to finding the solution of the linear system $A\mathbf{x} = \mathbf{b}$. Once the triangular factorization for A has been calculated by Algorithm 3.2, the calculation of $A^{-1}\mathbf{b}$ can therefore be accomplished by Algorithm 3.4 in exactly the same number of multiplications and additions as it takes to form the product of A^{-1} with the vector $\mathbf{b}$, as was pointed out earlier. Hence, once the triangular factorization is known, no advantage for calculating $A^{-1}\mathbf{b}$ can be gained by knowing A^{-1} explicitly. (Since forming the product $A^{-1}B$ amounts to multiplying each column of B by A^{-1}, these remarks apply to calculating such matrix products as well.) On the other hand, a first step toward calculating A^{-1} is finding the triangular factorization for A, which is then followed by n applications of the substitution algorithm; hence calculating A^{-1} presents a considerable initial computational outlay when compared with the work of calculating $A^{-1}\mathbf{b}$. In addition, the matrix so computed is only an *approximate* inverse and is, in a sense, less accurate than the triangular factorization, since it is derived from the factorization by further calculations. Hence nothing can be gained, and accuracy can be lost, by using A^{-1} explicitly in the calculation of matrix products involving A^{-1}.

Below, we have listed a FORTRAN program for the calculation of the inverse of a given N × N matrix A. This program uses the subprograms FACTOR and SUBST mentioned earlier. Also, sample input and the resulting output are listed, with the input the matrix of Example 3.7. The following remarks might help in the understanding of the coding. The order N of the matrix A is part of the input to this program; hence it is not possible to specify the exact dimension of the matrix A during compilation. On the other hand, both FACTOR and SUBST expect matrices A and/or W of exact dimension N × N. In the FORTRAN program below, the matrix A is therefore stored in a *one*-dimensional array, making use of the FORTRAN convention that the (I,J) entry of a two-dimensional (N,M) array is the $((J-1)*N+I)$ entry in an equivalent one-dimensional array. The same convention is followed in storing the entries of the Jth column of A^{-1} in the one-dimensional array AINV: the subroutine SUBST is given the $((J-1)*N+1)$ entry of AINV as the first entry of the N-vector called X in SUBST, into which the solution of the system $A\mathbf{x} = \mathbf{i}_j$ is to be stored.

FORTRAN PROGRAM FOR CALCULATING THE INVERSE OF A GIVEN MATRIX

```
        DIMENSION  A(900),AINV(900),B(30),IPIVOT(30)
      1 READ (5,501) N
    501 FORMAT(I2)
C       READ IN MATRIX ROW BY ROW.
        NSQ = N*N
        DO 10 I = 1,N
     10 READ   (5,510) (A(J),J = I,NSQ,N)
    510 FORMAT(5E15.7)
C
        CALL  FACTOR(A,A,IPIVOT,B,N,IFLAG)
                                GO TO (20,11),IFLAG
     11 WRITE (6,611)
    611 FORMAT(19H1MATRIX IS SINGULAR)
                                GO TO 1
C
     20 DO 21 I = 1,N
     21 B(I) = 0.
```

```
        IBEG = 1
        DO 30 J = 1,N
        B(J) = 1.
        CALL SUBST(A,B,AINV(IBEG),IPIVOT,N)
        B(J) = 0.
     30 IBEG = IBEG + N
        WRITE (6,630)
    630 FORMAT(24H1THE COMPUTED INVERSE IS //)
        DO 31 I = 1,N
     31 WRITE   (6,631) I,(AINV(J),J = I,NSQ,N)
    631 FORMAT(5H0ROW I2,8E15.7/(7X8E15.7))
                                                       GO TO 1
        END
```

SAMPLE INPUT

```
 3
2.      3.      −1.
4.      4.      −3.
−2.     3.      −1.
```

RESULTING OUTPUT

THE COMPUTED INVERSE IS

ROW 1   0.2500000E 00   0.0   −0.2499999E 00
ROW 2   0.5000000E 00   −0.1999998E 00   0.9999996E−01
ROW 3   0.1000000E 01   −0.6000000E 00   −0.2000000E 00

EXERCISES

3.4-1. Modify the FORTRAN program for the calculation of A^{-1} given in the text to obtain a program which solves the more general problem of calculating the product $C = A^{-1}B$, where A is a given (invertible) $n \times n$ matrix and B is a given $n \times m$ matrix

3.4-2. Calculate the inverse of the coefficient matrix A of the system of Exercise 3.2-8; then check the accuracy of the computed inverse A_{comp}^{-1} by calculating $A_{comp}^{-1}A$ and AA_{comp}^{-1}.

3.4-3. Show that the matrix

$$A = \begin{bmatrix} 2 & 2 & 1 \\ 1 & 1 & 1 \\ 3 & 2 & 1 \end{bmatrix}$$

is invertible, but that A cannot be written as the product of a lower-triangular matrix with an upper-triangular matrix.

3.4-4. Prove that the sum and the product of two lower- (upper-) triangular matrices is lower- (upper-) triangular and that the inverse of a lower- (upper-) triangular matrix is lower- (upper-) triangular.

3.4-5. Prove that a triangular factorization is unique in the following sense: If A is invertible and $L_1 U_1 = A = L_2 U_2$, where L_1, L_2 are unit-lower-triangular matrices and U_1, U_2 are upper-triangular matrices, then $L_1 = L_2$ and $U_1 = U_2$. (*Hint:* Use Exercise 3.1-8 to prove that U_1, L_2 must be invertible; then show that $L_2^{-1}L_1 = U_2 U_1^{-1}$ must hold, which implies, with Exercise 3.4-4, that $L_2^{-1}L_1$ must be a diagonal matrix; hence, since both L_1 and L_2 have 1's on their diagonal, $L_2^{-1}L_1 = I$.)

*3.5 COMPACT SCHEMES

The elimination algorithm 3.2 arrives at the entries of the factorization

$$PLU = A$$

for the coefficient matrix A by repeated modifications of the entries of the working array W, making it necessary to record many intermediate results. In the days of hand computations, this was found to be both arduous and a source of frequent errors.   Because of this, algorithms were developed which derive each entry of L and U in *one* operation, the so-called compact schemes. These algorithms are still useful today, since they make it possible (on some computers) to control the buildup of round-off error relatively cheaply by employing double-precision accumulation of scalar products (see below).

In a compact scheme, the entries of the unit-lower-triangular factor $L = (l_{ij})$ and the upper-triangular factor $U = (u_{ij})$ for A are calculated directly from the requirement that

$$LU = P^{-1}A \tag{3.35}$$

Consider first the general (i,j) entry

$$\sum_{r=1}^{n} l_{ir} u_{rj} \tag{3.36}$$

of the product LU.   Since $l_{ir} = 0$ for $i < r$, the summation in (3.36) need only be carried out for $r \le i$.   Again, since $u_{rj} = 0$ for $r > j$, only $r \le j$ need be considered in (3.36).   Hence

$$(i,j) \text{ entry of } LU = \sum_{r=1}^{\min(i,j)} l_{ir} u_{rj} \tag{3.37}$$

Further, let **p** be the permutation such that

$$P\mathbf{i}_j = \mathbf{i}_{p_j} \qquad j = 1, \ldots, n \tag{3.38}$$

Then the (i,j) entry of $P^{-1}A$ is $a_{p_i j}$.   Hence, in terms of the entries of L, U, and A, (3.35) reads

$$\sum_{r=1}^{\min(i,j)} l_{ir} u_{rj} = a_{p_i j} \qquad i, j = 1, \ldots, n \tag{3.39}$$

* This section may be omitted with no loss of continuity.

These equations can be solved for u_{ij} and l_{ij} as follows:

$$u_{ij} = a_{p_i j} - \sum_{r=1}^{i-1} l_{ir} u_{rj} \qquad i \le j \tag{3.40a}$$

(keeping in mind that $l_{ii} = 1$), and

$$l_{ij} = \frac{a_{p_i j} - \sum_{r=1}^{j-1} l_{ir} u_{rj}}{u_{jj}} \qquad i > j \tag{3.40b}$$

Now note that (3.40a) expresses the entries of the ith row of U in terms of the first $i-1$ rows of U and the first $i-1$ columns of L. Again, (3.40b) expresses the entries of the jth column of L in terms of the first $j-1$ rows of U, the first $j-1$ columns of L, and the jth diagonal entry of U. Hence, if we know already rows $1, 2, \ldots, k-1$ of U and columns $1, 2, \ldots, k-1$ of L, we can calculate row k of U, and after that, column k of L. In this way, we can build up U row by row, and L column by column.

Example 3.8 For the matrix

$$A = \begin{bmatrix} 2 & 3 & -1 \\ 4 & 4 & -3 \\ -2 & 3 & -1 \end{bmatrix}$$

we found, in Example 3.5, a factorization $PLU = A$, with the permutation matrix P derived from the pivoting strategy

$$\mathbf{p}^T = \begin{bmatrix} 2 & 3 & 1 \end{bmatrix}$$

by (3.38). We now calculate the entries of L and U using (3.40). By (3.40a),

$$u_{1j} = a_{p_1 j} - 0 = a_{2j} \qquad j \ge 1$$

Hence the first row of U is

$$u_{11} = 4 \qquad u_{12} = 4 \qquad u_{13} = -3$$

By (3.40b),

$$l_{i1} = \frac{a_{p_i 1} - 0}{u_{11}} = \frac{a_{p_i 1}}{4} \qquad i > 1$$

so that the first column of L is

$$(l_{11} = 1) \qquad l_{21} = \frac{a_{31}}{4} = -\tfrac{1}{2} \qquad l_{31} = \frac{a_{11}}{4} = \tfrac{1}{2}$$

Hence, writing the nontrivial entries of L and U into one matrix, we now know that

$$\begin{bmatrix} u_{11} & u_{12} & u_{13} \\ l_{21} & u_{22} & u_{23} \\ l_{31} & l_{32} & u_{33} \end{bmatrix} = \begin{bmatrix} 4 & 4 & -3 \\ -\tfrac{1}{2} & & \\ \tfrac{1}{2} & & \end{bmatrix}$$

Next, we get the second row of U. By (3.40a),

$$u_{2j} = a_{p_2j} - l_{21}u_{1j} \qquad j \geq 2$$

so that

$$u_{22} = a_{32} - l_{21}u_{12} = 3 - (-\tfrac{1}{2})4 = 5$$

$$u_{23} = a_{33} - l_{21}u_{13} = -1 - (-\tfrac{1}{2})(-3) = -\tfrac{5}{2}$$

As for the second column of L, (3.40b) states that

$$l_{i2} = \frac{a_{p_i2} - l_{i1}u_{12}}{u_{22}} \qquad i > 2$$

Therefore

$$l_{32} = \frac{a_{12} - l_{31}u_{12}}{u_{22}} = \frac{3 - \tfrac{1}{2}\cdot 4}{5} = \tfrac{1}{5}$$

We now know that

$$\begin{bmatrix} u_{11} & u_{12} & u_{13} \\ l_{21} & u_{22} & u_{23} \\ l_{31} & l_{32} & u_{33} \end{bmatrix} = \begin{bmatrix} 4 & 4 & -3 \\ -\tfrac{1}{2} & 5 & -\tfrac{5}{2} \\ \tfrac{1}{2} & \tfrac{1}{5} & \end{bmatrix}$$

Finally, we get the sole nonzero entry u_{33} of row 3 of U. By (3.40a),

$$\begin{aligned} u_{33} &= a_{p_33} - l_{31}u_{13} - l_{32}u_{23} \\ &= -1 - \tfrac{1}{2}(-3) - \tfrac{1}{5}(-\tfrac{5}{2}) = 1 \end{aligned}$$

A comparison with the results of Example 3.5 verifies the correctness of these calculations.

Before describing an algorithm for the calculation of P, L, and U, based on (3.40), we want to discuss briefly the possibility of controlling the buildup of round-off error through double-precision accumulation of scalar products. Equations (3.40) require the evaluation of an expression of the general form

$$s = \frac{\sum\limits_{r=1}^{m} c_r d_r}{e}$$

Such an expression is usually calculated by the algorithm

Set $s = 0$

For $r = 1, \ldots, m$, do:

$\quad\lfloor$ Set $s = s + c_r d_r$

Set $s = \dfrac{s}{e}$

But on many computers, formation of the product $c_r d_r$ of the two single-precision numbers c_r and d_r results in a double-precision number (as it does on any desk calculator), which is then usually rounded to single precision before it is used in further calculations. In double-precision accumulation of scalar products, the double-precision results of forming the products $c_r d_r$, $r = 1, \ldots, m$, are retained and summed in double precision; then the single-precision divisor e (if $\neq 1$) is divided into the full double-precision sum, and only then is the result rounded to single precision. Since the details of this procedure depend on the computer used, we will not discuss it here further. It is clearly easy to implement on a desk calculator (if the exponents in the floating-point numbers do not fluctuate too wildly).

We now discuss an algorithm for the calculation of the factors P, L, and U for a given matrix A based on (3.40). Recall from (3.28) and (3.32) that the nontrivial entries of L and U are contained in the working array W of Algorithm 3.2 as follows:

$$
\begin{aligned}
l_{ij} &= w_{p_ij} & i > j \\
u_{ij} &= w_{p_ij} & i \leq j
\end{aligned}
\tag{3.41}
$$

where $\mathbf{p}$ is the pivoting strategy used. Hence, in terms of the final content of the working array W of Algorithm 3.2, (3.40) reads

$$
\begin{aligned}
u_{ij} &= w_{p_ij} = a_{p_ij} - \sum_{r=1}^{i-1} w_{p_ir} w_{p_rj} & i \leq j \\
l_{ij} &= w_{p_ij} = \frac{a_{p_ij} - \sum_{r=1}^{j-1} w_{p_ir} w_{p_rj}}{w_{p_jj}} & i > j
\end{aligned}
\tag{3.42}
$$

Initially, we write the given matrix A of order n into the working array W (of order n). Also, we initialize the n-vector $\mathbf{p}$ to

$$
p_i = i \qquad i = 1, \ldots, n
$$

and calculate the sizes

$$
d_i = \max_{1 \leq j \leq n} |w_{ij}| \qquad i = 1, \ldots, n
$$

of the rows of A for use in scaled partial pivoting. Starting with step 1, the general, or kth, step proceeds as follows:

Step k At the beginning of this step, the ith row of W contains

$$
\begin{aligned}
&[u_{i1} \quad u_{i2} \quad \cdots \quad u_{i,k-1} \quad u_{ik} \quad \cdots \quad u_{in}] && \text{if } i = p_1 \\
&[l_{i1} \quad u_{i2} \quad \cdots \quad u_{i,k-1} \quad u_{ik} \quad \cdots \quad u_{in}] && \text{if } i = p_2 \\
&\cdots\cdots\cdots\cdots\cdots\cdots\cdots\cdots\cdots\cdots\cdots\cdots\cdots\cdots\cdots\cdots \\
&[l_{i1} \quad l_{i2} \quad \cdots \quad u_{i,k-1} \quad u_{ik} \quad \cdots \quad u_{in}] && \text{if } i = p_{k-1} \\
&[l_{i1} \quad l_{i2} \quad \cdots \quad l_{i,k-1} \quad a_{ik} \quad \cdots \quad a_{in}] && \text{otherwise}
\end{aligned}
\tag{3.43}
$$

According to (3.40),

$$
u_{kk} = a_{p_kk} - \sum_{r=1}^{k-1} l_{kr} u_{rk}
$$

$$
l_{ik} = \frac{a_{p_ik} - \sum_{r=1}^{k-1} l_{ir} u_{rk}}{u_{kk}} \qquad i > k
$$

if row p_k is the pivotal row for step k. To select the final value for p_k, we therefore calculate the numbers

$$c_{p_i} = a_{p_i k} - \sum_{r=1}^{k-1} l_{ir} u_{rk} \qquad i = k, \ldots, n$$

and then find the smallest $j \geq k$ such that

$$\frac{|c_{p_j}|}{d_{p_j}} \geq \frac{|c_{p_i}|}{d_{p_i}} \qquad \text{for } i = k, \ldots, n$$

Having determined this j, we interchange the contents of p_k and p_j. Then $u_{kk} = c_{p_k}$ is stored in $w_{p_k k}$, and $l_{ik} = c_{p_i}/c_{p_k}$ is stored in $w_{p_i k}, i = k + 1, \ldots, n$. Finally,

$$u_{kj} = a_{p_k j} - \sum_{r=1}^{k-1} l_{kr} u_{rj}$$

is calculated and stored in $w_{p_k j}, j = k + 1, \ldots, n$. The contents of W now look as described in (3.43), with every k replaced by $k + 1$.

Algorithm 3.5 Compact scheme with scaled partial pivoting Given the matrix W of order n containing the $n \times n$ matrix A.

For $i = 1, \ldots, n$, do:

> Set $p_i = i$
> Set $d_i = \max_{1 \leq j \leq n} |w_{ij}|$
> If $d_i = 0$, signal that A is not invertible and stop
> Otherwise, continue

For $k = 1, \ldots, n - 1$, do:

> For $i = k, \ldots, n$, do:
> > Set $w_{p_i k} = w_{p_i k} - \sum_{r=1}^{k-1} w_{p_i r} w_{p_r k}$
>
> Find the smallest $j \geq k$ such that $\dfrac{|w_{p_j k}|}{d_{p_j}} \geq \dfrac{|w_{ik}|}{d_i}$, for $i = p_k, \ldots, p_n$
> Interchange the contents of p_k and p_j
> If $w_{p_k k} = 0$, signal that A is not invertible and stop
> Otherwise, for $i = k + 1, \ldots, n$, do:
> > Set $w_{p_i k} = \dfrac{w_{p_i k}}{w_{p_k k}}$
> > Set $w_{p_k i} = w_{p_k i} - \sum_{r=1}^{k-1} w_{p_k r} w_{p_r i}$

Set $w_{p_n n} = w_{p_n n} - \sum_{r=1}^{n-1} w_{p_n r} w_{p_r n}$

If $w_{p_n n} = 0$, signal that A is not invertible and stop

Otherwise, A is now known to be invertible; further, if P, L, U are the
matrices whose entries are given in terms of W and $\mathbf{p}$ by (3.30),
(3.28), and (3.32), respectively, then $PLU = A$.

It is important to realize that the *only* virtue of the compact scheme for
computer calculations lies in the possibility for reducing round-off-error
effects by calculating all scalar products or sums using double-precision
accumulation, as discussed earlier. If the compact scheme is carried out
without such special techniques, the resulting factorization for A is *exactly
the same* (including round-off errors) as the one produced earlier by the
elimination algorithm 3.2 with scaled partial pivoting. On the other hand,
the indexing is slightly more complex in the compact scheme than it is in the
elimination algorithm 3.2. Hence, if one does not intend to use double-
precision accumulation of scalar products, one should prefer Algorithm 3.2
(as realized in the FORTRAN subprogram FACTOR in Sec. 3.4) to
Algorithm 3.5.

EXERCISES

3.5-1. *Choleski's method.* If the matrix A of order n is real, symmetric $(A = A^T)$, and
positive definite (that is, $\mathbf{x}^T A \mathbf{x} > 0$ for all nonzero n-vectors $\mathbf{x}$), then it is possible to
factor A as $A = LL^T$, where L is a real lower-triangular matrix.
     Develop an algorithm for the calculation of the entries of this matrix L (column
by column, say).

3.5-2. Show that Choleski's method is applicable whenever the matrix A is of the form
BB^T, where B is an invertible matrix.

3.5-3. Solve the system of Exercises 3.2-8 and 3.3-4 using Algorithm 3.5 with double-
precision accumulation of scalar products, and compare the results with those of
Exercises 3.2-8 and 3.3-4.

3.5-4. Prove: If the tridiagonal matrix A can be factored as $A = LU$, where L is lower-
triangular and U is upper-triangular, then both L and U are also tridiagonal. Interpret
Algorithm 3.3 as a way to factor tridiagonal matrices.

3.6 ERROR AND RESIDUAL OF AN APPROXIMATE SOLUTION; NORMS

Any computed solution of a linear system must, because of round-off, be
considered an approximate solution. In this section, we discuss the difficult
problem of ascertaining the error of an approximate solution (without
knowing the solution). In the discussion, we introduce and use norms as a
convenient means of measuring the "size" of vectors and matrices.

If $\hat{x}$ is a computed solution for the linear system $Ax = b$, then its *error* is the difference

$$e = x - \hat{x}$$

This error is, of course, usually not known to us (for otherwise, we would know the solution x, making any further discussions unnecessary). But we can always compute the *residual* (error)

$$r = Ax - A\hat{x}$$

since Ax is just the right side b. The residual then measures how well $\hat{x}$ satisfies the linear system $Ax = b$. If r is the zero vector, then $\hat{x}$ is the (exact) solution; that is, e is then zero. One would expect each entry of r to be small, at least in a relative sense, if $\hat{x}$ is a good approximation to the solution x.

Example 3.9 Consider the simple linear system

$$1.01x_1 + 0.99x_2 = 2$$
$$0.99x_1 + 1.01x_2 = 2$$

whose unique solution x has the entries $x_1 = x_2 = 1$. The approximate solution $\hat{x} = \begin{bmatrix} 1.01 \\ 1.01 \end{bmatrix}$ has error $e = \begin{bmatrix} -0.01 \\ -0.01 \end{bmatrix}$ and residual $r = \begin{bmatrix} -0.02 \\ -0.02 \end{bmatrix}$, so that a "small" residual (relative to the right side) corresponds to a relatively "small" error in this case. On the other hand, the approximate solution $\hat{x} = \begin{bmatrix} 2 \\ 0 \end{bmatrix}$ has error $e = \begin{bmatrix} -1 \\ 1 \end{bmatrix}$, but residual $r = \begin{bmatrix} -0.02 \\ 0.02 \end{bmatrix}$, hence still a relatively "small" residual, while the error is now relatively "large." By taking a different right side, we can achieve the opposite effect. The linear system

$$1.01x_1 + 0.99x_2 = 2 \qquad\qquad\qquad (3.44)$$
$$0.99x_1 + 1.01x_2 = -2$$

has the unique solution $x_1 = 100$, $x_2 = -100$. The approximate solution $\hat{x} = \begin{bmatrix} 101 \\ -99 \end{bmatrix}$ has error $e = \begin{bmatrix} -1 \\ -1 \end{bmatrix}$, but residual $r = \begin{bmatrix} -2 \\ -2 \end{bmatrix}$; hence the residual is now relatively "large," while the error is relatively "small" (only 1 percent of the solution).

As this example shows, the size of the *residual* $r = b - A\hat{x}$ of an approximate solution $\hat{x}$ is not always a reliable indicator of the size of the error $e = x - \hat{x}$ in this approximate solution. Whether or not a "small" residual implies a "small" error depends on the "size" of the coefficient matrix and of its inverse, in a manner to be made precise below. For this discussion, we need a means of measuring the "size" of n-vectors and $n \times n$ matrices.

The absolute value provides a convenient way to measure the "size" of real numbers or even of complex numbers. It is much less certain how one should measure the size of an n-vector or an $n \times n$ matrix. There is certainly not any *one* way of doing this which is acceptable in all situations.

For example, a frequently used measure for the size of an n-vector $\mathbf{a}$ is the nonnegative number

$$\|\mathbf{a}\|_\infty = \max_{1 \le i \le n} |a_i| \tag{3.45}$$

Assume now that the computed solution $\hat{\mathbf{x}}$ to $A\mathbf{x} = \mathbf{b}$ is known to have six-place accuracy in this way of measuring size; i.e.,

$$\frac{\|\mathbf{x} - \hat{\mathbf{x}}\|_\infty}{\|\mathbf{x}\|_\infty} < 10^{-6} \tag{3.46}$$

Then this would indicate a very satisfactory computed solution in case the unknowns are, say, approximate values of the well-behaved solution of a certain differential equation. But if one of the unknowns happens to be your annual income while another is the gross national product, then (3.46) gives no hint as to whether or not $\mathbf{x}$ is a satisfactory computed solution (as far as you are concerned), since, with (3.46) holding, the error in your computed yearly income (even if received for only one year) might make you independently wealthy or put you in debt for life. A measure like

$$\|\mathbf{a}\| = \max \{10^{10}|a_1|, \max_{2 \le i \le n} |a_i|\}$$

(assuming your yearly income to be the first unknown) would give you much more information, as would certain measures of size, which use several numbers (rather than just one nonnegative number) to describe the "size" of an n-vector.

For most situations, however, it suffices to measure the size of an n-vector by a *norm*. A norm retains certain properties of the absolute value for numbers. Specifically, a norm assigns to each n-vector $\mathbf{a}$ a real number $\|\mathbf{a}\|$, called *the norm of* $\mathbf{a}$, subject to the following reasonable restrictions:

(i) For all n-vectors $\mathbf{a}$, $\|\mathbf{a}\| \ge 0$, and $\|\mathbf{a}\| = 0$ if and only if $\mathbf{a} = \mathbf{0}$
(ii) For all n-vectors $\mathbf{a}$ and all numbers α, $\|\alpha\mathbf{a}\| = |\alpha|\,\|\mathbf{a}\|$ (3.47)
(iii) For any two n-vectors $\mathbf{a}$ and $\mathbf{b}$, $\|\mathbf{a} + \mathbf{b}\| \le \|\mathbf{a}\| + \|\mathbf{b}\|$

The first restriction forces all n-vectors but the zero vector to have positive "length." The second restriction states, for example, that $\mathbf{a}$ and its negative $-\mathbf{a}$ have the same "length" and that the length of $3\mathbf{a}$ is three times the length of $\mathbf{a}$. The third restriction is the *triangle inequality*, so called since it states that the sum of the lengths of two sides of a triangle is never smaller than the length of the third side.

The student is presumably familiar with the *euclidean* length or norm,

$$\|\mathbf{a}\|_2 = \sqrt{\mathbf{a}^T\mathbf{a}} = \sqrt{|a_1|^2 + |a_2|^2 + \cdots + |a_n|^2}$$

of the *n*-vector $\mathbf{a} = (a_i)$, at least for the case $n = 2$ or $n = 3$. But, for a reason made clear below, we prefer to use, in the numerical examples below, the *maximum norm* (3.45) as a way to measure the size or length of the *n*-vector $\mathbf{a}$. It is not difficult to verify that (3.45) defines a norm, i.e., that $\|\mathbf{a}\| = \|\mathbf{a}\|_\infty$ satisfies the three properties of a norm listed in (3.47): As to (i), $\|\mathbf{a}\|_\infty$ is the maximum of nonnegative quantities, hence nonnegative; also, $\|\mathbf{a}\|_\infty = 0$ if and only if, for all *i*, $|a_i| = 0$, which is the same as saying that $\mathbf{a} = \mathbf{0}$. Further, if α is any scalar, then

$$\|\alpha\mathbf{a}\|_\infty = \max_i |\alpha a_i| = \max_i |\alpha|\,|a_i| = |\alpha| \max_i |a_i| = |\alpha|\,\|\mathbf{a}\|_\infty$$

proving (ii). Finally,

$$\|\mathbf{a} + \mathbf{b}\| = \max_i |a_i + b_i| \leq \max_i (|a_i| + |b_i|)$$

$$\leq \max_i |a_i| + \max_i |b_i| = \|\mathbf{a}\|_\infty + \|\mathbf{b}\|_\infty$$

proving (iii).

Other vector norms in frequent use include the 1-norm

$$\|\mathbf{a}\| = \|\mathbf{a}\|_1 = \sum_{i=1}^{n} |a_i|$$

and various instances of the weighted *p*-norm

$$\|\mathbf{a}\| = \|\mathbf{a}\|_{p,w} = \left(\sum_{i=1}^{n} |a_i|^p w_i\right)^{1/p}$$

where *p* is some number between 1 and ∞ and the numbers $w_1, \ldots, w_n$ are fixed positive quantities. The case $p = 2$, $w_i = 1$ (all *i*) leads to the familiar euclidean norm.

Once a vector norm is chosen, we then measure the corresponding size of an $n \times n$ matrix A by comparing the size of $A\mathbf{x}$ with the size of $\mathbf{x}$. Precisely, we define the corresponding *matrix norm* of A by

$$\|A\| = \max \frac{\|A\mathbf{x}\|}{\|\mathbf{x}\|} \tag{3.48}$$

where the maximum is taken over all (nonzero) *n*-vectors $\mathbf{x}$. It can be shown that this maximum exists for every $n \times n$ matrix A (and any choice of the vector norm). The matrix norm $\|A\|$ is characterized by the following two facts:

For all n-vectors $\mathbf{x}$: $\|A\mathbf{x}\| \leq \|A\| \, \|\mathbf{x}\|$

and   (3.49)

For some nonzero n-vector $\mathbf{x}$: $\|A\mathbf{x}\| \geq \|A\| \, \|\mathbf{x}\|$

Further, the following properties can be shown to hold for the matrix norm (3.48):

(i) For all $n \times n$ matrices A: $\|A\| \geq 0$, and $\|A\| = 0$ if and only if $A = O$

(ii) For all $n \times n$ matrices A and all numbers α:
$$\|\alpha A\| = |\alpha| \, \|A\| \quad (3.50)$$

(iii) For any two $n \times n$ matrices A and B:
$$\|A + B\| \leq \|A\| + \|B\|$$

so that the term "norm" for the number $\|A\|$ is justified.

In addition,

(iv) For any two $n \times n$ matrices A and B: $\|AB\| \leq \|A\| \, \|B\|$ (3.50a)

Finally, if the matrix A is invertible, then $\mathbf{x} = A^{-1}(A\mathbf{x})$; hence $\|\mathbf{x}\| \leq \|A^{-1}\| \, \|A\mathbf{x}\|$. Combining this with (3.49), one gets

For all n-vectors $\mathbf{x}$: $\dfrac{\|\mathbf{x}\|}{\|A^{-1}\|} \leq \|A\mathbf{x}\| \leq \|A\| \, \|\mathbf{x}\|$ (3.51)

and both inequalities are *sharp*; i.e., each can be made an equality by an appropriate choice of a (nonzero) $\mathbf{x}$.

As it turns out, the matrix norm

$$\|A\|_2 = \max \frac{\|A\mathbf{x}\|_2}{\|\mathbf{x}\|_2}$$

based on the euclidean vector norm, is usually quite difficult to calculate, while the matrix norm

$$\|A\|_\infty = \max \frac{\|A\mathbf{x}\|_\infty}{\|\mathbf{x}\|_\infty}$$

based on the maximum norm, can be calculated quite easily, it being the number

$$\|A\|_\infty = \max_{1 \leq i \leq n} \sum_{j=1}^{n} |a_{ij}| \qquad (3.52)$$

To prove this, we have to show that the number $\|A\| = \max_i \sum_j |a_{ij}|$ satisfies the two statements in (3.49), i.e., that

For all n-vectors $\mathbf{x}$: $\qquad \|A\mathbf{x}\|_\infty \le \left(\max_i \sum_{j=1}^n |a_{ij}| \right) \|\mathbf{x}\|_\infty$

and

For some nonzero $\mathbf{x}$: $\qquad \|A\mathbf{x}\|_\infty \ge \left(\max_i \sum_{j=1}^n |a_{ij}| \right) \|\mathbf{x}\|_\infty$

But for an arbitrary $\mathbf{x}$:

$$\|A\mathbf{x}\|_\infty = \max_{1 \le i \le n} \left| \sum_{j=1}^n a_{ij} x_j \right| \le \max_{1 \le i \le n} \sum_{j=1}^n |a_{ij}| \, |x_j|$$

$$\le \max_{1 \le i \le n} \left(\left(\max_{1 \le j \le n} |x_j| \right) \sum_{j=1}^n |a_{ij}| \right) = \|\mathbf{x}\|_\infty \max_{1 \le i \le n} \sum_{j=1}^n |a_{ij}|$$

which proves the first statement. As to the second statement, let i_0 be an integer between 1 and n so that

$$\sum_{j=1}^n |a_{i_0 j}| = \max_{1 \le i \le n} \sum_{j=1}^n |a_{ij}|$$

and let $\mathbf{x}$ be an n-vector of max-norm 1 such that

$$a_{i_0 j} x_j = |a_{i_0 j}| \qquad j = 1, \ldots, n$$

e.g., take

$$x_j = \left\{ \begin{array}{ll} 1 & \text{if } a_{i_0 j} \ge 0 \\ -1 & \text{if } a_{i_0 j} < 0 \end{array} \right\} \qquad j = 1, \ldots, n$$

Then, for this clearly nonzero vector $\mathbf{x}$, $\|\mathbf{x}\|_\infty = 1$ and

$$\|A\mathbf{x}\|_\infty = \max_{1 \le i \le n} \left| \sum_{j=1}^n a_{ij} x_j \right| \ge \left| \sum_{j=1}^n a_{i_0 j} x_j \right|$$

$$= \sum_{j=1}^n |a_{i_0 j}| = \|\mathbf{x}\|_\infty \left(\max_{1 \le i \le n} \sum_j |a_{ij}| \right)$$

which proves the second statement.

Example 3.10 For the coefficient matrix A of Example 3.9, one readily finds

$$\|A\|_\infty = \max \{|1.01| + |0.99|, |0.99| + |1.01|\} = 2$$

We have seen that

$$A\begin{bmatrix}1\\1\end{bmatrix} = \begin{bmatrix}2\\2\end{bmatrix} \quad \text{and} \quad A\begin{bmatrix}100\\-100\end{bmatrix} = \begin{bmatrix}2\\-2\end{bmatrix}$$

Hence

$$A\left(\begin{bmatrix}1\\1\end{bmatrix} + \begin{bmatrix}100\\-100\end{bmatrix}\right) = \begin{bmatrix}4\\0\end{bmatrix} \quad \text{and} \quad A\left(\begin{bmatrix}1\\1\end{bmatrix} - \begin{bmatrix}100\\-100\end{bmatrix}\right) = \begin{bmatrix}0\\4\end{bmatrix}$$

Therefore $A\begin{bmatrix}\frac{101}{4} & -\frac{99}{4}\\ -\frac{99}{4} & \frac{101}{4}\end{bmatrix} = \begin{bmatrix}1 & 0\\0 & 1\end{bmatrix}$, showing that $A^{-1} = \begin{bmatrix}25.25 & -24.75\\-24.75 & 25.25\end{bmatrix}$

Consequently, $\|A^{-1}\|_\infty = \max\{|25.25| + |-24.75|, |-24.75| + |25.25|\} = 50$.

For this example, then, (3.51) states that

For all 2-vectors $\mathbf{x}$: $0.02\|\mathbf{x}\|_\infty \le \|A\mathbf{x}\|_\infty \le 2\|\mathbf{x}\|_\infty$

Choosing $\mathbf{x} = \begin{bmatrix}1\\1\end{bmatrix}$, we get $A\mathbf{x} = \begin{bmatrix}2\\2\end{bmatrix}$; hence $\|\mathbf{x}\|_\infty = 1$, $\|A\mathbf{x}\|_\infty = 2$, and the second inequality becomes equality.   Choosing $\mathbf{x} = \begin{bmatrix}100\\-100\end{bmatrix}$, we get $A\mathbf{x} = \begin{bmatrix}2\\-2\end{bmatrix}$; hence $\|\mathbf{x}\|_\infty = 100$ and $\|A\mathbf{x}\|_\infty = 2$, and the first inequality is an equality for this choice.

We now return to our discussion of the relationship between the *error* $\mathbf{e} = \mathbf{x} - \hat{\mathbf{x}}$ in the approximate solution $\hat{\mathbf{x}}$ of $A\mathbf{x} = \mathbf{b}$ and the *residual* $\mathbf{r} = \mathbf{b} - A\hat{\mathbf{x}}$. We have

$$\mathbf{r} = A\mathbf{x} - A\hat{\mathbf{x}} = A(\mathbf{x} - \hat{\mathbf{x}}) = A\mathbf{e}$$

Hence $\mathbf{e} = A^{-1}\mathbf{r}$.   Therefore, remembering that $(A^{-1})^{-1} = A$, we get from (3.51)

$$\frac{\|\mathbf{r}\|}{\|A\|} \le \|\mathbf{e}\| \le \|A^{-1}\|\,\|\mathbf{r}\| \tag{3.53}$$

Since $A\mathbf{x} = \mathbf{b}$, hence $\mathbf{x} = A^{-1}\mathbf{b}$, we get, similarly,

$$\frac{\|\mathbf{b}\|}{\|A\|} \le \|\mathbf{x}\| \le \|A^{-1}\|\,\|\mathbf{b}\| \tag{3.54}$$

On combining (3.53) and (3.54), we get, finally, the following *sharp bounds* for the *relative error* $\|\mathbf{e}\|/\|\mathbf{x}\|$ in terms of the relative residual $\|\mathbf{r}\|/\|\mathbf{b}\|$:

$$\frac{1}{\|A\|\,\|A^{-1}\|}\frac{\|\mathbf{r}\|}{\|\mathbf{b}\|} \le \frac{\|\mathbf{e}\|}{\|\mathbf{x}\|} \le \|A\|\,\|A^{-1}\|\frac{\|\mathbf{r}\|}{\|\mathbf{b}\|} \tag{3.55}$$

Because of its importance, we state (3.55) in words: If, for the invertible coefficient matrix A of the linear system $A\mathbf{x} = \mathbf{b}$, we have $\|A\|\,\|A^{-1}\| = K$, then the relative error of an approximate solution can be as large as K times its relative residual, but it can also be as small as $1/K$ times its relative residual.   Hence, if $K \approx 1$, then relative error and relative residual are always of the same size, and the relative residual can then be safely used as an estimate for the relative error. But the larger K is, the less information about the relative error can be obtained from the relative residual.

The number $\|A\| \, \|A^{-1}\|$ is called the *condition number of A* and is at times abbreviated

$$\text{cond}\,(A) = \|A\| \, \|A^{-1}\|$$

Note that the condition number cond (A) for A depends on the matrix norm used and can, for some matrices, vary considerably as the matrix norm is changed. On the other hand, the condition number is always at least 1, since for the identity matrix I, $\|I\| = \max \|\mathbf{x}\|/\|\mathbf{x}\| = 1$, and by (3.50a), $\|I\| = \|AA^{-1}\| \leq \|A\| \, \|A^{-1}\|$.

Example 3.11 We find from earlier calculations that, for the coefficient matrix A of Example 3.9, cond $(A) = \|A\|_\infty \|A^{-1}\|_\infty = 2 \cdot 50 = 100$. Further, we saw in Example 3.9 that indeed the relative error of an approximate solution can be as large as 100 times its relative residual, but can also be just $\frac{1}{100}$ of its relative residual.

EXERCISES

3.6-1. Verify that

$$\|\mathbf{a}\| = \|\mathbf{a}\|_1 = \sum_{i=1}^{n} |a_i|$$

defines a norm for all n-vectors $\mathbf{a}$.

3.6-2. Prove that the matrix norm $\|A\|_1$ associated with the vector norm $\|\mathbf{a}\|_1$ of Exercise 3.6-1 can be calculated by

$$\|A\|_1 = \max_{1 \leq j \leq n} \sum_{i=1}^{n} |a_{ij}|$$

3.6-3. If we interpret a 2-vector $\mathbf{a}$ as a point in the plane with coordinates $\{a_1, a_2\}$, then its 2-norm $\|\mathbf{a}\|_2$ is the euclidean distance of this point from the origin. Further, the set of all vectors of euclidean norm 1 forms a circle around the origin of radius 1. Draw the "circle of radius 1 around the origin" when the distance of the "point" $\mathbf{a}$ is measured by (a) the 1-norm $\|\mathbf{a}\|_1$, (b) the norm $\|\mathbf{a}\|_{3/2}$, (c) the euclidean norm $\|\mathbf{a}\|_2$, (d) the norm $\|\mathbf{a}\|_4$, (e) the max-norm $\|\mathbf{a}\|_\infty$.

3.6-4. With the same interpretation of 2-vectors as points in the plane as used in Exercise 3.6-3, show that, for any two 2-vectors $\mathbf{a}$ and $\mathbf{b}$, the three "points" $\mathbf{0}$, $\mathbf{a}$, and $\mathbf{a} + \mathbf{b}$ are the vertices of a triangle with sides of (euclidean) length $\|\mathbf{a}\|_2$, $\|\mathbf{b}\|_2$, and $\|\mathbf{a} + \mathbf{b}\|_2$, and explain the term "triangle inequality" for property (iii) of norms [Eq. (3.47)].

3.6-5. Show that, for any 2-vectors $\mathbf{a}$ and $\mathbf{b}$ and any particular vector norm,

$$\left| \|\mathbf{a}\| - \|\mathbf{b}\| \right| \leq \|\mathbf{a} - \mathbf{b}\|$$

3.6-6. Show that, for any 2-vectors $\mathbf{a}$ and $\mathbf{b}$, any number λ between 0 and 1,

$$\|\lambda \mathbf{a} + (1 - \lambda)\mathbf{b}\| \leq \max\,(\|\mathbf{a}\|, \|\mathbf{b}\|)$$

3.6-7. Show that the matrix norm $\|A\| = \max(\|A\mathbf{x}\|/\|\mathbf{x}\|)$ can also be calculated as

$$\|A\| = \max_{\|\mathbf{x}\|=1} \|A\mathbf{x}\|$$

3.6-8. Prove all the statements in (3.50) regarding matrix norms.

3.6-9. Use Exercise 3.6-7 to calculate $\|A\|_2$, where

$$A = \begin{bmatrix} 3 & -5 \\ 6 & 1 \end{bmatrix}$$

(*Hint:* A 2-vector $\mathbf{x}$ has 2-norm $\|\mathbf{x}\|_2 = 1$ if and only if $x_1 = \cos\theta$, $x_2 = \sin\theta$ for some θ.)

3.6-10. Use Exercise 3.4-2 to calculate the condition number of the coefficient matrix A of the system of Exercise 3.2-8; then discuss relative error and relative residuals of the solutions calculated in Exercises 3.2-8 and 3.3-4 in terms of this condition number.

3.7 THE CONDITION NUMBER AND ITERATIVE IMPROVEMENT

In the preceding Sec. 3.6, we identified the condition number

$$\text{cond}\,(A) = \|A\|\,\|A^{-1}\| \tag{3.56}$$

of the coefficient matrix A of the linear system $A\mathbf{x} = \mathbf{b}$ as the critical quantity in estimating the error of an approximate solution. To summarize: The condition number (3.56) provides a measure of how reliably the relative residual $\|\mathbf{b} - A\hat{\mathbf{x}}\|/\|\mathbf{b}\|$ of an approximate solution $\hat{\mathbf{x}}$ reflects the relative error $\|\mathbf{x} - \hat{\mathbf{x}}\|/\|\mathbf{x}\|$ of the approximate solution. The condition number is therefore a measure of how well we can hope to distinguish a "good" (approximate) solution from a "bad" one by looking at the residual error.

It is clearly quite difficult to calculate the condition number for a given matrix even if the matrix norm can be calculated relatively easily, since one must know A^{-1}. At times, cond (A) can be *estimated* with the aid of the following theorem, which might also help to explain further the significance of the condition number.

Theorem 3.8 For any invertible $n \times n$ matrix A and any matrix norm, the condition number of A indicates the relative distance of A from the nearest noninvertible $n \times n$ matrix. Specifically,

$$\frac{1}{\text{cond}\,(A)} = \min\left\{\frac{\|A - B\|}{\|A\|}\,\middle|\, B \text{ is not invertible}\right\}$$

A complete proof of this theorem is beyond the scope of this book. We only show that

$$\frac{1}{\text{cond}\,(A)} \leq \inf\left\{\frac{\|A - B\|}{\|A\|}\,\middle|\, B \text{ is not invertible}\right\}$$

i.e., that for any noninvertible $n \times n$ matrix B,

$$\frac{1}{\|A^{-1}\|} \leq \|A - B\| \tag{3.57}$$

Indeed, if B is not invertible, then by Theorem 3.4, there is a nonzero n-vector $\mathbf{x}$ such that $B\mathbf{x} = \mathbf{0}$. But then

$$\|A - B\| \, \|\mathbf{x}\| \geq \|(A - B)\mathbf{x}\| = \|A\mathbf{x} - B\mathbf{x}\| = \|A\mathbf{x}\| \geq \frac{\|\mathbf{x}\|}{\|A^{-1}\|}$$

using (3.51), and since $\mathbf{x} \neq \mathbf{0}$, we can divide by $\|\mathbf{x}\| \neq 0$ to obtain (3.57).

The argument just given establishes the following useful corollary.

Corollary If A is invertible and B is a matrix such that

$$\|A - B\| < \frac{1}{\|A^{-1}\|}$$

then B is invertible.

To give an example, we find for the matrix

$$A = \begin{bmatrix} 1.01 & 0.99 \\ 0.99 & 1.01 \end{bmatrix}$$

of Example 3.9 that $\|A^{-1}\|_\infty \geq 1/0.02 = 50$, since the matrix $B = \begin{bmatrix} 1 & 1 \\ 1 & 1 \end{bmatrix}$ is not invertible, and $A - B = \begin{bmatrix} 0.01 & -0.01 \\ -0.01 & 0.01 \end{bmatrix}$ has max-norm $\|A - B\|_\infty$ $= 0.02$. Hence, since $\|A\|_\infty = 2$, we get that cond $(A) \geq 100$. A different example is provided by invertible triangular matrices. If A is triangular, we know from Theorem 3.6 that all diagonal entries of A are nonzero, and that replacing any diagonal entry of A by 0 makes A noninvertible. Consequently, if A is triangular, then

$$\text{cond } (A) \geq \frac{\|A\|_\infty}{\min_i |a_{ii}|}$$

The condition number also plays a role in the analysis of a further complication in solving linear systems. If the linear system $A\mathbf{x} = \mathbf{b}$ derives from a practical problem, we must expect the coefficients of this system to be subject to error, either because they result from other calculations or from physical measurement, or even only because of round-off resulting from the conversion to a binary representation during read-in. Hence, assuming for the moment that the right side is accurate, we are, in fact, solving the linear system

$$\hat{A}\hat{\mathbf{x}} = \mathbf{b} \tag{3.58}$$

instead of $A\mathbf{x} = \mathbf{b}$, where $A = \hat{A} + E$, the matrix E containing the errors in the coefficients. Even if all calculations are carried out exactly, we still compute only the solution $\hat{\mathbf{x}}$ of (3.58) rather than the solution $\mathbf{x}$ of $A\mathbf{x} = \mathbf{b}$. Now, we have $\mathbf{x} = A^{-1}\mathbf{b}$; hence, assuming that (3.58) has a solution,

$$\mathbf{x} = A^{-1}\mathbf{b} = A^{-1}\hat{A}\hat{\mathbf{x}} = A^{-1}(A + \hat{A} - A)\hat{\mathbf{x}} = \hat{\mathbf{x}} + A^{-1}(\hat{A} - A)\hat{\mathbf{x}}$$

Therefore, with $\hat{A} - A = -E$,

$$\mathbf{x} - \hat{\mathbf{x}} = A^{-1}(-E)\hat{\mathbf{x}}$$

Hence

$$\|\mathbf{x} - \hat{\mathbf{x}}\| \le \|A^{-1}\| \, \|E\| \, \|\hat{\mathbf{x}}\| = \|A^{-1}\| \, \|A\| \frac{\|E\|}{\|A\|} \|\hat{\mathbf{x}}\|$$

giving the final result

$$\frac{\|\mathbf{x} - \hat{\mathbf{x}}\|}{\|\hat{\mathbf{x}}\|} \le \text{cond}\,(A) \frac{\|E\|}{\|A\|} \tag{3.59}$$

In words, the change in the solution from $\mathbf{x}$ to $\hat{\mathbf{x}}$ relative to $\|\hat{\mathbf{x}}\|$ can be as large as cond (A) times the relative change $\|E\|/\|A\|$ in the coefficient matrix. If the coefficients of the linear system $A\mathbf{x} = \mathbf{b}$ are known to be accurate only to about 10^{-s} (relative to the size of A) and cond $(A) \approx 10^t$, then there is no point in calculating the solution to a relative accuracy better than 10^{t-s}.

Example 3.12 Consider once more the linear system (3.44) in Example 3.9. We found earlier that cond $(A) = 100$ for its coefficient matrix A. By (3.59), a 1 percent change in the coefficients of the system could therefore change its solution drastically. Indeed, a 1 percent change (in the right direction) produces the linear system

$$x_1 + x_2 = 2$$
$$x_1 + x_2 = -2$$

which has no solution at all, for the coefficient matrix now fails to be invertible.

The preceding analysis can be put to good use in gauging the effect of round-off errors incurred during elimination and back-substitution on the accuracy of the computed solution. Roughly, it can be shown that the computed solution $\hat{\mathbf{x}}$ of the linear system $A\mathbf{x} = \mathbf{b}$ satisfies (exactly) a perturbed system

$$(A + E)\hat{\mathbf{x}} = \mathbf{b} \tag{3.60}$$

where the error matrix E depends on A, $\mathbf{b}$ and the arithmetic used during the calculations. The proof of these facts goes beyond the scope of this book. A detailed analysis can be found, for example, in Forsythe and Moler [18]. From that book, we quote the following typical result.

Theorem 3.9 Suppose we use t binary-digit floating-point arithmetic for all calculations in Algorithms 3.2 (with scaled partial pivoting) and 3.4. If the coefficient matrix A is of order n, then

$$\|E\|_\infty \le 1.01(n^3 + 3n^2)\rho\|A\|_\infty 2^{-t} \tag{3.61}$$

where

$$\rho = \max\{|a_{ij}^{(k-1)}| \mid i, j, k = 1, \ldots, n\}$$

The bound (3.61) is much too conservative. In most cases, the bound

$$\|E\|_\infty \le n\|A\|_\infty 2^{-t} \tag{3.62}$$

is much more realistic. In any event, such a bound gives some insight into the effect of the precision used in the calculations on the accuracy of the computed solution. For we get, for example, from (3.59) and (3.62), that the error of the computed solution relative to the size of this solution is usually bounded as follows:

$$\frac{\|\mathbf{x} - \hat{\mathbf{x}}\|}{\|\hat{\mathbf{x}}\|} \le \text{cond}\,(A)\cdot n\cdot 2^{-t} \tag{3.63}$$

Quite loosely, the linear system $A\mathbf{x} = \mathbf{b}$ is often called *ill-conditioned* if cond (A) is "large." Somewhat more to the point, one should say that the linear system is *ill-conditioned with respect to the precision used* if cond (A) is about 2^t, for then, by (3.63), a computed solution might well bear no resemblance to the (exact) solution of the system.

Example 3.13 Consider the linear system

$$\begin{aligned}
0.24x_1 + 0.36x_2 + 0.12x_3 &= 0.84 \\
0.12x_1 + 0.16x_2 + 0.24x_3 &= 0.52 \\
0.15x_1 + 0.21x_2 + 0.25x_3 &= 0.64
\end{aligned} \tag{3.64}$$

We attempt to solve this system by the elimination algorithm 3.2, using two-decimal-digit floating-point arithmetic and scaled partial pivoting. The pivoting strategy turns out to be $\mathbf{p}^T = [1 \quad 2 \quad 3]$, and the final content of the working array is

$$\begin{bmatrix} 0.24 & 0.36 & 0.12 & 0.84 \\ 0.50 & -0.02 & 0.18 & 0.10 \\ 0.63 & 1.0 & -0.01 & 0.01 \end{bmatrix}$$

Continuing the calculations, we find by back-substitution the approximate solution

$$\hat{\mathbf{x}} = \begin{bmatrix} 25 \\ -14 \\ -1 \end{bmatrix}. \quad \text{The residual is } \mathbf{r} = \begin{bmatrix} 0.0 \\ 0.0 \\ 0.08 \end{bmatrix}. \quad \text{In fact, the solution is } \mathbf{x} = \begin{bmatrix} -3 \\ 4 \\ 1 \end{bmatrix}, \text{ so}$$

that the computed solution $\hat{\mathbf{x}}$ is in error in the first significant digit.

The max-norm for the coefficient matrix A of this system is $\|A\|_\infty = 0.72$. Further, the matrix

$$B = \begin{bmatrix} 0.252 & 0.36 & 0.12 \\ 0.112 & 0.16 & 0.24 \\ 0.147 & 0.21 & 0.25 \end{bmatrix}$$

is noninvertible (its first column is 0.7 times its second column) while $\|A - B\|_\infty = 0.012$. Hence we get from Theorem 3.8 that

$$\text{cond } (A) \geq \frac{0.72}{0.012} \geq 60$$

This system is therefore very ill-conditioned with respect to the precision used, and the very large error in the computed solution is not surprising.

Next, we repeat the calculations, using three-decimal-digit floating-point arithmetic this time. Since cond $(A) \approx 60$, we still do not expect a very accurate computed solution. After Algorithm 3.2, the working matrix has the content

$$\begin{bmatrix} 0.24 & 0.36 & 0.12 & 0.84 \\ 0.5 & -0.02 & 0.18 & 0.10 \\ 0.625 & 0.75 & 0.04 & 0.04 \end{bmatrix} \tag{3.65}$$

and back-substitution gives the computed solution $\hat{x}^T = [-3 \quad 4 \quad 1]$; i.e., we get the (exact) solution, even though the system is still somewhat ill-conditioned with respect to the precision used. This becomes evident when we change the right side of (3.64) to

$$\mathbf{b} = \begin{bmatrix} 0.852 \\ 0.620 \\ 0.740 \end{bmatrix}.$$ Using the factorization (3.65), we calculate by Algorithm 3.4 the

(approximate) solution $\hat{\mathbf{x}} = \begin{bmatrix} -3.30 \\ 4.05 \\ 1.53 \end{bmatrix}$ (still using three-decimal-digit floating-point

arithmetic), which has residual $\mathbf{r} = \begin{bmatrix} 0.0024 \\ 0.0008 \\ 0.0020 \end{bmatrix}$. The exact solution is $\mathbf{x} = \begin{bmatrix} -3.6 \\ 4.25 \\ 1.55 \end{bmatrix}$;

hence our computed solution has about 10 percent error, as could be expected from (3.63).

As this example shows, a large condition number relative to the precision used *may* lead to a relatively large error in the computed solution but is not guaranteed to do so.

Whether or not a given linear system is ill-conditioned with respect to the precision used can be conveniently ascertained [even without knowledge of cond (A)] during *iterative improvement*, which we now discuss. With $\mathbf{e} = \mathbf{x} - \hat{\mathbf{x}}^{(1)}$ the (unknown) error in the approximate solution $\hat{\mathbf{x}}^{(1)}$ for $A\mathbf{x} = \mathbf{b}$, we found in Sec. 3.6 that

$$A\mathbf{e} = \mathbf{r} \tag{3.66}$$

where $\mathbf{r} = \mathbf{b} - A\hat{\mathbf{x}}^{(1)}$ is the *computable* residual for $\hat{\mathbf{x}}^{(1)}$. Here we have, then, a linear system whose solution is the error $\mathbf{e}$ and whose coefficient matrix agrees with the coefficient matrix of the original system. If $\hat{\mathbf{x}}^{(1)}$ is obtained by the elimination algorithm 3.2, we can solve (3.66) rather quickly by the substitution algorithm 3.4. Let $\hat{\mathbf{e}}^{(1)}$ be the (approximate) solution for (3.66) so computed. Then $\hat{\mathbf{e}}^{(1)}$ will, in general, not agree with $\mathbf{e}$. But at the very least, $\hat{\mathbf{e}}^{(1)}$ should give an indication of the size of $\mathbf{e}$. If $\|\hat{\mathbf{e}}^{(1)}\|/\|\hat{\mathbf{x}}^{(1)}\| \approx 10^{-s}$, we conclude that the first s decimal places of $\hat{\mathbf{x}}^{(1)}$ probably agree with those of $\mathbf{x}$. We would then also expect $\hat{\mathbf{e}}^{(1)}$ to be that accurate an approximation to $\mathbf{e}$. Hence we expect

$$\hat{\mathbf{x}}^{(2)} = \hat{\mathbf{x}}^{(1)} + \hat{\mathbf{e}}^{(1)}$$

to be a better approximation to $\mathbf{x}$ than is $\hat{\mathbf{x}}^{(1)}$. We can now, if necessary, compute the new residual $\mathbf{r} = \mathbf{b} - A\hat{\mathbf{x}}^{(2)}$ and solve (3.66) again to obtain a new correction $\hat{\mathbf{e}}^{(2)}$ and a new approximation $\hat{\mathbf{x}}^{(3)} = \hat{\mathbf{x}}^{(2)} + \hat{\mathbf{e}}^{(2)}$ to $\mathbf{x}$. The number of places in agreement in the successive approximations $\hat{\mathbf{x}}^{(1)}, \hat{\mathbf{x}}^{(2)}, \ldots,$ as well as an examination of the successive residuals, should give an indication of the accuracy of these approximate solutions. One normally carries out this iteration until $\|\hat{\mathbf{e}}^{(k)}\|/\|\hat{\mathbf{x}}^{(k)}\| \approx 10^{-t}$ if t decimal places are carried during the calculations. The number of iteration steps necessary to achieve this end can be shown to increase with cond (A). When cond (A) is "very large," the corrections $\hat{\mathbf{e}}^{(1)}, \hat{\mathbf{e}}^{(2)}, \ldots$ may never decrease in size, thus signaling extreme ill-conditioning of the original system.

For the success of iterative improvement, it is absolutely mandatory that the residuals be computed as accurately as possible. If, as is usual, floating-point arithmetic is used, the residual should always be calculated in double-precision arithmetic or by double-precision accumulation of scalar products (see Sec. 3.5).

Algorithm 3.6 Iterative improvement Given the linear system $A\mathbf{x} = \mathbf{b}$ and the approximate solution $\hat{\mathbf{x}}$.

> Calculate $\mathbf{r} = \mathbf{b} - A\hat{\mathbf{x}}$, using double-precision arithmetic
> Use Algorithm 3.2 (or if possible, only Algorithm 3.4) to compute an
> (approximate) solution $\hat{\mathbf{e}}$ of the linear system $A\mathbf{e} = \mathbf{r}$
> If $\|\hat{\mathbf{e}}\|/\|\hat{\mathbf{x}}\|$ is "small enough," stop and take $\hat{\mathbf{x}} + \hat{\mathbf{e}}$ as the solution
> Otherwise, set $\hat{\mathbf{x}} = \hat{\mathbf{x}} + \hat{\mathbf{e}}$ and repeat the procedure

Iterative improvement can be used whenever an approximate solution has been found by any means. It should always be used after an approximate solution has been found by elimination, since the corrections can then be calculated relatively cheaply by forward- and back-substitution. Also, the rate of convergence of the process (if any) gives a good indication of the condition of the system (with respect to the precision used).

Example 3.14 We apply iterative improvement to the approximate solution of (3.64) calculated in Example 3.13. The correctly computed residual is $\mathbf{r} = \begin{bmatrix} 0.0 \\ 0.0 \\ 0.08 \end{bmatrix}$ rounded to two significant digits. Applying Algorithm 3.4 to this right side (using two-decimal-digit floating-point arithmetic), we get the correction $\hat{\mathbf{e}}^{(1)} = \begin{bmatrix} 120 \\ -75 \\ -8 \end{bmatrix}$, which is of the same size as the computed solution. Hence we conclude that the given linear system is too ill-conditioned for the precision used and that a higher precision should be employed if we wish to calculate the solution of (3.64).

In Example 3.13 we also calculated an approximate solution $\hat{\mathbf{x}} = \begin{bmatrix} -3.30 \\ +4.05 \\ 1.53 \end{bmatrix}$ for the linear system with the same coefficient matrix but a different right side, using three-decimal-digit floating-point arithmetic. The correctly computed residual is $\mathbf{r} = \begin{bmatrix} 0.0024 \\ 0.0008 \\ 0.0020 \end{bmatrix}$. Applying Algorithm 3.4 to this $\mathbf{r}$ as right side (using the same precision as before), we get the correction $\hat{\mathbf{e}}^{(1)} = \begin{bmatrix} -0.3 \\ 0.2 \\ 0.02 \end{bmatrix}$, which is only 10 percent of the computed solution and gives the corrected solution $\hat{\mathbf{x}}^{(2)} = \begin{bmatrix} -3.6 \\ 4.25 \\ 1.55 \end{bmatrix}$. The residual for this approximate solution turns out to be $\mathbf{0}$, so that just one step of iterative improvement produces the (exact) solution in this example.

EXERCISES

3.7-1. Use Theorem 3.8 to estimate the condition number of the following matrix:

$$A = \begin{bmatrix} 7 & 8 & 9 \\ 8 & 9 & 10 \\ 9 & 10 & 8 \end{bmatrix}$$

3.7-2. Use iterative improvement on the computed solution in Exercise 3.3-4.

3.7-3. We say that a matrix A of order n is (strictly row) diagonally dominant if $|a_{ii}| > \sum_{j \neq i} |a_{ij}|$, $i = 1, \ldots, n$. Use the corollary to Theorem 3.8 to prove that a diagonally dominant matrix is invertible. (*Hint:* Write $A = DB$, where D is the diagonal matrix with diagonal entries equal to those of A; then show that $\|I - B\|_\infty < 1$.)

3.7-4. Estimate the condition number of the matrix of Exercise 3.7-1 by solving the linear system $A\mathbf{x} = \mathbf{b}$ with (a) $\mathbf{b}^T = [24,27,27]$, (b) $\mathbf{b}^T = [24.1,26.9,26.9]$. Use iterative improvement.

3.8 ITERATIVE METHODS

The computational effort in solving a linear system by elimination is in general proportional to the cube of its order, while storage requirements are proportional to the square of the order. Because of this, the solution of large linear systems, say, of order 500 or more, with a dense coefficient matrix is considered extremely difficult, if not impossible. Nevertheless, systems of order up to 1,000 and even 10,000 have been solved successfully, though not by elimination, but by *iteration*. These systems arise, for example, in the numerical solution of partial differential equations, and have a co-efficient matrix which is quite sparse, so that storage requirements are proportional only to the order of the system rather than its square. In addition, the coefficient matrix of such systems has certain recognizable properties which imply that iterative methods can be used successfully for their solution.

The simplest and best-known iterative methods for the solution of linear systems are generalization of fixed-point iteration, as discussed in Chap. 2 for the solution of one (nonlinear) equation in one unknown. To recall, with $f(x)$ a given function of one variable, a solution ξ to the equation

$$f(x) = 0 \tag{3.67}$$

is found as the limit of a sequence $x^{(0)}, x^{(1)}, x^{(2)}, \ldots$, whose terms are calculated iteratively by the prescription

$$x^{(m+1)} = g(x^{(m)}) \qquad m = 0, 1, 2, \ldots$$

Here $x^{(0)}$ is a suitable first guess, and the *iteration function* $g(x)$ is chosen so that the solution ξ of (3.67) is a fixed point for $g(x)$, that is, so that

$$\xi = g(\xi)$$

Further, to ensure convergence of the sequence, $x^{(0)}, x^{(1)}, x^{(2)}, \ldots, g(x)$ is usually constructed in such a way that, for y and z "close to" ξ,

$$|g(y) - g(z)| \le K|y - z| \tag{3.68}$$

where K is some positive constant less than 1.

Exactly the same technique can be used to construct iterative methods for the solution of a linear system $A\mathbf{x} = \mathbf{b}$, that is, of the vector equation

$$A\mathbf{x} - \mathbf{b} = 0 \tag{3.69}$$

Specifically, we find a matrix B and a vector $\mathbf{c}$ so that the vector equation

$$\mathbf{x} = B\mathbf{x} + \mathbf{c} \tag{3.70}$$

is *equivalent to* (3.69), i.e., so that a solution of one is also a solution of the other. We then compute the sequence $\mathbf{x}^{(0)}, \mathbf{x}^{(1)}, \mathbf{x}^{(2)}, \ldots$ of vectors iteratively by the prescription

$$\mathbf{x}^{(m+1)} = B\mathbf{x}^{(m)} + \mathbf{c} \qquad m = 0, 1, 2, \ldots \tag{3.71}$$

starting with some initial guess $\mathbf{x}^{(0)}$. Hopefully, the resulting sequence "converges" to the solution $\mathbf{x}$ of (3.70) [and therefore of (3.69)]. Here the sequence $\mathbf{x}^{(0)}, \mathbf{x}^{(1)}, \mathbf{x}^{(2)}, \ldots$ of n-vectors is said to *converge to* the n-vector $\mathbf{x}$ provided

$$\lim_{m \to \infty} x_i^{(m)} = x_i \qquad i = 1, \ldots, n \tag{3.72}$$

A simple iterative method constructed along these lines is *Jacobi iteration*. If all diagonal entries of the coefficient matrix A of the given linear system $A\mathbf{x} = \mathbf{b}$ are nonzero, we can construct an equivalent vector equation of the form (3.70) by choosing

$$b_{ij} = \begin{cases} \dfrac{-a_{ij}}{a_{ii}} & i \neq j \\ 0 & i = j \end{cases}$$

$$c_i = \dfrac{b_i}{a_{ii}} \qquad \text{all } i, j \tag{3.73}$$

Explicitly, (3.70) reads in this case

$$x_1 = \qquad\qquad -\frac{a_{12}}{a_{11}} x_2 - \frac{a_{13}}{a_{11}} x_3 - \cdots - \frac{a_{1n}}{a_{11}} x_n + \frac{b_1}{a_{11}}$$

$$x_2 = -\frac{a_{21}}{a_{22}} x_1 \qquad\qquad - \frac{a_{23}}{a_{22}} x_3 - \cdots - \frac{a_{2n}}{a_{22}} x_n + \frac{b_2}{a_{22}}$$

$$\cdots \cdots \cdots \cdots \cdots \cdots \cdots \cdots \cdots \cdots \cdots \cdots \cdots$$

$$x_n = -\frac{a_{n1}}{a_{nn}} x_1 - \frac{a_{n2}}{a_{nn}} x_2 - \cdots \cdots \cdots - \frac{a_{n,n-1}}{a_{nn}} x_{n-1} + \frac{b_n}{a_{nn}}$$

In effect, we obtain (3.70) from (3.69) by solving the ith equation of (3.69) for the ith unknown x_i, $i = 1, \ldots, n$.

Example 3.15 The linear system

$$\begin{aligned} 10x_1 + x_2 + x_3 &= 12 \\ x_1 + 10x_2 + x_3 &= 12 \\ x_1 + x_2 + 10x_3 &= 12 \end{aligned}$$

has the unique solution $x_1 = x_2 = x_3 = 1$. Starting with $\mathbf{x}^{(0)} = \mathbf{0}$, Jacobi iteration produces the vectors $\mathbf{x}^{(1)}, \ldots, \mathbf{x}^{(6)}$ listed below in Table 3.1. The sequence seems to converge nicely to the solution of the given system.

Table 3.1

	Jacobi				Gauss-Seidel	
$x_1^{(m)}$	$x_2^{(m)}$	$x_3^{(m)}$	m	$x_1^{(m)}$	$x_2^{(m)}$	$x_3^{(m)}$
0	0	0	0	0	0	0
1.2	1.2	1.2	1	1.2	1.08	0.972
0.96	0.96	0.96	2	0.9948	1.0033	1.00019
1.008	1.008	1.008	3	0.99965	1.000016	1.000033
0.9984	0.9984	0.9984	4			
1.00032	1.00032	1.00032	5			
0.999936	0.999936	0.999936	6			

By contrast, Jacobi iteration applied to the linear system

$$2x_1 + 5x_2 + 5x_3 = 12$$
$$5x_1 + 2x_2 + 5x_3 = 12$$
$$5x_1 + 5x_2 + 2x_3 = 12$$

does not converge. This system has also the unique solution $x_1 = x_2 = x_3 = 1$. But starting Jacobi iteration again with $\mathbf{x}^{(0)} = \mathbf{0}$, we now get iterates given in the table below which clearly diverge.

To investigate conditions for convergence of the iterative scheme (3.71), we note first that convergence of sequences of vectors can be expressed more compactly than (3.72) in terms of vector norms. It can be shown that a sequence $\mathbf{x}^{(0)}, \mathbf{x}^{(1)}, \mathbf{x}^{(2)}, \ldots$ of vectors converges to the vector $\mathbf{x}$ if and only if

$$\lim_{m \to \infty} \|\mathbf{x} - \mathbf{x}^{(m)}\| = 0 \tag{3.74}$$

i.e., if and only if, given $\varepsilon > 0$, there is an M such that, for $m \geq M$,

$$\|\mathbf{x} - \mathbf{x}^{(m)}\| \leq \varepsilon$$

The student should recognize that this is, word for word, the definition of convergence of a real-number sequence, except that the role of the absolute

Table 3.2

$x_1^{(m)}$	$x_2^{(m)}$	$x_3^{(m)}$	m
0	0	0	0
6	6	6	1
-24	-24	-24	2
126	126	126	3
-624	-624	-624	4

value is taken over by the vector norm. Which particular vector norm is chosen in (3.74) turns out to be immaterial; if (3.74) holds for one vector norm, it holds for any other.

We now show that a sufficient condition for the convergence of the iterative process (3.71) is the existence of a positive constant $K < 1$ so that, for all vectors $\mathbf{y}$ and $\mathbf{z}$,

$$\|(B\mathbf{y} + \mathbf{c}) - (B\mathbf{z} + \mathbf{c})\| \le K\|\mathbf{y} - \mathbf{z}\| \tag{3.75}$$

This is clearly analogous to the condition (3.68), which ensures convergence of fixed-point iteration for one equation in one unknown. Note that

$$(B\mathbf{y} + \mathbf{c}) - (B\mathbf{z} + \mathbf{c}) = B\mathbf{y} - B\mathbf{z} = B(\mathbf{y} - \mathbf{z})$$

so that

$$\|(B\mathbf{y} + \mathbf{c}) - (B\mathbf{z} + \mathbf{c})\| = \|B(\mathbf{y} - \mathbf{z})\| \le \|B\| \, \|\mathbf{y} - \mathbf{z}\|$$

Hence, if (3.75) is to hold for all vectors $\mathbf{y}$ and $\mathbf{z}$ and some $K < 1$, we need $\|B\| < 1$.

Lemma 3.4 Assume that, in some matrix norm, $\|B\| < 1$, and let $\mathbf{x}^{(0)}$, $\mathbf{x}^{(1)}$, $\mathbf{x}^{(2)}$, . . . be the sequence generated by (3.71). Then this sequence converges to the unique solution $\mathbf{x}$ of the vector equation

$$\mathbf{x} = B\mathbf{x} + \mathbf{c} \tag{3.70}$$

no matter how the initial guess $\mathbf{x}^{(0)}$ is chosen.

For the proof, we observe first that (3.70) has indeed exactly one solution. By Theorem 3.4, we merely have to show that the homogeneous system

$$\mathbf{x} = B\mathbf{x}$$

has only the trivial solution $\mathbf{x} = \mathbf{0}$. But if $\mathbf{x}$ solves this system, then

$$0 \le \|\mathbf{x}\| \le \|B\| \, \|\mathbf{x}\|$$

which cannot hold with $\|B\| < 1$ unless $\|\mathbf{x}\| = 0$, i.e., unless $\mathbf{x} = \mathbf{0}$. Further, for any m, we have

$$\mathbf{x} - \mathbf{x}^{(m)} = (B\mathbf{x} + \mathbf{c}) - (B\mathbf{x}^{(m-1)} + \mathbf{c}) = B(\mathbf{x} - \mathbf{x}^{(m-1)})$$

Hence, by induction on m,

$$\mathbf{x} - \mathbf{x}^{(m)} = B^m(\mathbf{x} - \mathbf{x}^{(0)}) \tag{3.76}$$

so that

$$0 \le \|\mathbf{x} - \mathbf{x}^{(m)}\| \le \|B^m\| \, \|\mathbf{x} - \mathbf{x}^{(0)}\| \tag{3.77}$$

If now $\|B\| < 1$, then

$$\|B^m\| \le \|B\|^m \xrightarrow[m \to \infty]{} 0$$

which finishes the proof.

As an application of this lemma, we now prove that Jacobi iteration converges if the diagonal entries of A are very much larger than the off-diagonal entries (as is the case in the first system considered in Example 3.15). We say that the matrix $A = (a_{ij})$ of order n is *strictly (row) diagonally dominant* if

$$|a_{ii}| > \sum_{j \ne i} |a_{ij}| \qquad \text{for } i = 1, \ldots, n \tag{3.78}$$

Corollary If the coefficient matrix A of the linear system $Ax = b$ is strictly diagonally dominant, then Jacobi iteration converges. In particular, A is then invertible (see Exercise 3.7-3).

For the proof, we note that, with (3.78), all diagonal entries of A are nonzero, so that Jacobi iteration can be carried out. Further, (3.78) states that

$$\sum_{j \ne i} \left| \frac{a_{ij}}{a_{ii}} \right| < 1 \qquad \text{for } i = 1, \ldots, n$$

But this implies, with the definition (3.73) of the iteration matrix B for Jacobi iteration, that

$$\|B\|_\infty = \max_{1 \le i \le n} \sum_{j \ne i} \left| \frac{a_{ij}}{a_{ii}} \right| < 1$$

Hence, by Lemma 3.4, Jacobi iteration converges. Further, by Lemma 3.4, the vector equation $x = Bx + c$ has exactly one solution. Since this equation is equivalent to the vector equation $Ax = b$, the latter equation has therefore exactly one solution; hence A is invertible.

For the first system in Example 3.15, one calculates $\|B\|_\infty = \frac{1}{5}$, implying that the error is reduced by at least a factor of 5 per iteration step. This is confirmed by Table 3.1.

Lemma 3.4 constitutes the easy part of the following basic theorem.

Theorem 3.10 Let x be the unique solution of the vector equation

$$x = Bx + c$$

where B is a given $n \times n$ matrix and c is a given n-vector. Then the sequence $x^{(0)}, x^{(1)}, x^{(2)}, \ldots$, generated by the iteration

$$x^{(m+1)} = Bx^{(m)} + c \qquad m = 0, 1, 2, \ldots$$

from some initial guess $\mathbf{x}^{(0)}$ converges to $\mathbf{x}$ (regardless of how $\mathbf{x}^{(0)}$ is chosen) if and only if some matrix norm for B is less than 1.

Note that this theorem does not require B to have a norm less than one in *every* matrix norm, but only in *some* matrix norm. The matrix

$$B = \begin{bmatrix} 0.9 & 0.9 \\ 0 & 0 \end{bmatrix}$$

for instance, has max-norm $\|B\|_\infty = 1.8 > 1$. Nevertheless, iteration with this matrix converges. For clearly,

$$B^m = \begin{bmatrix} (0.9)^m & (0.9)^m \\ 0 & 0 \end{bmatrix} \qquad m = 1, 2, 3, \ldots$$

so that $\|B^m\|_\infty = 2(0.9)^m \xrightarrow[m \to \infty]{} 0$, which, by (3.77), is really all that is required to show convergence. In this case, a matrix norm for which $\|B\| < 1$ is, for example, the matrix norm $\|B\|_1$ associated with the vector norm $\|\mathbf{a}\|_1 = \sum_i |a_i|$ (see Exercise 3.6-2), for which $\|B\|_1 = 0.9 < 1$.

It remains to discuss how one might find, for the given linear system $A\mathbf{x} = \mathbf{b}$, a matrix B and a vector $\mathbf{c}$ so that the vector equation

$$\mathbf{x} = B\mathbf{x} + \mathbf{c}$$

is equivalent to $A\mathbf{x} = \mathbf{b}$. This can be done as follows: If C is any invertible matrix (of the same order as A), then the vector equation

$$\mathbf{x} = \mathbf{x} + C^{-1}(\mathbf{b} - A\mathbf{x})$$

holds if and only if $C^{-1}(\mathbf{b} - A\mathbf{x}) = \mathbf{0}$, that is (since C is invertible), if and only if $A\mathbf{x} - \mathbf{b} = \mathbf{0}$. Hence, with

$$B = I - C^{-1}A \qquad \mathbf{c} = C^{-1}\mathbf{b}$$

the vector equation $\mathbf{x} = B\mathbf{x} + \mathbf{c}$ is equivalent to $A\mathbf{x} = \mathbf{b}$. For the resulting iterative method to be useful, C must satisfy two conditions:

(i) C should be "easily invertible"; i.e., it should be possible to calculate the vector $C^{-1}\mathbf{r}$ for any given vector $\mathbf{r}$ with considerably fewer operations than it takes to calculate $A^{-1}\mathbf{r}$; otherwise, just *one* step in the iteration would take as much work as finding the solution $A^{-1}\mathbf{b}$ directly. Hence one usually takes C to be a diagonal matrix (as in the Jacobi method), or a triangular matrix (as in the Gauss-Seidel method below), or the product of two triangular matrices (as in iterative improvement), or even a tridiagonal matrix, etc.

(ii) C^{-1} should be a good enough approximation to A^{-1} so that

$$\|I - C^{-1}A\| < 1$$

in some matrix norm; for by Theorem 3.10, only under this condition will the iteration converge.

It is always easy to satisfy one of these two conditions. Thus $C = I$ certainly satisfies condition (i), while $C = A$ is guaranteed to satisfy condition (ii). The difficulty in constructing useful iterative schemes lies precisely in finding a C which satisfies *both* conditions.

Algorithm 3.7 Fixed-point iteration for linear systems Given the linear system $A\mathbf{x} = \mathbf{b}$ of order n.

> Pick a matrix C of order n such that
>   (i) For given $\mathbf{r}$, the vector $C^{-1}\mathbf{r}$ is "easily" calculated
>   (ii) In some matrix norm, $\|I - C^{-1}A\| < 1$
> Pick an n-vector $\mathbf{x}^{(0)}$, for example, $\mathbf{x}^{(0)} = \mathbf{0}$
> For $m = 0, 1, 2, \ldots$, until satisfied, do:
>   Set $\mathbf{x}^{(m+1)} = \mathbf{x}^{(m)} + C^{-1}(\mathbf{b} - A\mathbf{x}^{(m)})$

In the absence of round-off error, the resulting sequence $\mathbf{x}^{(0)}, \mathbf{x}^{(1)}, \mathbf{x}^{(2)}, \ldots$ converges to the solution of the given linear system.

As in Chap. 2, we employ here the phrase "until satisfied" to stress the incompleteness of the description given. To complete the algorithm, one has to specify precise termination criteria. Typical criteria are:

Terminate if (a): $\|\mathbf{x}^{(m)} - \mathbf{x}^{(m-1)}\| < \varepsilon$

or if (b): $\dfrac{\|\mathbf{x}^{(m)} - \mathbf{x}^{(m-1)}\|}{\|\mathbf{x}^{(m)}\|} < \varepsilon$ for some prescribed ε (3.79)

or if (c): $m > M$ for some given M

The last criterion should always be present in any program implementing the algorithm. We repeat the warning first voiced in Sec. 1.6: The fact that

$$\|\mathbf{x}^{(m)} - \mathbf{x}^{(m-1)}\| < \varepsilon \qquad (3.80)$$

does not imply that

$$\|\mathbf{x}^{(m)} - \mathbf{x}\| < \varepsilon$$

In fact, (3.80) implies offhand *nothing* about the size of the error $\mathbf{x} - \mathbf{x}^{(m)}$ unless additional information about the convergence behavior of the sequence of iterates is known. We study this convergence behavior in more detail in the next section. Here we merely note the following (usually conservative) error bound which can be used if (a bound for) $\|B\| = \|I - C^{-1}A\|$ is known: We have

$$\mathbf{x} - \mathbf{x}^{(m-1)} = (\mathbf{x} - \mathbf{x}^{(m)}) + (\mathbf{x}^{(m)} - \mathbf{x}^{(m-1)})$$

Therefore, using the triangle inequality (3.47iii),

$$\|\mathbf{x} - \mathbf{x}^{(m-1)}\| \leq \|\mathbf{x} - \mathbf{x}^{(m)}\| + \|\mathbf{x}^{(m)} - \mathbf{x}^{(m-1)}\|$$

But by the proof of Lemma 3.4,

$$\|\mathbf{x} - \mathbf{x}^{(m)}\| = \|B(\mathbf{x} - \mathbf{x}^{(m-1)})\| \leq \|B\| \, \|\mathbf{x} - \mathbf{x}^{(m-1)}\|$$

Hence

$$(1 - \|B\|)\|\mathbf{x} - \mathbf{x}^{(m-1)}\| \leq \|\mathbf{x}^{(m)} - \mathbf{x}^{(m-1)}\|$$

Therefore, if $\|B\| < 1$, then

$$\|\mathbf{x} - \mathbf{x}^{(m-1)}\| \leq \frac{\|\mathbf{x}^{(m)} - \mathbf{x}^{(m-1)}\|}{1 - \|B\|} \tag{3.81a}$$

and

$$\|\mathbf{x} - \mathbf{x}^{(m)}\| \leq \frac{\|B\|}{1 - \|B\|} \|\mathbf{x}^{(m)} - \mathbf{x}^{(m-1)}\| \tag{3.81b}$$

To give an example, we found for the Jacobi iteration for the first system in Example 3.15 that $\|B\|_\infty \leq \frac{1}{5}$ and $\|\mathbf{x}^{(6)} - \mathbf{x}^{(5)}\|_\infty = 0.000384$. Therefore (3.81b) gives the estimate

$$\|\mathbf{x} - \mathbf{x}^{(6)}\|_\infty \leq \frac{\frac{1}{5}}{1 - \frac{1}{5}} 0.000384 = 0.000096$$

In fact, $\|\mathbf{x} - \mathbf{x}^{(6)}\|_\infty = 0.000064$, so that the error is overestimated by *only* 50 percent. Unfortunately, it is usually difficult to obtain a good estimate for $\|B\|$, or else the estimate for $\|B\|$ is so close to 1 as to make the denominator in (3.81a) or (3.81b) excessively small.

We now discuss specific examples of fixed-point iteration for linear systems. One such example is iterative improvement discussed in the preceding section. To recall, one computes the residual $\mathbf{r}^{(m)} = \mathbf{b} - A\mathbf{x}^{(m)}$ for the mth approximate solution $\mathbf{x}^{(m)}$; then, using the triangular factorization of A calculated during elimination, one finds the (approximate) solution $\mathbf{y}^{(m)}$ of the linear system $A\mathbf{y} = \mathbf{r}^{(m)}$ and, adding $\mathbf{y}^{(m)}$ to $\mathbf{x}^{(m)}$, obtains the hopefully better approximate solution $\mathbf{x}^{(m+1)} = \mathbf{x}^{(m)} + \mathbf{y}^{(m)}$. The vector $\mathbf{y}^{(m)}$ is in general not the (exact) solution of $A\mathbf{y} = \mathbf{r}^{(m)}$. This is partially due to rounding errors during forward- and back-substitution. But the major contribution to the error in $\mathbf{y}^{(m)}$ can be shown to come, usually, from inaccuracies in the computed triangular factorization PLU for A, that is, from the fact that PLU is only an approximation to A. If we ignore rounding errors during forward- and back-substitution, we have

$$\mathbf{y}^{(m)} = (PLU)^{-1}\mathbf{r}^{(m)} = (PLU)^{-1}(\mathbf{b} - A\mathbf{x}^{(m)})$$

Hence

$$\mathbf{x}^{(m+1)} = \mathbf{x}^{(m)} + (PLU)^{-1}(\mathbf{b} - A\mathbf{x}^{(m)})$$

This shows *iterative improvement* to be a special case of fixed-point iteration, C being the computed triangular factorization PLU for A. But for certain classes of matrices A, a matrix C satisfying (i) and (ii) of Algorithm 3.7 can be found with far less computational effort than it takes to calculate the triangular factorization for A. For a linear system with such a coefficient matrix, it then becomes more economical to dispense with elimination and to calculate the solution directly by Algorithm 3.7.

To discuss the two most common choices for C, we write the coefficient matrix $A = (a_{ij})$ as the sum of a strictly lower-triangular matrix $\hat{L} = (\hat{l}_{ij})$ a diagonal matrix $\hat{D} = (\hat{d}_{ij})$, and a strictly upper-triangular matrix $\hat{U} = (\hat{u}_{ij})$,

$$A = \hat{L} + \hat{D} + \hat{U}$$

with

$$\hat{l}_{ij} = \begin{cases} a_{ij} & i > j \\ 0 & i \leq j \end{cases} \qquad \hat{d}_{ij} = \begin{cases} a_{ij} & i = j \\ 0 & i \neq j \end{cases} \qquad \hat{u}_{ij} = \begin{cases} 0 & i \geq j \\ a_{ij} & i < j \end{cases}$$

Further, we assume that all diagonal entries of A are nonzero; i.e., we assume that $\hat{D}$ is invertible. If this is not so at the outset, we first rearrange the equations so that this condition is satisfied; this can always be done if A is invertible (see Exercise 3.10-5).

In the *Jacobi iteration*, or *method of simultaneous displacements*, one chooses $C = \hat{D}$. This gives the iteration formula

$$\mathbf{x}^{(m)} = (I - \hat{D}^{-1}A)\mathbf{x}^{(m-1)} + \hat{D}^{-1}\mathbf{b}$$

or $\mathbf{x}^{(m)} = B\mathbf{x}^{(m-1)} + \mathbf{c}$, with

$$B = I - \hat{D}^{-1}A = I - \hat{D}^{-1}(\hat{L} + \hat{D} + \hat{U}) = -\hat{D}^{-1}(\hat{L} + \hat{U})$$

and

$$\mathbf{c} = \hat{D}^{-1}\mathbf{b}$$

which agrees with our earlier description (3.73).

Algorithm 3.8 Jacobi iteration Given the linear system $A\mathbf{x} = \mathbf{b}$ of order n whose coefficient matrix $A = (a_{ij})$ has all diagonal entries nonzero.

Calculate the entries of $B = (b_{ij})$ and of $\mathbf{c} = (c_i)$ by

$$b_{ij} = \begin{cases} -a_{ij}/a_{ii} & i \neq j \\ 0 & i = j \end{cases}$$

$$c_i = b_i/a_{ii} \qquad \text{all } i$$

Pick an n-vector $\mathbf{x}^{(0)}$, for example, $\mathbf{x}^{(0)} = \mathbf{0}$
For $m = 1, 2, \ldots$, until satisfied, do:

$\quad$ Set $x_i^{(m)} = \sum_{j \neq i} b_{ij}x_j^{(m-1)} + c_i \qquad i = 1, \ldots, n$

If some matrix norm of B is less than 1, the sequence $\mathbf{x}^{(0)}, \mathbf{x}^{(1)}, \mathbf{x}^{(2)}, \ldots$ so generated converges to the solution of the given linear system.

If Jacobi iteration converges, the diagonal part $\hat{D}$ of A is a good enough approximation to A to give

$$\|B\| = \|I - \hat{D}^{-1}A\| < 1$$

But in this circumstance, one would expect the lower-triangular part $\hat{L} + \hat{D}$ of A to be an even better approximation to A; that is, one would expect to have

$$\|I - (\hat{L} + \hat{D})^{-1}A\| \leq \|I - \hat{D}^{-1}A\| < 1$$

Fixed-point iteration with $C = \hat{L} + \hat{D}$ would then seem a faster convergent iteration than the Jacobi method. Although this is not true in general, it is true for various classes of matrices A, for example, when A is strictly row diagonally dominant, or when A is tridiagonal (and more generally, when A is block-tridiagonal with diagonal diagonal blocks), or when A has positive diagonal entries and nonpositive off-diagonal entries.

Fixed-point iteration with $C = \hat{L} + \hat{D}$ is called *Gauss-Seidel iteration*, or the *method of successive displacements*. In this method, one has

$$\mathbf{x}^{(m+1)} = \mathbf{x}^{(m)} + (\hat{L} + \hat{D})^{-1}(\mathbf{b} - A\mathbf{x}^{(m)})$$

or

$$(\hat{L} + \hat{D})\mathbf{x}^{(m+1)} = (\hat{L} + \hat{D} - A)\mathbf{x}^{(m)} + \mathbf{b}$$

or

$$\hat{D}\mathbf{x}^{(m+1)} = -\hat{L}\mathbf{x}^{(m+1)} - \hat{U}\mathbf{x}^{(m)} + \mathbf{b}$$

giving the formulas

$$x_i^{(m+1)} = \frac{-\sum_{j<i} a_{ij}x_j^{(m+1)} - \sum_{j>i} a_{ij}x_j^{(m)} + b_i}{a_{ii}} \qquad i = 1, \ldots, n$$

Apparently, we can calculate the ith entry of $\mathbf{x}^{(m+1)}$ once we know $x_1^{(m+1)}$, $\ldots, x_{i-1}^{(m+1)}$.

Algorithm 3.9 Gauss-Seidel iteration Given the linear system $A\mathbf{x} = \mathbf{b}$ of order n whose coefficient matrix $A = (a_{ij})$ has all diagonal entries nonzero.

Calculate the entries of $B = (b_{ij})$ and of $\mathbf{c} = (c_i)$ by

$$b_{ij} = \begin{cases} -a_{ij}/a_{ii} & i \neq j \\ 0 & i = j \end{cases}$$

$$c_i = \frac{b_i}{a_{ii}} \qquad \text{all } i \text{ and } j$$

Pick $\mathbf{x}^{(0)}$, for example, $\mathbf{x}^{(0)} = \mathbf{0}$
For $m = 1, 2, \ldots$, until satisfied, do:

> For $i = 1, \ldots, n$, do:
>> Set $x_i^{(m)} = \sum_{j=1}^{i-1} b_{ij} x_j^{(m)} + \sum_{j=i+1}^{n} b_{ij} x_j^{(m-1)} + c_i$

If some matrix norm of $(\hat{L} + \hat{D})^{-1}\hat{U}$ is less than one, then the sequence $\mathbf{x}^{(0)}, \mathbf{x}^{(1)}, \ldots$ so generated converges to the solution of the given system.

The vectors $\mathbf{x}^{(1)}, \mathbf{x}^{(2)}, \mathbf{x}^{(3)}$ resulting from Gauss-Seidel iteration applied to the first linear system of Example 3.15 are listed in Table 3.1. Note that, for this example, Gauss-Seidel iteration converges much faster than does Jacobi iteration. After three steps, the accuracy is already better than that obtained at the end of six steps of Jacobi iteration.

In Jacobi iteration, the entries of $\mathbf{x}^{(m)}$ are used only in the calculation of the next iterate $\mathbf{x}^{(m+1)}$, while in Gauss-Seidel iteration, each entry of $\mathbf{x}^{(m)}$ is already used in the calculation of all succeeding entries of $\mathbf{x}^{(m)}$; hence the names simultaneous displacement and successive displacement. In particular, Jacobi iteration requires that *two* iterates be kept in memory, while Gauss-Seidel iteration requires only one vector.

Gauss-Seidel iteration can be shown to converge if the coefficient matrix A is strictly (row) diagonally dominant. It also converges if A is positive definite, i.e., if A is real symmetric and for all nonzero vectors $\mathbf{y}$,

$$\mathbf{y}^T A \mathbf{y} > 0$$

As pointed out earlier, iterative methods are usually applied to large linear systems with a sparse coefficient matrix. For sparse matrices, the number of nonzero entries is small, and hence the number of arithmetic operations to be performed per step is small. Moreover, iterative methods are less vulnerable to the growth of round-off error. Only the size of the round-off generated in a single iteration is important. On the other hand, iterative methods will not always converge, and even when they do converge, they may require a prohibitively large number of iterations. For large systems, the total number of iterations required for convergence to four or five places may be of the order of several hundred.

Example 3.16 Solve the linear system

$$
\begin{aligned}
2x_1 \quad - \quad x_2 \qquad\qquad &= 1 \\
-x_{i-1} + 2x_i \quad - \quad x_{i+1} &= 0 \qquad i = 2, \ldots, n-1 \\
- \quad x_{n-1} + 2x_n \quad &= 1
\end{aligned}
$$

for $n = 20$ by Gauss-Seidel iteration. Use the termination criterion (3.79b) with $\varepsilon = 10^{-6}$, and begin with the initial approximation $\mathbf{x}^{(0)} = \mathbf{0}$.

The coefficient matrix of this system is sparse; it is tridiagonal. Below we reproduce a FORTRAN program which solves this problem.

FORTRAN PROGRAM FOR EXAMPLE 3.16

```
      DIMENSION AL(20),AD(20),AR(20),B(20),X(20)
      DO 10 J = 1,20
      AL(J) = −1.
      AD(J) = 2.
      AR(J) = −1.
      B(J) = 0.
   10 X(J) = 0.
      B(1) = 1.
      B(20) = 1.
C
      CALL GSTRI(20,AL,AD,AR,B,X,1.E − 6)
      PRINT 600, (J,X(J),J = 1,20)
  600 FORMAT (16H1THE SOLUTION IS/(I5,E20.8))
      STOP
      END
C
      SUBROUTINE GSTRI(N,AL,AD,AR,B,X,EPS)
C
C     TO SOLVE A TRIDIAGONAL LINEAR SYSTEM OF THE FORM
C         AD(1)*X(1) + AR(1)*X(2)               = B(1)
C         AL(I)*X(I − 1) + AD(I)*X(I) + AR(I)*X(I + 1) = B(I), I = 2, . . . ,
C             N − 1, AL(N)*X(N − 1) + AD(N)*X(N) = B(N)
C     BY GAUSS-SEIDEL ITERATION. STARTING WITH THE GIVEN X,
C     THE ITERATION IS CARRIED OUT UNTIL EITHER MORE THAN
C     1000 STEPS HAVE BEEN TAKEN OR ELSE THE RELATIVE CHANGE
C     IN X DURING AN ITERATION STEP IS LESS THAN THE GIVEN
C     EPS.
C
      DIMENSION AL(1),AD(1),AR(1),B(1),X(1)
      DO 10 J = 1,N
      IF (AD(J) .EQ. 0.)                      GO TO 999
      AL(J) = AL(J)/AD(J)
      AR(J) = AR(J)/AD(J)
   10 B(J) = B(J)/AD(J)
C
      DO 30 ITER = 1,1000
      I = 1
      DIFMAX = 0.
      XMAX = 0.
C
      XNEW = B(1) − AR(1)*X(2)
                                             GO TO 13
   11 XNEW = B(N) − AL(N)*X(N − 1)
                                             GO TO 13
   12 XNEW = B(I) − AL(I)*X(I − 1) − AR(I)*X(I + 1)
C
   13 DIFF = XNEW − X(I)
      X(I) = XNEW
      XMAX = AMAX1(XMAX,ABS(XNEW))
      DIFMAX = AMAX1(DIFMAX,ABS(DIFF))
```

```
C
        I = I + 1
        IF (I − N)                                    12,11,19
C
     19 TEST = DIFMAX/XMAX
        IF (TEST .LT. EPS)                    RETURN
     30 CONTINUE
    999 PRINT 600
    600 FORMAT (23H ITERATION UNSUCCESSFUL)
                                             RETURN
        END
```

     To conserve space, the table below gives the value of $\|\mathbf{x}^{(m)} - \mathbf{x}^{(m-1)}\|_\infty / \|\mathbf{x}^{(m-1)}\|_\infty$ and the components $x_1^{(m)}$ and $x_{10}^{(m)}$ of $\mathbf{x}^{(m)}$ for selected values of m. Since, as is easily verified, the exact solution of this problem is $x_i = 1$, all i, the actual error can be seen at once. After 456 iterations, the termination criterion is satisfied; i.e.,

$$\frac{\|\mathbf{x}^{(456)} - \mathbf{x}^{(455)}\|_\infty}{\|\mathbf{x}^{(456)}\|_\infty} < 10^{-6}$$

But note that the error satisfies only

$$\|\mathbf{x} - \mathbf{x}^{(456)}\|_\infty \approx 5 \cdot 10^{-5}$$

showing that this error criterion is not always a satisfactory indicator of the accuracy of the computed solution, as was pointed out earlier.

EXERCISES

3.8-1. Prove: If the sequence $\mathbf{x}^{(0)}, \mathbf{x}^{(1)}, \mathbf{x}^{(2)}, \ldots$ of n-vectors converges to the n-vector $\mathbf{x}$ in the sense that $\lim_{m \to \infty} \|\mathbf{x} - \mathbf{x}^{(m)}\|_\infty = 0$, then (3.72) holds.

Table 3.3

m	$x_1^{(m)}$	$x_{10}^{(m)}$	$\dfrac{\|\mathbf{x}^{(m)} - \mathbf{x}^{(m-1)}\|_\infty}{\|\mathbf{x}^{(m)}\|_\infty}$	$r_{\min}^{(m)}$	$r_{\max}^{(m)}$
30	0.89844144	0.34722738	1.63 (−2)	0.963 · · ·	0.988 · · ·
100	0.97746982	0.86366559	3.15 (−3)	0.977969 · · ·	0.977976 · · ·
140	0.99082111	0.94448888	1.27 (−2)	0.97778708 · · ·	0.97779869 · · ·
· · ·	· · · · · · · · ·	· · · · · · · · ·	· · · · · · · · ·	· · · · · · · · · · · · ·	· · · · · · · · · · · · ·
200	0.99761522	0.98557816	3.28 (−4)	0.97778641 · · ·	0.97778660 · · ·
· · ·	· · · · · · · · ·	· · · · · · · · ·	· · · · · · · · ·	· · · · · · · · · · · · ·	· · · · · · · · · · · · ·
300	0.99974774	0.99847447	3.47 (−5)	0.97778640 · · ·	0.97778640 · · ·
400	0.99997332	0.99983863	3.67 (−6)	0.97778640 · · ·	0.97778640 · · ·
455	0.99999224	0.99995309	1.07 (−6)	0.97778640 · · ·	0.97778640 · · ·
456	0.99999275	0.99995615	9.60 (−7)	0.97778640 · · ·	0.97778640 · · ·

3.8-2. Show that fixed-point iteration with the iteration matrix

$$B = \begin{bmatrix} 0.9 & 1,000 \\ 0 & 0.9 \end{bmatrix}$$

converges even though $\|B\|_1$, $\|B\|_\infty > 1,000$. (*Hint:* Show that $\|B^m\|_\infty \to 0$ as $m \to \infty$.)

3.8-3. Let B be a *strictly* upper-triangular matrix; that is, B is upper-triangular with all diagonal entries equal to zero. Show that fixed-point iteration with such a B converges regardless of the size of its nonzero entries. (*Hint:* Assuming B to be of order n, show that $B^n = 0$.)

3.8-4. Use Exercise 3.8-3 to show that both Jacobi and Gauss-Seidel iterations converge in a finite number of steps whenever A is an (invertible) upper-triangular matrix.

3.8-5. Solve the system

$$\begin{bmatrix} 4 & -1 & 0 & 0 \\ -1 & 4 & -1 & 0 \\ 0 & -1 & 4 & -1 \\ 0 & 0 & -1 & 4 \end{bmatrix} \begin{bmatrix} x_1 \\ x_2 \\ x_3 \\ x_4 \end{bmatrix} = \begin{bmatrix} 1 \\ 1 \\ 1 \\ 1 \end{bmatrix}$$

by Jacobi iteration and by Gauss-Seidel iteration. Compare their rates of convergence.

3.8-6. Obtain the solution of the system

$$\begin{bmatrix} 6 & -4 & 1 & 0 & 0 \\ -4 & 6 & -4 & 1 & 0 \\ 1 & -4 & 6 & -4 & 1 \\ 0 & 1 & -4 & 6 & -4 \\ 0 & 0 & 1 & -4 & 6 \end{bmatrix} \begin{bmatrix} x_1 \\ x_2 \\ x_3 \\ x_4 \\ x_5 \end{bmatrix} = \begin{bmatrix} 0 \\ 0 \\ 0 \\ 0 \\ 1 \end{bmatrix}$$

by Gauss-Seidel iteration.

3.8-7. Derive a factorization of the coefficient matrix of the system in 3.8-5 by Algorithm 3.3; then use iterative improvement to solve the system, starting with the same initial guess as in Exercise 3.8-5, and compare with the results of Exercise 3.8-5. Estimate the work (= floating-point operations) required for each of the three methods to get an approximate solution of absolute accuracy less than 10^{-6}.

3.8-8. Prove that Jacobi iteration converges if the coefficient matrix A of the system is strictly column diagonally dominant, i.e.,

$$|a_{jj}| > \sum_{i \neq j} |a_{ij}| \qquad j = 1, \ldots, n$$

and $|a_{jj}| = 1$, all j
(*Hint;* Use the 1-norm.)

3.9 EIGENVALUES AND THE CONVERGENCE OF FIXED-POINT ITERATION

Let $x^{(0)}$, $x^{(1)}$, $x^{(2)}$, . . . be a sequence generated by fixed-point iteration,

$$x^{(m+1)} = Bx^{(m)} + c \qquad m = 0, 1, 2, \ldots$$

If $\mathbf{x}$ is a fixed point for this iteration, i.e., if

$$\mathbf{x} = B\mathbf{x} + \mathbf{c}$$

then the error

$$\mathbf{e}^{(m)} = \mathbf{x} - \mathbf{x}^{(m)}$$

in the mth iterate is given by

$$\mathbf{e}^{(m)} = B^m \mathbf{e}^{(0)} \qquad m = 0, 1, 2, \ldots$$

as we saw in the proof of Lemma 3.4. It follows that convergence or non-convergence of fixed-point iteration is intimately connected with the behavior of sequences of the form

$$\mathbf{z}, B\mathbf{z}, B^2\mathbf{z}, B^3\mathbf{z}, \ldots \tag{3.82}$$

where $\mathbf{z}$ is some fixed n-vector, for example, $\mathbf{z} = \mathbf{e}^{(0)}$. For the understanding of such sequences, the algebraic concept of an eigenvalue of a matrix turns out to be essential.

We say that the (real or complex) number λ is an *eigenvalue of the matrix B* provided for some nonzero (real or complex) vector $\mathbf{y}$,

$$B\mathbf{y} = \lambda\mathbf{y} \tag{3.83}$$

The n-vector $\mathbf{y}$ is then called an *eigenvector* of B belonging to the eigenvalue λ. We can write (3.83) in the form

$$(B - \lambda I)\mathbf{y} = \mathbf{0} \tag{3.84}$$

Since $\mathbf{y}$ is to be a nonzero vector, we see that λ is an eigenvalue of B if and only if the homogeneous system (3.84) has nontrivial solutions. Hence the following lemma is a consequence of Theorem 3.4.

Lemma 3.5 The number λ is an eigenvalue for the matrix B if and only if $(B - \lambda I)$ is not invertible.

Note that (3.83) or (3.84) determines an eigenvector for λ only up to scalar multiples. If $\mathbf{y}$ is an eigenvector belonging to λ, and $\mathbf{z}$ is a scalar multiple of $\mathbf{y}$, $\mathbf{z} = \alpha\mathbf{y}$, then $\mathbf{z}$ is also an eigenvector belonging to λ, since

$$B\mathbf{z} = B(\alpha\mathbf{y}) = \alpha(B\mathbf{y}) = \alpha(\lambda\mathbf{y}) = \lambda(\alpha\mathbf{y}) = \lambda\mathbf{z}$$

Examples The identity matrix I satisfies

$$I\mathbf{y} = \mathbf{y} = 1\mathbf{y}$$

for every vector $\mathbf{y}$. Hence 1 is an eigenvalue of I, and every nonzero vector is an eigenvector for I belonging to 1. Since a vector can belong to only one eigenvalue (or none), it follows that 1 is the only eigenvalue of I.

The null matrix O has the number 0 as its one and only eigenvalue. The matrix

$$B = \begin{bmatrix} 1 & 2 & 0 \\ 2 & 1 & 0 \\ 0 & 0 & -1 \end{bmatrix}$$

has the eigenvalue -1, since $B\mathbf{i}_3 = -\mathbf{i}_3$. Also, $B(\mathbf{i}_1 + \mathbf{i}_2) = 3(\mathbf{i}_1 + \mathbf{i}_2)$, so that $\lambda = 3$ is also an eigenvalue for B. Finally, $B(\mathbf{i}_1 - \mathbf{i}_2) = -(\mathbf{i}_1 - \mathbf{i}_2)$, so that the eigenvalue -1 has the two linearly independent eigenvectors $\mathbf{i}_3$ and $(\mathbf{i}_1 - \mathbf{i}_2)$.

If the matrix $B = (b_{ij})$ is upper-triangular, then λ is an eigenvalue of B if and only if $\lambda = b_{ii}$ for some i. For the matrix $(B - \lambda I)$ is then also upper-triangular; hence, by Theorem 3.6, $(B - \lambda I)$ is not invertible if and only if one of its diagonal entries is zero, i.e., if and only if $b_{ii} - \lambda = 0$ for some i. Hence the set of eigenvalues of a triangular matrix coincides with the set of numbers to be found on its diagonal.

In particular, the only eigenvalue of the matrix

$$B = \begin{bmatrix} 0 & 0 & 1 \\ 0 & 0 & 0 \\ 0 & 0 & 0 \end{bmatrix}$$

is the number 0, and both $\mathbf{i}_1$ and $\mathbf{i}_2$ are eigenvectors for this B belonging to this eigenvalue. Any other eigenvector of B must be a linear combination of these two eigenvectors. For suppose that the nonzero 3-vector $\mathbf{y}$ $(= y_1\mathbf{i}_1 + y_2\mathbf{i}_2 + y_3\mathbf{i}_3)$ is an eigenvector for B (belonging therefore to the only eigenvalue 0). Then

$$\begin{aligned} \mathbf{0} = 0\mathbf{y} = B\mathbf{y} &= y_1 B\mathbf{i}_1 + y_2 B\mathbf{i}_2 + y_3 B\mathbf{i}_3 \\ &= \mathbf{0} + \mathbf{0} + y_3 B\mathbf{i}_3 \end{aligned}$$

Since $B\mathbf{i}_3 = \mathbf{i}_1 \neq \mathbf{0}$, it follows that $y_3 = 0$, that is, $\mathbf{y} = y_1\mathbf{i}_1 + y_2\mathbf{i}_2$, showing that $\mathbf{y}$ is a linear combination of the eigenvectors $\mathbf{i}_1$ and $\mathbf{i}_2$.

We present a more detailed discussion of eigenvalues and eigenvectors in a later section, after we have considered determinants. In this section, we merely show the connection between eigenvalues and the convergence of fixed-point iteration, as much for a better understanding of fixed-point iteration as to motivate consideration of eigenvalues.

To begin with, we observe that no eigenvalue of the matrix B can be bigger in absolute value than any matrix norm of B. For if λ is an eigenvalue of B with $\mathbf{y}$ an associated nonzero eigenvector, then

$$|\lambda| \, \|\mathbf{y}\| = \|\lambda \mathbf{y}\| = \|B\mathbf{y}\| \leq \|B\| \, \|\mathbf{y}\|$$

Since $\mathbf{y} \neq \mathbf{0}$, we can divide through by $\|\mathbf{y}\| \neq 0$ to get

$$|\lambda| \leq \|B\| \tag{3.85}$$

regardless of the particular vector norm and corresponding matrix norm used. Hence we get from Theorem 3.10 the following lemma.

Lemma 3.6 Iteration with the iteration matrix B cannot converge (for all initial guesses $\mathbf{x}^{(0)}$) if B has an eigenvalue of modulus ≥ 1.

To give an example, consider the iteration matrix B for Jacobi iteration applied to the second system in Example 3.15,

$$
B = \begin{bmatrix} 0 & -2.5 & -2.5 \\ -2.5 & 0 & -2.5 \\ -2.5 & -2.5 & 0 \end{bmatrix}
$$

Hence $B(\mathbf{i}_1 + \mathbf{i}_2 + \mathbf{i}_3) = -5(\mathbf{i}_1 + \mathbf{i}_2 + \mathbf{i}_3)$, so that $\lambda = -5$ is an eigenvalue for B. Since this eigenvalue is greater than one in absolute value, iteration must therefore fail to converge, by Lemma 3.6 (at least for some choice of $\mathbf{x}^{(0)}$), as it did in Example 3.15.

Consider now, once more, the sequence

$$\mathbf{z}, B\mathbf{z}, B^2\mathbf{z}, B^3\mathbf{z}, \ldots$$

in (3.82), and assume that we can write $\mathbf{z}$ as a sum of eigenvectors of B, that is,

$$\mathbf{z} = \mathbf{y}_1 + \mathbf{y}_2 + \cdots + \mathbf{y}_r \tag{3.86}$$

where

$$B\mathbf{y}_i = \lambda_i \mathbf{y}_i \qquad i = 1, \ldots, r$$

The mth term in the sequence (3.82) then has the simple form

$$B^m\mathbf{z} = \lambda_1{}^m\mathbf{y}_1 + \lambda_2{}^m\mathbf{y}_2 + \cdots + \lambda_r{}^m\mathbf{y}_r \tag{3.87}$$

Hence the behavior of the *vector* sequence (3.82) is completely determined by the simple *numerical* sequences

$$\lambda_i{}^0, \lambda_i{}^1, \lambda_i{}^2, \lambda_i{}^3, \ldots \qquad i = 1, \ldots, r$$

It follows, for example, that

$$\lim_{m \to \infty} B^m\mathbf{z} = \mathbf{0} \qquad \text{if } |\lambda_i| < 1, \text{ for all } i \tag{3.88}$$

By taking, in particular,

$$\mathbf{z} = \mathbf{e}^{(0)} = \mathbf{x} - \mathbf{x}^{(0)}$$

the error in the initial guess for fixed-point iteration, we get that fixed-point iteration converges if all eigenvalues of the iteration matrix B are less than one in absolute value, and if $\mathbf{e}^{(0)}$ can be written as a sum of eigenvectors of B.

We take a moment to discuss this second assumption. Since we do not know $e^{(0)}$, we can be sure that $e^{(0)}$ can be written as a sum of eigenvectors of the $n \times n$ matrix B only if we know that every n-vector can be written as a sum of eigenvectors of B. But then we are asking, in effect, that B have enough eigenvectors to staff a basis. A basis for all n-vectors which consists entirely of eigenvectors for the $n \times n$ matrix B is called a *complete* set of eigenvectors for B. Clearly, if $z_1, \ldots, z_n$ is a complete set of eigenvectors for the $n \times n$ matrix B—hence a basis for all n-vectors—then any particular n-vector z can be written as a linear combination of these eigenvectors,

$$z = a_1 z_1 + a_2 z_2 + \cdots + a_n z_n$$

for suitable coefficients $a_1, \ldots, a_n$. If $a_i \neq 0$, then $y_i = a_i z_i$ is also an eigenvector for B, while if $a_i = 0$, we can drop the term $a_i z_i$ from the sum without loss. In this way, we obtain z as a sum of eigenvectors for B (except for the uninteresting case $z = 0$).

Unfortunately, not every matrix has a complete set of eigenvectors, as we saw earlier for the example

$$B = \begin{bmatrix} 0 & 0 & 1 \\ 0 & 0 & 0 \\ 0 & 0 & 0 \end{bmatrix}$$

On the other hand, this annoying assumption that B has a complete set of eigenvectors is not really necessary in order to prove (3.88) for arbitrary z. One can prove (by tools beyond the level of this book) that, for all z,

$$\lim_{m \to \infty} B^m z = 0 \qquad \text{if all eigenvalues of } B \text{ are less than 1 in absolute value}$$

Combining this statement with Lemma 3.6 establishes the following theorem.

Theorem 3.11   Fixed-point iteration with the iteration matrix B converges (regardless of the initial guess $x^{(0)}$) if and only if all eigenvalues of B are less than one in absolute value.

Iteration with the iteration matrix

$$B = \begin{bmatrix} 0.9 & 0.9 \\ 0 & 0 \end{bmatrix}$$

for instance, has to converge, as we established with some effort in the preceding section. For B is upper-triangular; hence its eigenvalues can be read off its diagonal; i.e., the eigenvalues of B are 0.9 and 0. Since these numbers are less than one in absolute value, convergence follows. In fact, Theorem 3.11 guarantees convergence even for the iteration matrix

$$B = \begin{bmatrix} 0.9 & 10^{10} \\ 0 & 0 \end{bmatrix}$$

although $\|B\|_\infty \geq 10^{10}$, so that for "almost all" possible initial guesses $\mathbf{x}^{(0)}$,

$$\|\mathbf{e}^{(0)}\|_\infty \ll \|\mathbf{e}^{(1)}\|_\infty$$

If, for example, $\mathbf{c} = \mathbf{0}$, so that $\mathbf{x} = \mathbf{0}$, and $\mathbf{x}^{(0)} = \mathbf{i}_1 + \mathbf{i}_2$, then

$$\mathbf{x}^{(m)} = (0.9 + 10^{10})(0.9)^{m-1}\mathbf{i}_1$$

Hence $\|\mathbf{e}^{(0)}\|_\infty = 1$, while $\|\mathbf{e}^{(1)}\|_\infty \geq 10^{10}$, and it is only for $m \geq 22$ that $\|\mathbf{e}^{(m)}\|_\infty$ is once again ≤ 1.

Although there are many other reasons for wanting to know the eigenvalues of a given matrix (see Sec. 3.11), Theorem 3.11 by itself makes it worthwhile to consider the problem of estimating or calculating eigenvalues. We discuss this problem in some detail in Sec. 3.11. Here we point out how fixed-point iteration itself can at times be used to calculate the absolutely largest eigenvalue of a matrix.

For this we return to the setup of (3.86) and (3.87) and make the following additional assumptions. We assume that the λ_i's are ordered by magnitude,

$$|\lambda_1| \geq |\lambda_2| \geq \cdots \geq |\lambda_r|$$

which can always be achieved by proper ordering of the $\mathbf{y}_i$'s. Further, we assume that

$$|\lambda_1| > |\lambda_2| \tag{3.89}$$

This assumption requires not only that λ_1 be different from all the other λ_i's [which can always be achieved by merely adding all $\mathbf{y}_i$'s in (3.86) which belong to λ_1, thereby getting just one eigenvector belonging to λ_1], but also that there be no other λ_i of the *same magnitude* as λ_1, and it is this part that makes (3.89) a nontrivial assumption.

Then, on dividing both sides of (3.87) by $\lambda_1{}^m$, we get that

$$(\lambda_1{}^{-1}B)^m\mathbf{z} = \mathbf{y}_1 + \sum_{i=2}^{r} \left(\frac{\lambda_i}{\lambda_1}\right)^m \mathbf{y}_i \qquad m = 0, 1, 2, \ldots$$

By our assumptions,

$$\left|\frac{\lambda_i}{\lambda_1}\right| < 1 \qquad i = 2, \ldots, r$$

Hence we conclude that

$$\lim_{m \to \infty} (\lambda_1{}^{-1}B)^m\mathbf{z} = \mathbf{y}_1 \tag{3.90}$$

In words, if $\mathbf{z}$ can be written in the form (3.86) in terms of eigenvectors of B so that the eigenvalue λ_1 corresponding to $\mathbf{y}_1$ is absolutely bigger than all the other eigenvalues, then a properly scaled version of $B^m\mathbf{z}$ converges to $\mathbf{y}_1$.

Actually, it is not necessary to scale $B^m z$ by λ_1^{-m} (which is not possible anyway if λ_1 is not known) to have the scaled sequence converge to some eigenvector belonging to λ_1. It is sufficient to pick an i so that the ith entry of y_1 is not zero and to scale each $B^m z$ so as to make its ith entry equal to 1. If we set

$$z^{(m)} = (i\text{th entry of } B^m z)^{-1} B^m z$$

then also

$$z^{(m)} = [i\text{th entry of } (\lambda_1^{-1} B)^m z]^{-1} (\lambda_1^{-1} B)^m z \qquad \text{for all } m$$

and with (3.90), we get that

$$\lim_{m \to \infty} z^{(m)} = y_1^* = (i\text{th entry of } y_1)^{-1} y_1 \tag{3.91}$$

Note that if i is picked so that the ith entry of y_1 is zero (as might happen in practice since i has to be picked without knowing y_1), then $\|z^{(m)}\| \to \infty$. One therefore would monitor the size of $z^{(m)}$, and should $\|z^{(m)}\|$ grow too large, one would change i so as to make the presently largest entry of $z^{(m)}$ equal to 1.

It follows that the sequence $z^{(0)}, z^{(1)}, z^{(2)}, \ldots$ converges to an eigenvector y_1^* belonging to the absolutely largest eigenvalue of B. But this implies that, for sufficiently large m,

$$B z^{(m)} \approx B y_1^* = \lambda_1 y_1^* \approx \lambda_1 z^{(m)}$$

Hence, for any j for which the jth entry of y_1 (or y_1^*) is not zero,

$$\frac{j\text{th entry of } B^{m+1} z}{j\text{th entry of } B^m z} = \frac{j\text{th entry of } B z^{(m)}}{j\text{th entry of } z^{(m)}} \approx \lambda_1 \tag{3.92}$$

Example 3.17 We saw earlier that the matrix

$$B = \begin{bmatrix} 1 & 2 & 0 \\ 2 & 1 & 0 \\ 0 & 0 & -1 \end{bmatrix}$$

has the eigenvectors $z_1 = i_1 + i_2$, $z_2 = i_1 - i_2$, $z_3 = i_3$ with corresponding eigenvalues $\lambda_1 = 3$, $\lambda_2 = \lambda_3 = -1$. These eigenvectors are linearly independent (see Exercise 3.1-10), hence form a basis for all 3-vectors. It follows that every 3-vector can be written as a sum of eigenvectors of B. In particular, the vector z given by $z^T = [1 \quad 2 \quad 3]$ can be written

$$z = y_1 + y_2$$

where

$$y_1 = 1.5 z_1 \qquad y_2 = -0.5 z_2 + 3 z_3$$

In Table 3.4, we have listed $B^m z$ and $z^{(m)}$ for $m = 0, \ldots, 5$. $z^{(m)}$ has been scaled to

Table 3.4

m		0	1	2	3	4	5
	1	1	5	13	41	121	365
$B^m\mathbf{z}$	2	2	4	14	40	122	364
	3	3	3	3	3	3	3
	1		1.0	1.00	1.000	1.000	1.000
$\mathbf{z}^{(m)}$	2		0.8	1.08	0.976	1.008	0.997
	3		0.6	0.23	0.073	0.025	0.008

make its first entry equal to 1. Evidently, the $\mathbf{z}^{(m)}$ converge to the eigenvector $\mathbf{y}_1^* = \mathbf{i}_1 + \mathbf{i}_2$ belonging to $\lambda_1 = 3$. Further, we calculate the ratios mentioned in (3.92). The ratios of first entries ($j = 1$) are

$$5, \quad 2.6, \quad 3.153 \cdots, \quad 2.951 \cdots, \quad 3.016 \cdots$$

From the second entries we get

$$2, \quad 3.5, \quad 2.857 \cdots, \quad 3.05 \cdots, \quad 2.983 \cdots$$

while the third entries give

$$1, \quad 1.0, \quad 1.000 \cdots, \quad 1.000 \cdots, \quad 1.000 \cdots$$

Hence the ratios of first entries, and of second entries, converge quite rapidly to $3 = \lambda_1$, while the ratios of third entries do not, illustrating that (3.92) holds only when the jth entry of the limit vector $\mathbf{y}_1^*$ is not zero.

The *power method* for the calculation of the absolutely largest eigenvalue of a given matrix B is based on (3.92). One picks some vector $\mathbf{z}$, for example, $\mathbf{z} = \mathbf{i}_1$; generates the (first few) terms of the sequence (3.82); and calculates the ratios mentioned in (3.92) as one goes along. As soon as these ratios agree sufficiently with each other, their common value is accepted as an approximation to the absolutely largest eigenvalue of B. If no scaling is used, the terms of the sequence (3.82) usually either grow without bound or else the sequence converges to $\mathbf{0}$. Hence scaling, such as the normalization

$$\mathbf{z}^{(m)} = (i\text{th entry of } B^m\mathbf{z})^{-1}B^m\mathbf{z} \qquad \text{for some fixed } i$$

serves to avoid possible overflow or underflow during the calculations.

Formula (3.92) is valid under much less restrictive assumptions on B than we used to prove it here. Essentially, a suitably scaled version of the sequence (3.82) converges to an eigenvector of B belonging to an eigenvalue λ of B of maximum modulus unless B has also an eigenvalue $\mu \neq \lambda$ for which $|\mu| = |\lambda|$.

We do not give a formal description of the power method since this would require consideration of many special cases whose understanding requires a good grasp of similarity theory. Instead, we illustrate by some simple examples what can happen when the power method is used.

1. We saw already, in Example 3.17, that (3.92) need not hold for all ratios of entries. Hence one has to allow for such an eventuality when deciding whether or not all ratios agree sufficiently.

2. If $B = \begin{bmatrix} 1 & 0 \\ 0 & -1 \end{bmatrix}$ and $z = \begin{bmatrix} 1 \\ 1 \end{bmatrix}$, then $B^m z = \begin{bmatrix} 1 \\ (-1)^m \end{bmatrix}$, all m. It follows that one ratio is always 1, the other always -1, reflecting the fact that B has the two eigenvalues 1 and -1 which are equal in absolute value.

If $B = \begin{bmatrix} 0 & 1 \\ -1 & 0 \end{bmatrix}$ and $z = \begin{bmatrix} 1 \\ 1 \end{bmatrix}$, then $z = \begin{bmatrix} 1 \\ 1 \end{bmatrix}$, $Bz = \begin{bmatrix} 1 \\ -1 \end{bmatrix}$, $B^2 z = \begin{bmatrix} -1 \\ -1 \end{bmatrix}$, $B^3 z = \begin{bmatrix} -1 \\ 1 \end{bmatrix}$, $B^4 z = \begin{bmatrix} 1 \\ 1 \end{bmatrix} = z$, etc. Hence here too, one ratio is always 1, the other always -1, but now neither number is an eigenvalue for B. The fact that, in this case, the sequence (3.82) does not converge indicates that B has two eigenvalues of the same modulus, namely, the numbers $\sqrt{-1}$ and $-\sqrt{-1}$. Finally, if $B = \begin{bmatrix} 1 & 2 \\ -2 & 1 \end{bmatrix}$ and $z = \begin{bmatrix} 1 \\ 1 \end{bmatrix}$, then

$$Bz = \begin{bmatrix} 3 \\ -1 \end{bmatrix} \qquad B^2 z = \begin{bmatrix} 1 \\ -7 \end{bmatrix} \qquad B^3 z = \begin{bmatrix} -13 \\ -9 \end{bmatrix} \qquad B^4 z = \begin{bmatrix} -31 \\ 17 \end{bmatrix}$$

$$B^5 z = \begin{bmatrix} 3 \\ 79 \end{bmatrix} \qquad \cdots$$

and the ratios of corresponding entries show no regularity whatsoever. Again, this indicates that B has two eigenvalues of the same modulus. In each of these three examples, it is possible to extract information about the two absolutely equal eigenvalues from the sequence (3.82), but we do not take the time to explain how this might be done. We merely point out that it might be difficult at times to distinguish this behavior from behavior due to the fact that the sequence has not yet settled down.

3. The following examples show yet another difficulty, very slow convergence.

With $B = \begin{bmatrix} 1 & 1 \\ 0 & 1 \end{bmatrix}$, $z = \begin{bmatrix} 1 \\ 1 \end{bmatrix}$, we get

$$Bz = \begin{bmatrix} 2 \\ 1 \end{bmatrix} \qquad B^2 z = \begin{bmatrix} 3 \\ 1 \end{bmatrix}$$

and in general

$$B^m\mathbf{z} = \begin{bmatrix} m + 1 \\ 1 \end{bmatrix} \quad \text{all } m$$

Hence the ratios computed from the entries of $B^m\mathbf{z}$ and $B^{m-1}\mathbf{z}$ are

$$\frac{m + 1}{m} \quad \text{and} \quad 1$$

and the first converges quite slowly to 1. Slow convergence is also evident in the calculations for Example 3.16. In that example, we solved a certain linear system by Gauss-Seidel iteration, getting a sequence $\mathbf{x}^{(0)}, \mathbf{x}^{(1)}, \mathbf{x}^{(2)}, \ldots$ converging to the solution. If B is the iteration matrix for this example, then

$$\mathbf{x}^{(m+1)} - \mathbf{x}^{(m)} = B(\mathbf{x}^{(m)} - \mathbf{x}^{(m-1)}) = \cdots = B^m(\mathbf{x}^{(1)} - \mathbf{x}^{(0)})$$

Hence in this, as in any other instance of fixed-point iteration, the differences of successive iterates form a sequence like that of (3.82), with $\mathbf{z} = \mathbf{x}^{(1)} - \mathbf{x}^{(0)}$. During the calculations for Example 3.16, we also calculated the ratios

$$r_i^{(m)} = \frac{x_i^{(m+1)} - x_i^{(m)}}{x_i^{(m)} - x_i^{(m-1)}} \quad \text{all } i$$

and we listed both

$$r_{\min}^{(m)} = \min_i r_i^{(m)} \quad \text{and} \quad r_{\max}^{(m)} = \max_i r_i^{(m)}$$

in Table 3.3 alongside information about the iterates $\mathbf{x}^{(m)}$. As these numbers indicate,

$$r_i^{(m)} \xrightarrow[m \to \infty]{} 0.97778640 \cdots \quad \text{all } i$$

so that $0.97778640 \cdots$ must be the eigenvalue of maximum modulus of the particular iteration matrix B used. But note that after 100 iterations we only get

$$r_{\min}^{(100)} = 0.977969 \cdots \qquad r_{\max}^{(100)} = 0.977976 \cdots$$

so that the ratios are accurate to three places only. Further, note that all the ratios agree to five places; i.e.,

$$r_{\max}^{(100)} - r_{\min}^{(100)} = 0.000007 \cdots$$

pointing up yet another difficulty: The extent to which all the ratios of entries of $B^m\mathbf{z}$ over corresponding entries of $B^{m-1}\mathbf{z}$ agree is no indication of how far these ratios are from the exact eigenvalue.

EXERCISES

3.9-1. Let a, b be scalars and A be a square matrix. Prove that, if λ is an eigenvalue of A, then $a\lambda + b$ is an eigenvalue of the matrix $aA + bI$. [*Hint:* Consider $(aA + bI)\mathbf{x}$, where $\mathbf{x}$ is an eigenvector of A belonging to λ.]

3.9-2. Prove that if λ is an eigenvalue of the square matrix A and $p(x)$ is some polynomial, then $p(\lambda)$ is an eigenvalue of $p(A)$ (see Exercise 3.1-12).

3.9-3. Let A be the tridiagonal matrix of order n with diagonal entries equal to zero and $a_{i,i+1} = a_{i+1,i} = 1$, $i = 1, \ldots , n - 1$. For $j = 1, \ldots , n$, let $\mathbf{x}^{(j)}$ be the n-vector whose ith entry is $x_i^{(j)} = \sin [ij\pi/(n+1)]$, $i = 1, \ldots , n$. Prove that

$$A\mathbf{x}^{(j)} = 2 \cos \left(\frac{j\pi}{n+1} \right) \mathbf{x}^{(j)} \qquad j = 1, \ldots , n$$

3.9-4. Use Exercises 3.9-1 and 3.9-3 to prove that if A is a tridiagonal matrix with $a_{ii} = d$, $a_{i+1,i} = a_{i,i+1} = e$, all i, then the eigenvalues of A consist of the numbers

$$d + 2e \cos \frac{j\pi}{n+1} \qquad j = 1, \ldots , n$$

3.9-5. Use the power method to estimate the eigenvalue of maximum modulus, and a corresponding eigenvector, for the tridiagonal matrix A of order 20 with $a_{ii} = 4$, $a_{i+1,i} = a_{i,i+1} = -1$, all i, and compare with the exact answer obtained from Exercise 3.9-4.

3.9-6. Try to estimate an eigenvalue of maximum modulus for the matrix A of 3.9-3 (with $n = 21$, say) using the power method. Explain any difficulties you encounter.

3.9-7. The power method breaks down if the matrix has two or more eigenvalues of the same maximum modulus. Discuss how one might use Exercise 3.9-1 to circumvent this difficulty. Try your remedy on the problem in Exercise 3.9-6.

3.9-8. Show that the matrix $B = \begin{bmatrix} 1 & 1 \\ 0 & 1 \end{bmatrix}$ does not have a complete set of eigenvectors.

3.9-9. Let $\mathbf{x}$ and $\mathbf{y}$ be two eigenvectors for the matrix A belonging to the eigenvalues λ and μ of A, respectively. Show that if $\lambda \neq \mu$, then $\mathbf{x}$ and $\mathbf{y}$ are linearly independent.

3.9-10. Use 3.9-9 to show that the matrix $\begin{bmatrix} 1 & 1 \\ 0 & 2 \end{bmatrix}$ must have a complete set of eigenvectors.

3.10 DETERMINANTS

Although the student is assumed to be familiar with the concept of a determinant, we take this section to give the formal definition of determinants and give some of their elementary properties.

Associated with every square matrix A of numbers is a number called the determinant of the matrix and denoted by det (A). If $A = (a_{ij})$ is an $n \times n$ matrix, then the determinant of A is defined by

$$\det (A) = \sum_{\mathbf{p}} \sigma_{\mathbf{p}} \, a_{1,p_1} a_{2,p_2} \cdots \cdot a_{n,p_n} \tag{3.93}$$

where the sum is taken over all $n!$ permutations $\mathbf{p}$ of degree n, and $\sigma_{\mathbf{p}}$ is 1 or -1, depending on whether $\mathbf{p}$ is even or odd (see Sec. 3.1). Hence, if $n = 1$, then

$$\det (A) = \det [a_{11}] = a_{11}$$

while if $n = 2$,

$$\det (A) = \det \begin{bmatrix} a_{11} & a_{12} \\ a_{21} & a_{22} \end{bmatrix} = a_{11}a_{22} - a_{12}a_{21} \tag{3.94}$$

Already, for $n = 3$, six products have to be summed, and for $n = 10$, over 3 million products, each with 10 factors, have to be computed and summed for the evaluation of the right side of (3.93). Hence the definition (3.93) is not very useful for the calculation of determinants. But we give below a list of rules regarding determinants which can be derived quite easily from the definition (3.93). With these rules, we then show how the determinant can be calculated, using the elimination algorithm 3.2, in about $O(n^3)$ [rather than $O(n!)$] operations.

The determinant of a matrix is of importance because of the following theorem.

Theorem 3.12 Let A be an $n \times n$ matrix; then A is invertible if and only if $\det (A) \neq 0$.

We make use of this theorem in the next section, which concerns the calculation of eigenvalues and eigenvectors of a matrix.

For certain matrices, the determinant is calculated quite easily.

Rule 1 If $A = (a_{ij})$ is an upper- (lower-) triangular matrix, then

$$\det (A) = a_{11}a_{22} \cdots a_{nn}$$

i.e., the determinant is just the product of the diagonal entries of A.

For if A is, for example, upper-triangular and $\mathbf{p}$ is any permutation other than the identity permutation, then, for some i, we must have $p_i < i$, and the corresponding product $a_{1,p_1}a_{2,p_2} \cdots a_{n,p_n}$ contains, therefore, the *sub-diagonal*, hence zero, entry a_{i,p_i} of A, and must be zero. Hence, if A is upper-triangular, then the only summand in (3.93) not guaranteed to be zero is the term $a_{11}a_{22} \cdots a_{nn}$ corresponding to the (even) identity permutation $\mathbf{p}^T = [1 \quad 2 \quad \cdots \quad n]$.

In particular,

$$\det (I) = 1 \tag{3.94a}$$

One proves similarly a second rule.

Rule 2 If P is the $n \times n$ permutation matrix given by

$$P\mathbf{i}_j = \mathbf{i}_{p_j} \quad j = 1, \ldots, n$$

with some permutation **p**, then

$$\det(P) = \begin{cases} 1 & \text{if } \mathbf{p} \text{ is even} \\ -1 & \text{if } \mathbf{p} \text{ is odd} \end{cases}$$

Rule 3 If the matrix B results from the matrix A by the interchange of two columns (rows) of A, then $\det(B) = -\det(A)$.

Example

$$\det \begin{bmatrix} 1 & 4 \\ 2 & 3 \end{bmatrix} = 3 - 8 = -5 \quad \text{and} \quad \det \begin{bmatrix} 4 & 1 \\ 3 & 2 \end{bmatrix} = 8 - 3 = 5$$

Consequently, if two columns (rows) of the matrix A agree (so that their interchange leaves A unchanged), then $\det(A) = 0$.

Rule 4 If the matrix B is obtained from the matrix A by multiplying all entries of one column (row) of A by the same number α, then $\det(B) = \alpha \det(A)$.

Example

$$\det \begin{bmatrix} 3 \cdot 1 & 4 \\ 3 \cdot 2 & 3 \end{bmatrix} = 9 - 24 = -15 = 3(-5) = 3 \det \begin{bmatrix} 1 & 4 \\ 2 & 3 \end{bmatrix}$$

Rule 5 Suppose that the three $n \times n$ matrices A_1, A_2, A_3 differ only in one column (row), say the jth, and that the jth column (row) of A_3 is the vector sum of the jth column (row) of A_1 and the jth column (row) of A_2; then

$$\det(A_1) + \det(A_2) = \det(A_3)$$

Example

$$\det \begin{bmatrix} 1 & 2 \\ 2 & 2 \end{bmatrix} + \det \begin{bmatrix} 1 & 2 \\ 1 & 1 \end{bmatrix} = (2 - 4) + (1 - 2) = 3 - 6 = \det \begin{bmatrix} 1 & 2 \\ 3 & 3 \end{bmatrix}$$

Rules 1 to 5 imply Theorems 3.13 and 3.14 below.

Theorem 3.13 If A and B are $n \times n$ matrices, then

$$\det(AB) = \det(A)\det(B)$$

Theorem 3.14 If A is an $n \times n$ matrix and $\mathbf{x} = (x_i)$ and $\mathbf{b}$ are n-vectors such that

$$A\mathbf{x} = \mathbf{b}$$

then, for $j = 1, \ldots, n$,

$$\det(A^{(j)}) = x_j \det(A) \tag{3.95}$$

where $A^{(j)}$ is the matrix one gets on replacing the jth column of A by $\mathbf{b}$.

If A is invertible, i.e. (by Theorem 3.12), if $\det(A) \neq 0$, then one can solve (3.95) for x_j, getting

$$x_j = \frac{\det(A^{(j)})}{\det(A)} \quad j = 1, \ldots, n$$

This is *Cramer's rule* for the entries of the solution **x** of the linear system $A\mathbf{x} = \mathbf{b}$. Because of the difficulty of evaluating determinants, Cramer's rule is, in general, only of *theoretical interest*.

In fact, the fastest known way to calculate $\det(A)$ for an arbitrary $n \times n$ matrix A is to apply the elimination algorithm 3.2 to the matrix A (ignoring the right side).   We saw in Sec. 3.4 that this algorithm produces a factorization

$$A = PLU$$

of A into a permutation matrix P determined by the pivoting strategy **p**, a lower-triangular matrix L with all diagonal entries equal to 1, and the final upper-triangular coefficient matrix $U = (u_{ij})$, which has all the pivots on its diagonal.   By Rule 1, $\det(L) = 1$, while by Rule 2, $\det(P) = 1$ or -1, depending on whether **p** is even or odd, i.e., depending on whether the number of interchanges made during the elimination is even or odd.   Finally, again by Rule 1, $\det(U) = u_{11}u_{22} \cdots u_{nn}$.   Hence

$$\det(A) = (-1)^i u_{11}u_{22} \cdots u_{nn} \tag{3.96}$$

with i the number of interchanges during the elimination algorithm.

Of course, the elimination algorithm 3.2 succeeds (at least theoretically) only when A is invertible.   But if A is not invertible, then the algorithm will so indicate, in which case we know that $\det(A) = 0$, by Theorem 3.12.

Finally, if the matrix A has special properties, it is at times profitable to make use of the following rule.

Rule 6   Expansion of a determinant by minors   The *minor* M_{ij} of the $n \times n$ matrix $A = (a_{ij})$ is, by definition, the determinant of the matrix of order $n - 1$ obtained from A by deleting the ith row and the jth column. One has

For any i: $\det(A) = a_{i1}(-1)^{i+1}M_{i1} + a_{i2}(-1)^{i+2}M_{i2} + \cdots$
$$+ a_{in}(-1)^{i+n}M_{in}$$

and

For any j: $\det(A) = a_{1j}(-1)^{1+j}M_{1j} + a_{2j}(-1)^{2+j}M_{2j} + \cdots$
$$+ a_{nj}(-1)^{n+j}M_{nj}$$

Rule 6 allows us to express a determinant of order n as a sum of determinants of order $n - 1$.   By applying the rule recursively, we can eventually express det (A) as a sum of determinants of order 1. This rule is particularly useful for the calculation of det (A) when A is a sparse matrix, so that most of the summands drop out. For example, expanding in minors for the first row,

$$\det \begin{bmatrix} 0 & 1 & 0 \\ 1 & 0 & 0 \\ 0 & 0 & 1 \end{bmatrix} = 0 \det \begin{bmatrix} 0 & 0 \\ 0 & 1 \end{bmatrix} - 1 \det \begin{bmatrix} 1 & 0 \\ 0 & 1 \end{bmatrix} + 0 \det \begin{bmatrix} 1 & 0 \\ 0 & 0 \end{bmatrix}$$

$$= -1 \det \begin{bmatrix} 1 & 0 \\ 0 & 1 \end{bmatrix} = -1 \cdot 1 = -1$$

EXERCISES

3.10-1. Use Theorem 3.13 and Eq. (3.94a) to prove that if A is invertible, then det $(A) \neq 0$.

3.10-2. Use Theorems 3.14 and 3.4 to prove that if det $(A) \neq 0$, then A is invertible.

3.10-3. Determine the number of arithmetic operations necessary to calculate the solution of a linear system of order 2 (a) by elimination and back-substitution, (b) by Cramer's rule.

3.10-4. If $n = 3$, then direct evaluation of (3.93) takes 12 multiplications and 5 additions. How many multiplications and additions does the evaluation of a determinant of order 3 take if expansion by minors (Rule 6) is used? How many multiplications/divisions and additions are necessary for the same task if elimination is used?

3.10-5. Prove: If the coefficient matrix of the linear system $A\mathbf{x} = \mathbf{b}$ is invertible, then it is always possible to reorder the equations (if necessary) so that the coefficient matrix of the reordered (equivalent) system has all diagonal entries nonzero. [*Hint:* By Theorem 3.12, at least one of the summands in (3.93) must be nonzero if A is invertible.]

3.10-6. Verify Rules 1 to 5 in case all matrices in question are of order 2. Try to prove Rules 4 and 5 for matrices of arbitrary order.

3.10-7. Prove Theorem 3.13 in case A and B are matrices of order 2.

3.10-8. Let A be a tridiagonal matrix of order n; for $p = 1, 2, \ldots, n$, let A_p be the $p \times p$ matrix obtained from A by omitting rows $p + 1, \ldots, n$ and columns $p + 1, \ldots, n$. Use Rule 6 to prove that, with det $(A_0) = 1$,

$$\det (A_p) = a_{pp} \det (A_{p-1}) - a_{p,p-1} a_{p-1,p} \det (A_{p-2}) \qquad p = 2, 3, \ldots, n$$

Write a program for the evaluation of the determinant of a tridiagonal matrix based on this recursion formula.

3.11 THE EIGENVALUE PROBLEM

In Sec. 3.9, eigenvalues were seen to play a major role in the study of convergence of iterative methods for solving linear systems of equations. Eigenvalues are also of great importance in many physical problems. The stability of an aircraft, for example, is determined by the location of the eigenvalues of a certain matrix in the complex plane. The natural frequencies of the vibrations of beams are actually eigenvalues of an (infinite) matrix.

This makes the calculation of the absolutely largest eigenvalue, or even all the eigenvalues, of a given matrix an important computational problem. Since, by Lemma 3.5, the number λ is an eigenvalue of the matrix A if and only if the matrix $(A - \lambda I)$ is not invertible, and since, by Theorem 3.12, the matrix $(A - \lambda I)$ is not invertible if and only if $\det (A - \lambda I) = 0$, it follows that

λ is an eigenvalue for A if and only if $\det (A - \lambda I) = 0$

Hence, finding all the eigenvalues for a given matrix A is equivalent to finding all the roots of the so-called *characteristic equation*

$\det (A - \lambda I) = 0$

The matrix $(A - \lambda I)$ differs from A only in that $-\lambda$ has been subtracted from each diagonal entry of A. If we use the *Kronecker symbol* δ_{ij} to denote the (i,j) entry of the identity matrix, so that

$$\delta_{ij} = \begin{cases} 1 & \text{if } i = j \\ 0 & \text{if } i \neq j \end{cases}$$

then

(i,j) entry of $(A - \lambda I) = a_{ij} - \lambda \delta_{ij}$

Hence

$$\det (A - \lambda I) = \sum_{\mathbf{p}} \sigma_{\mathbf{p}} (a_{1p_1} - \lambda \delta_{1p_1})(a_{2p_2} - \lambda \delta_{2p_2}) \cdot (a_{np_n} - \lambda \delta_{np_n})$$

$$= \sum_{\mathbf{p}} \sigma_{\mathbf{p}} \left(\prod_{i \neq p_i} a_{ip_i} \right) \left[\prod_{i = p_i} (a_{ip_i} - \lambda) \right]$$

showing $\det (A - \lambda I)$ to be the sum of *polynomials* in the variable λ. Since each summand has n factors, each summand is a polynomial in λ of degree at most n, while the summand corresponding to the identity permutation $\mathbf{p}^T = [1 \quad 2 \quad \cdots \quad n]$ is simply

$(a_{11} - \lambda)(a_{22} - \lambda) \cdots (a_{nn} - \lambda)$

hence of exact degree n in λ. It follows that $\det (A - \lambda I)$, considered as a function of λ, is a polynomial in λ of exact degree n,

$p(\lambda) = \det (A - \lambda I) = (-\lambda)^n + \text{a polynomial of degree } < n$

This polynomial is called the *characteristic polynomial* of A.

Example 3.18   If

$$A = \begin{bmatrix} 1 & 2 & 0 \\ 2 & 1 & 0 \\ 0 & 0 & -1 \end{bmatrix}$$

then

$$p(\lambda) = \det(A - \lambda I) = \det \begin{bmatrix} 1 - \lambda & 2 & 0 \\ 2 & 1 - \lambda & 0 \\ 0 & 0 & -1 - \lambda \end{bmatrix}$$

and expansion by elements of the last row or column gives

$$p(\lambda) = (-1 - \lambda) \det \begin{bmatrix} 1 - \lambda & 2 \\ 2 & 1 - \lambda \end{bmatrix} = -(1 + \lambda)[(1 - \lambda)^2 - 4]$$

$$= -(1 + \lambda)(1 - \lambda + 2)(1 - \lambda - 2)$$

Hence the eigenvalues of A, that is, the zeros of $p(\lambda)$, are -1 and 3, as found earlier by different means in Sec. 3.9.

Since a polynomial of degree n can have at most n distinct zeros (see Sec. 2.6), it follows that an $n \times n$ matrix can have at most n eigenvalues. On the other hand, by the fundamental theorem of algebra, every polynomial of positive degree has at least one zero (see Sec. 1.7); hence every square matrix has at least one eigenvalue. These eigenvalues may well be complex even if A is a real matrix.

In theory, then, the problem of calculating the eigenvalues of a given matrix is completely solved. Merely calculate the characteristic polynomial for A and find its zeros, using the techniques discussed in Chap. 2.

The method of quadratic interpolation (Muller's method), for instance, discussed in Sec. 2.7, can be employed to find one or more eigenvalues, real or complex, of a given matrix. To use this method we must be able only to evaluate the polynomial $p(\lambda)$ for any value of λ. Since for a given value of λ, $p(\lambda)$ is simply a determinant of order n, any method for evaluating a determinant can be used. In particular, this can be done by elimination, as explained in Sec. 3.10. To apply quadratic interpolation to find a root $\lambda = \xi_1$ of $p(\lambda)$, we proceed as follows:

1. Let $\lambda_0, \lambda_1, \lambda_2$ be any three approximations to $\lambda = \xi_1$ (or if no information is available, take $\lambda_0 = -1$, $\lambda_1 = 1$, $\lambda_2 = 0$).
2. Evaluate

$$p(\lambda_i) = \det \begin{bmatrix} a_{11} - \lambda_i & a_{12} & \cdots & a_{1n} \\ a_{21} & a_{22} - \lambda_i & \cdots & a_{2n} \\ \vdots & & & \vdots \\ a_{n1} & a_{n2} & \cdots & a_{nn} - \lambda_i \end{bmatrix} \qquad i = 0, 1, 2$$

3. Apply Algorithm 2.11 until convergence to a root ξ_1 results.
4. To find the next root, repeat this process using, instead of $p(\lambda)$, the deflated function

$$\frac{p(\lambda)}{\lambda - \xi_1}$$

5. Continue as described in Sec. 2.7.

The method of quadratic interpolation is not competitive, relative to computational efficiency, with some of the more advanced methods. However, it is simple to apply, it is completely general, it almost invariably converges, and it provides satisfactory accuracy in most cases. It can also be applied to solve the more general eigenvalue problem

$$\det (A - \lambda B) = 0$$

where A and B are both matrices of order n.

Example 3.19   Free vibrations of simple structures   In civil engineering a problem frequently encountered is to determine the natural frequencies λ of the free vibrations of an undamped structure for several masses and degrees of freedom. This problem can be expressed in the form

$$A\mathbf{x} = \lambda M\mathbf{x} \tag{3.97}$$

where M = mass matrix of system
A = stiffness of system
$\mathbf{x}$ = natural mode

Since (3.97) represents a homogeneous system of equations, it will have a nontrivial solution $\mathbf{x}$ if the determinant of the coefficients vanishes, i.e., if

$$\det (A - \lambda M) = 0 \tag{3.98}$$

Thus, if the matrices A and M are given, the values of λ for which (3.98) is satisfied are the required natural frequencies. Muller's method can be applied directly to find these eigenvalues. For example, for a certain system, $M = I$, and the stiffness matrix A is given by

$$A = \begin{bmatrix} 4 & -1 & -1 & -1 \\ -1 & 4 & -1 & -1 \\ -1 & -1 & 4 & -1 \\ -1 & -1 & -1 & 4 \end{bmatrix}$$

Find the natural frequencies λ of this system.

A computer program using the gaussian elimination algorithm 3.2 to evaluate the determinants and the Muller algorithm 2.11 as a root finder produced the following estimates for the eigenvalues:

$$\lambda_1 = 1.0000000$$
$$\lambda_2 = 5.0000234$$
$$\lambda_3 = 4.9999954$$
$$\lambda_4 = 4.9999973$$

The exact eigenvalues are easily seen to be 1,5,5,5. The effectiveness of Muller's method as a root finder is demonstrated by this example, where a triple root has been found to fairly good accuracy.

Example 3.20   The elements of the tridiagonal matrix B are generated as follows:

$$b_{i,i+1} = 0.5 \quad i = 1, 2, \ldots, n - 1$$
$$b_{i+1,i} = 0.5 \quad i = 1, 2, \ldots, n - 1$$
$$b_{ij} \quad = 0 \quad \text{for all other } i, j$$

Write a computer program to find the eigenvalues of B for $n = 20$.

For $n = 20$, Muller's method produced the following machine results on an IBM 7094:

±0.074730093	±0.73305187
±0.22252094	±0.82623877
±0.36534102	±0.90096886
±0.50000001	±0.95557281
±0.62348980	±0.98883083

Note that the eigenvalues are all real, are symmetrically placed with respect to the origin, and are all less than one in modulus. For this matrix the eigenvalues are known explicitly (see Exercise 3.9-4) and are given by

$$\lambda_k = \cos \frac{k\pi}{n + 1} \quad k = 1, 2, \ldots, n$$

The accuracy of the machine results can be checked from this formula. For $k = 7$ and $n = 20$, $\lambda_7 = \cos (\pi/3) = \frac{1}{2}$, and the machine result underlined above indicates an accuracy of seven significant figures.

The repeated evaluation of determinants necessary for this and similar methods can be quite expensive in machine time, and possibly in accuracy for large n. It is usually more efficient to employ *similarity transformations* to produce, from A, a matrix B having the same characteristic polynomial, hence the same eigenvalues, as A, but a more easily calculable determinant. We say that *the matrix B is similar to A* provided there exists an invertible matrix C such that

$$B = C^{-1}AC \tag{3.99}$$

Clearly, if (3.99) holds, then

$$B - \lambda I = C^{-1}AC - \lambda I = C^{-1}AC - \lambda C^{-1}C = C^{-1}(A - \lambda I)C$$

Hence, by Theorem 3.13,

$$\det (B - \lambda I) = \det (C^{-1}) \det (A - \lambda I) \det (C) = \det (A - \lambda I)$$

since $\det (C^{-1}) \det (C) = \det (C^{-1}C) = \det (I) = 1$, by (3.94a).

Typically, one determines (in Hessenberg's method and its variants) an invertible matrix C such that

$$B = C^{-1}AC$$

is an upper Hessenberg matrix; that is, $B = (b_{ij})$ satisfies

$$b_{ij} = 0 \qquad \text{for } i > j + 1$$

In words, an upper Hessenberg matrix is almost upper-triangular, all sub-diagonal entries, except those adjacent to the diagonal, being zero. If B is an upper Hessenberg matrix, then so is $B - \lambda I$ for every λ. Hence, when $\det (B - \lambda I)$ is calculated by elimination (using the pivoting strategy $\mathbf{p}^T = [1,2, \ldots ,n]$), only one entry has to be eliminated at each step; hence $\det (B - \lambda I)$ can be calculated in $O(n^2)$ operations. It is even possible to choose C so that the characteristic polynomial for B can be read off directly from the entries of B (Danilevski's method).

If the original matrix is real symmetric, i.e., if $A^T = A$, then it is possible to choose C so that the resulting B is tridiagonal and real symmetric (Householder's method and Givens' method). But all these methods are based on advanced topics from the theory of linear algebra and will therefore not be pursued here.

At times it is only necessary to estimate the eigenvalues of A. A typical example of how this might be done is provided by the following theorem.

Theorem 3.15 Gershgorin's circle theorem   Each eigenvalue λ of the $n \times n$ matrix $A = (a_{ij})$ satisfies

$$|a_{ii} - \lambda| \leq \sum_{\substack{j=1 \\ j \neq i}}^{n} |a_{ij}| \qquad \text{for some } i$$

For if

$$|a_{ii} - \lambda| > \sum_{j \neq i} |a_{ij}| \qquad \text{for } i = 1, \ldots , n$$

then the matrix $(A - \lambda I)$ is strictly (row) diagonally dominant; hence, by the corollary to Lemma 3.4 (in Sec. 3.8), $A - \lambda I$ is then invertible; that is, λ is then not an eigenvalue for A.

For example, for the matrix A of Example 3.18, we get from this theorem that each eigenvalue λ of A satisfies

either $\quad |1 - \lambda| \leq 2 \quad$ or $\quad |-1 - \lambda| = 0$

We saw already, in Chap. 2, that we have to employ some iterative technique to find (good approximations to) the zeros of a given polynomial. This being so, it is at times advantageous to apply some iterative technique directly to the given matrix A in order to find its eigenvalues. One such technique, the power method, was discussed in some detail in Sec. 3.9. With a deeper understanding of the eigenvalue-eigenvector structure of matrices than we have been able to transmit here, it is possible to develop from the power method more advanced iterative techniques, such as the LR method or the QR method, which attempt to find all the eigenvalues of a given matrix by iteration.

EXERCISES

3.11-1. Find all the eigenvalues of the matrix

$$A = \begin{bmatrix} 4 & -1 & -1 & -1 \\ -1 & 4 & -1 & -1 \\ -1 & -1 & 4 & -1 \\ -1 & -1 & -1 & 4 \end{bmatrix}$$

by determining explicitly its characteristic polynomial, and then the zeros of this polynomial.

3.11-2. Use Muller's method to find the natural frequencies in Example 3.19 in case

$$A = \begin{bmatrix} -2 & 0 & 1 & 0 \\ 0 & -2 & 0 & 1 \\ 1 & 0 & -2 & 0 \\ 0 & 1 & 0 & -2 \end{bmatrix} \qquad M = \begin{bmatrix} 2 & 1 & 0 & 0 \\ 1 & 2 & 1 & 0 \\ 0 & 1 & 2 & 1 \\ 0 & 0 & 1 & 2 \end{bmatrix}$$

3.11-3. Do Example 3.20 for $n = 10$, using the FORTRAN program developed in Exercise 3.10-8 for the evaluation of the requisite determinants.

3.11-4. Suppose the matrix A of order n has a complete set of eigenvectors $\mathbf{x}^{(1)}, \ldots, \mathbf{x}^{(n)}$. Prove that then A is similar to a diagonal matrix (whose diagonal entries must be the eigenvalues of A). [*Hint:* Consider the matrix $C^{-1}AC$, where $Ci_j = \mathbf{x}^{(j)}, j = 1, \ldots, n$. Why must C be invertible?]

3.11-5. *Deflation for the power method.* Suppose that we have calculated, by the power method or by any other method, an eigenvalue λ for the matrix A of order n, with corresponding eigenvector $\mathbf{x}$, and assume that $x_n \neq 0$. Let B be the matrix of order $n - 1$ obtained from the matrix $C^{-1}AC$ by omitting its last row and last column, where $Ci_j = i_j, j = 1, \ldots, n - 1$, and $Ci_n = \mathbf{x}$. Prove that all the eigenvalues of A are also eigenvalues of B, with the possible exception of the eigenvalue λ.

4
Interpolation and Approximation

In this chapter we consider the problem of approximating a general function by a class of simpler functions. There are two uses for approximating functions. The first is to replace complicated functions by some simpler functions so that many common operations such as differentiation and integration can be more easily performed. The second major use is for interpolating in tables, i.e., for evaluating a function at some unknown point when values of the functions are known at a set of tabular points. The most commonly used classes of approximating functions are polynomials, trigonometric functions, exponentials, and rational functions. Of these, the interpolating polynomial is by far the most widely used on computers, and most of this chapter will be concerned with the derivation of properties of this class of functions.

4.1 THE INTERPOLATING POLYNOMIAL: LAGRANGE FORM

Let $x_0, x_1, \ldots, x_n$ be $n + 1$ distinct points on the real axis and let $f(x)$ be a real-valued function defined on some interval $I = [a,b]$ containing these

points.   We wish to construct a polynomial $p(x)$ of degree $\leq n$ which interpolates $f(x)$ at the points $x_0, \ldots, x_n$, that is, satisfies

$$p(x_i) = f(x_i) \qquad i = 0, \ldots, n$$

As it turns out, there are many ways to write down such a polynomial.
It is therefore important to establish at the outset that *there is at most one
polynomial of degree $\leq n$ which interpolates $f(x)$ at the $n + 1$ distinct points*
$x_0, \ldots, x_n$.   To see this, assume that both $p(x)$ and $q(x)$ are polynomials
of degree $\leq n$ which interpolate $f(x)$ at the distinct points $x_0, \ldots, x_n$.
If we set

$$h(x) = p(x) - q(x)$$

then $h(x)$ is a polynomial of degree $\leq n$, and

$$h(x_i) = p(x_i) - q(x_i) = f(x_i) - f(x_i) = 0 \qquad i = 0, \ldots, n$$

that is, $h(x)$ has at least $n + 1$ distinct zeros.   But this implies, since the
only polynomial of degree $\leq n$ with $n + 1$ zeros is the zero polynomial (see
Sec. 2.6), that $h(x)$ vanishes identically, and $p(x) \equiv q(x)$ follows.

Next we show that *there is at least one polynomial of degree $\leq n$ which
interpolates $f(x)$ at the $n + 1$ distinct points* $x_0, x_1, \ldots, x_n$.   This is almost
evident in the special case when $f(x)$ vanishes at all the interpolation points
but one,

$$f(x_i) = \begin{cases} 1 & i = k \\ 0 & i \neq k \end{cases}$$

say.   In this case, we seek a polynomial of degree $\leq n$ which vanishes at all
the x_i's, with the exception of x_k.   The function

$$g_k(x) = \prod_{\substack{i=0 \\ i \neq k}}^{n} (x - x_i)$$

$$= (x - x_0)(x - x_1) \cdots (x - x_{k-1})(x - x_{k+1}) \cdots (x - x_n)$$

is such a polynomial.   Further,

$$g_k(x_k) = \prod_{\substack{i=0 \\ i \neq k}}^{n} (x_k - x_i) \neq 0$$

since the x_i's are assumed to be distinct.   Hence

$$l_k(x) = \frac{g_k(x)}{g_k(x_k)} = \prod_{\substack{i=0 \\ i \neq k}}^{n} \frac{x - x_i}{x_k - x_i} \qquad\qquad (4.1)$$

is the solution to the interpolation problem in this special case, i.e.,

$$l_k(x_i) = \begin{cases} 1 & i = k \\ 0 & i \neq k \end{cases} \qquad i = 0, \ldots, n$$

But then, for an arbitrary function $f(x)$,

$$p(x) = \sum_{k=0}^{n} f(x_k) l_k(x) \tag{4.2}$$

is a polynomial of degree $\leq n$ which interpolates $f(x)$ at $x_0, \ldots, x_n$. This establishes the following theorem.

Theorem 4.1 Given a real-valued function $f(x)$ and $n + 1$ distinct points $x_0, \ldots, x_n$, there exists exactly one polynomial of degree $\leq n$ which interpolates $f(x)$ at $x_0, \ldots, x_n$.

The right side of (4.2) is called the *Lagrange form* of the interpolating polynomial. The polynomials $l_0(x), \ldots, l_n(x)$ defined by (4.1) are called the Lagrange polynomials for the points $x_0, \ldots, x_n$.

As a simple application, we consider the case $n = 1$; i.e., we are given $f(x)$ and two distinct points x_0, x_1. Then

$$l_0(x) = \frac{x - x_1}{x_0 - x_1} \qquad l_1(x) = \frac{x - x_0}{x_1 - x_0}$$

and

$$p(x) = f(x_0) l_0(x) + f(x_1) l_1(x) = f(x_0) \frac{x - x_1}{x_0 - x_1} + f(x_1) \frac{x - x_0}{x_1 - x_0}$$

$$= \frac{f(x_0)(x - x_1) - f(x_1)(x - x_0)}{x_0 - x_1} = f(x_0) + \frac{f(x_1) - f(x_0)}{x_1 - x_0}(x - x_0)$$

This is the familiar case of *linear interpolation* written in some of its many equivalent forms.

Example 4.1 An integral related to the complete elliptic integral is defined by

$$K(k) = \int_0^{\pi/2} \frac{dx}{[1 - (\sin k)^2 \sin^2 x]^{1/2}} \tag{4.3}$$

From a table of values of these integrals we find that, for various values of k measured in degrees,

$$K(1) = 1.5709$$
$$K(4) = 1.5727$$
$$K(6) = 1.5751$$

Find $K(3.5)$, using a second-degree interpolating polynomial.

We have

$$l_0(3.5) = \frac{(3.5 - 4)(3.5 - 6)}{(1 - 4)(1 - 6)} = \frac{1.25}{15} = 0.08333$$

$$l_1(3.5) = \frac{(3.5 - 1)(3.5 - 6)}{(4 - 1)(4 - 6)} = \frac{-6.25}{-6} = 1.04167$$

$$l_2(3.5) = \frac{(3.5 - 1)(3.5 - 4)}{(6 - 1)(6 - 4)} = \frac{-1.25}{10} = -0.12500$$

Then

$$K(3.5) \approx (1.5709)(0.08333) + (1.5727)(1.04167) + (1.5751)(-0.12500)$$
$$= 1.57225$$

This approximation is in error in the last place.

EXERCISES

4.1-1. In Example 4.1 use a second-degree interpolating polynomial to find $K(3.0)$.

4.1-2. For the integral defined in (4.3), some values of K obtained from a table are

$$K(2) = 1.5713$$
$$K(3) = 1.5719$$
$$K(5) = 1.5738$$
$$K(6) = 1.5751$$

Find $K(4.0)$ using a second-degree interpolating polynomial and a third-degree polynomial. Round the final results off to four decimal places. Is there any advantage in this case in using a third-degree polynomial?

4.1-3. Show that the polynomials $l_k(x)$ defined by (4.1) can also be written in the form

$$l_k(x) = \frac{\psi(x)}{(x - x_k)\psi'(x_k)}$$

where

$$\psi(x) = \prod_{j=0}^{n} (x - x_j)$$

and that the interpolating polynomial (4.2) can therefore be written in the form

$$p(x) = \psi(x) \sum_{k=0}^{n} \frac{f(x_k)}{(x - x_k)\psi'(x_k)}$$

4.1-4. Prove: If $f(x)$ is a polynomial of degree $\leq n$, then the polynomial of degree $\leq n$ which interpolates $f(x)$ at $x_0, \ldots, x_n$ is $f(x)$ itself.

4.1-5. Use Exercise 4.1-4 to prove that

$$\sum_{i=0}^{n} l_i(x) \equiv 1$$

where $l_0(x), \ldots, l_n(x)$ are the Lagrange polynomials given in (4.1). Then try to verify this identity directly for the case $n = 2$.

4.1-6. Given the numbers $a_0, a_1, \ldots, a_k$, present a formula for the polynomial $p(x)$ of degree $\leq k$ which satisfies

$$p(x_i) = a_i \qquad i = 0, \ldots, k$$

where $x_0, \ldots, x_k$ are $k + 1$ distinct points.

4.2 THE INTERPOLATING POLYNOMIAL: NEWTON FORM

The Lagrange form (4.2) for the interpolating polynomial makes it easy to show the existence of an interpolating polynomial. But its evaluation at a point x takes at least $(3n + 1)$ multiplications/divisions and $(2n + 1)$ additions and subtractions *after* the denominators of the Lagrange polynomals have been calculated once for all. This is to be compared with n multiplications and n additions necessary for the evaluation of a polynomial of degree n by nested multiplication (see Algorithm 2.9).

A more serious objection to the Lagrange form arises as follows: In practice, one is often uncertain as to how many interpolation points to use. Hence, with $p_j(x)$ denoting the polynomial of degree $\leq j$ which interpolates $f(x)$ at $x_0, \ldots, x_j$, one calculates $p_0(x), p_1(x), p_2(x), \ldots$, increasing the number of interpolation points, and hence the degree of the interpolating polynomial, until hopefully, a satisfactory approximation $p_k(x)$ to $f(x)$ has been found. In such a process, use of the Lagrange form seems wasteful since, in calculating $p_k(x)$, no advantage can be taken of the fact that one already has $p_{k-1}(x)$ available. For this purpose and others, the Newton form of the interpolating polynomial is much better suited.

Assume that we have somehow determined the polynomial $p_{k-1}(x)$ of degree $\leq k - 1$ which interpolates $f(x)$ at the points $x_0, \ldots, x_{k-1}$. To make use of $p_{k-1}(x)$ in calculating $p_k(x)$, we consider the following problem: What function $h(x)$ do we have to add to $p_{k-1}(x)$ to get $p_k(x)$? Clearly,

$$h(x) = p_k(x) - p_{k-1}(x)$$

Hence (1) $h(x)$ is a polynomial of degree $\leq k$, and (2) $h(x_0) = h(x_1) = \cdots = h(x_{k-1}) = 0$, since

$$\text{For } 0 \leq i \leq k - 1: \qquad h(x_i) = p_k(x_i) - p_{k-1}(x_i) = f(x_i) - f(x_i) = 0$$

In short, $h(x)$ is a polynomial of degree $\leq k$ having (at least) the k distinct zeros $x_0, \ldots, x_{k-1}$. But this implies (see Sec. 2.6) that

$$h(x) = A_k(x - x_0)(x - x_1) \cdot \cdots \cdot (x - x_{k-1})$$

for some constant A_k. For reasons given below and in the next section, this number A_k is called *the kth divided difference of $f(x)$ at the points $x_0, \ldots, x_k$*, and is denoted by

$$f[x_0, x_1, \ldots, x_k]$$

With this notation, we get that

$$p_k(x) = p_{k-1}(x) + f[x_0, \ldots , x_k](x - x_0)(x - x_1) \cdots (x - x_{k-1})$$
$$(4.4)$$

Using the Lagrange form for $p_k(x)$, it is possible to give an explicit expression for the kth divided difference appearing in (4.4). For since $p_{k-1}(x)$ is a polynomial of degree $< k$, while

$$(x - x_0)(x - x_1) \cdots (x - x_{k-1}) = x^k + \text{a polynomial of degree} < k$$

we conclude from (4.4) that

$$p_k(x) = f[x_0, x_1, \ldots , x_k]x^k + \text{a polynomial of degree} < k \qquad (4.5)$$

Hence

$$p_k^{(k)}(x) = k! f[x_0, \ldots , x_k] \qquad (4.6)$$

showing the kth divided difference $f[x_0, \ldots , x_k]$ to be $1/k!$ times the (constant) kth derivative of the polynomial of degree $\leq k$ which interpolates $f(x)$ at $x_0, \ldots , x_k$. Now, by (4.2), we can also write

$$p_k(x) = \sum_{i=0}^{k} f(x_i) \prod_{\substack{j=0 \\ j \neq i}}^{k} \frac{x - x_j}{x_i - x_j}$$

$$= \sum_{i=0}^{k} \frac{f(x_i)}{\prod_{\substack{j=0 \\ j \neq i}}^{k} (x_i - x_j)} x^k + \text{a polynomial of degree} < k$$

Therefore, on comparing this with (4.5), we get that

$$f[x_0, x_1, \ldots , x_k]$$

$$= \sum_{i=0}^{k} \frac{f(x_i)}{(x_i - x_0) \cdots (x_i - x_{i-1})(x_i - x_{i+1}) \cdots (x_i - x_k)} \qquad (4.7)$$

This explicit formula for the kth divided difference shows that

$$f[y_0, \ldots , y_k] = f[x_0, \ldots , x_k]$$

if $y_0, \ldots , y_k$ is a reordering of the sequence $x_0, \ldots , x_k$. Also, for $k = 1$, we get that

$$f[x_0, x_1] = \frac{f(x_0)}{x_0 - x_1} + \frac{f(x_1)}{x_1 - x_0} = \frac{f(x_0) - f(x_1)}{x_0 - x_1}$$

so that the first divided difference is, indeed, a divided difference. Further, for $k = 2$, (4.7) gives

$$f[x_0,x_1,x_2] = \frac{f(x_0)}{(x_0 - x_1)(x_0 - x_2)} + \frac{f(x_1)}{(x_1 - x_0)(x_1 - x_2)}$$
$$+ \frac{f(x_2)}{(x_2 - x_0)(x_2 - x_1)}$$

which, after some manipulations, can be simplified to

$$\frac{f[x_0,x_1] - f[x_1,x_2]}{x_0 - x_2}$$

showing the second divided difference to be a divided difference of divided differences. But for $k \geq 2$, (4.7) is too cumbersome for the actual calculation of $f[x_0, \dots ,x_k]$.

If we define the 0th divided difference of $f(x)$ at x_0 by

$$f[x_0] = f(x_0)$$

which is consistent with (4.5) or (4.7), then we get from (4.4), by induction on n, that

$$p_n(x) = f[x_0] + f[x_0,x_1](x - x_0) + f[x_0,x_1,x_2](x - x_0)(x - x_1)$$
$$+ \cdots + f[x_0,x_1,\dots,x_n](x - x_0)(x - x_1)\cdots(x - x_{n-1})$$

This is the *Newton form* for the interpolating polynomial, which can also be written more compactly as

$$\boxed{p_n(x) = \sum_{i=0}^{n} f[x_0, \dots ,x_i] \prod_{j=0}^{i-1} (x - x_j)} \tag{4.8}$$

if we make use of the convention that

$$\prod_{m=r}^{s} a_m = \begin{cases} a_r a_{r+1} \cdots a_s & \text{for } r \leq s \\ 1 & \text{for } r > s \end{cases}$$

In particular, for $n = 1$, we get that

$$p_1(x) = f[x_0] + f[x_0,x_1](x - x_0)$$
$$= f(x_0) + \frac{f(x_1) - f(x_0)}{x_1 - x_0}(x - x_0)$$

which coincides with a formula for $p_1(x)$ derived in Sec. 4.1.

Example 4.2 Solve Example 4.1 using the Newton form.

In this example, we have to determine the polynomial $p_2(x)$ of degree ≤ 2 which satisfies

$$p_2(1) = 1.5709 \qquad p_2(4) = 1.5727 \qquad p_2(6) = 1.5751$$

By the discussion following (4.7), we can calculate

$$K[1,4] = \frac{1.5709 - 1.5727}{1 - 4} = 0.0006$$

$$K[4,6] = \frac{1.5727 - 1.5751}{4 - 6} = 0.0012$$

Therefore

$$K[1,4,6] = \frac{0.0006 - 0.0012}{1 - 6} = 0.00012$$

and (4.8) now gives

$$p_2(x) = 1.5709 + 0.0006(x - 1) + 0.00012(x - 1)(x - 4)$$

Substituting into this the value $x = 3.5$, we obtain

$$p_2(3.5) = 1.5709 + (0.0006)(2.5) + (0.00012)(2.5)(-0.5) = 1.57225$$

which agrees with the result obtained in Example 4.1.

Before attacking the problem of the efficient calculation of the coefficients $f[x_0], f[x_0,x_1], \ldots, f[x_0,x_1, \ldots, x_n]$ of the Newton form (4.8) for the interpolating polynomial in the next section, we show how to evaluate the Newton form efficiently, using a variant of the nested multiplication algorithm 2.9. To recall, if we are given the coefficients $a_0, a_1, \ldots, a_k$ for the polynomial $p(x)$ in the power form

$$p(x) = a_0 + a_1 x + a_2 x^2 + \cdots + a_k x^k$$

and a point z, then the calculations

Set $b_k = a_k$
For $i = k - 1, \ldots, 0$, do:
$\quad$ Set $b_i = a_i + z b_{i+1}$

produce numbers $b_0, \ldots, b_k$ so that

$$p(x) = b_0 + (x - z)(b_1 + b_2 x + \cdots + b_k x^{k-1})$$

In particular, for $x = z$, we get $p(z) = b_0$. Assume now that we are given, more generally, the coefficients $a_0, a_1, \ldots, a_k$ for the polynomial $p(x)$ written in its Newton form based on the points $y_1, y_2, \ldots, y_k$, that is,

$$p(x) = a_0 + a_1(x - y_1) + a_2(x - y_1)(x - y_2) + \cdots$$
$$+ a_k(x - y_1) \cdots (x - y_k) \tag{4.9}$$

and given further a point z. Then the calculations

Set $b_k = a_k$
For $i = k - 1, \ldots, 0$, do:
$\quad$ Set $b_i = a_i + (z - y_{i+1}) b_{i+1}$

produce numbers $b_0, \ldots, b_k$ so that

$$p(x) = b_0 + b_1(x - z) + b_2(x - z)(x - y_1) + \cdots$$
$$+ b_k(x - z)(x - y_1) \cdots (x - y_{k-1}) \quad (4.10)$$

that is, $b_0, \ldots, b_k$ so calculated are the coefficients in the Newton form for $p(x)$ but based on the points $z, y_1, \ldots, y_{k-1}$ (rather than $y_1, \ldots, y_k$). In particular, on substituting $x = z$ into (4.10), we get that $p(z) = b_0$. Note that it takes just $2k$ additions and k multiplications to produce the number b_0.

For the proof of (4.10), we note that, from the calculations,

$$a_k = b_k$$
$$a_i = b_i + b_{i+1}(y_{i+1} - z) \quad i = 0, \ldots, k - 1$$

On substituting these expressions for the a_i's into (4.9), we get

$$p(x) = a_0 + a_1(x - y_1) + a_2(x - y_1)(x - y_2) + \cdots + a_k(x - y_1) \cdots (x - y_k)$$
$$= b_0 + b_1(y_1 - z)$$
$$+ [b_1 + b_2(y_2 - z)](x - y_1)$$
$$+ [b_2 + b_3(y_3 - z)](x - y_1)(x - y_2)$$
$$\cdot$$
$$\cdot$$
$$\cdot$$
$$+ [b_{k-1} + b_k(y_k - z)](x - y_1) \cdots (x - y_{k-1})$$
$$+ b_k(x - y_1) \cdots (x - y_{k-1})(x - y_k)$$
$$= b_0 + b_1(x - z) + b_2(x - z)(x - y_1) + \cdots + b_k(x - z)(x - y_1) \cdots (x - y_{k-1})$$

which proves (4.10).

Algorithm 4.1 Nested multiplication for the Newton form Given the $k + 1$ coefficients $a_0, \ldots, a_k$ for the Newton form (4.9), based on the points $y_1, \ldots, y_k$, of the polynomial $p(x)$. Given further the number z.

> Set $b_k = a_k$
> For $i = k - 1, \ldots, 0$, do:
> > Set $b_i = a_i + (z - y_{i+1})b_{i+1}$

Then $b_0, \ldots, b_k$ are the coefficients in the Newton form (4.10) based on the points $z, y_1, \ldots, y_{k-1}$ for $p(x)$. In particular, $p(z) = b_0$.

Aside from producing the value of the polynomial (4.9) at any particular point z economically, this algorithm is useful in changing from one Newton form to another. Suppose, for example, that we wish to express the polynomial

$$p_2(x) = 1.5709 + 0.0006(x - 1) + 0.00012(x - 1)(x - 4)$$

calculated in Example 4.2, in terms of powers of x, that is, in the Newton form based on the points 0,0. Then, applying Algorithm 4.1 with $z = 0$ (and $k = 2$), we get

$$b_2 = a_2 = 0.00012$$
$$b_1 = a_1 + (z - y_2)b_2 = 0.0006 + (0 - 4)(0.00012) = 0.00012$$
$$b_0 = a_0 + (z - y_1)b_1 = 1.5709 + (0 - 1)(0.00012) = 1.57078$$

Hence

$$p_2(x) = 1.57078 + 0.00012(x - 0) + 0.00012(x - 0)(x - 1)$$

Applying Algorithm 4.1 to this polynomial, again with $z = 0$, gives

$$b_2 = a_2 = 0.00012$$
$$b_1 = a_1 + (z - y_2)b_2 = 0.00012 + (0 - 1)(0.00012) = 0.0$$
$$b_0 = a_0 + (z - y_1)b_1 = 1.57078 + (0 - 0)(0.0) = 1.57078$$

Therefore

$$p_2(x) = 1.57078 + 0.0(x - 0) + 0.00012(x - 0)(x - 0)$$
$$= 1.57078 + 0.00012x^2$$

In this simple example, we can verify this result quickly by multiplying out the terms in the original expression.

$$p_2(x) = 1.5709 + 0.0006(x - 1) + 0.00012(x^2 - 5x + 4)$$
$$= [1.5709 - 0.0006 + (0.00012)(4)]$$
$$+ [0.0006 + (0.00012)(-5)]x + 0.00012x^2$$
$$= 1.57078 + 0.00012x^2$$

EXERCISES

4.2-1. In Example 4.1, find (an approximation to) $K(3.0)$ using the Newton form of the second-degree interpolating polynomial.

4.2-2. Verify that for any three distinct points x_0, x_1, x_2,

$$f[x_0,x_1,x_2] = f[x_2,x_0,x_1] = f[x_1,x_2,x_0]$$

4.2-3. Let $p(x)$ be the polynomial given in (4.9). Prove: If $y_1 = y_2 = \cdots = y_{r+1}$, then $p^{(j)}(y_1) = j! \, a_j, j = 0, \ldots, r$. [*Hint:* Under these assumptions, $p(x)$ can be written

$$p(x) = \sum_{j=0}^{r} a_j(x - y_1)^j + (x - y_1)^{r+1}q(x)$$

where $q(x)$ is some polynomial. Now differentiate.]

4.2-4. Find the first derivative of

$$p(x) = 3 - 4(x - 1) + 5(x - 1)(x + 1) - 6(x - 1)(x + 1)x$$
$$+ (x - 1)(x + 1)x(x + 2)$$

at $x = 2$.   [*Hint:* Apply Algorithm 4.1 twice to get the Newton form for $p(x)$ based on 2, 2, 1, -1; then use Exercise 4.2-3.]

4.2-5. Find also the second derivative of the polynomial $p(x)$ of Exercise 4.2-4 at $x = 2$.

4.2-6. Find the Taylor expansion around $c = 3$ for the polynomial of Exercise 4.2-4. (*Hint:* The Taylor expansion for a polynomial around a point c is just the Newton form for this polynomial based on the points $c, c, c, \ldots$; hence can be obtained from any Newton form for this polynomial by repeated applications of Algorithm 4.1.)

4.3 THE DIVIDED-DIFFERENCE TABLE

In the preceding section, we introduced the Newton form

$$p_n(x) = \sum_{i=0}^{n} f[x_0, \ldots, x_i] \prod_{j=0}^{i-1} (x - x_j) \tag{4.11}$$

for the polynomial of degree $\leq n$ which interpolates the function $f(x)$ at the $n + 1$ distinct points $x_0, \ldots, x_n$, but left open the question of how to calculate the divided differences $f[x_0], f[x_0, x_1], \ldots, f[x_0, \ldots, x_n]$ which appear as coefficients in (4.11).

Clearly, (4.11) is the Newton form for the polynomial $p_n(x)$ based on the points $x_0, x_1, \ldots, x_{n-1}$.   Hence, if we apply Algorithm 4.1 to it, with $z = x_n$ (and $k = n$), then we get that

$$p_n(x) = b_0 + b_1(x - x_n) + b_2(x - x_n)(x - x_0) + \cdots$$

$$+ b_n(x - x_n)(x - x_0) \cdots (x - x_{n-2}) \tag{4.12}$$

where the numbers $b_0, \ldots, b_n$ are given recursively by

$$b_n = f[x_0, \ldots, x_n]$$
$$b_i = f[x_0, \ldots, x_i] + (x_n - x_i)b_{i+1} \qquad i = n - 1, \ldots, 0$$

In particular, this gives

$$b_{n-1} = f[x_0, \ldots, x_{n-1}] + (x_n - x_{n-1})b_n$$

or solving this for b_n,

$$b_n = \frac{b_{n-1} - f[x_0, \ldots, x_{n-1}]}{x_n - x_{n-1}} \tag{4.13}$$

On the other hand, since $p_n(x)$ interpolates $f(x)$ at $x_0, \ldots, x_n$, it also interpolates $f(x)$ at $x_n, x_0, \ldots, x_{n-1}$.   Therefore

$$p_n(x) = f[x_n] + f[x_n, x_0](x - x_n) + f[x_n, x_0, x_1](x - x_n)(x - x_0)$$

$$+ \cdots + f[x_n, x_0, \ldots, x_{n-1}](x - x_n)(x - x_0) \cdots$$

$$(x - x_{n-2}) \tag{4.14}$$

On comparing (4.12) and (4.14), we find that

$$b_0 = f[x_n] \qquad b_1 = f[x_n,x_0], \ldots , b_{n-1} = f[x_n,x_0, \ldots , x_{n-2}]$$

Hence, since $b_n = f[x_0, \ldots ,x_n]$, we get from (4.13) that

$$f[x_0, \ldots ,x_n] = \frac{f[x_n,x_0, \ldots ,x_{n-2}] - f[x_0, \ldots ,x_{n-1}]}{x_n - x_{n-1}} \qquad (4.15)$$

which shows the nth divided difference to be a divided difference of $(n-1)$st divided differences, justifying the name "nth divided difference."

Now recall from (4.7) that the kth divided difference on $k+1$ points depends only on these $k+1$ points, and not on the order in which we write them down; i.e.,

$$f[y_0, \ldots ,y_k] = f[z_0, \ldots ,z_k]$$

if $z_0, \ldots , z_k$ are just the numbers $y_0, \ldots , y_k$ written in a different order. Since the x_i's appearing in (4.15) are $n+1$ arbitrary points, we conclude from (4.15) that the nth divided difference on a set M of $n+1$ distinct points can always be calculated as follows: Take any $n-1$ of these points and call their collection N; this leaves two points, call them α and β. Then

nth divided difference of $f(x)$ on the points of M

$$= \frac{[(n-1)\text{st div.diff. on } N \text{ and } \alpha] - [(n-1)\text{st div.diff. on } N \text{ and } \beta]}{\alpha - \beta}$$

In particular, we will from now on use the formula

$$f[x_0, \ldots ,x_n] = \frac{f[x_1, \ldots ,x_n] - f[x_0, \ldots ,x_{n-1}]}{x_n - x_0} \qquad (4.16)$$

i.e., with $M = \{x_0, \ldots ,x_n\}$, we pick $N = \{x_1, \ldots ,x_{n-1}\}$, $\alpha = x_n$, $\beta = x_0$. This formula allows us to generate all the divided differences needed for the Newton form (4.11) in a simple manner with the aid of a so-called *divided-difference table*.

Such a table is depicted in Fig. 4.1, for $n = 4$.

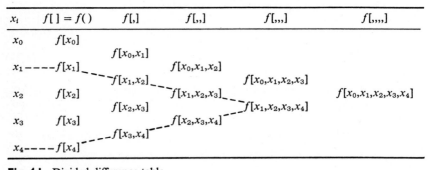

x_i	$f[\ ] = f(\ )$	$f[,]$	$f[,,]$	$f[,,,]$	$f[,,,,]$
x_0	$f[x_0]$				
		$f[x_0,x_1]$			
x_1	$f[x_1]$		$f[x_0,x_1,x_2]$		
		$f[x_1,x_2]$		$f[x_0,x_1,x_2,x_3]$	
x_2	$f[x_2]$		$f[x_1,x_2,x_3]$		$f[x_0,x_1,x_2,x_3,x_4]$
		$f[x_2,x_3]$		$f[x_1,x_2,x_3,x_4]$	
x_3	$f[x_3]$		$f[x_2,x_3,x_4]$		
		$f[x_3,x_4]$			
x_4	$f[x_4]$				

Fig. 4.1 Divided-difference table.

The entries in the table are calculated, for example, column by column, according to the following algorithm.

Algorithm 4.2   Divided-difference table   Given the first two columns of the table, containing $x_0, x_1, \ldots, x_n$ and, correspondingly, $f[x_0], f[x_1],$ $\ldots, f[x_n]$.

For $k = 1, \ldots, n$, do:
> For $i = 0, \ldots, n - k$, do:
> > Calculate
> > $$f[x_i, \ldots, x_{i+k}] = \frac{f[x_{i+1}, \ldots, x_{i+k}] - f[x_i, \ldots, x_{i+k-1}]}{x_{i+k} - x_i}$$

If this algorithm is carried out by hand, the following directions might be helpful.   Draw the two diagonals from the entry to be calculated through its two neighboring entries to the left.   If these lines terminate at $f[x_i]$ and $f[x_j]$, respectively, divide the difference of the two neighboring entries by the corresponding difference $x_j - x_i$ to get the desired entry.   This is illustrated in Fig. 4.1 for the entry $f[x_1, \ldots, x_4]$.

When the divided-difference table is filled out, the coefficients $f[x_0, \ldots, x_i]$, $i = 0, \ldots, n$, for the Newton form (4.11) can be found at the head of their respective columns.

For reasons of storage requirements, and because the DO variables in FORTRAN can only increase, one would use a somewhat modified version of Algorithm 4.2 in a FORTRAN program.   First, for the evaluation of the Newton form according to Algorithm 4.1, it is more convenient to use the form

$$p_n(x) = \sum_{i=0}^{n} f[x_i, \ldots, x_n] \prod_{j=i+1}^{n} (x - x_j)$$

i.e., to use the Newton form based on the points $x_n, x_{n-1}, \ldots, x_1$.   For then the value $v = p_n(z)$ can be calculated, according to Algorithm 4.1, by

Set $v = f[x_0, \ldots, x_n]$
For $i = 1, \ldots, n$, do:
> Set $v = f[x_i, \ldots, x_n] + (z - x_i)v$

Second, since we are then only interested in the numbers $f[x_i, \ldots, x_n]$, $i = 0, \ldots, n$, it is not necessary to store the entire divided-difference table (requiring a two-dimensional array in which roughly half the entries would not be used anyway, because of the triangular character of the divided-difference table).   For if we use the abbreviation

$$d_{ij} = f[x_i, \ldots, x_{i+j}]$$

then the calculations of Algorithm 4.2 read

> For $k = 1, \ldots, n$, do:
> > For $i = 0, \ldots, n - k$, do:
> > > Set $d_{ik} = (d_{i+1,k-1} - d_{i,k-1})/(x_{i+k} - x_i)$

In particular, the number $d_{i,k-1}$ is not used any further once d_{ik} has been calculated, so that we can safely store d_{ik} over $d_{i,k-1}$.

Algorithm 4.3 Calculation of the coefficients for the Newton form

Given the $n + 1$ distinct points $x_0, \ldots, x_n$ and, correspondingly, the numbers $f(x_0), \ldots, f(x_n)$, with $f(x_i)$ stored in d_i, $i = 0, \ldots, n$.

> For $k = 1, \ldots, n$, do:
> > For $i = 0, \ldots, n - k$, do:
> > > Set $d_i = (d_{i+1} - d_i)/(x_{i+k} - x_i)$

Then $d_i = f[x_i, \ldots, x_n]$, $i = 0, \ldots, n$.

Example 4.3 Let $f(x) = (1 + x^2)^{-1}$. For $n = 2, 4, \ldots, 16$, calculate the polynomial $p_n(x)$ of degree $\leq n$ which interpolates $f(x)$ at the $n + 1$ equally spaced points

$$x_i = i\frac{10}{n} - 5 \qquad i = 0, \ldots, n$$

Then estimate the maximum interpolation error

$$E_n = \max_{-5 \leq x \leq 5} |f(x) - p_n(x)| \qquad n = 2, 4, \ldots, 16$$

on the interval $[-5,5]$ by computing

$$E_n \approx \max_i |f(y_i) - p_n(y_i)|$$

where

$$y_i = \frac{i}{10} - 5 \qquad i = 0, \ldots, 100$$

The FORTRAN program below utilizes Algorithms 4.1 and 4.3 to solve this problem. As the output indicates, E_n decreases slightly initially but then increases quite rapidly as n increases. Thus, for this example, interpolation with a low-degree polynomial gives better results than interpolation with a high-degree polynomial. We discuss this important phenomenon later, in Sec. 4.7.

FORTRAN PROGRAM FOR EXAMPLE 4.3

```
      DIMENSION X(17),D(17)
      F(X) = 1./(1. + X*X)
      WRITE (6,600)
  600 FORMAT(1H1,3X1HN5X13HMAXIMUM ERROR)
      DO 40 N = 2,16,2
```

```
      NP1 = N + 1
      H = 10./FLOAT(N)
      DO 10 I = 1,NP1
      X(I) = FLOAT(I − 1)*H − 5.
   10 D(I) = F(X(I))
```
CALCULATE THE COEFFICIENTS OF INTERP. POL. BY ALGORITHM 4.3
```
      DO 20 K = 1,N
      NP1MK = NP1 − K
      DO 20 I = 1,NP1MK
      IPK = I + K
   20 D(I) = (D(I + 1) − D(I))/(X(IPK) − X(I))
C     ESTIMATE MAXIMUM INTERPOLATION ERROR ON (−5,5).
      Y = −5.
      ERRMX = 0.
      DO 30 J = 1,101
```
CALCULATE PN(Y) BY ALGORITHM 4.1
```
      PNOFY = D(1)
      DO 29 K = 2,NP1
   29 PNOFY = D(K) + (Y − X(K))*PNOFY
      ERROR = ABS(F(Y) − PNOFY)
      IF (ERROR .GT. ERRMX) ERRMX = ERROR
   30 Y = Y + .1
   40 WRITE (6,640) N,ERRMX
  640 FORMAT(I5,E18.7)
                                              STOP
      END
```

COMPUTER OUTPUT FOR EXAMPLE 4.3

N	MAXIMUM ERROR
2	6.4615385E−01
4	4.3813387E−01
6	6.1666759E−01
8	1.0451739E+00
10	1.9156431E+00
12	3.6052745E+00
14	7.1920080E+00
16	1.4051542E+01

Consider now the problem of estimating $f(x)$ at a point $x = \bar{x}$, using polynomial interpolation at distinct points $x_0, x_1, x_2, \ldots$. With $p_k(x)$ the polynomial of degree $\leq k$ which interpolates $f(x)$ at $x_0, \ldots, x_k$, we calculate successively $p_0(\bar{x}), p_1(\bar{x}), p_2(\bar{x}), \ldots$ until, hopefully, the difference between $p_{k+1}(\bar{x})$ and $p_k(\bar{x})$ is sufficiently small. The Newton form for the interpolating polynomial

$$p_k(x) = \sum_{i=0}^{k} f[x_0, \ldots, x_i]\psi_i(x)$$

with

$$\psi_i(x) = (x - x_0) \cdots (x - x_{i-1})$$

is expressly designed for such calculations. If we know $p_k(\bar{x})$, $\psi_k(\bar{x})$, and $f[x_0, \ldots, x_{k+1}]$, then we can calculate $p_{k+1}(\bar{x})$ by

$$p_{k+1}(\bar{x}) = p_k(\bar{x}) + f[x_0, \ldots, x_{k+1}]\psi_k(\bar{x})(\bar{x} - x_k)$$

Algorithm 4.4 Interpolation using an increasing number of inter-polation points Given distinct points $x_0, x_1, x_2, \ldots$ and the values $f(x_0)$, $f(x_1), f(x_2), \ldots$ of a function $f(x)$ at these points. Also, given a point $\bar{x}$.

Set $f[x_0] = f(x_0)$, $p_0(\bar{x}) = f(x_0)$, $\psi_0(\bar{x}) = 1$
For $k = 0, 1, 2, \ldots$, until satisfied, do:

> Set $f[x_{k+1}] = f(x_{k+1})$
> For $i = k, \ldots, 0$, do:
> > Calculate
> > $$f[x_i, \ldots, x_{k+1}] = \frac{f[x_{i+1}, \ldots, x_{k+1}] - f[x_i, \ldots, x_k]}{x_{k+1} - x_i}$$
>
> Set $\psi_{k+1}(\bar{x}) = \psi_k(\bar{x})(\bar{x} - x_k)$
> Set $p_{k+1}(\bar{x}) = p_k(\bar{x}) + f[x_0, \ldots, x_{k+1}]\psi_{k+1}(\bar{x})$

This algorithm generates the entries of the divided-difference table for $f(x)$ at $x_0, x_1, x_2, \ldots$ a diagonal at a time. During the calculation of $p_{k+1}(\bar{x})$, the upward diagonal emanating from $f[x_{k+1}]$ is calculated up to and including the number $f[x_0, \ldots, x_{k+1}]$, using the number $f[x_{k+1}] = f(x_{k+1})$ and the previously calculated entries $f[x_k], f[x_{k-1}, x_k], \ldots, f[x_0, \ldots, x_k]$ in the preceding diagonal. Hence, even if only the most recently calculated diagonal is saved (in a FORTRAN program, say), the algorithm provides incidentally the requisite coefficients for the Newton form for $p_{k+1}(x)$ based on the points $x_{k+1}, \ldots, x_1$:

$$p_{k+1}(x) = \sum_{i=0}^{k+1} f[x_i, \ldots, x_{k+1}] \prod_{j=i+1}^{k+1} (x - x_j) \tag{4.17}$$

Example 4.4 We apply Algorithm 4.4 to the problem of Examples 4.1 and 4.2, using $x_0 = 1$, $x_1 = 4$, $x_2 = 6$, and in addition, $x_3 = 0$. For this example, $\bar{x} = 3.5$. We get $p_0(\bar{x}) = K[x_0] = 1.5709$ and $\psi_0(\bar{x}) = 1$. Next, with $K[x_1] = 1.5727$, we get $K[x_0, x_1] = 0.0006$, and with $\psi_1(\bar{x}) = (\bar{x} - x_0)\psi_0(\bar{x}) = 2.5$, we get $p_1(\bar{x}) = 1.5709 + 0.0015 = 1.5724$.
Adding the point $x_2 = 6$, we have $K[x_2] = 1.5751$; hence $K[x_1, x_2] = 0.0012$, $K[x_0, x_1, x_2] = 0.00012$; therefore, as $\psi_2(\bar{x}) = (-0.5)(2.5) = -1.25$,

$$p_2(\bar{x}) = 1.5724 - 0.00015 = 1.57225$$

the number calculated earlier in Example 4.2.   To check the error for this approximation to $K(3.5)$, we add the point $x_3 = 0$.   With $K[x_3] = 1.5708$, we compute $K[x_2,x_3] = 0.000717$, $K[x_1,x_2,x_3] = 0.000121$, $K[x_0,x_1,x_2,x_3] = -0.000001$, and get, with $\psi_3(\bar{x}) = (-2.5)(-1.25) = 3.125$, that

$$p_3(\bar{x}) = 1.57225 - 0.000004$$

indicating that 1.5722 or 1.5723 is probably the value of $K(3.5)$ to within the accuracy of the given values of $K(x)$.

These calculations, if done by hand, are conveniently arranged in a table as shown in Fig. 4.2, which also shows how Algorithm 4.4 gradually builds up the divided-difference table.

We have listed below a FORTRAN FUNCTION, called TABLE, which uses Algorithm 4.4 to interpolate in a given table of abscissas and ordinates X(I), F(I), I = 1, . . . , NTABLE, with $F(I) = f(X(I))$, and $X(1) < X(2) < \cdots$, in order to find a good approximation to $f(x)$ at $x =$ XBAR.   The program generates $p_0(\text{XBAR}), p_1(\text{XBAR}), \ldots,$ until

$$|p_k(\text{XBAR}) - p_{k-1}(\text{XBAR})| \leq \text{TOL}$$

where TOL is a given error requirement, or until $k + 1 = \min(20, \text{NTABLE})$, and then returns the number $p_k(\text{XBAR})$.   The sequence $x_0, x_1, x_2, \ldots$ of points of interpolation is chosen from the tabular points X(1), X(2), . . . , X(NTABLE) as follows: If X(I) < XBAR $\leq$ X(I + 1), then $x_0 = X(I + 1)$, $x_1 = X(I)$, $x_2 = X(I + 2)$, $x_3 = X(I - 2)$, . . . , except near the beginning or the end of the given table, where eventually only points to the right or to the left of XBAR are used.   To protect the program (and the user!) against an unreasonable choice for TOL, the program should be modified so as to terminate also if and when the successive differences $|p_{k+1}(\text{XBAR}) - p_k(\text{XBAR})|$ begin to *increase* as k increases.   (See also Exercise 4.3-4.)

k	$p_k(\bar{x})$	$\psi_k(\bar{x})$	x_k	$K[\ ]$	$K[,]$	$K[,,]$	$K[,,,]$
0	1.5709	1.	1	1.5709			
	$+$ 15				0.0006		
1	1.5724	2.5	4	1.5727		0.00012	
	$-$ 15				0.0012		-0.000001
2	1.57225	-1.25	6	1.5751		0.000121	
	$-$ 3				0.000717		
3	1.572247	3.125	0	1.5708			

Fig. 4.2

FORTRAN SUBPROGRAM FOR INTERPOLATION IN A FUNCTION TABLE

```
      FUNCTION TABLE(XBAR,X,F,NTABLE,TOL,IFLAG)
      DIMENSION X(100),F(100),XK(20),A(20)
C  LOCATE XBAR IN THE X-ARRAY, WHICH IS ASSUMED TO BE
C     INCREASING.
      IF (XBAR .GE. X(1))                    GO TO 9
      TABLE = F(1)
                                             GO TO 11
    9 DO 10 NEXT = 2,NTABLE
      IF (XBAR .LE. X(NEXT))                 GO TO 12
   10 CONTINUE
      TABLE = F(NTABLE)
   11 WRITE (6,611) XBAR
  611 FORMAT(E16.7,19H NOT IN TABLE RANGE)
      IFLAG = 3
                                             RETURN
   12 IFLAG = 1
      A(1) = F(NEXT)
      TABLE = A(1)
      XK(1) = X(NEXT)
      PSIK = 1.
      IDIF = -1
      IEND = 1
C     USE ALGORITHM 4.4, WITH THE NEXT XK ALWAYS THE TABLE
C     POINT NEAREST XBAR OF THOSE NOT YET USED.
      KP1MAX = MIN0(20,NTABLE)
      DO 20 KP1 = 2,KP1MAX
      NEXT = NEXT + IDIF
      XK(KP1) = X(NEXT)
      A(KP1) = F(NEXT)
      KMI = KP1
      DO 13 I = 2,KP1
      KMI = KMI - 1
   13 A(KMI) = (A(KMI + 1) - A(KMI))/(XK(KP1) - XK(KMI))
C     FOR I = 1, . . . , KP1, A(I) CONTAINS NOW THE DIV.DIFF. OF
C     F(X) AT XK(I), . . . , XK(KP1).
      PSIK = PSIK*(XBAR - XK(KP1 - 1))
      ERROR = A(1)*PSIK
C  TEMPORARY PRINT OUT
      WRITE (6,613) KP1, TABLE,ERROR
  613 FORMAT(I10,2E17.7)
      TABLE = TABLE + ERROR
      IF (ABS(ERROR) .LE. TOL)               RETURN
                                             GO TO (14,15,20),IEND
   14 IDIF = 1 - IDIF
      IF (NEXT + IDIF .LE. NTABLE)           GO TO 19
      IDIF = -1
                                             GO TO 18
```

```
    15 IDIF = −1 − IDIF
       IF (NEXT + IDIF .GT. 0)              GO TO 19
       IDIF = 1
    18 IEND = 0
    19 IEND = 3 − IEND
    20 CONTINUE
       IFLAG = 2
       WRITE (6,620) KP1MAX
   620 FORMAT(19H NO CONVERGENCE IN I3,11H ITERATIONS)
                                            RETURN
       END
```

EXERCISES

4.3-1. From a table of logarithms we obtain the following values of log x at the indicated tabular points.

x	$\log x$
1.0	0.0
1.5	0.17609
2.0	0.30103
3.0	0.47712
3.5	0.54407
4.0	0.60206

Form a divided-difference table based on these values.

4.3-2. Using the divided-difference table in Exercise 4.3-1, interpolate for the following values: log 2.5, log 1.25, log 3.25.   Use a third-degree interpolating polynomial in its Newton form.

4.3-3. Estimate the error in the result obtained for log 2.5 in Exercise 4.3-2 by computing the next term in the interpolating polynomial.   Also estimate it by comparing the approximation for log 2.5 with the sum of log 2 and the approximation for log 1.25.

4.3-4. The FORTRAN function TABLE given in the text terminates as soon as $|p_{k+1}(\text{XBAR}) - p_k(\text{XBAR})| \leq \text{TOL}$.   Show that this does not guarantee that the value $p_{k+1}(\text{XBAR})$ returned by TABLE is within TOL of the desired number $f(\text{XBAR})$ by the following examples:

(a) $f(x) = x^2$; for some I, $X(I) = -10, X(I + 1) = 10, \text{XBAR} = 0, \text{TOL} = 10^{-5}$.

(b) $f(x) = x^3$; for some I, $X(I) = -100$, $X(I + 1) = 0$, $X(I + 2) = 100$, $\text{XBAR} = -50, \text{TOL} = 10^{-5}$.

4.3-5. By Exercise 4.1-4, the polynomial of degree $\leq k$ which interpolates a function $f(x)$ at $x_0, \ldots, x_k$ is $f(x)$ itself if $f(x)$ is a polynomial of degree $\leq k$.   This fact may be used to check the accuracy of the *computed* interpolating polynomial.   Adapt the FORTRAN program given in Example 4.3 to carry out such a check as follows: For $n = 4, 8, 12, \ldots, 32$, find the polynomial $p_n(x)$ of degree $\leq n$ which interpolates the function $f_n(x) = \prod_{j=1}^{n} (x - j - \frac{1}{2})$ at $0, 1, 2, \ldots, n$.   Then estimate $E_n = \max_{0 \leq x \leq n} |f_n(x) - p_n(x)|$ by $\max_i |f_n(y_i) - p_n(y_i)|$, where the y_i's are a suitably large number of points in $[0,n]$.

What can you say about the error E_n as a function of n? Does E_n grow faster (with n) than $\max_{0 \le x \le n} |f_n(x)|$? Theoretically, what should E_n be?

4.3-6. In *inverse interpolation* in a table, one is given a number $\bar{y}$ and wishes to find the point $\bar{x}$ so that $f(\bar{x}) = \bar{y}$, where $f(x)$ is the tabulated function. If $f(x)$ is (continuous and) strictly monotone-increasing or -decreasing, this problem can always be solved by considering the given table $x_i, f(x_i), i = 0, 1, 2, \ldots$ to be a table $y_i, g(y_i), i = 0, 1, 2, \ldots$ for the inverse function $g(y) = f^{-1}(y) = x$ by taking $y_i = f(x_i), g(y_i) = x_i, i = 0, 1, 2, \ldots$, and to interpolate for the unknown value $g(\bar{y})$ in this table. Use the FORTRAN function TABLE to find $\bar{x}$ so that $\sin \bar{x} = 0.6$.

4.4 THE ERROR OF THE INTERPOLATING POLYNOMIAL

Let $f(x)$ be a real-valued function on the interval $I = [a,b]$, and let $x_0, \ldots, x_n$ be $n + 1$ distinct points in I. With $p_n(x)$ the polynomial of degree $\le n$ which interpolates $f(x)$ at $x_0, \ldots, x_n$, the *interpolation error $e_n(x)$* of $p_n(x)$ is given by

$$e_n(x) = f(x) - p_n(x) \tag{4.18}$$

Let now $\bar{x}$ be any point different from $x_0, \ldots, x_n$. If $p_{n+1}(x)$ is the polynomial of degree $\le n + 1$ which interpolates $f(x)$ at $x_0, \ldots, x_n$ and at $\bar{x}$, then $p_{n+1}(\bar{x}) = f(\bar{x})$, while by (4.4) and (4.8),

$$p_{n+1}(x) = p_n(x) + f[x_0, \ldots, x_n, \bar{x}] \prod_{j=0}^{n} (x - x_j)$$

It follows that

$$f(\bar{x}) = p_{n+1}(\bar{x}) = p_n(\bar{x}) + f[x_0, \ldots, x_n, \bar{x}] \prod_{j=0}^{n} (\bar{x} - x_j)$$

Therefore,

For all $\bar{x} \ne x_0, \ldots, x_n$: $\qquad e_n(\bar{x}) = f[x_0, \ldots, x_n, \bar{x}] \prod_{j=0}^{n} (\bar{x} - x_j)$

$$\tag{4.19}$$

showing the error to be "like the next term" in the Newton form.

We cannot evaluate the right side of (4.19) without knowing the number $f(\bar{x})$. But as we now prove, the number $f[x_0, \ldots, x_n, \bar{x}]$ is closely related to the $(n + 1)$st derivative of $f(x)$, and using this information, we can at times estimate $e_n(\bar{x})$.

Theorem 4.2 Let $f(x)$ be a real-valued function, defined on $[a,b]$ and k times differentiable in (a,b). If $x_0, \ldots, x_k$ are $k + 1$ distinct points in $[a,b]$, then there exists $\xi \in (a,b)$ such that

$$f[x_0, \ldots, x_k] = \frac{f^{(k)}(\xi)}{k!} \tag{4.20}$$

For $k = 1$, this is just the mean-value theorem for derivatives (see Sec. 1.7). For the general case, observe that the error function $e_k(x) = f(x) - p_k(x)$ has (at least) the $k + 1$ distinct zeros $x_0, \ldots, x_k$ in $I = [a,b]$. Hence, if $f(x)$, and therefore $e_k(x)$, is k times differentiable on (a,b), then it follows from Rolle's theorem (see Sec. 1.7) that $e'(x)$ has at least k zeros in (a,b); hence $e''(x)$ has at least $k - 1$ zeros in (a,b), and continuing in this manner, we finally get that $e_k^{(k)}(x)$ has at least one zero in (a,b). Let ξ be one such zero. Then

$$0 = e_k^{(k)}(\xi) = f^{(k)}(\xi) - p_k^{(k)}(\xi)$$

On the other hand, we know from (4.6) that, for any x,

$$p_k^{(k)}(x) = f[x_0, \ldots, x_k]k!$$

and (4.20) now follows.

By taking $a = \min_i x_i$, $b = \max_i x_i$, it follows that the unknown point ξ in (4.20) can be assumed to lie somewhere between the x_i's.

If we apply Theorem 4.2 to (4.19), we get Theorem 4.3.

Theorem 4.3 Let $f(x)$ be a real-valued function defined on $[a,b]$ and $n + 1$ times differentiable on (a,b). If $p_n(x)$ is the polynomial of degree $\leq n$ which interpolates $f(x)$ at the $n + 1$ distinct points $x_0, \ldots, x_n$ in $[a,b]$, then for all $\bar{x} \in [a,b]$, there exists $\xi = \xi(\bar{x}) \in (a,b)$ such that

$$e_n(\bar{x}) = f(\bar{x}) - p_n(\bar{x}) = \frac{f^{(n+1)}(\xi)}{(n + 1)!} \prod_{j=0}^{n} (\bar{x} - x_j) \tag{4.21}$$

It is important to note that $\xi = \xi(\bar{x})$ depends on the point $\bar{x}$ at which the error estimate is required. This dependence need not even be continuous. As we have need in Chap. 5 to integrate and differentiate $e_n(x)$ with respect to x, we usually prefer for such purposes the formula (4.19). For, as we show in Sec. 4.6, $f[x_0, \ldots, x_n, x]$ is a well-behaved function of x.

The error formula (4.21) is of only limited practical utility since, in general, we will seldom know $f^{(n+1)}(x)$, and we will almost never know the point ξ. But when a *bound* on $|f^{(n+1)}(x)|$ is known over the entire interval $[a,b]$, then we can use (4.21) to obtain a (usually crude) bound on the error of the interpolating polynomial in that interval.

Example 4.5 Find a bound for the error in linear interpolation.

The linear polynomial interpolating $f(x)$ at x_0 and x_1 is

$$p_1(x) = f(x_0) + f[x_0,x_1](x - x_0) = \frac{(x_1 - x)f(x_0) + (x - x_0)f(x_1)}{x_1 - x_0}$$

Equation (4.21) then yields the error formula

$$f(\bar{x}) - p_1(\bar{x}) = (\bar{x} - x_0)(\bar{x} - x_1)\frac{f''(\xi)}{2!}$$

where ξ depends on $\bar{x}$. If $\bar{x}$ is a point between x_0 and x_1, then ξ lies between x_0 and x_1. Hence, if we know that $|f''(x)| \leq M$ on $[x_0,x_1]$, then

$$|f(\bar{x}) - p_1(\bar{x})| \leq |(\bar{x} - x_0)(\bar{x} - x_1)|\frac{M}{2}$$

The maximum value of $|(\bar{x} - x_0)(\bar{x} - x_1)|$ for $\bar{x} \in [x_0,x_1]$ occurs at $\bar{x} = (x_0 + x_1)/2$; hence is $(x_1 - x_0)^2/4$. It follows that, for any $\bar{x} \in [x_0,x_1]$,

$$|f(\bar{x}) - p_1(\bar{x})| \leq (x_1 - x_0)^2\frac{M}{8}$$

Example 4.6 Determine the spacing h in a table of equally spaced values of the function $f(x) = \sqrt{x}$ between 1 and 2, so that interpolation with a second-degree polynomial in this table will yield a desired accuracy.

By assumption, the table will contain $f(x_i)$, with $x_i = 1 + ih$, $i = 0, \ldots, N$, where $N = (2 - 1)/h$. If $\bar{x} \in [x_{i-1},x_{i+1}]$, then we approximate $f(\bar{x})$ by $p_2(\bar{x})$, where $p_2(x)$ is the quadratic polynomial which interpolates $f(x)$ at x_{i-1}, x_i, x_{i+1}. By (4.21), the error is then

$$f(\bar{x}) - p_2(\bar{x}) = (\bar{x} - x_{i-1})(\bar{x} - x_i)(\bar{x} - x_{i+1})\frac{f'''(\xi)}{3!}$$

for some ξ in (x_{i-1},x_{i+1}). Since we do not know ξ, we can merely estimate $f'''(\xi)$,

$$|f'''(\xi)| \leq \max_{1 \leq x \leq 2} |f'''(x)|$$

One calculates $f'''(x) = \frac{3}{8}x^{-5/2}$; hence $|f'''(\xi)| \leq \frac{3}{8}$. Further,

$$\max_{x \in [x_{i-1},x_{i+1}]} |(x - x_{i-1})(x - x_i)(x - x_{i+1})| = \max_{y \in [-h,h]} |(y + h)y(y - h)|$$

$$= \max_{y \in [-h,h]} |y(y^2 - h^2)|$$

using the linear change of variables $y = x - x_i$. Since the function $\psi(y) = y(y^2 - h^2)$ vanishes at $y = -h$ and $y = h$, the maximum of $|\psi(y)|$ on $[-h,h]$ must occur at one of the extrema of $\psi(y)$. These extrema are found by solving the equation $\psi'(y) = 3y^2 - h^2 = 0$, giving $y = \pm h/\sqrt{3}$. Hence

$$\max_{x \in [x_{i-1},x_{i+1}]} |(x - x_{i-1})(x - x_i)(x - x_{i+1})| = \frac{2h^3}{3\sqrt{3}}$$

We are now assured that, for any $\bar{x} \in [1,2]$,

$$|f(\bar{x}) - p_2(\bar{x})| \leq \frac{(2h^3/3\sqrt{3})(3/8)}{6} = \frac{h^3}{24\sqrt{3}}$$

if $p_2(x)$ is chosen as the quadratic polynomial which interpolates $f(x) = \sqrt{x}$ at the three tabular points nearest $\bar{x}$. If we wish to obtain seven-place accuracy this way, we would have to choose h so that

$$\frac{h^3}{24\sqrt{3}} < 5 \cdot 10^{-8}$$

giving $h \approx 0.0128$, or $N \approx 79$.

EXERCISES

4.4-1. A table of values of $\cos x$ is required so that linear interpolation will yield six-decimal-place accuracy for any value of x in $[0,\pi]$. Assuming that the tabular values are to be equally spaced, what is the minimum number of entries needed in the table?

4.4-2. The function defined by

$$f(x) = \int_0^x \sin s^2 \, ds$$

has been tabulated for equally spaced values of x with step $h = 0.1$. What is the maximum error encountered if cubic interpolation is to be used to calculate $f(\bar{x})$ for $\bar{x}$ any point on the interval $[0,\pi/2]$?

4.4-3. Prove: If the values $f(x_0), \ldots, f(x_n)$ are our *only* information about the function $f(x)$, then we can say *nothing* about the error $e_n(\bar{x}) = f(\bar{x}) - p_n(\bar{x})$ at a point $\bar{x} \neq x_0$, $\ldots, x_n$; that is, the error may be "very large" or may be "very small." [*Hint:* Consider interpolation at $x_0, x_1, \ldots, x_n$ to the function $f(x) = K(x - x_0) \cdots (x - x_n)$, where K is an unknown constant.] What does this imply about programs like the FUNCTION TABLE in Sec. 4.3 or Algorithm 4.4?

4.4-4. Use (4.21) to give a *lower* bound on the interpolation error $|f(\bar{x}) - p_n(\bar{x})|$ when $f(x) = \ln x$, $n = 3$, $x_0 = 1$, $x_1 = \frac{4}{3}$, $x_2 = \frac{5}{3}$, $x_3 = 2$, and $\bar{x} = \frac{3}{2}$.

4.5 INTERPOLATION IN A FUNCTION TABLE BASED ON EQUALLY SPACED POINTS

Much of engineering and scientific calculation uses functions such as $\sin x$, e^x, $J_n(x)$, erf (x), etc., which are defined by an infinite series, or as the solution of a certain differential equation, or by similar processes involving limits, and can therefore, in general, not be evaluated in a finite number of steps. Computer installations provide subroutines for the evaluation of such functions which use approximations to these functions either by polynomials or by ratios of polynomials. But before the advent of high-speed computers, the only tool for the use of such functions in calculations was the *function table*. Such a table contains function values $f(x_i)$ for certain points $x_0, \ldots, x_n$, and the user has to interpolate (literally, "put in between") the given values whenever the value of $f(x)$ at a point not already listed is desired. Polynomial interpolation was initially developed to facilitate this process. Since in such tables $f(x)$ is given at a usually increasing sequence of *equally spaced*

points, certain simplifications in the calculation of the interpolating polynomial can be made, which we discuss in this section.

Throughout this section, we assume that $f(x)$ *is tabulated for* $x = a(h)b$,
that is, we have the numbers $f(x_i)$, $i = 0, \ldots, N$, available, where

$$x_i = a + ih \qquad i = 0, \ldots, N, \text{ with } N = \frac{b - a}{h} \tag{4.22}$$

It is convenient to introduce a linear change of variables

$$s = s(x) = \frac{x - x_0}{h} \qquad \text{so that} \qquad x = x(s) = x_0 + sh \tag{4.23}$$

and to abbreviate

$$f(x) = f(x_0 + sh) = f_s \tag{4.24}$$

This has the effect of standardizing the situation to one where $f(x)$ is known
at the first $N + 1$ nonnegative integers, thus simplifying notation. It should
be noted that the *linear* change of variables (4.23) carries polynomials of
degree n in x into polynomials of degree n in s.

To calculate the polynomial of degree $\leq n$ which interpolates $f(x)$ at
$x_k, \ldots, x_{k+n}$, we need not calculate in this case a *divided-difference* table.
Rather, it is sufficient to calculate a *difference* table. To make this precise,
we introduce the *forward difference*

$$\Delta^i f_s = \begin{cases} f_s & i = 0 \\ \Delta(\Delta^{i-1} f_s) = \Delta^{i-1} f_{s+1} - \Delta^{i-1} f_s & i > 0 \end{cases} \tag{4.25}$$

The forward difference is related to the divided difference in the following way.

Lemma 4.1   For all $i \geq 0$

$$f[x_k, \ldots, x_{k+i}] = \frac{1}{i! \, h^i} \Delta^i f_k \tag{4.26}$$

Since both sides of (4.26) are defined by induction on i, the proof of
Lemma 4.1 has to be by induction. For $i = 0$, (4.26) merely asserts the
validity of the conventions

$$f[x_k] = f(x_k) = f_k = \Delta^0 f_k$$

and is therefore true. Assuming (4.26) to hold for $i = n \geq 0$, we have

$$f[x_k, \ldots, x_{k+n+1}] = \frac{f[x_{k+1}, \ldots, x_{k+n+1}] - f[x_k, \ldots, x_{k+n}]}{x_{k+n+1} - x_k}$$

$$= \frac{\Delta^n f_{k+1}/(n! \, h^n) - \Delta^n f_k/(n! \, h^n)}{(n + 1)h}$$

$$= \frac{\Delta^{n+1} f_k}{(n + 1)! \, h^{n+1}}$$

showing (4.26) to hold, then, for $i = n + 1$ too.

With this, the polynomial of degree $\leq n$ interpolating $f(x)$ at $x_k, \ldots,$ x_{k+n} becomes

$$p_n(x) = \sum_{i=0}^{n} \frac{1}{i! \, h^i} \Delta^i f_k \prod_{j=0}^{i-1} (x - x_{k+j}) \qquad (4.27)$$

In terms of s, we have

$$x - x_{k+j} = x_0 + sh - [x_0 + (k+j)h] = (s - k - j)h$$

Hence

$$p_n(x) = p_n(x_0 + sh) = \sum_{i=0}^{n} \Delta^i f_k \prod_{j=0}^{i-1} \frac{s - k - j}{j + 1}$$

A final definition shortens this expression still further. For real y and for i a nonnegative integer, we define the *binomial function*

$$\binom{y}{i} = \begin{cases} 1 & i = 0 \\ \displaystyle\prod_{j=0}^{i-1} \frac{y - j}{j + 1} = \frac{(y)(y - 1) \cdots (y - i + 1)}{1 \cdot 2 \cdots \cdots i} & i > 0 \end{cases} \qquad (4.28)$$

The word "binomial" is justified, since (4.28) is just the binomial coefficient $\binom{y}{i}$ whenever y is an integer. With this, (4.27) takes the simple form

$$p_n(x_0 + sh) = \sum_{i=0}^{n} \Delta^i f_k \binom{s - k}{i}$$

$$= f_k + (s - k) \Delta f_k + \frac{(s - k)(s - k - 1)}{2} \Delta^2 f_k$$

$$+ \cdots + \frac{(s - k) \cdots (s - k - n + 1)}{n!} \Delta^n f_k \qquad (4.29)$$

which goes under the name of *Newton forward-difference form* for the polynomial of degree $\leq n$, which interpolates $f(x)$ at $x_k + ih$, $i = 0, \ldots, n$.

The coefficients $\Delta^i f_k$ for (4.29) are conveniently read off a (*forward*)-*difference table* for $f(x)$. Such a table is shown in Fig. 4.3. According to (4.25), each entry is merely the difference between the entry to the left below and the entry to the left above.

If in (4.29) we set $k = 0$, which is customary, the Newton forward-difference form becomes

$$\boxed{p_n(x_0 + sh) = \sum_{i=0}^{n} \Delta^i f_0 \binom{s}{i}} \qquad (4.30)$$

The differences which appear in this form lie along the diagonal marked ① in Fig. 4.3.

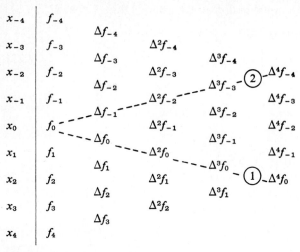

Fig. 4.3 Forward-difference table.

Example 4.7 From a table of logarithms we obtain the values of log x for $x = 2(0.2)3$. Form a difference table based on these values.

x	$\log x$	Δf	$\Delta^2 f$	$\Delta^3 f$	$\Delta^4 f$
2.0	0.30103				
		4139			
2.2	0.34242		-360		
		3779		57	
2.4	0.38021		-303		-11
		3476		46	
2.6	0.41497		-257		-12
		3219		34	
2.8	0.44716		-223		
		2996			
3.0	0.47712				

It is customary to omit the decimal point and leading zeros in difference tables. Note that the fourth differences are approximately constant, indicating that a fourth-degree polynomial should provide a very good fit for interpolating purposes.

Difference tables are also used to check the smoothness of a tabulated function and to detect errors in one or more of the function values. Consider, for example, the difference table given as Fig. 4.4. From a book of interplanetary coordinates we have selected the x coordinate of Mars in a heliocentric coordinate system corresponding to the dates given. These coordinates are given at intervals of 10 days, and have been obtained by

t	$x = f(t)$	Δf	$\Delta^2 f$	$\Delta^3 f$	$\Delta^4 f$	$\Delta^5 f$	$\Delta^6 f$
1,250.5	1.39140						
		−1444					
1,260.5	1.37696		−1469				
		−2913		55			
1,270.5	1.34783		−1414		17		
		−4327		72		−3	
1,280.5	1.30456		−1342		14		−2
		−5669		86		−5	
1,290.5	1.24787		−1256		9		8
		−6925		95		3	
1,300.5	1.17862		−1161		12		−11
		−8086		107		−8	
1,310.5	1.09776		−1054		4		8
		−9140		111		0	
1,320.5	1.00636		−943		4		
		−10083		115			
1,330.5	0.90553		−828				
		−10911					
1,340.5	0.79642						

Fig. 4.4 Heliocentric, equational X coordinate of Mars.

astronomers by various means. The first four differences have the same sign, diminish in magnitude, and are reasonably smooth. The fifth differences are of differing signs, and succeeding differences actually become larger with alternating signs. This behavior of the fifth and higher derivatives indicates that the function values are probably in error in the fifth decimal place. If those differences were to be used for interpolation purposes, only differences through the fourth should be retained. The use of higher differences might very well lead to a poorer approximation.

Because of the former importance of function tables, a rather large body of material concerning interpolation in function tables has been developed over the centuries. Difference operators other than the forward-difference operator Δ have been introduced to provide a compact notation for various forms for the interpolating polynomial, all of which differ only in the order in which interpolation points appear. These forms have been associated with the names of Newton, Gauss, Bessel, Stirling, Gregory, Everett, etc., often by tradition rather than by historical fact. A complete treatment of these forms can be found in Hildebrand [5].

We choose not to discuss these forms, with the exception of the Newton backward-difference form, which is convenient for the description of predictor-corrector methods in Chap. 6. We feel that Algorithm 4.4 and the FORTRAN subprogram TABLE discussed in Sec. 4.3 are sufficient equipment for the few occasions the student is likely to make use of tables.

The Newton forward-difference form (4.29) is useless when $k + n > N$, since it is based on the interpolation points $x_k, x_{k+1}, \ldots, x_{k+n}$. When interpolating near the end of a table, it is better to have a form which uses interpolation points in the order $x_k, x_{k-1}, \ldots, x_{k-n}$. Starting again with the Newton form for the polynomial $p_n(x)$ of degree $\leq n$ which interpolates $f(x)$ at $x_k, \ldots, x_{k-n}$, we get with Lemma 4.1 that

$$p_n(x) = \sum_{i=0}^{n} f[x_{k-i}, \ldots, x_k] \prod_{j=-i+1}^{0} (x - x_{k+j})$$

$$= \sum_{i=0}^{n} \frac{1}{i! \, h^i} \Delta^i f_{k-i} \prod_{j=-i+1}^{0} (x - x_{k+j})$$

Further,

$$\prod_{j=-i+1}^{0} (x - x_{k+j}) = \prod_{j=-i+1}^{0} (s - k - j)h = (-h)^i \prod_{j=0}^{i-1} (k - s - j)$$

Hence with (4.28),

$$p_n(x_0 + sh) = \sum_{i=0}^{n} (-1)^i \Delta^i f_{k-i} \binom{k-s}{i}$$

$$= f_k - \binom{k-s}{1} \Delta f_{k-1} + \binom{k-s}{2} \Delta^2 f_{k-2}$$

$$+ \cdots + (-1)^n \binom{k-s}{n} \Delta^n f_{k-n} \tag{4.31}$$

the *Newton backward-difference form* for the polynomial $p_n(x)$ of degree $\leq n$ which interpolates $f(x)$ at $x_k, x_{k-1}, \ldots, x_{k-n}$. Again, if we set $k = 0$ in (4.31), we obtain the simplified form

$$p_n(x_0 + sh) = \sum_{i=0}^{n} (-1)^i \Delta^i f_{-i} \binom{-s}{i} \tag{4.31a}$$

Note that the differences $\Delta^i f_{-i}$ lie along the diagonal marked ② in Fig. 4.3. Since by (4.21)

$$f(x) - p_n(x) = \frac{1}{(n+1)!} f^{(n+1)}(\xi) \prod_{j=-n}^{0} (x - x_j)$$

in this case, we get, similarly, the error in terms of the binomial function as

$$f(x_0 + sh) - p_n(x_0 + sh) = h^{n+1} f^{(n+1)}(\xi) \binom{-s}{n+1} \tag{4.32}$$

for some $\xi = \xi(s)$ in the smallest interval containing $x_{k-n}, \ldots, x_k$ and $x_0 + sh$ [provided $f(x)$ is sufficiently smooth].

Example 4.8 Using the difference table of Example 4.7, find log 2.15 as accurately as possible.

Since 2.15 is between 2.0 and 2.2, we take $x_0 = 2.00$ and use the Newton forward-difference form (4.30) with $n = 4$,

$$p_4(x_0 + sh) = f_0 + \binom{s}{1}\Delta f_0 + \binom{s}{2}\Delta^2 f_0 + \binom{s}{3}\Delta^3 f_0 + \binom{s}{4}\Delta^4 f_0$$

With $s = (x - x_0)/h$ and $h = 0.2$, $x_0 = 2.0$, we find that $\bar{x} = 2.15$ corresponds to $s = (2.15 - 2.0)/0.2 = 0.75$, and

$$\binom{s}{1} = 0.75$$

$$\binom{s}{2} = \binom{s}{1}\frac{s-1}{2} = \frac{0.75(-0.25)}{2} = -0.09375$$

$$\binom{s}{3} = \binom{s}{2}\frac{s-2}{3} = -0.09375\frac{-1.25}{3} = 0.03906$$

$$\binom{s}{4} = \binom{s}{3}\frac{s-3}{4} = 0.03906\frac{-2.25}{4} = -0.02197$$

Hence

$$\log 2.15 \approx p_4(0.75) = 0.30103 + (0.75)(0.04139) + (-0.09375)(-0.00360)$$
$$+ (0.03906)(0.00057) + (-0.02197)(-0.00011)$$
$$= 0.332435$$

An estimate of the error can be obtained from the next term in the Newton form. Thus, since $\binom{s}{5}\Delta^5 f_0 = -0.0000014$, we would expect the result above to be correct to five significant figures. The correctly rounded value of log 2.15 is actually 0.33244, in agreement with the result obtained here.

Example 4.9 Using the difference table of Example 4.7, find log 2.9 as accurately as possible.

Since 2.9 is near the end of the table, we choose $x_0 = 3.0$ and use Newton's backward-difference form (4.31a). With $h = 0.2$, we compute $s = (2.9 - 3.0)/0.2 = -\frac{1}{2}$. The formula (4.31a) with $n = 4$ is

$$p_4(x_0 + sh) = f_0 - \binom{-s}{1}\Delta f_{-1} + \binom{-s}{2}\Delta^2 f_{-2} - \binom{-s}{3}\Delta^3 f_{-3} + \binom{-s}{4}\Delta^4 f_{-4}$$

Then

$$\binom{-s}{1} = -s = \frac{1}{2}$$

$$\binom{-s}{2} = \binom{-s}{1}\frac{-s-1}{2} = \frac{1}{2}\cdot\frac{-1/2}{2} = -\frac{1}{8}$$

$$\binom{-s}{3} = \binom{-s}{2}\frac{-s-2}{3} = -\frac{1}{8}\cdot\frac{-3/2}{3} = \frac{1}{16}$$

$$\binom{-s}{4} = \binom{-s}{3}\frac{-s-3}{4} = \frac{1}{16}\cdot\frac{-5/2}{4} = -\frac{5}{128}$$

Hence

$$\log 2.9 \approx p_4\left(-\frac{1}{2}\right) = 0.47712 - \frac{1}{2}(0.02996) - \frac{1}{8}(-0.00223)$$

$$- \frac{1}{16}(0.00034) - \frac{5}{128}(-0.00012)$$

$$= 0.46240$$

EXERCISES

4.5-1. To see how an individual error in a tabular entry spreads through a table, we may proceed as follows: In Fig. 4.3 set $f_0 = \varepsilon$ and all other $f_i = 0$. Then form the difference columns. From the results determine the law which governs the growth of this isolated error.

4.5-2. The values of $f(x)$ given below are those of a certain polynomial of degree 4. Form a difference table, and from this table find $f(5)$. (See Exercise 4.5-6.)

x	0	1	2	3	4
$f(x)$	1	5	31	121	341

4.5-3. Form a difference table for the following data, and estimate the degree of the interpolating polynomial needed to produce interpolated values correct to the number of significant figures given.

x	$f(x)$
1.0	1.5709
2.0	1.5713
3.0	1.5719
4.0	1.5727
5.0	1.5738
6.0	1.5751
7.0	1.5767
8.0	1.5785
9.0	1.5805

4.5-4. Using the difference table in Fig. 4.4 find

(a) $f(1252.5)$ (b) $f(1332.5)$

In each case estimate the error.

4.5-5. Prove that if $p_n(x)$ is a polynomial of degree n with leading coefficient a_n, and x_0 is an arbitrary point, then

$$\Delta^n p_n(x_0) = a_n n! \, h^n$$

and

$$\Delta^{n+1} p_n(x_0) = 0$$

Use the definition (4.25) of the forward-difference operator Δ. [Else, use Lemma 4.1 and (4.6) or (4.20).]

4.5-6. Let $x_i = x_0 + ih$, $i = 0, 1, 2, \ldots$, and assume that you know the numbers $\Delta^0 p_n(x_n), \Delta^1 p_n(x_{n-1}), \ldots, \Delta^n p_n(x_0)$ for a certain polynomial $p_n(x)$ of degree $\leq n$. Show how to get from this information the values $p_n(x_{n+1}), p_n(x_{n+2}), \ldots$, using just n additions per value. [*Hint:* By Exercise 4.5-5, $\Delta^n p_n(x_i)$ does not depend on i, while for all i, j, $\Delta^j p_n(x_i) = \Delta^j p_n(x_{i-1}) + \Delta^{j+1} p_n(x_{i-1})$, by definition of the forward difference.] This method is useful for graphing polynomials. What is its connection with Algorithm 4.1?

4.6 THE DIVIDED DIFFERENCE AS A FUNCTION OF ITS ARGUMENTS AND OSCULATORY INTERPOLATION

We have so far dealt with divided differences only in their role as coefficients in the Newton form for the interpolating polynomial, i.e., as constants to be calculated from the given numbers $f(x_i)$, $i = 0, \ldots, n$. But the appearance of the *function* $g_n(x) = f[x_0, x_1, \ldots, x_n, x]$ in the error term (4.19) for polynomial interpolation makes it necessary to understand how the divided difference $f[x_0, \ldots, x_k]$ behaves as one or all of the points $x_0, \ldots, x_k$ vary.

To begin with, we noted in Sec. 4.2 that $f[x_0, \ldots, x_k]$ is a *symmetric* function of its arguments; that is, $f[x_0, \ldots, x_k]$ depends only on the numbers $x_0, \ldots, x_k$, and not on the order in which they appear in the argument list.

As it stands, $f[x_0, \ldots, x_k]$ is defined only when $x_0, \ldots, x_k$ are $k + 1$ *distinct* points. For example, for $k = 1$,

$$f[x_0, x_1] = \frac{f(x_1) - f(x_0)}{x_1 - x_0}$$

and the right-hand side makes sense only when $x_c \neq x_1$. But if $f(x)$ is continuously differentiable, then

$$\lim_{x_0, x_1 \to y} \frac{f(x_1) - f(x_0)}{x_1 - x_0} = f'(y)$$

Hence it then makes sense to define

$$f[x_0, x_1] = f'(x_0) \qquad \text{whenever } x_0 = x_1 \tag{4.33}$$

More generally, we have the following theorem.

Theorem 4.4 Let $f(x)$ be defined on $[a,b]$ and k times continuously differentiable there. Let $x_0, \ldots , x_k$ be distinct points in $[a,b]$ and let $y \in [a,b]$. Then

$$\lim_{x_0,\ldots,x_k \to y} f[x_0, \ldots ,x_k] = \frac{1}{k!} f^{(k)}(y) \tag{4.34}$$

For the proof, recall from Theorem 4.2 that with these assumptions

$$f[x_0, \ldots ,x_k] = \frac{1}{k!} f^{(k)}(\xi) \quad \text{for some } \xi \in \left(\min_i x_i, \max_i x_i \right)$$

Hence, if $x_0, \ldots , x_k$ all approach y, then the corresponding ξ must approach y. Therefore

$$\lim_{x_0,\ldots,x_k \to y} f[x_0, \ldots ,x_k] = \lim_{\xi \to y} \frac{1}{k!} f^{(k)}(\xi) = \frac{1}{k!} f^{(k)}(y)$$

the last equality by the continuity of $f^{(k)}(x)$.

Let now $p_n(x)$ be the polynomial of degree $\leq n$ which interpolates $f(x)$ at the $n + 1$ distinct points $x_0, \ldots , x_n$. Then, as we showed in Sec. 4.2,

$$p_n(x) = \sum_{i=0}^{n} f[x_0, \ldots ,x_i] \prod_{j=0}^{i-1} (x - x_j)$$

Assume that $f(x)$ is n times continuously differentiable. Then Theorem 4.4 implies that $p_n(x)$ goes over into the polynomial

$$\hat{p}_n(x) = \sum_{i=0}^{n} \frac{1}{i!} f^{(i)}(y) \prod_{j=0}^{i-1} (x - y) \tag{4.35}$$

as all the interpolation points $x_0, \ldots , x_n$ approach the point y. Since

$$\prod_{j=0}^{i-1} (x - y) = (x - y)^i$$

we recognize in (4.35) the truncated Taylor series for $f(x)$ around y (see Sec. 1.7), i.e.,

$$\hat{p}_n(x) = \sum_{i=0}^{n} \frac{f^{(i)}(y)(x - y)^i}{i!} \tag{4.36}$$

In the case $n = 1$, this limit process is familiar from calculus. In this case, the straight line

$$p_1(x) = f(x_0) + f[x_0,x_1](x - x_0)$$

is a *secant* to (the graph of) $f(x)$ which goes over into the *tangent*

$$\hat{p}_1(x) = f(y) + f'(y)(x - y)$$

as both x_0 and x_1 approach y. Clearly, $\hat{p}_1(x)$ agrees with $f(x)$ in value *and* slope at $x = y$.

More generally, one verifies that the Taylor polynomial (4.36) satisfies

$$\hat{p}_n^{(j)}(y) = f^{(j)}(y) \qquad j = 0, \ldots, n \tag{4.37}$$

since

$$\left(\frac{d}{dx}\right)^j (x - y)^i \bigg|_{x=y} = \begin{cases} i! & j = i \\ 0 & j \neq i \end{cases}$$

We speak of *osculatory* interpolation whenever the interpolating polynomial $\hat{p}_n(x)$ has higher than first-order contact with $f(x)$ at an interpolation point (*osculus* is the Latin word for "kiss"). Since $\hat{p}_n(x)$ is the limiting case of interpolation to $f(x)$ at $n + 1$ distinct points (as all approach the point y), we also say that $\hat{p}_n(x)$ *interpolates* $f(x)$ *at the* $n + 1$ (*equal*) *points* $y, \ldots, y$.

If we define the kth divided difference of $f(x)$ at $k + 1$ *equal* points to be

$$f[x_0, \ldots, x_k] = \frac{f^{(k)}(y)}{k!} \qquad \text{if } x_0 = x_1 = \cdots = x_k = y \tag{4.38}$$

then we can continue to use the Newton form

$$p_n(x) = \sum_{i=0}^{n} f[x_0, \ldots, x_i] \prod_{j=0}^{i-1} (x - x_j)$$

to describe the polynomial interpolating $f(x)$ at $x_0, \ldots, x_n$ even in the case when all the x_i's coincide [provided $f(x)$ is n times continuously differentiable].

Guided by (4.16) and the definition (4.38), we now extend the definition of $f[x_0, \ldots, x_k]$ still further to *all* point sets $x_0, \ldots, x_k$, distinct or partially coincident, as follows:

Case 1   If $x_0 \leq x_1 \leq \cdots \leq x_k$, then we define

$$f[x_0, \ldots, x_k] = \begin{cases} \dfrac{f[x_1, \ldots, x_k] - f[x_0, \ldots, x_{k-1}]}{x_k - x_0} & \text{if } x_0 \neq x_k \\[2ex] \dfrac{f^{(k)}(x_0)}{k!} & \text{if } x_0 = x_k \end{cases}$$

$$\tag{4.39}$$

Case 2 If not $x_0 \leq x_1 \leq \cdots \leq x_k$, then take any reordering y_0, $\ldots$, y_k of the points $x_0, \ldots, x_k$ such that $y_0 \leq y_1 \leq \cdots \leq y_k$. For such a point set, $f[y_0, \ldots, y_k]$ is defined by (4.39) in Case 1; hence, setting

$$f[x_0, \ldots, x_k] = f[y_0, \ldots, y_k]$$

then defines $f[x_0, \ldots, x_k]$ unambiguously, in this case.

It is clear that this definition is consistent with Eq. (4.9) or (4.16) as long as $x_0, \ldots, x_k$ are all distinct. The next theorem shows that this extension of $f[x_0, \ldots, x_k]$ to coincident arguments is not arbitrary, but is dictated by the desire to make $f[x_0, \ldots, x_k]$ a *continuous* function of its arguments, as was already indicated by (4.34).

Theorem 4.5 Assume that $f(x)$ is k times continuously differentiable on $[a,b]$, and let $y_0, \ldots, y_k$ be points in $[a,b]$, distinct or not. Then

(i) There exists $\xi \in (\min_i y_i, \max_i y_i)$ such that

$$f[y_0, \ldots, y_k] = \frac{1}{k!} f^{(k)}(\xi)$$

(ii) If $x_0^{(r)}, \ldots, x_k^{(r)}$ are $k+1$ points in $[a,b]$ for $r = 1, 2, \ldots$, and

$$\lim_{r \to \infty} x_i^{(r)} = y_i \qquad i = 0, \ldots, k$$

then

$$\lim_{r \to \infty} f[x_0^{(r)}, \ldots, x_k^{(r)}] = f[y_0, \ldots, y_k]$$

The proof of this theorem is by induction on k (since $f[y_0, \ldots, y_k]$ is defined inductively), and is a straightforward but *lengthy* exercise in the concept of a continuous function of several variables. The interested reader is referred to Ref. 19.

We conclude this section with some interesting consequences of Theorem 4.5. It follows at once that the function

$$g_n(x) = f[x_0, \ldots, x_n, x]$$

which appears in the error term for polynomial interpolation is defined for all x and is a *continuous* function of x if $f(x)$ is sufficiently smooth. Thus it follows that

$$f(x) = \sum_{i=0}^{n} f[x_0, \ldots, x_i] \prod_{j=0}^{i-1} (x - x_j) + f[x_0, \ldots, x_n, x] \prod_{j=0}^{n} (x - x_j)$$

$$(4.40)$$

for all x, and not only for $x \neq x_0, \ldots, x_n$ [see (4.19)].

Further, if $f(x)$ is sufficiently often differentiable, then $g_n(x)$ is differentiable. For by the definition of derivatives,

$$g_n'(x) = \lim_{h \to 0} g[x, x + h]$$

if this limit exists. On the other hand,

$$g_n[x, x + h] = f[x_0, \ldots, x_n, x, x + h] \xrightarrow[h \to 0]{} f[x_0, \ldots, x_n, x, x]$$

by Theorem 4.5. Hence

$$\frac{d}{dx} f[x_0, \ldots, x_n, x] = f[x_0, \ldots, x_n, x, x] \tag{4.41}$$

Finally, it is now easy to carry out osculatory polynomial interpolation at several points.

Theorem 4.6 Assume that $f(x)$ is $n + 1$ times continuously differentiable on $[a,b]$, and let $y_0, \ldots, y_n$ be $n + 1$ points in $[a,b]$ not necessarily distinct.

Then

$$f(x) = \hat{p}_n(x) + f[y_0, \ldots, y_n, x] \prod_{j=0}^{n} (x - y_j) \tag{4.42}$$

where

$$\hat{p}_n(x) = \sum_{i=0}^{n} f[y_0, \ldots, y_i] \prod_{j=0}^{i-1} (x - y_j) \tag{4.43}$$

Further, $\hat{p}_n(x)$ is the polynomial of degree $\leq n$ which interpolates $f(x)$ at $y_0, \ldots, y_n$ in the following sense: If the point z appears $k + 1$ times among the numbers $y_0, \ldots, y_n$, then

$$\hat{p}_n^{(j)}(z) = f^{(j)}(z) \quad j = 0, \ldots, k \tag{4.44}$$

For the proof, we start out with the identity (4.40), valid whenever the interpolation points $x_0, \ldots, x_n$ are distinct. By Theorem 4.5, this identity goes over into (4.42), with $\hat{p}_n(x)$ given by (4.43), as $x_0, \ldots, x_n$ approach $y_0, \ldots, y_n$, thus proving (4.42). In particular, $\hat{p}_n(x)$ as given by (4.43) does not depend on the order in which the y_i's are written down [although the *form* for the right side of (4.43) changes when we change the order of the

y_i's]. Hence, to prove (4.44), we can assume without loss of generality that $z = y_0 = \cdots = y_k$. Then

$$\hat{p}_n(x) = \sum_{i=0}^{k} f[y_0, \ldots, y_i] \prod_{j=0}^{i-1} (x - y_j)$$

$$+ \sum_{i=k+1}^{n} f[y_0, \ldots, y_i] \prod_{j=0}^{i-1} (x - y_j)$$

$$= \sum_{i=0}^{k} \frac{f^{(i)}(z)(x - z)^i}{i!} + (x - z)^{k+1}q(x)$$

where $q(x)$ is a polynomial of no further interest. Because of the factor $(x - z)^{k+1}$, the function $(x - z)^{k+1}q(x)$ and its first k derivatives vanish at $x = z$, while the sum is just the truncated Taylor series expansion for $f(x)$ around z. Hence (4.44) follows from (4.37).

Example 4.10 With $f(x) = \ln x$, calculate $f(1.5)$ by cubic interpolation, using $f(1) = 0$, $f(2) = 0.693147, f'(1) = 1, f'(2) = 0.5$.

In this case, the four interpolation points are $y_0 = y_1 = 1$, $y_2 = y_3 = 2$. We calculate

$$f[y_0, y_1] = f'(y_0) = 1 \qquad f[y_1, y_2] = 0.693147 \qquad f[y_2, y_3] = f'(y_2) = 0.5$$

$$f[y_0, y_1, y_2] = \frac{0.693147 - 1}{2 - 1} = -0.306853$$

$$f[y_1, y_2, y_3] = \frac{0.5 - 0.693147}{2 - 1} = -0.193147$$

$$f[y_0, y_1, y_2, y_3] = \frac{-0.193147 + 0.306853}{2 - 1} = 0.113706$$

The complete divided-difference table is written as follows:

y_i	$f[\,]$	$f[,]$	$f[,,]$	$f[,,,]$
1	0.0			
		1.0		
1	0.0		−0.306853	
		0.693147		0.113706
2	0.693147		−0.193147	
		0.5		
2	0.693147			

With this,

$$\hat{p}_3(x) = 0. + (1.)(x - 1) + (-0.306853)(x - 1)^2 + (0.113706)(x - 1)^2(x - 2)$$

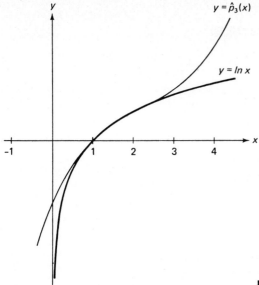

Fig. 4.5 Osculatory interpolation.

is the cubic polynomial which agrees with $\ln x$ in value *and* slope at the two points $x = 1$ and $x = 2$.   The osculatory character of the approximation of $\ln x$ by $\hat{p}_3(x)$ is evident from Fig. 4.5.   Using Algorithm 4.1 to evaluate $\hat{p}_3(x)$ at 1.5, we get

$$\ln 1.5 \approx \hat{p}_3(1.5) = 0.409074$$

With $e_3(x) = f(x) - \hat{p}_3(x)$ the error, we get from (4.42) and Theorem 4.5(*i*) the estimate

$$|e_3(1.5)| \leq \frac{1}{4!} \max_{1 \leq \xi \leq 2} |f^{(4)}(\xi)|(1.5 - 1)^2(1.5 - 2)^2 = 0.015625$$

Since $\ln 1.5 = 0.405465$, the error is actually only 0.00361.   This shows once again that the uncertainty about the location of ξ makes error estimates based on (4.21) rather conservative—to put it nicely.

We conclude this section with a FORTRAN program which calculates the coefficients for $\hat{p}_n(x)$ as given by (4.43) and then evaluates $\hat{p}_n(x)$ at a given set of equally spaced points.

```
      CALCULATION OF THE NEWTON FORM FOR THE POLYNOMIAL OF
C        DEGREE .LE. N, WHICH INTERPOLATES F(X) AT Y(I), I = 1, . . . , NP1.
C        SOME OR ALL OF THE INTERPOLATION POINTS MAY COINCIDE,
C        SUBJECT ONLY TO THE FOLLOWING RESTRICTIONS.
C        (1) IF Y(I) = Y(I + K), THEN Y(I) = Y(I + J), J = 1, . . . , K,
C        (2) IF ALSO Y(I − 1) .NE. Y(I), OR IF I = 1, THEN
C              F(I + J) = VALUE OF THE J-TH DERIVATIVE OF F(X) AT X = Y(I),
C                     J = 0, . . . , K.
C
         DIMENSION Y(30),F(30)
```

```
        READ (5,500) NP1,(Y(I),F(I),I = 1,NP1)
    500 FORMAT(I2/(2F10.3))
CALCULATE DIVIDED DIFFERENCES
        N = NP1 − 1
        IF (N .EQ. 0)                              GO TO 20
        DO 10 K = 1,N
        FLOATK = K
        NP1MK = NP1 − K
        FLAST = F(1)
        DO 9 I = 1,NP1MK
        IPK = I + K
        DY = Y(IPK) − Y(I)
        IF (DY .EQ. 0.)                            GO TO 8
        F(I) = (F(I + 1) − FLAST)/DY
        FLAST = F(I + 1)
                                                   GO TO 9
      8 F(I) = F(I + 1)/FLOATK
      9 CONTINUE
     10 F(NP1MK + 1) = FLAST
CALCULATE PN(X) FOR VARIOUS VALUES OF X.
     20 READ (5,501) NPOINT,X,DX
    501 FORMAT(I3,2F10.3)
        DO 30 J = 1,NPOINT
        PNOFX = 0.
        DO 29 I = 1,NP1
     29 PNOFX = F(I) + (X − Y(I))*PNOFX
        WRITE (6,600) J,X,PNOFX
    600 FORMAT(I10,2E20.7)
     30 X = X + DX
        STOP
        END
```

The calculation of divided differences corresponds to Algorithm 4.3 if all interpolation points are distinct. If some interpolation points coincide, the input must contain values of derivatives of the interpolant. Specifically, the input is assumed to consist of the array of interpolation points $Y(I)$, $I = 1, \ldots, NP1 = n + 1$, together with an array of numbers $F(I)$, $I = 1, \ldots, NP1$. For simplicity of programming, the sequence of interpolation points is assumed to satisfy the restriction that

$$\text{If } Y(I) = Y(I + K), \text{ then } Y(I) = Y(I + 1) = \cdots = Y(I + K)$$

i.e., all repeated interpolation points appear together. With this restriction, it is further assumed that, for each I,

$$F(I) = f^{(j)}(Y(I)) \text{ if } Y(I) = Y(I - j) \neq Y(I - j - 1)$$

Thus, with $f(x) = 1/x$, $n = 6$, the following input would be correct, in the sense that it would produce the polynomial of degree ≤ 6, which interpolates $f(x) = 1/x$ at the given $Y(I)$, $I = 1, \ldots, 7$.

I	1	2	3	4	5	6	7
Y(I)	2.	2.	2.	1.	4.	4.	5.
F(I)	0.5	−0.25	0.25	1.	0.25	−0.0625	0.2

The student is encouraged to take an example like this and trace through the calculations in the FORTRAN program. The following flow chart describing the calculations of the divided differences might help in this endeavor.

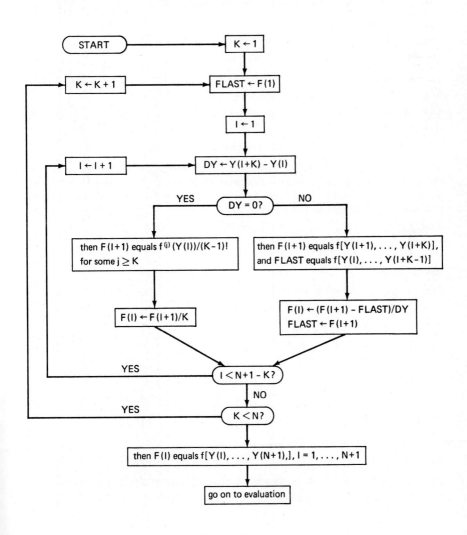

EXERCISES

4.6-1. For $f(x) = e^x$ calculate $f(0.5)$, using quadratic interpolation, given that $f(0) = 1$, $f'(0) = 1$, $f(1) = 2.7183$. Compare with the correctly rounded result $f(0.5) = 1.6487$.

4.6-2. For $f(x) = \sinh x$ we are given that

$$f(0) = 0 \qquad f'(0) = 1 \qquad f(1) = 1.1752 \qquad f'(1) = 1.5431$$

Form a divided-difference table and calculate $f(0.5)$ using cubic interpolation. Compare with the result $\sinh 0.5 = 0.5211$.

4.6-3. A function $f(x)$ has a double root at z_1 and a triple root at z_2. Determine the form of the polynomial of degree ≤ 5 which interpolates $f(x)$ twice at z_1, three times at z_2, and once at some point z_3.

4.6-4. Find the coefficients a_0, a_1, a_2, a_3 for the cubic polynomial $p_3(x) = a_0 + a_1(x - y) + a_2(x - y)^2 + a_3(x - y)^3$, so that

$$p_3(y) = f_y \qquad p_3'(y) = f_y' \qquad p_3(z) = f_z \qquad p_3'(z) = f_z'$$

where y, z, f_y, f_y', f_z, f_z' are given numbers (and $y \neq z$).

4.6-5. Get a simple expression for $p_3[(y + z)/2]$ in terms of the given numbers y, z, f_y, f_y', f_z, f_z', where $p_3(x)$ is the polynomial determined in Exercise 4.6-4.

4.6-6. In Sec. 4.2, we introduced the divided difference $f[x_0, \ldots, x_k]$ as that number A_k for which

$$p_k(x) = A_k x^k + \text{a polynomial of degree} < k$$

where $p_k(x)$ is the polynomial of degree $\leq k$ which interpolates $f(x)$ at $x_0, \ldots, x_k$. Prove that our extension of divided differences to (partially or completely) coincident point sets still satisfies this condition. Conclude that we could have used this condition to *define* divided differences at coincident points.

4.6-7. Let $g(x) = f[x_0, \ldots, x_k, x]$. Prove that

$$g[y_0, \ldots, y_n] = f[x_0, \ldots, x_k, y_0, \ldots, y_n]$$

(use induction).

4.6-8. Use Exercise 4.6-7 to prove that if $g(x) = f[x_0, \ldots, x_k, x]$, then

$$g^{(n)}(x) = n! \, f[x_0, \ldots, x_k, \overbrace{x, \ldots, x}^{n + 1 \text{ times}}]$$

4.6-9. Let $f(x) = g(x)h(x)$. Prove that

$$f[x_0, \ldots, x_k] = \sum_{i=0}^{k} g[x_0, \ldots, x_i]h[x_i, \ldots, x_k]$$

(use induction; else identify the right side as the leading coefficient of a polynomial of degree $\leq k$ which interpolates $g(x)h(x)$ at $x_0, \ldots, x_k$).

4.7 THE CASE FOR PIECEWISE-POLYNOMIAL INTERPOLATION

Polynomial interpolation is usually applied (1) to recover a function $f(x)$ from a known set of its values, e.g., from a function table, or (2) to replace the known function $f(x)$ in further calculations by a more tractable polynomial.   In either case, one may be faced with the prospect of interpolating $f(x)$ by a polynomial of "large" degree, say of degree greater than 15 or 20. In Case 1, this may come about simply because the number of given function values is that large.   In Case 2, one may feel forced into using that many points in an effort to bring the interpolation error down to an acceptable size.

A first objection to polynomial interpolation at a "large" number of points must be raised because the calculation and evaluation of the interpolating polynomial become costly and unreliable as the number of interpolation points becomes "large."   In Exercise 4.3-5 the student is invited to establish this fact experimentally.   The discussion, in Sec. 4.5, of the propagation of errors through a difference table also supports this statement.

A more serious objection to the use of interpolating polynomials of high degree is the fact that this may well *increase* the interpolation error. This was illustrated earlier in Example 4.3.   Although a rigorous discussion of this phenomenon is beyond the scope of this book, we try to indicate the salient points of the argument.   Assume that we are to approximate the function $f(x)$ on the interval $[a,b]$, and that we choose to approximate $f(x)$ by the polynomial $p_n(x)$ which interpolates $f(x)$ at the points $x_0, \ldots, x_n$ in the interval $[a,b]$.   If $f(x)$ is sufficiently smooth, then, by (4.21), the error is

$$e_n(x) = f(x) - p_n(x) = \frac{1}{(n+1)!} f^{(n+1)}(\xi) \prod_{j=0}^{n} (x - x_j) \qquad (4.45)$$

where ξ is a point in $[a,b]$ whose precise location depends in an unknown way on x.

Consider first the part

$$\frac{1}{(n+1)!} f^{(n+1)}(\xi)$$

of the error which depends on $f(x)$ but not on the interpolation points. Since ξ is not known, we have to consider its size to be

$$\frac{1}{(n+1)!} \max_{a \leq \xi \leq b} |f^{(n+1)}(\xi)| \qquad (4.46)$$

Only for very special functions, such as $f(x) = e^x$ or $f(x) = \sin x$, does (4.46) decrease rapidly as n increases.   Even for "smooth" functions such as $(x) = 1/x$ on $[1,2]$ or $f(x) = \tan x$ on $[-1,1]$, (4.46) decreases very slowly as n increases or merely stays bounded.   For functions one is most likely to meet in practice, (4.46) often increases sharply with n, or in the extreme case, $f^{(n+1)}(x)$ ceases to exist from some n on.

Hence a "small" interpolation error over $[a,b]$ can usually be expected only if the second part of the error,

$$\max_{a \leq x \leq b} \left| \prod_{j=0}^{n} (x - x_j) \right| \tag{4.47}$$

is "small." The problem of choosing the interpolation points $x_0, \ldots, x_n$ so as to minimize (4.47) is known (see Sec. 4.12) to have the unique solution

$$x_j = \frac{1}{2}\left\{ b + a - (b - a) \cos\left[\frac{2j + 1}{2(n + 1)}\pi\right]\right\} \quad j = 0, \ldots, n \tag{4.48}$$

the so-called Chebyshev points for the interval $[a,b]$. For this special choice,

$$\max_{a \leq x \leq b} \left| \prod_{j=0}^{n} (x - x_j) \right| = 2\left(\frac{b - a}{4}\right)^{n+1}$$

while, for example, for equally spaced x_j's, the number (4.47) is much larger.

It follows that the only way open to *guaranteeing* a "small" error, even for small n, is to make the interval $[a,b]$ "small." Since the interval over which $f(x)$ is to be approximated is usually given in advance, this can be accomplished only by partitioning this interval into sufficiently small subintervals and approximating $f(x)$ in each subinterval by a suitable polynomial. This leads to *piecewise-polynomial interpolation*.

A simple and familiar example of piecewise-polynomial interpolation is linear interpolation in a table of values $f(x_i)$, $i = 1, \ldots, N + 1$, where $a = x_1 < x_2 < \cdots < x_{N+1} = b$. Here $f(x)$ is approximated at a point $\bar{x}$ by locating the interval $[x_k, x_{k+1}]$ which contains $\bar{x}$ and then taking

$$p_1(\bar{x}) = f(x_k) + f[x_k, x_{k+1}](\bar{x} - x_k)$$

as the approximation to $f(\bar{x})$. In effect, $f(x)$ is approximated over $[a,b]$ by the "broken line" or piecewise-linear function $g_1(x)$ (see Fig. 4.6) with

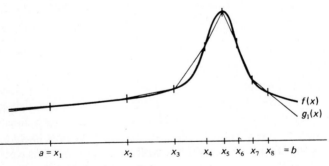

Fig. 4.6 Broken-line interpolation.

breakpoints $x_2, \ldots, x_N$, which interpolates $f(x)$ at $x_1, \ldots, x_{N+1}$. It follows from Example 4.5, applied to each of the subintervals $[x_k, x_{k+1}]$, $k = 1, \ldots, N$, that

$$\text{For all } x \in [a,b]: \quad |f(x) - g_1(x)| \le \max_{a \le \xi \le b} |f''(\xi)| \tfrac{1}{8} \Big(\max_k \Delta x_k \Big)^2 \quad (4.49)$$

provided that $f(x)$ is twice differentiable on $[a,b]$. Note that we can make the interpolation error as small as we wish by making Δx_k small for all k. Note further that such an increase in interpolation points does not complicate further work with $g_1(x)$, since $g_1(x)$ is "locally" a very simple function.

By using a piecewise-polynomial function $g_r(x)$ of degree $r > 1$ instead of the piecewise-linear $g_1(x)$, we can produce approximations to $f(x)$ whose error term contains the $(r + 1)$st power of $\max_k \Delta x_k$; hence goes to zero faster than the error (4.49) for piecewise-linear interpolation as $\max \Delta x_k$ becomes small. Piecewise-cubic approximation has become particularly popular. Several piecewise-cubic interpolation methods are discussed in the next section.

EXERCISES

4.7-1. Carry out the calculations of Example 4.3, but use the Chebyshev points (4.48) as interpolation points rather than equally spaced interpolation points. Compare your results with those of Example 4.3.

4.7-2. Show that a linear change in the independent variable can always be used to make *either* (4.46) *or* (4.47) as "small" as one would wish. Conclude that the argument given in the text is not very rigorous. How could it be made more rigorous?

*4.8 PIECEWISE-CUBIC INTERPOLATION

Let $f(x)$ be a real-valued function defined on some interval $[a,b]$. We wish to construct a piecewise-cubic (polynomial) function $g_3(x)$ which interpolates $f(x)$ at the points $x_1, \ldots, x_{N+1}$, where

$$a = x_1 < x_2 < \cdots < x_{N+1} = b \quad (4.50)$$

As with piecewise-linear interpolation, we choose the interior interpolation points $x_2, \ldots, x_N$ to be the breakpoints for $g_3(x)$; that is, on each interval $[x_i, x_{i+1}]$, we construct $g_3(x)$ as a certain cubic polynomial $P_i(x)$, $i = 1, \ldots, N$.

To facilitate the use of $g_3(x)$ in subsequent calculations, we write each cubic piece $P_i(x)$ of $g_3(x)$ as

$$P_i(x) = c_{1,i} + c_{2,i}(x - x_i) + c_{3,i}(x - x_i)^2 + c_{4,i}(x - x_i)^3 \quad (4.51)$$

Once we know the coefficients $c_{j,1}$, $j = 1, \ldots, 4$, $i = 1, \ldots, N$, then the following FORTRAN function PCUBIC efficiently evaluates $g_3(x)$ for any particular point $x = \bar{x}$.

```
      FUNCTION PCUBIC(XBAR,N,XI,C)
      DIMENSION XI(50),C(4,50)
      DATA I / 1 /
      DX = XBAR − XI(I)
      IF (DX)                                    10,30,20
   10 IF (I .EQ. 1)                              GO TO 30
      I = I − 1
      DX = XBAR − XI(I)
      IF (DX)                                    10,30,30
   19 I = I + 1
      DX = DDX
   20 IF (I .EQ. N)                              GO TO 30
      DDX = XBAR − XI(I + 1)
      IF (DDX)                                   30,19,19
   30 PCUBIC = C(1,I) + DX*(C(2,I) + DX*(C(3,I) + DX*C(4,I)))
                                                 RETURN
      END
```

We now turn to the determination of the piecewise-cubic interpolating function $g_3(x)$. Since we want

$$g_3(x_i) = f(x_i) \qquad i = 1, \ldots, N + 1$$

we must have

$$P_i(x_i) = f(x_i) \qquad P_i(x_{i+1}) = f(x_{i+1}) \qquad i = 1, \ldots, N \qquad (4.52)$$

Note that (4.52) implies

$$P_{i-1}(x_i) = P_i(x_i) \qquad i = 2, \ldots, N$$

so that $g_3(x)$ is guaranteed to be continuous on $[a,b]$.

Recall from Theorem 4.1 or 4.6 that we can always interpolate a given function at *four* points by a cubic polynomial. So far, each of the cubic pieces $P_i(x)$ is required to interpolate $f(x)$ only at *two* points. Hence we have still quite a bit of freedom in choosing the $P_i(x)$. Different interpolation methods differ only in how this freedom is used.

In piecewise-cubic Hermite interpolation, one determines $P_i(x)$ so as to interpolate $f(x)$ at $x_i, x_i, x_{i+1}, x_{i+1}$, that is, so that also

$$P_i'(x_i) = f'(x_i) \qquad P_i'(x_{i+1}) = f'(x_{i+1}) \qquad i = 1, \ldots, N \qquad (4.53)$$

It then follows by Theorem 4.6 that, for $i = 1, \ldots, N$,

$$P_i(x) = f(x_i) + f[x_i,x_i](x - x_i) + f[x_i,x_i,x_{i+1}](x - x_i)^2$$
$$+ f[x_i,x_i,x_{i+1},x_{i+1}](x - x_i)^2(x - x_{i+1})$$

Since $(x - x_{i+1}) = (x - x_i) + (x_i - x_{i+1})$, this gives

$$P_i(x) = f(x_i) + f'(x_i)(x - x_i) + (f[x_i,x_i,x_{i+1}] - f[x_i,x_i,x_{i+1},x_{i+1}]\Delta x_i)$$
$$\times (x - x_i)^2 + f[x_i,x_i,x_{i+1},x_{i+1}](x - x_i)^3$$

where $\Delta x_i = x_{i+1} - x_i$, from which we can read off directly the coefficients $c_{1,i}, c_{2,i}, c_{3,i}, c_{4,i}$ for $P_i(x)$. Using the abbreviations

$$f_i = f(x_i) \qquad s_i = f'(x_i) \qquad i = 1, \ldots, N+1 \tag{4.54}$$

we get

$$c_{1,i} = f_i \qquad c_{2,i} = s_i$$

$$c_{3,i} = f[x_i,x_i,x_{i+1}] - f[x_i,x_i,x_{i+1},x_{i+1}]\Delta x_i$$

$$= \frac{f[x_i,x_{i+1}] - s_i}{\Delta x_i} - c_{4,i}\Delta x_i$$

$$c_{4,i} = \frac{f[x_i,x_{i+1},x_{i+1}] - f[x_i,x_i,x_{i+1}]}{\Delta x_i} \tag{4.55}$$

$$= \frac{s_{i+1} + s_i - 2f[x_i,x_{i+1}]}{(\Delta x_i)^2}$$

With f_i stored in $c_{1,i}$ and s_i stored in $c_{2,i}$, $i = 1, \ldots, N+1$, the following FORTRAN subroutine utilizes (4.55) to calculate $c_{3,i}, c_{4,i}, i = 1, \ldots, N$.

```
      SUBROUTINE CALCCF(N,XI,C)
      DIMENSION XI(50),C(4,50)
      DO 10 I = 1,N
      DX = XI(I + 1) − XI(I)
      DIVDF1 = (C(1,I + 1) − C(1,I))/DX
      DIVDF3 = C(2,I) + C(2,I + 1) − 2.*DIVDF1
      C(3,I) = (DIVDF1 − C(2,I) − DIVDF3)/DX
   10 C(4,I) = DIVDF3/DX/DX
                                     RETURN
      END
```

Example 4.11 Solve the interpolation problem of Example 4.3 using piecewise-cubic Hermite interpolation; i.e., for $N = 2, 4, \ldots, 16$, choose

$$x_i = \frac{(i-1)10}{N} - 5 \qquad i = 1, \ldots, N+1$$

and interpolate

$$f(x) = (1 + x^2)^{-1}$$

at these points, estimating as before the maximum interpolation error in $[-5,5]$.

The following FORTRAN program solves this problem:

```
      DIMENSION X(17),C(4,17)
      F(X) = 1./(1. + X*X)
C        FPRIME(X) = −2.*X*F(X)**2
```

```
        WRITE (6,600)
    600 FORMAT(1H1,3X1HN5X13HMAXIMUM ERROR)
        DO 40 N = 2,16,2
        NP1 = N + 1
        H = 10./FLOAT(N)
        DO 10 I = 1,NP1
        X(I) = FLOAT(I - 1)*H - 5.
        C(1,I) = F(X(I))
     10 C(2,I) = -2.*X(I)*C(1,I)**2
        CALL CALCCF(N,X,C)
C    ESTIMATE MAXIMUM INTERPOLATION ERROR ON (-5,5).
        Y = -5.
        ERRMX = 0.
        DO 30 J = 1,101
        ERROR = ABS(F(Y) - PCUBIC(Y,N,X,C))
        IF (ERROR .GT. ERRMX) ERRMX = ERROR
     30 Y = Y + .1
     40 WRITE (6,640) N,ERRMX
    640 FORMAT(I5,E18.7)
                                                    STOP
        END
```

COMPUTER OUTPUT FOR EXAMPLE 4.11

N	MAXIMUM ERROR
2	4.9188219E−01
4	2.1947326E−01
6	9.1281965E−02
8	3.5128250E−02
10	1.2705882E−02
12	4.0849234E−03
14	1.6011164E−03
16	1.6953134E−03

In contrast to polynomial interpolation (see Example 4.3), the maximum error now decreases quite nicely as N increases.

The error in piecewise-cubic Hermite interpolation is easily estimated. Since, for $x \in [x_i, x_{i+1}]$, $g_3(x) = P_i(x)$, where $P_i(x)$ interpolates $f(x)$ at x_i, x_i, x_{i+1}, x_{i+1}, it follows from Theorem 4.6 that, for $x \in [x_i, x_{i+1}]$,

$$f(x) - g_3(x) = f[x_i, x_i, x_{i+1}, x_{i+1}, x](x - x_i)^2(x - x_{i+1})^2$$

$$= \frac{1}{4!} f^{(4)}(\xi_i)(x - x_i)^2(x - x_{i+1})^2 \qquad \text{some } \xi_i \in (x_i, x_{i+1})$$

provided $f(x)$ is four times continuously differentiable. Further,

$$\max_{x \in [x_i, x_{i+1}]} |(x - x_i)^2(x - x_{i+1})^2| = (\tfrac{1}{2}\Delta x_i)^4 \leq \frac{(\max_j \Delta x_j)^4}{16}$$

Therefore

$$\text{For } a \le x \le b: \qquad |f(x) - g_3(x)| \le \max_{\xi \in [a,b]} |f^{(4)}(\xi)| \frac{(\max_i \Delta x_i)^4}{384} \qquad (4.56)$$

Piecewise-cubic Hermite interpolation requires knowledge of $f'(x)$. In practice, it is often difficult, if not impossible, to acquire the needed numbers $f'(x_i)$, $i = 1, \ldots, N + 1$. In such a case, one uses for s_i some reasonable approximation to $f'(x_i)$, $i = 1, \ldots, N + 1$. Thus, in *piece-wise-cubic Bessel* interpolation, one uses

$$s_i = f[x_{i-1}, x_{i+1}] \qquad (4.57)$$

instead of $s_i = f'(x_i)$, but proceeds otherwise as before, determining the coefficients $c_{j,i}$ for the cubic pieces by (4.55). Note that (4.57) requires the two additional points x_0, x_{N+2} to give some number for the boundary derivatives s_1, s_{n+1} of $g_3(x)$. One chooses these points somehow, e.g.,

$$x_0 = a \qquad x_{N+2} = b$$

Otherwise, one uses

$$s_1 = f'(a) \qquad s_{N+1} = f'(b) \qquad (4.58)$$

if these numbers are available. Yet another possibility is to choose s_1 and s_{N+1} in such a way that $g_3(x)$ satisfies the "free-end" conditions

$$g_3''(a) = g_3''(b) = 0 \qquad (4.59)$$

If we continue to use $f_i = f(x_i)$, $i = 1, \ldots, N + 1$, in (4.55), then regardless of the particular choice of numbers s_i, $i = 1, \ldots, N + 1$, the resulting piecewise-cubic function $g_3(x)$ interpolates $f(x)$ at $x_1, \ldots, x_{N+1}$. Further, $g_3(x)$ is not only continuous, but also continuously differentiable on $[a,b]$, since (4.55) implies that

$$P_{i-1}'(x_i) = s_i = P_i'(x_i) \qquad i = 2, \ldots, N$$

As we now show, it is always possible to determine the numbers $s_1, \ldots, s_{N+1}$ in such a way that the resulting $g_3(x)$ is even *twice* continuously differentiable. This method of determining $g_3(x)$ is known as *cubic spline interpolation*. The name "spline" has been given to the interpolant $g_3(x)$ in this case, since its graph approximates the position which a draftman's spline (i.e., a thin flexible rod) would occupy if it were constrained to pass through the points $\{x_i, f_i\}$, $i = 1, \ldots, N + 1$.

The requirement that $g_3(x)$ be twice continuously differentiable is equivalent to the condition that

$$P_{i-1}''(x_i) = P_i''(x_i) \qquad i = 2, \ldots, N$$

or with (4.51),

$$2c_{3,i-1} + 6c_{4,i-1} \Delta x_{i-1} = 2c_{3,i} \qquad i = 2, \ldots, N$$

Hence, with (4.55) we want

$$\frac{2(f[x_{i-1},x_i] - s_{i-1})}{\Delta x_{i-1}} + 4c_{4,i-1}\Delta x_{i-1} = \frac{2(f[x_i,x_{i+1}] - s_i)}{\Delta x_i} - 2c_{4,i}\Delta x_i$$

$$i = 2, \ldots, N$$

If we use (4.55) to express $c_{4,i-1}$ and $c_{4,i}$ in terms of the f_j's and s_j's, and simplify, we get

$$(\Delta x_i)s_{i-1} + 2(\Delta x_{i-1} + \Delta x_i)s_i + (\Delta x_{i-1})s_{i+1}$$

$$= 3(f[x_{i-1},x_i]\Delta x_i + f[x_i,x_{i+1}]\Delta x_{i-1}) \qquad i = 2, \ldots, N \quad (4.60)$$

This is a system of $N - 1$ linear equations in the $N + 1$ unknowns $s_1, \ldots, s_{N+1}$. If we somehow choose s_1 and s_{N+1}, for example, by (4.57) or (4.58), we can solve (4.60) for $s_2, \ldots, s_N$ by Gauss elimination (see Chap. 3). The coefficient matrix of (4.60) is then strictly row diagonally dominant, hence (see the corollary to Lemma 3.4) invertible, so that (4.60) has then a unique solution.

The FORTRAN subprogram SPLINE below uses Gauss elimination adapted to take advantage of the tridiagonal character of the coefficient matrix of (4.60) (see Algorithm 3.3) to calculate $c_{2,i} = s_i$, $i = 2, \ldots, N$, as the solution of (4.60), given the numbers $c_{1,i} = f_i$, $i = 1, \ldots, N + 1$, and $c_{2,1} = s_1$, $c_{2,N+1} = s_{N+1}$.

```
SUBROUTINE SPLINE(N,XI,C)
DIMENSION XI(50),C(4,50),D(50),DIAG(50)
DATA DIAG(1),D(1)/1.,0. /
NP1 = N + 1
DO 10 M = 2,NP1
D(M) = XI(M) − XI(M − 1)
10 DIAG(M) = (C(1,M) − C(1,M − 1))/D(M)
DO 20 M = 2,N
C(2,M) = 3.*(D(M)*DIAG(M + 1) + D(M + 1)*DIAG(M))
20 DIAG(M) = 2.*(D(M) + D(M + 1))
DO 30 M = 2,N
G = −D(M + 1)/DIAG(M − 1)
DIAG(M) = DIAG(M) + G*D(M − 1)
30 C(2,M) = C(2,M) + G*C(2,M − 1)
NJ = NP1
DO 40 M = 2,N
NJ = NJ − 1
40 C(2,NJ) = (C(2,NJ) − D(NJ)*C(2,NJ + 1))/DIAG(NJ)
                                    RETURN
END
```

Example 4.12 Approximating a design curve by a cubic spline We are given a design curve, a cross section of part of a car door, say, as pictured in Fig. 4.7a. The

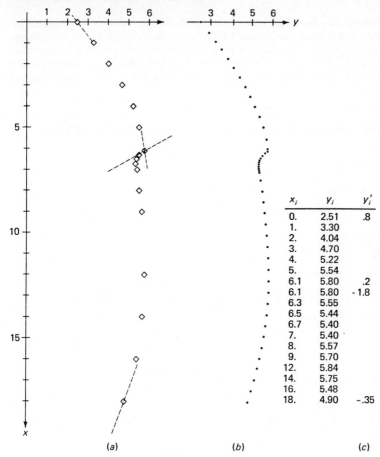

x_i	y_i	y_i'
0.	2.51	.8
1.	3.30	
2.	4.04	
3.	4.70	
4.	5.22	
5.	5.54	
6.1	5.80	.2
6.1	5.80	-1.8
6.3	5.55	
6.5	5.44	
6.7	5.40	
7.	5.40	
8.	5.57	
9.	5.70	
12.	5.84	
14.	5.75	
16.	5.48	
18.	4.90	-.35

(a)   (b)   (c)

Fig. 4.7   Cubic spline approximation to a design curve.

curve has a slope discontinuity at $x = 6.1$.   Measurements have been taken and end slopes have been estimated graphically, as indicated in Fig. 4.7a and c.   The problem is to find a function $s(x)$ which fits the data and "looks smooth."

A solution to this problem is easily provided by cubic spline interpolation to the given data, using two cubic splines which join continuously, but with differing slopes, at $x = 6.1$.   The following FORTRAN program accomplishes this, using the subprograms SPLINE and CALCCF discussed earlier.   The program reads in the data up to $x = 6.1$, including the two given end slopes, and stores the calculated polynomial coefficients of the first six polynomial pieces in

$C(J,I), J = 1, \ldots , 4 \quad I = 1, \ldots , 6$

Then the data from $x = 6.1$ to $x = 18$ are read in, together with the two end slopes, and using SPLINE and CALCCF once again, the coefficients

$C(J,I), J = 1, \ldots , 4 \quad I = 7, \ldots , 16$

of the remaining 10 polynomial pieces are found. Finally, the calculated piecewise-cubic function $s(x)$ is evaluated, using PCUBIC, for various values of x; some of these values are plotted in Fig. 4.7b. Even without the slope discontinuity, polynomial interpolation to these data would produce an "unsmooth," i.e., oscillatory, approximation because the region of relatively high curvature near 6.1 is followed by a rather flat and enigmatic section (see Exercise 4.8-2).

FORTRAN PROGRAM FOR CUBIC SPLINE INTERPOLATION (EXAMPLE 4.12)

```
        DIMENSION XI(50),C(4,50)
        READ (5,500) N1
  500 FORMAT(I2)
        READ (5,501) (XI(I),C(1,I),I = 1,N1),C(2,1),C(2,N1)
        N = N1 − 1
        CALL SPLINE(N,XI,C)
        CALL CALCCF(N,XI,C)
C
        READ (5,500) N2
        N1N2 = N + N2
        READ (5,501) (XI(I),C(1,I),I = N1,N1N2),C(2,N1),C(2,N1N2)
  501 FORMAT(2E10.3)
        N = N2 − 1
        CALL SPLINE(N,XI(N1),C(1,N1))
        CALL CALCCF(N,XI(N1),C(1,N1))
C
        N = N1N2 − 1
        X = XI(1)
        DO 10 J = 1,200
        FX = PCUBIC(X,N,XI,C)
        WRITE (6,600) J,X,FX
  600 FORMAT(I5,F10.1,E20.9)
   10 X = X + .1
                                                    STOP
        END
```

EXERCISES

4.8-1. In the notation employed in this section, derive the equation which f_1, f_2, s_1, s_2 must satisfy in order for the "free-end" condition

$$g_3''(a) = 0$$

to hold.

4.8-2. Calculate the polynomial of appropriate degree which interpolates the design curve of Example 4.12 at all the given data points from 6.1 to 18 (including slopes), and compare it with the spline approximation calculated in Example 4.12.

4.8-3. Interpolate the data of Example 4.12 by cubic Bessel interpolation and compare.

4.8-4. Cubic Bessel interpolation is *local* in the sense that the value of the interpolating function $g_3(x)$ at any point $\bar{x}$ depends only on the four given function values nearest $\bar{x}$.

By contrast, cubic spline interpolation is *global*; i.e., the value of $g_3(x)$ at any given point depends on all the given information about $f(x)$. Prove these two assertions.

4.8-5. Try to construct a reasonable scheme of interpolating a given function by a piecewise-parabolic function $g_2(x)$. Can you make $g_2(x)$ continuously differentiable?

4.9 DATA FITTING

We have so far discussed the approximation of a function $f(x)$ by means of interpolation at certain points. Such a procedure presupposes that the values of $f(x)$ at these points are known. Hence interpolation is of little use (if not outright dangerous) in the following common situation: The function $f(x)$ describes the relationship between two physical quantities x and $y = f(x)$, and through measurement or other experiment, one has obtained numbers f_n which merely *approximate* the value of $f(x)$ at x_n, that is

$$f(x_n) = f_n + \varepsilon_n \qquad n = 1, \ldots, N$$

where the experimental errors ε_n are unknown. The problem of *data fitting* is to recover $f(x)$ from the given (approximate) data f_n, $n = 1, \ldots, N$.

Strictly speaking, one never *knows* that the numbers f_n are in error. Rather, based on other information about $f(x)$ or even by mere feeling, one decides that $f(x)$ is not as complicated or as quickly varying a function as the numbers f_n would seem to indicate, and therefore believes that the numbers f_n must be in error.

Consider, for example, the data plotted in Fig. 4.8. Here

$$x_n = n \qquad n = 1, \ldots, 11$$

x_i	f_i
1	.0
2	.6
3	1.77
4	1.92
5	3.31
6	3.52
7	4.59
8	5.31
9	5.79
10	7.06
11	7.17

Fig. 4.8 Least-squares straight-line approximation to certain data.

If we have reason to believe that $f(x)$ is a straight line, the given data are most certainly in error.   If we only know that $f(x)$ is a convex function, we still can conclude that the data are erroneous.   Even if we know nothing about $f(x)$, we might still be tempted to conclude from Fig. 4.8 that $f(x)$ is a straight line, although we would now be on shaky ground.   But whether or not we know anything about $f(x)$, we can conclude from the plotted data that most of the information about $f(x)$ contained in the data f_n can be adequately represented by a straight line.

To summarize, data fitting is based on the belief that the given data f_n contain a slowly varying component, the *trend* of, or the *information* about, $f(x)$, and a comparatively fast varying component of comparatively small amplitude, the *error* or *noise* in the data.   The task is to approximate or fit the data by some function $F^*(x)$ in such a way that $F^*(x)$ contains or represents most (if not all) the information about $f(x)$ contained in the data and little (if any) of the error or noise.

This is accomplished in practice by picking a function

$$F(x) = F(x;c_1, \ldots ,c_k) \tag{4.61}$$

which depends on the parameters $c_1, \ldots , c_k$.   Normally, one will try to select a function $F(x)$ which depends *linearly* on the parameters, so that $F(x)$ will have the form

$$F(x) = c_1\phi_1(x) + c_2\phi_2(x) + \cdots + c_k\phi_k(x) \tag{4.62}$$

where the $\{\phi_i\}$ are an a priori selected set of functions and the $\{c_i\}$ are parameters which must be determined.   The $\{\phi_i\}$ may, for example, be the set of monomials $\{x^{i-1}\}$ or the set of trigonometric functions $\{\sin \pi i x\}$.   Normally, k is small compared with the number N of data points.   The hope is that k is large enough so that the information about $f(x)$ in the data can be well represented by proper choice of the parameters $c_1, \ldots , c_k$, while at the same time k is too small to also allow for reproduction of the error or noise.

Once the practitioner of the art of data fitting has decided on the right form (4.61) for the approximating function, he has to determine particular values $c_1^*, \ldots , c_k^*$ for the parameters c_i to get a "good" approximation $F^*(x) = F(x;c_1^*, \ldots ,c_k^*)$.   In general, there will be many ways of doing this.   One way is to choose the $\{c_i^*\}$ so as to minimize the expression

$$\sum_{n=1}^{N} |d_n|$$

where

$$d_n = f_n - F(x_n;c_1, \ldots ,c_k)$$

In effect, this choice of the $\{c_i\}$ will minimize the sum of the absolute value of the deviations d_n.   Figure 4.8 illustrates these deviations in a typical example. Another way is to minimize

$$\max_{1 \le n \le N} |d_n|$$

i.e., to make all deviations uniformly as small as possible.

Both these criteria lead to a *nonlinear* system of equations for the determination of the c_i^*'s.   It is therefore customary to determine the c_i^*'s so as to minimize the sum of squares of the deviations, i.e., to minimize

$$E(c_1, \ldots, c_k) = \sum_{n=1}^{N} [f_n - F(x_n; c_1, \ldots, c_k)]^2 \tag{4.63}$$

for this leads to a *linear* system of equations for the determination of the c_i^*'s. The resulting approximation is then known as the *least-squares approximation* to the given data.

The problem of minimizing $E(c_1, \ldots, c_k)$ can be solved as follows: First we note that $E(c_1, \ldots, c_k)$ is continuously differentiable as a function of its arguments, and then we recall that at a minimum the first partial derivatives must vanish.   On differentiating $E(c_1, \ldots, c_k)$ with respect to the c_i, we obtain

$$\frac{\partial}{\partial c_i} E(c_1, \ldots, c_k) = \sum_{n=1}^{N} \frac{\partial}{\partial c_i} [f_n - F(x_n; c_1, \ldots, c_k)]^2$$

$$= -2 \sum_{n=1}^{N} [f_n - F(x_n; c_1, \ldots, c_k)]$$

$$\times \frac{\partial}{\partial c_i} F(x_n; c_1, \ldots, c_k) \quad (4.64)$$

Since $F(x; c_1, \ldots, c_k)$ is of the form (4.62), we get

$$\frac{\partial}{\partial c_i} F(x_n; c_1, \ldots, c_k) = \phi_i(x_n)$$

Using this in (4.64) and setting the result to zero, we obtain, for $i = 1, \ldots, k,$

$$-2 \sum_{n=1}^{N} [f_n - F(x_n; c_1^*, \ldots, c_k^*)] \phi_i(x_n) = \frac{\partial}{\partial c_i} E(c_1, \ldots, c_k)|_{c_j = c_j^*} = 0$$

$$(4.65)$$

This system of equations is therefore a necessary condition for $c_1^*, \ldots, c_k^*$ to minimize $E(c_1, \ldots, c_k)$.   The equations (4.65) are known as the *normal* equations of the least-squares approximation. Using the particular form (4.62) of $F(x;c_1, \ldots ,c_k)$ once more, the normal equations can be rewritten

$$c_1^* \sum_{n=1}^{N} \phi_i(x_n)\phi_1(x_n) + \cdots + c_k^* \sum_{n=1}^{N} \phi_i(x_n)\phi_k(x_n) = \sum_{n=1}^{N} f_n\phi_i(x_n)$$

$$i = 1, \ldots , k \quad (4.66)$$

a system of k linear equations in the k unknowns $c_1^*, \ldots , c_k^*$. As it turns out, this system always has at least one solution [regardless of what the $\phi_i(x)$ are]; further, any solution of (4.66) minimizes $E(c_1, \ldots ,c_k)$.

To give an example, we now find the least-squares approximation to the data plotted in Fig. 4.8 by a straight line.

In this example, $x_n = n, n = 1, \ldots , 11$, and

$$F(x;c_1,c_2) = c_1 + c_2x$$

so that $k = 2$ and $\phi_1(x) = 1$, $\phi_2(x) = x$. The linear system (4.66) takes the form

$$11c_1^* + 66c_2^* = 41.04$$
$$66c_1^* + 506c_2^* = 328.05$$

which, when solved by Gauss elimination, gives the unique solution

$$c_1^* = -0.7314 \cdots \qquad c_2^* = 0.7437 \cdots$$

The resulting straight line is plotted also in Fig. 4.8.

At this point, all would be well if it were not for the unhappy fact that the coefficient matrix of (4.66) is quite often ill-conditioned, enough so that straightforward application of the elimination algorithm 3.2 produces unreliable results. This is illustrated by the following simple example.

Example 4.13 We are given approximate values $f_n \approx f(x_n)$ with

$$x_n = 10 + \frac{n - 1}{5} \qquad n = 1, \ldots , 6$$

and we have reason to believe that these data can be adequately represented by a parabola. Accordingly, we choose

$$\phi_1(x) = 1 \qquad \phi_2(x) = x \qquad \phi_3(x) = x^2$$

For this case, the coefficient matrix A of (4.66) is

$$A = \begin{bmatrix} 6 & 63 & 662.2 \\ 63 & 662.2 & 6{,}967.8 \\ 662.2 & 6{,}967.8 & 73{,}393.5664 \end{bmatrix}$$

It follows that $\|A\|_\infty \approx 8 \cdot 10^4$. On the other hand, with

$$\mathbf{x} = \begin{bmatrix} 10.07 \\ -2. \\ 0.099 \end{bmatrix} \qquad \text{we get} \qquad A\mathbf{x} = \begin{bmatrix} -0.02 \\ -0.18 \\ -1.28 \end{bmatrix}$$

Hence, from the inequality (3.51),

$$\|A\mathbf{x}\| \geq \frac{\|\mathbf{x}\|}{\|A^{-1}\|}$$

we get

$$1.28 = \|A\mathbf{x}\|_\infty \geq \frac{10.07}{\|A^{-1}\|_\infty} \qquad \text{or} \qquad \|A^{-1}\|_\infty \geq 7.8$$

Therefore the condition number of A is

$$\text{cond}(A) = \|A\|_\infty \|A^{-1}\|_\infty \geq 10^5$$

Actually, the condition number of A is much larger than 10^5, as the following specific results show. We pick

$$f(x) = 10 - 2x + \frac{x^2}{10}$$

and use exact data,

$$f_n = f(x_n) \qquad n = 1, \ldots, 6$$

Then, since $f(x)$ is a polynomial of degree 2, $F^*(x)$ should be $f(x)$ itself; therefore we should get

$$c_1^* = 10 \qquad c_2^* = -2 \qquad c_3^* = 0.1$$

Using the elimination algorithm 3.2 to solve (4.66) for this case on the CDC 6500 produces the result

$$c_1^* = 9.9999997437 \cdots \qquad c_2^* = -1.9999999511 \cdots \qquad c_3^* = 0.0999999976 \cdots$$

so that 14-decimal-digit floating-point arithmetic for this 3×3 system gives only about 8 correct decimal digits. If we round the (3,3) entry of A to 73,393.6 and repeat the calculation, the computed answer turns out to be an astonishing

$$c_1^* = 6.035 \cdots \qquad c_2^* = -1.243 \cdots \qquad c_3^* = 0.0639 \cdots$$

Similarly, if all calculations are carried out in seven-decimal-digit floating-point arithmetic, the results are

$$c_1^* = 8.492 \cdots \qquad c_2^* = -1.712 \cdots \qquad c_3^* = 0.0863 \cdots$$

This example should make clear that it can be dangerous to rush into solving the normal equations without some preliminary work. This work should consist in choosing the $\phi_i(x)$ carefully.

A seemingly simple way to avoid the condition problem is to choose the $\phi_i(x)$ to be *orthogonal* on the points $x_1, \ldots, x_N$, that is, so that

$$\sum_{n=1}^{N} \phi_i(x_n)\phi_j(x_n) = 0 \qquad \text{whenever } i \neq j \qquad (4.67)$$

For if (4.67) holds, Eqs. (4.66) reduce to

$$c_i^* \sum_{n=1}^{N} \phi_i(x_n)\phi_i(x_n) = \sum_{n=1}^{N} f_n\phi_i(x_n) \qquad i = 1, \ldots, k \qquad (4.68)$$

whose solution offers, offhand, no further difficulty.

Of course, this nice way out of the condition problem merely replaces one problem by another, for now we have to get hold of orthogonal functions. If we also want the ϕ_i's to be polynomials, it is possible to construct such orthogonal polynomial functions quite efficiently using a three-term recurrence relation valid for sequences of orthogonal polynomials. This we discuss in Secs. 4.10 and 4.11. If, as is often the case in practice, $f(x)$ cannot be assumed to be of polynomial form, other means for constructing appropriate orthogonal functions have to be used. One such technique, the modified Gram-Schmidt algorithm, is discussed in some texts (see, for example, Ref. 17). Alternatively, one has to be satisfied with choosing $\phi_1(x), \ldots, \phi_k(x)$ to be "nearly" orthogonal. This vague term is meant to describe the fact that the coefficient matrix of (4.66) for such $\phi_i(x)$ is "nearly" diagonal, e.g., diagonally dominant. If the points $x_1, \ldots, x_N$ are distributed nearly uniformly in some interval (a,b), then $\phi_1(x), \ldots, \phi_k(x)$ tend to be "nearly" orthogonal if each $\phi_i(x)$ changes sign in (a,b) one more time than does $\phi_{i-1}(x)$ (see Exercise 4.9-3).

EXERCISES

4.9-1. Calculate the least-squares approximation to the data plotted in Fig. 4.8 by functions of the form

$$F(x) = c_1 + c_2 x + c_3 \sin [123(x - 1)]$$

by solving the appropriate normal equations. Do you feel that this approximation represents all the information about $f(x)$ contained in the data? Why?

4.9-2. Derive the normal equations for the best c_1^*, c_2^*, in case

$$F(x) = F(x;c_1,c_2) = c_1 e^{c_2 x}$$

following the argument given in the text. Are these normal equations still linear?

4.9-3. Repeat all the calculations in Example 4.13 using the functions

$$\phi_1(x) = 1 \qquad \phi_2(x) = x - 10.5 \qquad \phi_3(x) = (x - 10.3)(x - 10.7)$$

According to the last paragraph of this section, the normal equations should now be much better conditioned. Are they?

*4.10   ORTHOGONAL POLYNOMIALS

In this section, we discuss briefly some pertinent properties and specific examples of sequences of orthogonal polynomials. Although our immediate motivation for this discussion comes from the problem of least-squares approximation by polynomials (to be discussed in the next section), we have use for orthogonal polynomials in different contexts later on, e.g., in Secs. 4.12 and 5.4.   In preparation for those sections, we use now a notion of orthogonality of functions which is somewhat more general than the one introduced in Sec. 4.9.

In what is to follow, let (a,b) be a given interval and let $w(x)$ be a given function defined (at least) on (a,b) and positive there.   Further, we define the *scalar product*

$$\langle g,h \rangle$$

of any two functions $g(x)$ and $h(x)$ [defined on (a,b)] in one of two ways:

$$\langle g,h \rangle = \int_a^b g(x)h(x)w(x)\,dx \tag{4.69}$$

or

$$\langle g,h \rangle = \sum_{n=1}^{N} g(x_n)h(x_n)w(x_n) \tag{4.70}$$

In the first case, we assume that the integral exists (at least as an improper integral) for all functions $g(x)$ and $h(x)$ of interest; in the second case, we assume that we have given N points $x_1, \ldots, x_N$ all in the interval (a,b) which are considered fixed during the discussion.   Note that, with $w(x) \equiv 1$, (4.70) reduces to the kind of "product" of functions which plays a major role in the discussion of least-squares approximation in Sec. 4.9.

With the scalar product of two functions defined, we say that the two functions $g(x)$ and $h(x)$ are *orthogonal* (to each other) in case

$$\langle g,h \rangle = 0$$

It is easy to verify, for example, that the functions $g(x) \equiv 1$, $h(x) = x$ are orthogonal if the scalar product is

$$\langle g,h \rangle = \int_{-1}^{1} g(x)h(x)\,dx$$

They are also orthogonal if the scalar product is

$$\langle g,h \rangle = \sum_{n=-10}^{10} g(n)h(n)$$

or if the scalar product is

$$\langle g,h \rangle = \int_{-1}^{1} \frac{g(x)h(x)}{(1-x^2)^{1/2}}\,dx$$

The functions $g(x) = \sin nx$, $h(x) = \sin mx$ are orthogonal, for n and m integers, if

$$\langle g,h \rangle = \int_0^{2\pi} g(x)h(x)\, dx$$

and $n \neq m$, as are the functions $g(x) = \sin nx$, $h(x) = \cos mx$.

Further, we say that $P_0(x), P_1(x), P_2(x), \ldots$ is a (finite or infinite) *sequence of orthogonal polynomials* provided the $P_i(x)$ are all orthogonal to each other and each $P_i(x)$ is a polynomial of exact degree i. In other words,

(i) For each i, $P_i(x) = \alpha_i x^i +$ a polynomial of degree $< i$, with $\alpha_i \neq 0$
(ii) Whenever $i \neq j$, then $\langle P_i, P_j \rangle = 0$

The functions

$$P_0(x) \equiv 1 \qquad P_1(x) = x \qquad P_2(x) = 3x^2 - 1$$

for instance, form a sequence of three orthogonal polynomials if

$$\langle g,h \rangle = \int_{-1}^{1} g(x)h(x)\, dx$$

We mentioned earlier that $\langle P_0, P_1 \rangle = 0$. Also

$$\langle P_0, P_2 \rangle = \int_{-1}^{1} 1(3x^2 - 1)\, dx = x^3 - x \Big|_{-1}^{1} = 0$$

while

$$\langle P_1, P_2 \rangle = \int_{-1}^{1} x(3x^2 - 1)\, dx = \tfrac{3}{4}x^4 - \tfrac{1}{2}x^2 \Big|_{-1}^{1} = 0$$

Let $P_0(x), P_1(x), \ldots, P_k(x)$ be a finite sequence of orthogonal polynomials. Then the following facts can be proved:

Property 1 If $p(x)$ is *any* polynomial of degree $\leq k$, the $p(x)$ can be written

$$p(x) = d_0 P_0(x) + d_1 P_1(x) + \cdots + d_k P_k(x) \tag{4.71}$$

with the coefficients $d_0, \ldots, d_k$ uniquely determined by $p(x)$. Specifically, if

$$p(x) = a_k x^k + \text{a polynomial of degree } < k$$

and if the leading coefficient of $P_k(x)$ is α_k, then

$$d_k = \frac{a_k}{\alpha_k}$$

This property follows from (i), above, by induction on k. For the example above, we can write the general polynomial of degree ≤ 2,

$$p_2(x) = a_0 + a_1 x + a_2 x^2$$

as

$$p_2(x) = \left(a_0 + \frac{a_2}{3}\right)P_0(x) + a_1 P_1(x) + \frac{a_2}{3}P_2(x)$$

By combining Property 1 with (ii), one gets Property 2.

Property 2   If $p(x)$ is a polynomial of degree $<k$, then $p(x)$ is orthogonal to $P_k(x)$, that is,

$$\langle p, P_k \rangle = 0$$

If in the example above we take $p(x) = 1 + x$, we find that

$$\langle p, P_2 \rangle = \int_{-1}^{1} (1 + x)(3x^2 - 1)\, dx = \tfrac{3}{4}x^4 + x^3 - \tfrac{1}{2}x^2 - x \Big|_{-1}^{1} = 0$$

This rather innocuous property has several important consequences.

Property 3   If the scalar product is given by (4.69), then $P_k(x)$ has k simple real zeros, all of which lie in the interval (a,b); that is, $P_k(x)$ is of the form

$$P_k(x) = \alpha_k(x - \xi_{1,k})(x - \xi_{2,k}) \cdots (x - \xi_{k,k}) \tag{4.72}$$

for certain k distinct points $\xi_{1,k}, \ldots, \xi_{k,k}$ in (a,b).

For our example,

$$P_0(x) \equiv \alpha_0 \equiv 1 \qquad P_1(x) = \alpha_1(x - \xi_{1,1}) = 1 \cdot (x - 0)$$

$$P_2(x) = \alpha_2(x - \xi_{1,2})(x - \xi_{2,2}) = 3\left(x + \frac{1}{\sqrt{3}}\right)\left(x - \frac{1}{\sqrt{3}}\right)$$

A simple proof of Property 3 goes as follows: Let $k > 0$ and let $\xi_{1,k}, \ldots, \xi_{r,k}$ be all the points in the interval (a,b) at which $P_k(x)$ changes sign. We claim that then

$$r \geq k$$

For if r were less than k, then, with $\bar{x} \in (\max_i \xi_{i,k}, b)$,

$$p(x) = P_k(\bar{x})(x - \xi_{1,k})(x - \xi_{2,k}) \cdots (x - \xi_{r,k})$$

would be a polynomial of degree $<k$ which, at every point in (a,b), has the same sign as $P_k(x)$. Hence, on the one hand, by Property 3,

$$\int_a^b p(x) P_k(x) w(x)\, dx = \langle p, P_k \rangle = 0$$

while on the other hand,

$$p(x)P_k(x)w(x) > 0 \qquad \text{for all } x \in (a,b) \text{ except } x = \xi_{1,k}, \ldots, \xi_{r,k}$$

and these two facts certainly contradict each other. Consequently, we must have $r \geq k$; that is, $P_k(x)$ must change sign in (a,b) at least k times. But since $P_k(x)$ is a polynomial of degree k and each $\xi_{i,k}$ is a root of $P_k(x)$, r cannot be bigger than k (see Sec. 2.6); therefore r must equal k, that is, the k distinct points $\xi_{i,k}, i = 1, \ldots, k$, are exactly the zeros of $P_k(x)$.

One proves similarly that (4.72) holds when the scalar product is given by (4.70), provided there are at least k distinct points among the x_n's.

Property 4   The orthogonal polynomials satisfy a three-term recurrence relation. If we set

$$A_i = \frac{\alpha_{i+1}}{\alpha_i} \qquad \text{all } i$$

$$P_{-1}(x) \equiv 0$$

and if

$$S_i = \langle P_i, P_i \rangle$$

is not zero for $i = 0, \ldots, k - 1$, then this recurrence relation can be written

$$P_{i+1}(x) = A_i(x - B_i)P_i(x) - C_iP_{i-1}(x) \qquad i = 0, 1, \ldots, k - 1 \tag{4.73}$$

where

$$B_i = \frac{\langle xP_i(x), P_i(x) \rangle}{S_i} \qquad i = 1, \ldots, k - 1$$

and

$$C_i = \begin{cases} \text{arbitrary} & i = 0 \\ \dfrac{A_iS_i}{A_{i-1}S_{i-1}} & i > 0 \end{cases}$$

This property can be used to generate sequences of orthogonal polynomials (provided the numbers S_i and B_i can be calculated and the S_i are not zero). In such a process, one usually chooses the leading coefficients α_i, or equivalently, the numbers A_i, so that the resulting sequence is particularly simple in some sense.

Example 4.14   Legendre polynomials   If the scalar product is given by

$$\langle g, h \rangle = \int_{-1}^{1} g(x)h(x)\, dx$$

then the resulting orthogonal polynomials are associated with Legendre's name. Starting with

$$P_0(x) \equiv 1$$

one gets

$$S_0 = \int_{-1}^{1} 1 \, dx = 2 \qquad B_0 = \int_{-1}^{1} x \cdot 1 \, dx = 0$$

Hence, from Property 4, with the choice $A_i = 1$, all i, we get

$$P_1(x) = x$$

Further,

$$S_1 = \int_{-1}^{1} x^2 \, dx = \tfrac{2}{3} \qquad B_1 = \int_{-1}^{1} x \cdot x^2 \, dx = 0 \qquad C_1 = \frac{S_1}{S_0} = \tfrac{1}{3}$$

so, again by Property 4,

$$P_2(x) = x^2 - \tfrac{1}{3}$$

Again,

$$S_2 = \int_{-1}^{1} (x^2 - \tfrac{1}{3})^2 \, dx = \tfrac{8}{45} \qquad B_2 = \int_{-1}^{1} x(x^2 - \tfrac{1}{3})^2 \, dx = 0 \qquad C_2 = \tfrac{4}{15}$$

so

$$P_3(x) = x^3 - \tfrac{3}{5}x$$

It is customary to normalize the Legendre polynomials so that

$$P_k(1) = 1 \qquad \text{all } k$$

With this normalization, the coefficients in the recurrence relation become

$$A_k = \frac{2k + 1}{k + 1} \qquad B_k = 0 \qquad C_k = \frac{k}{k + 1} \qquad k = 0, 1, 2, \ldots$$

so that

$$P_{k+1}(x) = \frac{(2k + 1)xP_k(x) - kP_{k-1}(x)}{k + 1}$$

Table 4.1 gives the first few Legendre polynomials.

Table 4.1

k	$P_k(x)$
0	1
1	x
2	$(3/2)(x^2 - 1/3)$
3	$(5/2)[x^3 - (3/5)x]$
4	$(35/8)[x^4 - (6/7)x^2 + 3/35]$

Example 4.15 Chebyshev polynomials If the scalar product is given by

$$\langle g,h \rangle = \int_{-1}^{1} \frac{g(x)h(x)}{(1 - x^2)^{1/2}} \, dx$$

then one gets the Chebyshev polynomials. It is customary to denote the kth such polynomial by $T_k(x)$. With the usual normalization, their recurrence relation is particularly simple. The coefficients are

$$
\begin{array}{llll}
A_0 = 1 & B_0 = 0 & & \\
A_k = 2 & B_k = 0 & C_k = 1 & k = 1, 2, \ldots
\end{array}
$$

so that

$$T_{k+1}(x) = 2xT_k(x) - T_{k-1}(x) \qquad k = 1, 2, \ldots \tag{4.74}$$

Most of the properties of Chebyshev polynomials can be derived from the remarkable fact that

$$T_k(\cos \theta) \equiv \cos k\theta \tag{4.75}$$

We consider Chebyshev polynomials in more detail in Sec. 4.12.

Example 4.16 Hermite polynomials $H_k(x)$ result when the scalar product

$$\langle g,h \rangle = \int_{-\infty}^{\infty} g(x)h(x)e^{-x^2} \, dx$$

is used. With the customary normalization, these polynomials satisfy the recurrence relation

$$H_{k+1}(x) = 2xH_k(x) - 2kH_{k-1}(x) \qquad k = 0, 1, 2, \ldots$$

The first few Hermite polynomials are given in Table 4.2.

Example 4.17 Generalized Laguerre polynomials $L_k^\alpha(x)$ are associated with the scalar product

$$\langle g,h \rangle = \int_{0}^{\infty} g(x)h(x)x^\alpha e^{-x} \, dx$$

The coefficients for the recurrence relation are

$$A_k = -\frac{1}{k+1} \qquad B_k = 2k + \alpha + 1 \qquad C_k = \frac{k+\alpha}{k+1}$$

Table 4.2

k	$H(x)$
0	1
1	$2x$
2	$4x^2 - 2$
3	$8x^3 - 12x$
4	$16x^4 - 48x^2 + 12$

We leave the generation of the first five Laguerre polynomials (with $\alpha = 0$) to the student (see Exercise 4.10-1).

The last two examples are of particular importance in the numerical quadrature over semi-infinite or infinite intervals (see Sec. 5.4).

We conclude this section with the discussion of an algorithm for the evaluation of a polynomial given in terms of orthogonal polynomials. Suppose that $P_0(x), P_1(x), \ldots, P_k(x)$ is a finite sequence of orthogonal polynomials, and suppose that we have given a polynomial $p(x)$ of degree $\leq k$ in terms of the $P_i(x)$, that is, we know the coefficients $d_0, \ldots, d_k$ so that

$$p(x) = d_0 P_0(x) + d_1 P_1(x) + \cdots + d_k P_k(x) \qquad (4.76)$$

In evaluating $p(x)$ at a particular point $\bar{x}$, we can make use of the three-term recurrence relation (4.73) for the $P_i(x)$ as follows: By (4.73),

$$P_k(\bar{x}) = A_{k-1}(\bar{x} - B_{k-1})P_{k-1}(\bar{x}) - C_{k-1}P_{k-2}(\bar{x})$$

Therefore

$$
\begin{aligned}
p(\bar{x}) = d_0 P_0(\bar{x}) + \cdots &+ d_{k-3}P_{k-3}(\bar{x}) + (d_{k-2} - d_k C_{k-1})P_{k-2}(\bar{x}) \\
&+ [d_{k-1} + d_k A_{k-1}(\bar{x} - B_{k-1})]P_{k-1}(\bar{x})
\end{aligned}
$$

or with the abbreviations

$$\bar{d}_k = d_k \qquad \bar{d}_{k-1} = d_{k-1} + \bar{d}_k A_{k-1}(\bar{x} - B_{k-1})$$

we have

$$
\begin{aligned}
p(\bar{x}) = d_0 P_0(\bar{x}) + \cdots &+ d_{k-3}P_{k-3}(\bar{x}) + (d_{k-2} - \bar{d}_k C_{k-1})P_{k-2}(\bar{x}) \\
&+ \bar{d}_{k-1}P_{k-1}(\bar{x}) \quad (4.77)
\end{aligned}
$$

Again by (4.73),

$$P_{k-1}(\bar{x}) = A_{k-2}(\bar{x} - B_{k-2})P_{k-2}(\bar{x}) - C_{k-2}P_{k-3}(\bar{x})$$

and substituting this into (4.77), we get

$$p(\bar{x}) = d_0 P_0(\bar{x}) + \cdots + (d_{k-3} - \bar{d}_{k-1}C_{k-2})P_{k-3}(\bar{x}) + \bar{d}_{k-2}P_{k-2}(\bar{x})$$

where we have used the abbreviation

$$\bar{d}_{k-2} = d_{k-2} + \bar{d}_{k-1}A_{k-2}(\bar{x} - B_{k-2}) - \bar{d}_k C_{k-1}$$

Proceeding in this fashion, we calculate sequentially

$$\bar{d}_j = d_j + \bar{d}_{j+1}A_j(\bar{x} - B_j) - \bar{d}_{j+2}C_{j+1} \qquad j = k - 2, \ldots, 0$$

getting finally that

$$p(\bar{x}) = \bar{d}_0 P_0(\bar{x}) = \bar{d}_0 \alpha_0$$

Algorithm 4.5 Nested multiplication for orthogonal polynomials
Given the coefficients $A_j, B_j, C_j, j = 0, \ldots, k - 1$, for the three-term recurrence relation (4.73) satisfied by the orthogonal polynomials $P_0(x), \ldots,$

$P_k(x)$; given also the constant $\alpha_0 = P_0(x)$, the coefficients $d_0, \ldots, d_k$ of $p(x)$ in (4.76), and a point $\bar{x}$.

Set $\bar{d}_k = d_k$

If $k = 0$, stop

Otherwise, set $\bar{d}_{k-1} = d_{k-1} + \bar{d}_k A_{k-1}(\bar{x} - B_{k-1})$ and continue

If $k = 1$, stop

Otherwise, for $j = k - 2, \ldots, 0$, do:

$\quad$ Set $\bar{d}_j = d_j + \bar{d}_{j+1} A_j(\bar{x} - B_j) - \bar{d}_{j+2} C_{j+1}$

Then $p(\bar{x})$ is given by

$$p(\bar{x}) = \bar{d}_0 P_0(x)$$

FORTRAN implementations of this algorithm have to contend with the minor difficulty that FORTRAN does not allow zero subscripts. Also, storage requirements and the number of necessary calculations vary from one set of orthogonal polynomials to another.

Example 4.18 Write a FORTRAN implementation of Algorithm 4.5 in case the orthogonal polynomials are the Chebyshev polynomials.

In this case, the A_i, B_i, C_i need not be stored in arrays since they do not depend on i. Also, the calculation of $\bar{d}_j$ requires only $\bar{d}_{j+1}$ and $\bar{d}_{j+2}$; hence it is not necessary to store the full array $\bar{d}_i$, $i = 0, \ldots, k$.

The FORTRAN FUNCTION CHEB below solves the given problem. NTERMS is the number of terms in $p(x)$; that is, $p(x)$ is of degree $\leq$ NTERMS $- 1$. Both NTERMS and the coefficients

$$D(i) = d_{i-1} \quad i = 1, \ldots, \text{NTERMS}$$

are assumed to be in the labeled COMMON POLY.

```
      FUNCTION CHEB(X)
      COMMON / POLY / NTERMS,D(30)
      K = NTERMS
      CHEB = D(K)
      K = K - 1
      IF (K .EQ. 0)                          RETURN
      TWOX = 2.*X
      PREV2 = 0.
   10 PREV = CHEB
      IF (K .EQ. 1)                          GO TO 20
      CHEB = D(K) + TWOX*PREV - PREV2
      PREV2 = PREV
      K = K - 1
                                             GO TO 10
   20 CHEB = D(1) + X*PREV - PREV2
                                             RETURN
      END
```

EXERCISES

4.10-1. Using the appropriate recurrence relation, generate the first five Laguerre polynomials (for $\alpha = 0$).

4.10-2. Find the zeros of the Legendre polynomials $P_2(x)$, $P_3(x)$, and $P_4(x)$.

4.10-3. Find the zeros of the Hermite polynomials $H_2(x)$, $H_3(x)$, $H_4(x)$.

4.10-4. Express the polynomial $p(x) = x^4 + 2x^3 + x^2 + 2x + 1$ as a sum of Legendre polynomials.

4.10-5. Verify directly that the Legendre polynomial $P_3(x)$ is orthogonal to any polynomial of degree 2.

4.10-6. Prove that if $P_k(x)$ is the Legendre polynomial of degree k, then

$$\int_{-1}^{1} [P_k(x)]^2 \, dx = \frac{2}{2k + 1}$$

Use the three-term recurrence relation satisfied by Legendre polynomials.

4.10-7. Let $P_0(x)$, $P_1(x)$, . . . be a sequence of orthogonal polynomials and let x_0, . . . , x_k be the $k + 1$ distinct zeros of $P_{k+1}(x)$. Prove that the Lagrange polynomials $l_i(x) = \prod_{j \neq i} (x - x_j)/(x_i - x_j)$, $i = 0$, . . . , k, for these points are orthogonal to each other. [*Hint:* Show that for $i \neq j$, $l_i(x)l_j(x) = P_{k+1}(x)g(x)$, where $g(x)$ is some polynomial of degree $\leq k$.]

*4.11 LEAST-SQUARES APPROXIMATION BY POLYNOMIALS

In this section, we discuss the use of sequences of orthogonal polynomials for the calculation of polynomial (weighted) least-squares approximations.

Let $f(x)$ be a function defined on some interval (a,b), and suppose that we wish to approximate $f(x)$ on (a,b) by a polynomial of degree $\leq k$. If we measure the difference between $f(x)$ and $p(x)$ by

$$\langle f(x) - p(x), f(x) - p(x) \rangle = \begin{cases} \int_a^b [f(x) - p(x)]^2 w(x) \, dx, \text{ or} \\ \sum_{n=1}^{N} [f(x_n) - p(x_n)]^2 w(x_n) \end{cases} \tag{4.78}$$

where the scalar product is given by (4.69) or (4.70), then it is natural to seek a polynomial of degree $\leq k$ for which (4.78) is as small as possible. Such a polynomial is called a (*weighted*) *least-squares approximation to* $f(x)$ *by polynomials of degree* $\leq k$.

The problem of finding such a polynomial is solved in Sec. 4.9 for the particular case that the scalar product is given by (4.70) with the weight function $w(x) = 1$. In the general case, one proceeds as follows: Suppose that we can find, for the chosen scalar product, a sequence $P_0(x)$, . . . , $P_k(x)$ of orthogonal polynomials. By Property 1 of such sequences (see Sec. 4.10), every polynomial $p(x)$ of degree $\leq k$ can be written in the form

$$p(x) = d_0 P_0(x) + \cdots + d_k P_k(x)$$

for suitable coefficients $d_0, \ldots, d_k$. Substituting this into (4.78), it follows that we want to minimize

$$E(d_0, \ldots, d_k) = \langle f(x) - d_0 P_0(x) - \cdots - d_k P_k(x),$$
$$f(x) - d_0 P_0(x) - \cdots - d_k P_k(x) \rangle$$

over all possible choices of $d_0, \ldots, d_k$. Proceeding as in Sec. 4.9, one shows that "best" coefficients $d_0^*, \ldots, d_k^*$ must satisfy the *normal equations*

$$d_0^* \langle P_0, P_i \rangle + d_1^* \langle P_1, P_i \rangle + \cdots + d_k^* \langle P_k, P_i \rangle = \langle f, P_i \rangle \quad i = 0, \ldots k$$

which, because of the orthogonality of the $P_j(x)$, reduce to

$$d_i^* \langle P_i, P_i \rangle = \langle f, P_i \rangle \quad i \doteq 0, \ldots, k$$

Hence, if

$$S_i = \langle P_i, P_i \rangle \quad i = 0, \ldots, k$$

are all nonzero, then the best coefficients are simply given by

$$d_i^* = \frac{\langle f, P_i \rangle}{S_i} \quad i = 0, \ldots, k \tag{4.79}$$

Example 4.19 Calculate the polynomial of degree ≤ 3 which minimizes

$$\int_{-1}^{1} [e^x - p(x)]^2 \, dx$$

over all polynomials $p(x)$ of degree ≤ 3.

In this case, $f(x) = e^x$, and the scalar product is given by

$$\langle g, h \rangle = \int_{-1}^{1} g(x) h(x) \, dx$$

From Example 4.14, we find the orthogonal polynomials for this scalar product to be the Legendre polynomials. Using Table 4.1 of these polynomials, we calculate

$$\langle f, P_0 \rangle = \int_{-1}^{1} e^x \, dx = e - \frac{1}{e}$$

$$\langle f, P_1 \rangle = \int_{-1}^{1} e^x x \, dx = \frac{2}{e}$$

$$\langle f, P_2 \rangle = \frac{3}{2} \int_{-1}^{1} e^x (x^2 - \tfrac{1}{3}) \, dx = e - \frac{7}{e}$$

$$\langle f, P_3 \rangle = \frac{5}{2} \int_{-1}^{1} e^x (x^3 - \tfrac{3}{5}x) \, dx = -5e + \frac{37}{e}$$

One can show that, for the Legendre polynomials (see Exercise 4.10-6),

$$S_i = \langle P_i, P_i \rangle = \frac{2}{2i + 1} \quad \text{all } i$$

so that $S_0 = 2$, $S_1 = \frac{2}{3}$, $S_2 = \frac{2}{5}$, $S_3 = \frac{2}{7}$. Using (4.79) to calculate the d_i^* and using $e = 2.71828183$, we find that the least-squares approximation to e^x on $(-1,1)$ by cubic polynomials is

$$p^*(x) = 1.175201194P_0(x) + 1.103638324P_1(x) + 0.3578143506P_2(x)$$
$$+ 0.07045563367P_3(x)$$

If we replace $P_i(x)$ by their equivalent expressions in powers of x using Table 4.1 and rearrange, we obtain

$$p^*(x) = 0.9962940183 + 0.9979548730x + 0.5367215260x^2 + 0.1761390842x^3$$

On $(-1,1)$, this polynomial has a maximum deviation from e^x of about 0.011.

If the appropriate orthogonal polynomials cannot be found in tables, one has to generate them. This can be done with the aid of the three-term recurrence relation (4.73). We now give an algorithmic description of this technique for the practically important case when the scalar product is

$$\langle g,h \rangle = \sum_{n=1}^{N} g(x_n)h(x_n)w(x_n) \tag{4.80}$$

with $x_1, \ldots, x_N$ certain fixed points in (a,b).

Algorithm 4.6 Generation of orthogonal polynomials For simplicity, we elect to get all orthogonal polynomials with leading coefficient 1, so that

$$A_i = \alpha_i = 1 \qquad \text{all } i$$

Step 0 Set $P_0(x) \equiv 1$. Further, calculate

$$S_0 = \langle P_0,P_0 \rangle = \sum_{n=1}^{N} w(x_n)$$

If $N \geq 1$ and $w(x) > 0$, then S_0 is not zero, and we can go on to calculate

$$P_1(x) = (x - B_0)P_0(x) = x - B_0$$

where, by Property 4 of orthogonal polynomials (see Sec. 4.10),

$$B_0 = \frac{\langle xP_0(x),P_0(x) \rangle}{S_0} = \sum_{n=1}^{N} \frac{x_n w(x_n)}{S_0}$$

With $P_0(x), \ldots, P_j(x)$ already constructed, the general, or jth, step proceeds as follows:

Step j Calculate

$$S_j = \langle P_j,P_j \rangle = \sum_{n=1}^{N} [P_j(x_n)]^2 w(x_n)$$

Since $P_j(x)$ is a polynomial of exact degree j, S_j can be zero only if no more than j of the points $x_1, \ldots, x_N$ are distinct. Hence, if there are more than j distinct points among the x_n's, we can calculate

$$B_j = \frac{\langle xP_j(x), P_j(x) \rangle}{S_j} = \sum_{n=1}^{N} x_n [P_j(x_n)]^2 \frac{w(x_n)}{S_j}$$

$$C_j = \frac{S_j}{S_{j-1}}$$

and get the next orthogonal polynomial as

$$P_{j+1}(x) = (x - B_j)P_j(x) - C_j P_{j-1}(x) \tag{4.81}$$

Example 4.20 Solve the least-squares approximation problem of Example 4.13 using orthogonal polynomials.

For this example, $f(x) = 10 - 2x + x^2/10$,

$$x_n = 10 + \frac{n-1}{5} \qquad f_n = f(x_n) \qquad n = 1, \ldots, 6$$

and we seek the polynomial of degree ≤ 2 which minimizes

$$\sum_{n=1}^{6} [f_n - p(x_n)]^2$$

i.e., we are dealing with the scalar product (4.70) with $w(x) \equiv 1$. Following the Algorithm 4.6, we calculate

$$P_0(x) \equiv 1 \qquad \text{hence} \qquad S_0 = \sum_{n=1}^{6} 1 = 6$$

$$B_0 = \sum_{n=1}^{6} \left[10 + \frac{n-1}{5} \right] S_0 = \frac{63}{6} = 10.5$$

Therefore

$$P_1(x) = x - 10.5 \qquad S_1 = \sum_{n=1}^{6} \left(\frac{n-1}{5} - 0.5 \right)^2 = 0.7$$

and, as $S_1 \neq 0$, we can go on to calculate $P_2(x)$. We get

$$B_1 = \sum_{n=1}^{N} \frac{[10 + (n-1)/5][(n-1)/5 - 0.5]^2}{S_1} = \frac{7.35}{0.7} = 10.5$$

$$C_1 = \frac{S_1}{S_0} = \frac{0.7}{6} = 0.1166667$$

if we carry seven decimal places and round. This gives

$$P_2(x) = (x - 10.5)^2 - 0.1166667 \qquad S_2 = 0.05973332$$

Next, we calculate the best coefficients d_0^*, d_1^*, d_2^* for the least-squares approximation

$$p^*(x) = d_0^* P_0(x) + d_1^* P_1(x) + d_2^* P_2(x)$$

using (4.79) and continuing with seven-decimal-digit floating-point arithmetic. This gives

$$d_0^* = \sum_{n=1}^{6} \frac{f_n}{6} = 0.03666667$$

$$d_1^* = \sum_{n=1}^{6} \frac{f_n P_1(x_n)}{0.7} = 0.1$$

$$d_2^* = \sum_{n=1}^{6} \frac{f_n P_2(x_n)}{0.05973332} = 0.0999999$$

To compare this with the results computed in Example 4.13, we write $p^*(x)$ in terms of 1, x, x^2. We get

$$p^*(x) = 0.03666667 + 0.1(x - 10.5)$$
$$+ 0.0999999[(x - 10.5)^2 - 0.1166667]$$
$$= 0.03666667 - 1.05 + 0.0999999(110.25 - 0.1166667)$$
$$+ [0.1 + 0.0999999(-21)]x + 0.0999999x^2$$

Hence, computed this way, the c_i^* of Example 4.13 become

$$c_1^* = 9.99998 \cdots \qquad c_2^* = -0.9999997 \cdots \qquad c_3^* = 0.0999999 \cdots$$

By contrast, we obtained in Example 4.13

$$c_1^* = 8.492 \cdots \qquad c_2^* = -1.712 \cdots \qquad c_3^* = 0.0863 \cdots$$

when we solved the normal equations (4.66) for the c_i^*'s directly, using seven-decimal-digit floating-point arithmetic. The results using orthogonal polynomials thus show an impressive improvement in this example.

Incidentally, one would normally not go to the trouble of expressing $p^*(x)$ in terms of the powers of x. Rather, one would use Algorithm 4.5 together with the computed d_i^* whenever $p^*(x)$ is to be evaluated, since one has the coefficients B_i and C_i of the recurrence relation available.

In a FORTRAN implementation, the generation of the orthogonal polynomials and the calculation of the best coefficients d_i^* are best combined into one operation to save storage. For the calculation of d_j^* and of $P_{j+1}(x)$, we only need the numbers

$$P_j(x_n) \qquad P_{j-1}(x_n) \qquad n = 1, \ldots, N$$

Hence, if d_j^* is calculated as soon as $P_j(x_n)$, $n = 1, \ldots, N$, become available, then $P_j(x_n)$, $n = 1, \ldots, N$, can safely be forgotten once $P_{j+1}(x)$ and $P_{j+2}(x)$ have been calculated. Again, there is no need to construct the $P_j(x)$ explicitly in terms of the powers of x, say, since we need only their values at the x_n, $n = 1, \ldots, N$.

The FORTRAN subroutine ORTPOL below is based on the preceding discussion.   Input consists of

$$X(n) = x_n \qquad F(n) = f_n \qquad W(n) = w(x_n) \qquad n = 1, \ldots, \text{NPOINT}$$

and the number NTERMS which is one larger than the degree of the desired polynomial approximation.   It is assumed that at least NTERMS $-$ 1 of the given x_n's are distinct, and that the $W(n)$ are all positive.   In addition, two arrays, PJM1 and PJ, are to be provided for temporary storage.   The program calculates the entries for the arrays $B(j)$, $C(j), j = 1, \ldots, \text{NTERMS}$ $-$ 1, and $D(j), j = 1, \ldots, \text{NTERMS}$ such that

$$P_{j+1}(x) = [x - B(j + 1)]P_j(x) - C(j + 1)P_{j-1}(x)$$

$$j = 0, 1, \ldots, \text{NTERMS} - 1$$

and such that

$$p^*(x) = D(1)P_0(x) + D(2)P_1(x) + \cdots + D(\text{NTERMS})P_{\text{NTERMS}-1}(x)$$

minimizes

$$\sum_{n=1}^{N} [f_n - p(x_n)]^2 w(x_n)$$

over all polynomials $p(x)$ of degree $<$ NTERMS.

The program also returns the array ERROR, where

$$\text{ERROR}(n) = f_n - p^*(x_n) \qquad n = 1, \ldots, \text{NPOINT}$$

```
      SUBROUTINE ORTPOL(NPOINT,X,F,W,ERROR,PJM1,PJ)
      COMMON / POLY / NTERMS,B(20),C(20),D(20)
      DIMENSION  X(100),F(100),W(100),ERROR(100),PJM1(100),PJ(100)
      DIMENSION  S(20)
C
      DO 9 J = 1,NTERMS
      B(J) = 0.
      D(J) = 0.
    9 S(J) = 0.
      C(1) = 0.
      DO 10 I = 1,NPOINT
      D(1) = D(1) + F(I)*W(I)
      B(1) = B(1) + X(I)*W(I)
   10 S(1) = S(1) + W(I)
      D(1) = D(1)/S(1)
      DO 11 I = 1,NPOINT
   11 ERROR(I) = F(I) - D(1)
      IF (NTERMS .EQ. 1)                        RETURN
      B(1) = B(1)/S(1)
      DO 12 I = 1,NPOINT
      PJM1(I) = 1.
```

```
    12 PJ(I) = X(I) − B(1)
       J = 1
C
    20 J = J + 1
       DO 21 I = 1,NPOINT
       P = PJ(I)*W(I)
       D(J) = D(J) + ERROR(I)*P
       P = P*PJ(I)
       B(J) = B(J) + X(I)*P
    21 S(J) = S(J) + P
       D(J) = D(J)/S(J)
       DO 22 I = 1,NPOINT
    22 ERROR(I) = ERROR(I) − D(J)*PJ(I)
       IF (J .EQ. NTERMS)                     RETURN
       B(J) = B(J)/S(J)
       C(J) = S(J)/S(J − 1)
       DO 27 I = 1,NPOINT
       P = PJ(I)
       PJ(I) = (X(I) − B(J))*PJ(I) − C(J)*PJM1(I)
    27 PJM1(I) = P
                                           GO TO 20
       END
```

The calculation of the $D(j)$ as carried out in this subprogram needs perhaps some clarification. Since $D(j) = d^*_{j-1}$, we get from (4.79) that

$$D(j) = \sum_{n=1}^{\text{NPOINT}} \frac{f_n P_{j-1}(x_n)w(x_n)}{S_{j-1}} \tag{4.82}$$

whereas in the program, $D(j)$ is calculated as

$$D(j) = \sum_{n=1}^{\text{NPOINT}} \frac{\text{ERROR}(n)P_{j-1}(x_n)w(x_n)}{S_{j-1}} \tag{4.83}$$

with

$$\text{ERROR}(n) = f_n - D(1)P_0(x_n) - \cdots - D(j-1)P_{j-2}(x_n) \qquad \text{all } n \tag{4.84}$$

If one substitutes (4.84) into (4.83), one gets

$$D(j) = \sum_{n=1}^{\text{NPOINT}} \frac{[f_n - D(1)P_0(x_n) - \cdots - D(j-1)P_{j-2}(x_n)]P_{j-1}(x_n)w(x_n)}{S_{j-1}}$$

$$= \sum_{n} \frac{f_n P_{j-1}(x_n)w(x_n) - D(1)\langle P_0,P_{j-1}\rangle - \cdots - D(j-1)\langle P_{j-2},P_{j-1}\rangle}{S_{j-1}}$$

$$= \sum_{n} \frac{f_n P_{j-1}(x_n)w(x_n)}{S_{j-1}}$$

since P_{j-1} is orthogonal to $P_0(x), \ldots, P_{j-2}(x)$. Hence, in exact or infinite-precision arithmetic, both (4.82) and (4.83) give the same value for $D(j)$. But in finite-precision arithmetic, (4.83) can be expected to be more accurate for the following reason: Since

$$p_r^*(x) = D(1)P_0(x) + \cdots + D(r+1)P_r(x)$$

is the (weighted) least-squares approximation to $f(x)$ by polynomials of degree $\leq r$, it follows that the numbers

$$\text{ERROR}(n) = f_n - p_{j-2}^*(x_n) \qquad n = 1, \ldots, \text{NPOINT}$$

can be expected to be of smaller size than are the numbers f_n, $n = 1, \ldots,$ NPOINT. Hence the calculation of (4.83) is less likely to produce loss of significance due to subtraction of quantities of nearly equal size than is the calculation of (4.82) (see Exercise 4.11-1).

Example 4.21   Given the values f_n of $f(x) = e^x$ at $x_n = (n-1)/10 - 1$ ($n = 1, \ldots, 21$), rounded to two places after the decimal point. Try to recover the information about $f(x)$ contained in these data.

We attempt to solve this problem by calculating the polynomial $p_3^*(x)$ which minimizes

$$\sum_{n=1}^{21} [f_n - p_3(x_n)]^2$$

over all polynomials $p_3(x)$ of degree ≤ 3. The following FORTRAN program calculates $p_3^*(x)$ with the aid of the subprogram ORTPOL mentioned earlier, then evaluates $p_3^*(x)$ at the x_n using the FUNCTION ORTVAL, which is based on Algorithm 4.5.

```
      COMMON / POLY / NTERMS,B(20),C(20),D(20)
      DIMENSION  X(100),F(100),W(100),ERROR(100),PJM1(100),PJ(100)
      NPOINT = 21
      DO 1 I = 1,NPOINT
      W(I) = 1.
      X(I) = -1. + FLOAT(I - 1)/10.
    1 F(I) = FLOAT(IFIX(EXP(X(I))*100. +.5))/100.
      NTERMS = 4
      CALL  ORTPOL(NPOINT,X,F,W,ERROR,PJM1,PJ)
      WRITE (6,601) (J,B(J),C(J),D(J),J = 1,NTERMS)
  601 FORMAT(I2,3E16.8)
      DO 60 I = 1,NPOINT
      PJM1(I) = EXP(X(I))
   60 PJ(I) = ORTVAL(X(I))
      WRITE (6,600)(X(I),F(I),PJ(I),ERROR(I),PJM1(I),I = 1,NPOINT)
  600 FORMAT(F5.1,F8.3,F10.5,E13.3,F10.5)
                                            STOP
      END
      FUNCTION ORTVAL(X)
      COMMON / POLY / NTERMS,B(20),C(20),D(20)
```

```
      K = NTERMS
      ORTVAL = D(K)
      PREV = 0.
10    K = K - 1
      IF (K .EQ. 0)                    RETURN
      PREV2 = PREV
      PREV = ORTVAL
      ORTVAL = D(K) + (X - B(K))*PREV - C(K + 1)*PREV2
                                       GO TO 10
      END
```

Table 4.3 gives the results of the calculations which were carried out on a CDC 6500. We have plotted the error, $f_n - p_3^*(x_n)$, in Fig. 4.9d, which shows the error to behave in a somewhat regular fashion, suggesting that $p_3^*(x)$ does not represent *all* the information contained in the given data. We therefore calculate also the least-squares approximation $p_4^*(x)$ to the given data by polynomials of degree ≤ 4. The results are also listed in Table 4.3. The error $f_n - p_4^*(x)$ is plotted in Fig. 4.9e, and is seen to behave quite irregularly. Hence $p_4^*(x)$ can be assumed to represent *all* the information contained in the given data f_n. Increasing the degree of the approximating polynomial any further would only serve to give the approximating function the additional freedom to approximate the noise in the data, too.

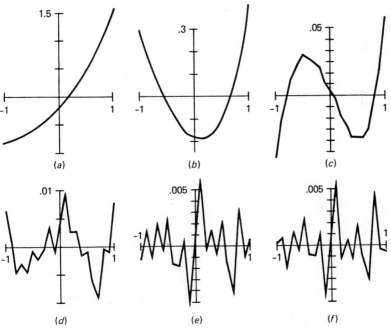

Fig. 4.9 The error in the least-squares approximation to the data of Example 4.21 by polynomials of degree (a) zero, (b) one, (c) two, (d) three, (e) four, (f) five.

Table 4.3   Computer results for Example 4.21

x_n	f_n	$p_3^*(x_n)$	$f_n - p_3^*(x_n)$	$p_4^*(x_n)$	$f_n - p_4^*(x_n)$	e^{x_n}
−1.0	0.370	0.36387	6.130E−03	0.37115	−1.154E−03	0.36788
−0.9	0.410	0.40874	1.263E−03	0.40874	1.263E−03	0.40657
−0.8	0.450	0.45481	−4.806E−03	0.45097	−9.719E−04	0.44933
−0.7	0.500	0.50315	−3.148E−03	0.49804	1.964E−03	0.49659
−0.6	0.550	0.55484	−4.836E−03	0.55021	−2.134E−04	0.54881
−0.5	0.610	0.61094	−9.436E−04	0.60789	2.108E−03	0.60653
−0.4	0.670	0.67254	−2.542E−03	0.67156	−1.565E−03	0.67032
−0.3	0.740	0.74070	−7.045E−04	0.74183	−1.832E−03	0.74082
−0.2	0.820	0.81650	3.497E−03	0.81940	6.029E−04	0.81873
−0.1	0.900	0.90101	−1.010E−03	0.90507	−5.070E−03	0.90484
0.0	1.000	0.99530	4.701E−03	0.99976	2.358E−04	1.00000
0.1	1.110	1.10044	9.558E−03	1.10450	5.499E−03	1.10517
0.2	1.220	1.21751	2.490E−03	1.22040	−4.045E−04	1.22140
0.3	1.350	1.34758	2.422E−03	1.34871	1.294E−03	1.34986
0.4	1.490	1.49172	−1.717E−03	1.49074	−7.399E−04	1.49182
0.5	1.650	1.65100	−1.000E−03	1.64795	2.052E−03	1.64872
0.6	1.820	1.82650	−6.499E−03	1.82188	−1.876E−03	1.82212
0.7	2.010	2.01929	−9.287E−03	2.01418	−4.176E−03	2.01375
0.8	2.230	2.23044	−4.368E−04	2.22660	3.397E−03	2.22554
0.9	2.460	2.46102	−1.020E−03	2.46102	−1.020E−03	2.45960
1.0	2.720	2.71211	7.890E−03	2.71939	6.061E−04	2.71828

EXERCISES

4.11-1. If $f(x) = 6{,}000 + x$, then any least-squares approximation to $f(x)$ by straight lines is $f(x)$ itself.   Calculate the polynomial

$$p_1^*(x) = d_0^* + d_1^* x$$

which minimizes

$$\sum_{n=-2}^{2} [f(n) - p_1(n)]^2$$

Note that 1 and x are already orthogonal, so that one merely has to calculate d_0^* and d_1^*. Show the difference between (4.82) and (4.83) by calculating d_1^* both ways, using four-decimal-digit floating-point arithmetic.

4.11-2. Calculate the polynomial of degree ≤ 2 which minimizes

$$\int_{-1}^{1} [\sin \pi x - p(x)]^2 \, dx$$

over all polynomials $p(x)$ of degree ≤ 2.   Use Legendre polynomials and carry out all calculations to five decimal places.   (*Note:* $\pi = 3.141593$.)

4.11-3. Implement the subroutine ORTPOL on your computer.   Then use this subroutine to solve the following problem.   From a table of values of $f(x) = \sin \pi x$, find

$f_n = \sin \pi x_n$ at $x_n = (n - 1)/10 - 1$ $(n = 1, \ldots, 21)$, rounded off to three decimal places.   Then find the polynomial $p_4^*(x)$ which minimizes

$$\sum_{n=1}^{21} [f_n - p_4(x_n)]^2$$

over all polynomials $p_4(x)$ of degree ≤ 4.

*4.12 CHEBYSHEV ECONOMIZATION

It is often important in practice to obtain an approximation $p(x)$ to a given function $f(x)$ which is guaranteed to deviate from $f(x)$ by no more than a given tolerance ε for all x in some interval $[a,b]$, that is, for which

$$|f(x) - p(x)| \leq \varepsilon \qquad \text{for all } x \in [a,b] \tag{4.85}$$

If this approximation is to be evaluated extensively, as for example in a FORTRAN library subroutine, then it becomes also important that $p(x)$ be computable as cheaply as possible, i.e., in as few arithmetic operations as possible.   This usually excludes getting $p(x)$ by interpolation in a sufficiently extensive table because of table look-up time; also, the resulting storage requirements are usually unacceptably high.   Rather, one calculates an approximation $p(x)$ to $f(x)$ which satisfies (4.85) yet is simple enough to be stored and evaluated cheaply in a computer.

If it has already been decided to use polynomial approximations, one is faced with the problem of finding the polynomial of *least degree* such that (4.85) holds.   If there is such a polynomial at all, one is guaranteed to find it as follows:

For $n = 0, 1, 2, \ldots$, find the polynomial $p_n^*(x)$ which minimizes

$$\max_{a \leq x \leq b} |f(x) - p_n(x)|$$

over all polynomials $p_n(x)$ of degree $\leq n$.   Stop as soon as

$$\max_{a \leq x \leq b} |f(x) - p_n^*(x)| \leq \varepsilon$$

for $p_n^*(x)$ is then a polynomial of least degree satisfying (4.85).

If $p_j^*(x)$ is a polynomial of degree $\leq j$ which minimizes

$$\max_{a \leq x \leq b} |f(x) - p_j(x)|$$

over all polynomials $p_j(x)$ of degree $\leq j$, then $p_j^*(x)$ is called a *Chebyshev*, or minimax, approximation to $f(x)$ (on $[a,b]$ by polynomials of degree $\leq j$). A discussion of how such minimax approximations can be calculated is, unfortunately, beyond the scope of this book.   The interested reader is referred to Ref. 17.   Instead, we give a description of a simple technique which sometimes produces low-degree polynomial approximations to $f(x)$ satisfying (4.85).

For simplicity, we assume that the approximation is sought on the interval $[-1,1]$. This state of affairs can always be achieved by a linear change in the independent variable x. We further assume that we can find arbitrarily good polynomial approximations to $f(x)$. In effect, we assume that we have available a power series expansion

$$f(x) = \sum_{r=0}^{\infty} a_r x^r \tag{4.86}$$

which converges uniformly to $f(x)$ on $[-1,1]$. This means that, for every $\varepsilon > 0$, we can find an $n = n(\varepsilon)$ so that

$$\left| f(x) - \sum_{r=0}^{n} a_r x^r \right| \le \varepsilon \qquad \text{for all } x \in [-1,1]$$

Typically, we have the Taylor series expansion for $f(x)$ around $x = 0$ available and know that this series converges uniformly on $[-1,1]$. If, for example, $f(x) = e^x$, then

$$f(x) = \sum_{r=0}^{\infty} \frac{x^r}{r!}$$

If we let

$$p_n(x) = \sum_{r=0}^{n} \frac{x^r}{r!}$$

then we know from Theorem 1.7 that

$$e^x - p_n(x) = R_{n+1}(x) = \frac{x^{n+1} e^\xi}{(n+1)!} \qquad \text{for some } \xi \text{ with } |\xi| < |x|$$

Hence

$$\max_{-1 \le x \le 1} |e^x - p_n(x)| = \max_{-1 \le x \le 1} |R_{n+1}(x)| \le \frac{1^{n+1} e^1}{(n+1)!} = \frac{e}{(n+1)!}$$

which can be made arbitrarily small by proper choice of n. But such a $p_n(x)$ is the result of interpolating $f(x)$ $n + 1$ times at $x = 0$ (see Sec. 4.6), so that, for all $x \ne 0$, $p_n(x)$ is in effect an extrapolated value. Consequently, by the time n is large enough for

$$\max_{-1 \le x \le 1} |f(x) - p_n(x)| \le \varepsilon \tag{4.87}$$

to hold for a given ε, n is usually unacceptably large. For the example $f(x) = e^x$, one has to take $n = 12$ if $\varepsilon = 10^{-8}$ is required, but then the Taylor series for e^x converges quite fast. By contrast, the Taylor series for

$$f(x) = \ln\left(\frac{3}{2} + \frac{x}{2}\right)$$

converges so slowly that n has to be well over 20 if $\varepsilon = 10^{-8}$ is desired.

To obtain a lower-degree polynomial approximation having the same accuracy, one uses a technique called *telescoping*, or *Chebyshev economization*, of power series. In this technique, one starts out with a polynomial approximation $p_n(x)$ which is somewhat better than required,

$$\max_{-1 \leq x \leq 1} |f(x) - p_n(x)| = \varepsilon_n < \varepsilon$$

Next, one finds the polynomial $p_{n-1}^*(x)$ of degree $\leq n - 1$ which is the minimax approximation to $p_n(x)$, that is, for which

$$\max_{-1 \leq x \leq 1} |p_n(x) - p_{n-1}^*(x)| \leq \max_{-1 \leq x \leq 1} |p_n(x) - p_{n-1}(x)|$$

for all polynomials $p_{n-1}(x)$ of degree $< n$. If we set

$$E_n = \max_{-1 \leq x \leq 1} |p_n(x) - p_{n-1}^*(x)|$$

then

$$\max_{-1 \leq x \leq 1} |f(x) - p_{n-1}^*(x)| \leq \max_{-1 \leq x \leq 1} |f(x) - p_n(x)|$$
$$+ \max_{-1 \leq x \leq 1} |p_n(x) - p_{n-1}^*(x)| = \varepsilon_n + E_n$$

If it is still true that

$$\varepsilon_n + E_n < \varepsilon$$

one repeats the procedure, getting the minimax approximation $p_{n-2}^*(x)$ to $p_{n-1}^*(x)$, then the minimax approximation $p_{n-3}^*(x)$ to $p_{n-2}^*(x)$, etc. If we set

$$E_j = \max_{-1 \leq x \leq 1} |p_j^*(x) - p_{j-1}^*(x)| \qquad \text{all } j < n$$

we carry out this procedure until

$$\varepsilon_n + E_n + \cdots + E_{j+1} \leq \varepsilon < \varepsilon_n + E_n + \cdots + E_{j+1} + E_j$$

Then $p_j^*(x)$ is the lowest-degree polynomial satisfying (4.87) that can be constructed this way.

This somewhat involved scheme is in fact quite effective because it is very easy to calculate the polynomials $p_{n-1}^*(x), p_{n-2}^*(x), \ldots$. To see this, we have to look more closely at the Chebyshev polynomials $T_0(x), T_1(x), \ldots$ introduced in Example 4.15 in Sec. 4.10. We noted that

$$T_n(\cos \theta) = \cos n\theta \qquad n = 0, 1, 2, \ldots \tag{4.88}$$

and that

$$T_{n+1}(x) = 2xT_n(x) - T_{n-1}(x) \qquad n = 1, 2, \ldots \tag{4.89}$$

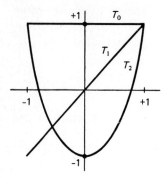

Fig. 4.10

From (4.88),

$$T_0(x) = 1$$
$$T_1(x) = x$$

and using the recurrence relation (4.89),

$$T_2(x) = 2xT_1(x) - T_0(x) = 2x^2 - 1$$
$$T_3(x) = 2xT_2(x) - T_1(x) = 2x(2x^2 - 1) - x = 4x^3 - 3x, \text{ etc.}$$

The first eight of these polynomials are listed in column A of Table 4.4. Graphs of the first five Chebyshev polynomials are plotted in Figs. 4.10 and 4.11.

Since $T_1(x) = x$, it is easily verified from the recurrence relation that

$$T_n(x) = 2^{n-1}x^n + \text{a polynomial of degree} < n \quad n = 1, 2, \ldots \quad (4.90)$$

More specific information about the zeros and the extrema of $T_n(x)$ can be obtained directly from (4.88) with the observation that $\cos \theta$ varies from 1 to -1 as θ varies from 0 to π. One can verify, for example, that

$$T_n(x) = 2^{n-1}(x - \xi_{1,n})(x - \xi_{2,n}) \cdots (x - \xi_{n,n}) \quad (4.91)$$

Table 4.4

A	B
$T_0(x) = 1$	$1 = T_0$
$T_1(x) = x$	$x = T_1$
$T_2(x) = 2x^2 - 1$	$x^2 = 2^{-1}(T_0 + T_2)$
$T_3(x) = 4x^3 - 3x$	$x^3 = 2^{-2}(3T_1 + T_3)$
$T_4(x) = 8x^4 - 8x^2 + 1$	$x^4 = 2^{-3}(3T_0 + 4T_2 + T_4)$
$T_5(x) = 16x^5 - 20x^3 + 5x$	$x^5 = 2^{-4}(10T_1 + 5T_3 + T_5)$
$T_6(x) = 32x^6 - 48x^4 + 18x^2 - 1$	$x^6 = 2^{-5}(10T_0 + 15T_2 + 6T_4 + T_6)$
$T_7(x) = 64x^7 - 112x^5 + 56x^3 - 7x$	$x^7 = 2^{-6}(35T_1 + 21T_3 + 7T_5 + T_7)$

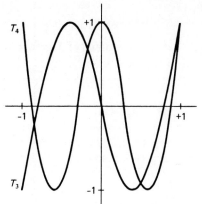

Fig. 4.11

with the zeros of $T_n(x)$ given by

$$\xi_{k,n} = \cos \frac{2k - 1}{2n} \pi \qquad k = 1, \ldots, n \tag{4.92}$$

These zeros are the so-called *Chebyshev points* referred to earlier in Sec. 4.7. It is also evident that

$$|T_n(x)| \leq 1 \qquad \text{for all } x \in [-1,1] \tag{4.93}$$

and that $T_n(x)$ attains this bound ± 1 alternately at the $n + 1$ points

$$x_k = \cos \frac{k\pi}{n} \qquad k = 0, \ldots, n \tag{4.94}$$

in $[-1,1]$; i.e., from (4.88),

$$T_n(x_k) = T_n\left(\cos \frac{k\pi}{n}\right) = \cos \frac{nk\pi}{n} = (-1)^k \qquad k = 0, \ldots, n \tag{4.95}$$

Lemma 4.2   If $p_n(x)$ is a polynomial of the form

$$p_n(x) = a_n x^n + q(x)$$

where $q(x)$ is a polynomial of degree $<n$, then the minimax approximation $p^*_{n-1}(x)$ to $p_n(x)$ by polynomials of degree $<n$ is given by

$$p^*_{n-1}(x) = p_n(x) - a_n 2^{1-n} T_n(x) \tag{4.96}$$

For the proof, observe first that $p^*_{n-1}(x)$ as given by (4.96) is indeed a polynomial of degree $<n$, since by (4.90),

$$p^*_{n-1}(x) = p_n(x) - a_n 2^{1-n} T_n(x)$$
$$= [a_n x^n + q(x)] - a_n 2^{1-n}(2^{n-1}x^n + \text{polynomial of degree} <n)$$
$$= q(x) - a_n 2^{1-n} \cdot (\text{polynomial of degree} <n)$$

We have to prove that

$$\max_{-1 \le x \le 1} |p_n(x) - p^*_{n-1}(x)| \le \max_{-1 \le x \le 1} |p_n(x) - p_{n-1}(x)|$$

for all polynomials $p_{n-1}(x)$ of degree $<n$. Suppose that this is not so; i.e., suppose that there is a polynomial $p_{n-1}(x)$ of degree $<n$ so that

$$\max_{-1 \le x \le 1} |p_n(x) - p^*_{n-1}(x)| > \max_{-1 \le x \le 1} |p_n(x) - p_{n-1}(x)| \qquad (4.97)$$

From (4.96), we get that

$$p_n(x) - p^*_{n-1}(x) = a_n 2^{1-n} T_n(x)$$

Hence, if we let $d(x)$ denote the difference

$$d(x) = p^*_{n-1}(x) - p_{n-1}(x)$$

then $d(x)$ is a nonzero polynomial of degree $<n$, and

$$p_n(x) - p_{n-1}(x) = p_n(x) - p^*_{n-1}(x) + d(x)$$

so that (4.97) can be written

$$\max_{-1 \le x \le 1} |a_n 2^{1-n} T_n(x)| > \max_{-1 \le x \le 1} |a_n 2^{1-n} T_n(x) + d(x)|$$

Using the fact that $|T_n(x)| \le 1$ for $x \in [-1,1]$, we therefore have

$$|a_n| 2^{1-n} > \max_{-1 \le x \le 1} |a_n 2^{1-n} T_n(x) + d(x)|$$

Hence

$$|a_n| 2^{1-n} > a_n 2^{1-n} T_n(x) + d(x) > -|a_n| 2^{1-n} \qquad (4.98)$$

for all $x \in [-1,1]$. Consider now, in particular, $x = x_k$, one of the extrema (4.94) of $T_n(x)$. With (4.95), we get from (4.98) that

$$a_n 2^{1-n} > a_n 2^{1-n}(-1)^k + d(x_k) > -a_n 2^{1-n}$$

Hence, assuming for simplicity that $a_n > 0$,

$$0 > d(x_k) \qquad \text{if } k \text{ is even}$$

and

$$d(x_k) > 0 \qquad \text{if } k \text{ is odd}$$

Since $x_0 > x_1 > \cdots > x_k$, this implies that the nonzero polynomial $d(x)$ of degree $\leq n - 1$ must change sign in $[-1,1]$ at least n times, which implies that $d(x)$ has at least n zeros. This, however, is impossible, since $d(x)$ is a nonzero polynomial of degree $\leq n - 1$. Hence (4.97) cannot hold, and the lemma is proved.

Equipped with this lemma, we return now to Chebyshev economization. If $p_n(x)$ is a given polynomial of degree $\leq n$, then, by Property 1 of orthogonal polynomials (see Sec. 4.10), $p_n(x)$ is uniquely expressible in terms of $T_0(x), \ldots, T_n(x)$; that is,

$$p_n(x) = d_0 T_0(x) + \cdots + d_n T_n(x) \tag{4.99}$$

for certain coefficients $d_0, \ldots, d_n$. In particular, if the leading coefficient of $p(x)$ is a_n, then, since x^n appears only in $T_n(x)$, we must have

$$a_n = d_n \cdot 2^{n-1}$$

or

$$d_n = a_n 2^{1-n}$$

Hence, once we have expressed $p_n(x)$ in the form (4.99), then we can obtain the minimax approximation $p_{n-1}^*(x)$ to $p_n(x)$ simply by dropping the last term:

$$p_{n-1}^*(x) = d_0 T_0(x) + \cdots + d_{n-1} T_{n-1}(x)$$

and

$$E_n = \max_{-1 \leq x \leq 1} |p_n(x) - p_{n-1}^*(x)| = a_n 2^{1-n} = d_n$$

More generally, using the same notation as before,

$$p_j^*(x) = d_0 T_0(x) + \cdots + d_j T_j(x)$$
$$[E_j = d_j] \qquad j = n - 1, n - 2, \ldots, 0$$

Algorithm 4.7 Economization of power series To get an "economical" polynomial approximation to $f(x)$ of absolute accuracy ε on the interval $[-1,1]$, proceed as follows:

Step 1 Get a power series expansion for $f(x)$ valid on $[-1,1]$; typically, calculate the Taylor series expansion for $f(x)$ around $x = 0$.

Step 2 Truncate the power series to obtain a polynomial

$$p_n(x) = a_0 + a_1 x + \cdots + a_n x^n$$

which approximates $f(x)$ on $[-1,1]$ to within an error ε_n, where ε_n is smaller than ε.

Step 3 Expand $p_n(x)$ into a Chebyshev series

$$p_n(x) = d_0 T_0(x) + \cdots + d_n T_n(x)$$

making use of a table like column B of Table 4.4.

Step 4   Retain the first $k + 1$ terms in this series; i.e., get

$$p_k^*(x) = d_0 T_0(x) + \cdots + d_k T_k(x)$$

choosing k as the smallest integer such that

$$\varepsilon_n + d_{k+1} + \cdots + d_n \leq \varepsilon$$

Step 5   Use the FORTRAN function CHEB, given in Example 4.18, whenever $p_k^*(x)$ is to be evaluated.   This assures minimum loss of significance in the evaluation of $p_k^*(x)$.

Example 4.22   Using Algorithm 4.7, find an economized polynomial which will yield the value of e^x on $[-1,1]$ with an error $\varepsilon \leq 0.005$.
Solution
   Step 1   The Taylor series expansion for e^x about $x = 0$ is

$$e^x = 1 + x + \frac{x^2}{2} + \cdots + \frac{x^n}{n!} + R_{n+1}(x)$$

   Step 2   Since

$$\max_{-1 \leq x \leq 1} |R_{n+1}(x)| \leq \max_{-1 \leq x \leq 1} |x|^{n+1} \max_{-1 \leq \xi \leq 1} \frac{e^\xi}{(n+1)!} = \frac{e}{(n+1)!}$$

we find that the error for $n = 5$ is

$$R = \frac{e}{6!} < 0.004 < 0.005$$

while for $n = 4$ the error estimate is greater than 0.005.   Hence we take $n = 5$ and obtain

$$e^x \approx p_5(x) = 1 + x + \frac{x^2}{2} + \frac{x^3}{6} + \frac{x^4}{24} + \frac{x^5}{120}$$

$$\varepsilon_5 \leq 0.004$$

   Step 3   Replacing each power of x in $p_5(x)$ in terms of Chebyshev polynomials as given in Table 4.4, column B, we find that

$$p_5(x) = 1.2656250 + 1.1302083 T_1 + 0.2708333 T_2 + 0.0442708 T_3$$
$$+ 0.0052083 T_4 + 0.0005208 T_5$$

   Step 4   Since

$$\varepsilon_5 + d_5 = 0.004 + 0.0005208 = 0.0045208 < 0.005$$

while $\varepsilon_5 + d_4 + d_5$ is clearly greater than 0.005, the economized polynomial approximation to $p_5(x)$ must be

$$p_4^*(x) = 1.2656250 + 1.1302083 T_1 + 0.2708333 T_2 + 0.0442708 T_3 + 0.0052083 T_4$$

To evaluate $p_k^*(x)$ for any argument, one can use the FORTRAN function CHEB in Sec. 4.10, which uses $p_4^*(x)$ in the form above.   One can of course write $p_4^*(x)$ in standard polynomial form by replacing the T_i ($i = 1,2,3,4$) by their standard polynomial equivalents and rearranging in powers of x.   If this is done, we arrive at the economized polynomial

$$p_4^*(x) = 1.0000000 + 0.9973959x + 0.5000002x^2 + 0.1770832x^3$$
$$+ 0.0416664x^4$$

As a check we list in the table below the errors in $p_5(x)$ and $p_4^*(x)$ at selected points.

x	e^x	$e^x - p_5(x)$	$e^x - p_4^*(x)$
-1.0	0.36788	0.0012	0.0007
-0.5	0.60653	0.0000	-0.0002
0.0	1.0000	0.0000	0.0000
0.5	1.6487	0.0000	0.0003
1.0	2.7183	0.0016	0.0022

For many functions, especially those with slowly converging power series, the telescoping effect can be quite dramatic. Hastings [7], for example, shows that the polynomial

$$p_6^*(x) = 0.99990167x - 0.49787544x^2 + 0.31765005x^3$$
$$- 0.19376149x^4 + 0.08556927x^5 - 0.01833851x^6$$

arrived at by Chebyshev economization, approximates $\ln(1 + x)$ to an accuracy of $\varepsilon = 0.0000016$ for all x on [0,1]. The Taylor series for $\ln(1 + x)$ (around $\frac{1}{2}$) converges so slowly that more than 16 terms would be required for this same accuracy.

Minimax polynomials, or more generally, minimax rational functions, are especially useful in library subroutines for the common elementary functions such as $\sin x$, $\cos x$, $\ln(1 + x)$, e^x, $\arctan x$, because these subroutines are used so often that efficiency is an important consideration.

EXERCISES

4.12-1. Find an economized polynomial which will approximate $\sin \pi x$ for $-1 \le x \le 1$ with a maximum error of 0.001.

4.12-2. Verify the statements in Eqs. (4.90) to (4.92) in the text.

4.12-3. Plot the graph of $T_5(x)$.

4.12-4. Find an economized polynomial which will approximate $\cosh x$ for $-1 \le x \le 1$ with a maximum error of 0.001.

5
Differentiation and Integration

In Chap. 4, we developed some techniques for approximating a given function by a polynomial (or piecewise-polynomial function), typically by interpolation. In this chapter, we consider a major use of such approximating polynomials—that of *analytic substitution*. Here we are concerned with replacing a complicated, or a merely tabulated, function by an approximating polynomial so that the fundamental operations of calculus can be performed more easily, or can be performed at all. These operations include

$$I(f) = \int_a^b f(x)\,dx \qquad D(f) = f'(a) \qquad S_n(f) = \frac{1}{2\pi}\int_{-\pi}^{\pi} f(x)\sin nx\,dx$$

and even

$$Z(f) = \lim_{h \to 0} f(h)$$

Abstractly, if L denotes one of these operations on functions (or a similar one), we approximate the number $L(f)$ by the number $L(p)$, where, for given

$f(x)$, $p(x)$ is an approximation to $f(x)$. The hope is that the operation L can be carried out easily on $p(x)$, and this hope is justified if $p(x)$ is a polynomial and L is any one of the above operations.

In estimating the error $L(f) - L(p)$, it is of some help that the operation L is usually *linear* (as are the operations mentioned above). This means that

$$L(f(x) + g(x)) = L(f) + L(g)$$
$$L(af(x)) = aL(f)$$

where $f(x)$ and $g(x)$ are functions and a is a number. The linearity implies that

$$L(f) - L(p) = L(e)$$

where $e(x)$ is the error in the approximation $p(x)$ to $f(x)$, that is,

$$f(x) = p(x) + e(x)$$

We will usually choose $p(x)$ to be an interpolating polynomial; say, $p(x)$ is the polynomial of degree $\leq k$ which interpolates $f(x)$ at the points $x_0, \ldots, x_k$. If these points are distinct, then, by (4.2),

$$p(x) = \sum_{i=0}^{k} f(x_i)l_i(x)$$

where the $l_i(x)$ are the Lagrange polynomials for the points $x_0, \ldots, x_k$. If now the operation L is linear, it follows that

$$L(p) = \sum_{i=0}^{k} f(x_i)w_i$$

where the numbers w_i are given by

$$w_i = L(l_i) \qquad i = 0, \ldots, k$$

and *do not depend on* $f(x)$; hence can be calculated once for all (for any particular point set $x_0, \ldots, x_k$). In this form, the approximation $L(p)$ is usually called a *rule* [for the approximation of $L(f)$], and the numbers w_i are called its *weights*, or coefficients. We obtain an expression for the error

$$E(f) = L(f) - L(p)$$

in such a rule by applying the operation L to the error function of polynomial interpolation as given by (4.21) or (4.40), making use of the fact that the divided difference is a well-behaved function of its arguments.

5.1 NUMERICAL DIFFERENTIATION

We consider first some numerical techniques for approximating the derivative $f'(x)$ of a given function. Before doing so we should point out that numerical differentiation based on the interpolating polynomial is basically an unstable process and that we cannot expect good accuracy even when the original data are known to be accurate. As we shall see, the error $f'(x) - p'(x)$ may be very large, especially when the values of $f(x)$ at the interpolating points are "noisy." These comments will be made more precise in what follows.

Let $f(x)$ be a function continuously differentiable on the interval $[c,d]$. If $x_0, \ldots, x_k$ are distinct points in $[c,d]$, we can write $f(x)$ according to (4.40) as

$$f(x) = p_k(x) + f[x_0, \ldots, x_k, x]\psi_k(x) \tag{5.1}$$

where $p_k(x)$ is the polynomial of degree $\leq k$ which interpolates $f(x)$ at $x_0, \ldots, x_k$, and

$$\psi_k(x) = \prod_{j=0}^{k} (x - x_j)$$

By (4.41),

$$\frac{d}{dx} f[x_0, \ldots, x_k, x] = f[x_0, \ldots, x_k, x, x]$$

if $f(x)$ is sufficiently smooth. Hence, in such a case, we can differentiate (5.1) to get

$$f'(x) = p_k'(x) + f[x_0, \ldots, x_k, x, x]\psi_k(x) + f[x_0, \ldots, x_k, x]\psi_k'(x) \tag{5.2}$$

Define the operator D as

$$D(f) = f'(a)$$

with a some point in $[c,d]$. If we approximate $D(f)$ by $D(p_k)$, then by (5.2), the error in this approximation is

$$E(f) = D(f) - D(p_k) = f[x_0, \ldots, x_k, a, a]\psi_k(a) + f[x_0, \ldots, x_k, a]\psi_k'(a)$$

or

$$E(f) = \frac{f^{(k+2)}(\xi)\psi_k(a)}{(k+2)!} + \frac{f^{(k+1)}(\eta)\psi_k'(a)}{(k+1)!} \tag{5.3}$$

for some $\xi, \eta \in (c,d)$.

The expression (5.3) for the error $E(f)$ in numerical differentiation tells us in general very little about the true error, since we will seldom know the derivatives $f^{(k+1)}$ and $f^{(k+2)}$ involved in $E(f)$ and we will almost never know the arguments ξ, η. In some cases this error term can be simplified greatly either by choosing the point a at which the derivative is to be evaluated or by choosing the interpolating points $x_0, \ldots, x_k$ appropriately.

We consider first the case when a is one of the interpolation points. Let $a = x_i$ for some i. Then, since $\psi_k(x)$ contains the factor $(x - x_i)$, it follows that $\psi_k(a) = 0$ and the first term in the error (5.3) drops out. Moreover (see Sec. 2.6), $\psi_k'(a) = q(a)$, where

$$q(x) = \frac{\psi_k(x)}{x - x_i} = (x - x_0) \cdots (x - x_{i-1})(x - x_{i+1}) \cdots (x - x_k)$$

Therefore, if we choose $a = x_i$, for some i, then (5.3) reduces to

$$E(f) = \frac{1}{(k + 1)!} f^{(k+1)}(\eta) \prod_{\substack{j=0 \\ j \neq i}}^{k} (x_i - x_j) \qquad \text{some } \eta \in (c,d) \tag{5.4}$$

Another way to simplify the error expression (5.3) is to choose a so that $\psi_k'(a) = 0$, for then the second term in (5.3) will vanish. If k is an odd number, we can achieve this by placing the x_i's *symmetrically around* a, that is, so that

$$x_{k-j} - a = a - x_j \qquad j = 0, \ldots, \frac{k-1}{2} \tag{5.5}$$

For then

$$(x - x_j)(x - x_{k-j}) = (x - a + a - x_j)(x - a + a - x_{k-j})$$

$$= (x - a)^2 - (a - x_j)^2 \qquad j = 0, \ldots, \frac{k-1}{2}$$

Hence

$$\psi_k(x) = \prod_{j=0}^{(k-1)/2} [(x - a)^2 - (a - x_j)^2]$$

Since

$$\frac{d}{dx}[(x - a)^2 - (a - x_j)^2]|_{x=a} = 2(x - a)|_{x=a} = 0 \qquad \text{all } j$$

it then follows that $\psi_k'(a) = 0$. To summarize, if (5.5) holds, then (5.3) reduces to

$$E(f) = \frac{1}{(k + 2)!} f^{(k+2)}(\xi) \prod_{j=0}^{(k-1)/2} [-(a - x_j)^2] \tag{5.6}$$

Note that the derivative of $f(x)$ in (5.6) is of one order higher than the one in (5.4).

We now consider specific examples. If $k = 0$, then $D(p_k) = 0$, which is a safe but (usually) not very good approximation to $D(f) = f'(a)$. We choose, therefore, $k \geq 1$. For $k = 1$,

$$p_k(x) = f(x_0) + f[x_0,x_1](x - x_0)$$

Hence

$$D(p_k) = f[x_0,x_1]$$

regardless of a. If $a = x_0$, then (5.2) and (5.4) give, with $h = x_1 - x_0$,

$$\boxed{f'(a) \approx f[a, a + h] = \frac{f(a + h) - f(a)}{h}} \qquad \boxed{E(f) = -\tfrac{1}{2}hf''(\eta)}$$

$$(5.7)$$

On the other hand, if we choose $a = \tfrac{1}{2}(x_0 + x_1)$, then x_0, x_1 are symmetric around a, and (5.6) gives, with $x_0 = a - h$, $x_1 = a + h$, $h = \tfrac{1}{2}(x_1 - x_0)$, that

$$\boxed{f'(a) \approx f[a - h, a + h] = \frac{f(a + h) - f(a - h)}{2h}}$$

$$(5.8)$$

$$\boxed{E(f) = -\frac{h^2}{6}f'''(\eta)}$$

Hence, if x_0, x_1 are "close together," then $f[x_0,x_1]$ is a much better approximation to $f'(a)$ at the midpoint $a = \tfrac{1}{2}(x_0 + x_1)$ than at either end point $a = x_0$ or $a = x_1$. This is not surprising since we know by the mean-value theorem for derivatives (see Sec. 1.7) that

$$f[x_0,x_1] = f'(a) \qquad \text{for } some \ a \ between \ x_0 \ and \ x_1$$

This is also illustrated in Fig. 5.1.

Next, we consider using three interpolation points so that $k = 2$. Then

$$p_k(x) = f(x_0) + f[x_0,x_1](x - x_0) + f[x_0,x_1,x_2](x - x_0)(x - x_1)$$

so that

$$p_k'(x) = f[x_0,x_1] + f[x_0,x_1,x_2](2x - x_0 - x_1)$$

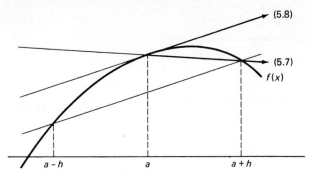

Fig. 5.1 Numerical differentiation.

Hence, if $a = x_0$, then (5.2) and (5.4) give

$$f'(a) = f[a,x_1] + f[a,x_1,x_2](a - x_1) + \tfrac{1}{6}(a - x_1)(a - x_2)f'''(\eta) \quad (5.9)$$

Let now, in particular, $x_1 = a + h$, $x_2 = a + 2h$. Then (5.9) reduces to

$$f'(a) \approx \frac{-3f(a) + 4f(a + h) - f(a + 2h)}{2h}$$

$$(5.10)$$

$$E(f) = \frac{h^2}{3} f'''(\xi), \text{ some } \xi \text{ between } a \text{ and } a + 2h$$

On the other hand, if we choose $x_1 = a - h$, $x_2 = a + h$, then we get

$$f'(a) \approx \frac{f(a + h) - f(a - h)}{2h}$$

$$(5.11)$$

$$E(f) = -\frac{h^2}{6} f'''(\xi) \quad \text{with } |\xi - a| < |h|$$

which is just (5.8).

Formulas for approximating higher derivatives of $f(x)$ can be obtained in a similar manner. Thus, on differentiating (5.1) twice, one gets

$$f''(x) = p_k''(x) + 2f[x_0, \ldots ,x_k,x,x,x]\psi_k(x) + 2f[x_0, \ldots ,x_k,x,x]\psi_k'(x) + f[x_0, \ldots ,x_k,x]\psi_k''(x) \quad (5.12)$$

With $k = 2$ and $a = x_0$, this gives

$$f''(a) = 2f[a,x_1,x_2] + 2f[a,x_1,x_2,a,a](a - x_1)(a - x_2) + f[a,x_1,x_2,a]2(a - x_1 + a - x_2)$$

Hence, with $x_1 = a + h$, $x_2 = a + 2h$,

$$f''(a) \approx \frac{f(a) - 2f(a + h) + f(a + 2h)}{h^2}$$

(5.13)

$$E(f) = \frac{h^2}{12} f^{\mathrm{iv}}(\xi) - \frac{h}{3} f'''(\eta)$$

By choosing $x_1 = a - h$, $x_2 = a + h$ instead, so that the interpolation points are symmetric around a, we get

$$f''(a) \approx \frac{f(a - h) - 2f(a) + f(a + h)}{h^2}$$

(5.14)

$$E(f) = -\frac{h^2}{12} f^{\mathrm{iv}}(\xi) \qquad \text{with } |\xi - a| < |h|$$

Note that placing the interpolation points symmetrically around a has resulted once again in a higher-order formula.

Finally, we infer from (4.20) that

$$k! f[x_0, \ldots , x_k]$$

is a "good" approximation to $f^{(k)}(a)$ provided the x_i's are all "close enough" to a.

Formulas (5.7), (5.8), and (5.10) are all of the general form

$$D(f) = D(p_k) + \text{const } h^r f^{(r+1)}(\xi)$$

(5.15)

with $D(f) = f'(a)$, and h the spacing of the points used for interpolation. Further, the number $D(p_k)$ involves just the values of $f(x)$ at a finite number of discrete points. The process of replacing $D(f)$ by $D(p_k)$ is therefore known as *discretization*, and the error-term const $h^r f^{(r+1)}(\xi)$ is called the *discretization error*.

It follows from (5.15) that we should be able to calculate $D(f)$ to any desired accuracy merely by calculating $D(p_k)$ for small enough h. However, the fact that computers have limited word length, together with loss of significance caused when nearly equal quantities are subtracted, combine to make high accuracy difficult to obtain. Indeed, for a computer with fixed

Table 5.1

h	EXP(h)	EXP($-h$)	D_h	$D_h{}^2$
1.0	0.27182817E 01	0.36787944E 00	0.11752012E 01	0.10861612E 01
0.1	0.11051708E 01	0.90483743E 00	0.10016673E 01	0.10008334E 01
0.01	0.10100501E 01	0.99004984E 00	0.10000161E 01	0.10000169E 01
0.001	0.10010005E 01	0.99900050E 00	0.99999458E 00	0.99837783E 00
0.0001	0.10000999E 01	0.99990001E 00	0.99994244E 00	0.14901161E 01

word length and for a given function, there is an optimum value of h below which the approximation will become worse. Consider, for instance, the values given in Table 5.1. These were computed using the IBM 7094 computer in single-precision floating-point arithmetic.

In this table, the column headed D_h gives $f'(a)$ as estimated by (5.8), while the column with $D_h{}^2$ gives $f''(a)$ as estimated by (5.14). The function $f(x)$ is e^x, and with $a = 0$, the exact values of $f'(a)$ and $f''(a)$ are obviously one. We see from the table that the D_h and $D_h{}^2$ continue to improve as h diminishes until $h = 0.01$. After this, the results worsen. For $h = 0.0001$, there is a loss of four significant figures in D_h and of seven significant figures in $D_h{}^2$. The only remedy for this loss of significance is to increase the number of significant digits to which $f(x)$ is computed as h becomes smaller. This will normally be impossible on most computers. Moreover, $f(x)$ will itself normally be the result of other computations which have introduced other numerical errors.

To analyze this phenomenon, consider formula (5.11), which gives

$$f'(a) = \frac{f(a + h) - f(a - h)}{2h} - \frac{h^2 f'''(\xi)}{6}$$

In calculations, we will in fact use the numbers $f(a + h) + E_+$ and $f(a - h) + E_-$ instead of the numbers $f(a + h)$ and $f(a - h)$, because of round-off. Therefore we compute

$$f'_{comp} = \frac{f(a + h) + E_+ - f(a - h) - E_-}{2h}$$

$$= \frac{f(a + h) - f(a - h)}{2h} + \frac{E_+ - E_-}{2h}$$

Hence, with (5.11),

$$f'(a) = f'_{comp} - \frac{E_+ - E_-}{2h} - \frac{h^2 f'''(\xi)}{6} \tag{5.16}$$

The error in the *computed* approximation f'_{comp} to $f'(a)$ is therefore seen to consist of two parts, one part due to round-off, and the other part due to discretization. If $f'''(x)$ is bounded, then the discretization error goes to zero as $h \to 0$, but the round-off error grows if we assume (as we must in practice) that $E_+ - E_-$ does not decrease (but see Exercise 5.1-5).

We define the *optimum* value of h as that value for which the sum of the magnitudes of the round-off error and of the discretization error is minimized. To illustrate the procedure for finding an optimum value of h, let us consider the problem above of computing $f'(0)$ when $f(x) = e^x$. Let us assume that the error in computing e^x is $\pm 1 \cdot 10^{-8}$ and that $E_+ - E_-$ remains finite and equal approximately to $\pm 2 \cdot 10^{-8}$. Then, from (5.16), the round-off error R is approximately

$$R = \pm \frac{2 \cdot 10^{-8}}{2h}$$

The discretization error T is approximately

$$T = -\tfrac{1}{6}h^2$$

since $f'''(\xi)$ is approximately one. To find the optimum h we must therefore minimize

$$|R| + |T| = \frac{10^{-8}}{h} + \tfrac{1}{6}h^2 = g(h)$$

To find the value of h for which $g(h)$ is a minimum, we differentiate $g(h)$ with respect to h and find its zero. Thus

$$g'(h) = \frac{-10^{-8}}{h^2} + \frac{h}{3} = 0$$

and its positive solution is

$$h^3 = 3 \cdot 10^{-8}$$

or

$$h = 10^{-3} \sqrt[3]{30} \approx 0.003$$

This is the optimum value of h. The student can verify by examining Table 5.1 that the best value of h falls between 0.01 and 0.001.

Formulas for numerical differentiation as derived in this section are very useful in the study of methods for the numerical solution of differential equations (see Chaps. 6 and 7). But the above analysis shows these formulas to be of limited utility for the approximate calculation of derivatives. The analysis shows that we can combat the round-off-error effect by using "sufficiently" high precision arithmetic. But this is impossible when $f(x)$ is known only *approximately* at *finitely* many points.

If the numerical calculation of derivatives cannot be avoided, it is usually more advantageous to estimate $D(f)$ by $D(p_k)$, with $p_k(x)$ the least-squares approximation to $f(x)$ by polynomials of low degree (see Sec. 4.11).

A very promising alternative is the approximation of $D(f)$ by $D(g_3)$, where $g_3(x)$ is the cubic spline interpolating $f(x)$ at a number of points, or best approximating $f(x)$ in the least-squares sense.

EXERCISES

5.1-1. From the following table find $f'(1.4)$, using (5.7), (5.8), and (5.10). Also find $f''(1.4)$, using (5.14). Compare your results with the results $f'(1.4) = \cosh 1.4 = 2.1509$ and $f''(1.4) = \sinh 1.4 = 1.9043$, which are correct to the places given.

x	$f(x)$
1.2	1.5095
1.3	1.6984
1.4	1.9043
1.5	2.1293
1.6	2.3756

5.1-2. From the following table of values of $f(x) = \sinh x$, find $f'(0.400)$, using (5.8) with $h = 0.001$ and $h = 0.002$. Which of these is the more accurate? The correct result is $f'(0.4) = \cosh 0.4 = 1.081072$.

x	$f(x)$
0.398	0.408591
0.399	0.409671
0.400	0.410752
0.401	0.411834
0.402	0.412915

5.1-3. In Eq. (5.16) let $f(x) = \sinh x$ and assume that the round-off error in computing $\sinh x$ remains constant, so that $E_+ - E_- = 0.5 \cdot 10^{-7}$. Determine the optimum value of h to be used if formula (5.11) is used to compute $f'(0)$.

5.1-4. Derive a formula for $f''(a)$ by differentiating (5.1) three times, choosing $k = 3$ and setting $a = x_0$, $x_1 = a - h$, $x_2 = a + h$, $x_3 = a + 2h$. Also derive the error term for this formula.

5.1-5. On your computer, calculate the sequence of numbers

$$a_n = f[2 - 2^{-n}, 2 + 2^{-n}] \qquad n = 1, 2, 3, \ldots$$

where $f(x) = \ln x$. Without round-off effects,

$$\lim_{n \to \infty} a_n = f'(2) = 0.5$$

According to the discussion in this section,

$$\lim_{n \to \infty} |a_n| = \infty$$

because of round-off. Does this really happen? If not, why not? Does this invalidate the discussion in the text?

5.2 NUMERICAL INTEGRATION: SOME BASIC RULES

The problem of numerical integration, or numerical quadrature, is that of estimating the number

$$I(f) = \int_a^b f(x)\, dx \tag{5.17}$$

This problem arises when the integration cannot be carried out exactly or when $f(x)$ is known only at a finite number of points.

Numerical integration, in contrast to differentiation, is basically a stable process, and many adequate formulas, or *rules*, exist for it. Some of these we derive in this section.

We assume that the integrand $f(x)$ is sufficiently smooth on some interval $[c,d]$ containing a and b so that we can write, as in (4.40),

$$f(x) = p_k(x) + f[x_0, \ldots, x_k, x]\psi_k(x)$$

where $p_k(x)$ is the polynomial of degree $\leq k$ which interpolates $f(x)$ at certain $k + 1$ points $x_0, \ldots, x_k$ in the interval $[c,d]$, and

$$\psi_k(x) = \prod_{j=0}^k (x - x_j)$$

We estimate $I(f)$ by $I(p_k)$. Then the error in this estimate is

$$E(f) = I(f) - I(p_k) = \int_a^b f[x_0, \ldots, x_k, x]\psi_k(x)\, dx \tag{5.18}$$

$f[x_0, \ldots, x_k, x]$ being a continuous, hence integrable, function of x, by Theorem 4.5.

This error term can, at times, be simplified. If, for example, $\psi_k(x)$ is *of one sign* on (a,b), then, by the mean-value theorem for integrals (see Sec. 1.7),

$$\int_a^b f[x_0, \ldots, x_k, x]\psi_k(x)\, dx = f[x_0, \ldots, x_k, \xi] \int_a^b \psi_k(x)\, dx$$

$$\text{some } \xi \in (a,b) \quad (5.19)$$

If, in addition, $f(x)$ is $k + 1$ times continuously differentiable on (c,d), we get from (5.18) and (5.19) that

$$E(f) = \frac{1}{(k + 1)!} f^{(k+1)}(\eta) \int_a^b \psi_k(x)\, dx \qquad \text{some } \eta \in (c,d) \tag{5.20}$$

Even if $\psi_k(x)$ is not of one sign, certain simplifications in the error term (5.18) are possible. A particularly desirable instance of this kind occurs when

$$\int_a^b \psi_k(x)\, dx = 0 \tag{5.21}$$

In such a case, we can make use of the identity

$$f[x_0, \ldots ,x_k,x] = f[x_0, \ldots ,x_k,x_{k+1}] + f[x_0, \ldots ,x_{k+1},x](x - x_{k+1})$$

which is valid for arbitrary x_{k+1} to get that

$$E(f) = \int_a^b f[x_0, \ldots ,x_{k+1}]\psi_k(x)\, dx$$

$$+ \int_a^b f[x_0, \ldots ,x_{k+1},x](x - x_{k+1})\psi_k(x)\, dx$$

$$= \int_a^b f[x_0, \ldots ,x_{k+1},x]\psi_{k+1}(x)\, dx$$

since

$$\int_a^b f[x_0, \ldots ,x_{k+1}]\psi_k(x)\, dx = f[x_0, \ldots ,x_{k+1}] \int_a^b \psi_k(x)\, dx = 0$$

If we now can choose x_{k+1} in such a way that $\psi_{k+1}(x) = (x - x_{k+1})\psi_k(x)$ is of one sign on (a,b), and if $f(x)$ is $(k + 2)$ times continuously differentiable, then it follows (as before) that

$$E(f) = \frac{1}{(k + 2)!} f^{(k+2)}(\eta) \int_a^b \psi_{k+1}(x)\, dx \qquad \text{some } \eta \in (c,d) \qquad (5.22)$$

Note that the derivative of $f(x)$ appearing in (5.22) is of one order higher than the one in (5.20).   As in numerical differentiation, this indicates that (5.22) is of higher order than (5.20).

We now consider specific examples.   Let $k = 0$.   Then

$$f(x) = f(x_0) + f[x_0,x](x - x_0)$$

Hence

$$I(p_k) = (b - a)f(x_0)$$

If $x_0 = a$, then this approximation becomes

$$\boxed{I(f) \approx R = (b - a)f(a)} \qquad (5.23)$$

the so-called *rectangle rule* (see Fig. 5.2).   Since, in this case, $\psi_0(x) = x - a$ is of one sign on (a,b), the error E^R of the rectangle rule can be computed from (5.20).   One gets

$$\boxed{E^R = f'(\eta) \int_a^b (x - a)\, dx = \frac{f'(\eta)(b - a)^2}{2}} \qquad (5.24)$$

If $x_0 = (a + b)/2$, then $\psi_0(x)$ fails to be of one sign. But then

$$\int_a^b (x - x_0)\, dx = 0$$

while $(x - x_0)^2$ is of one sign. Hence, in this case, the error in $I(p_k)$ can be computed from (5.22), with $x_1 = x_0$. One gets

$$I(f) \approx M = (b - a)f\left(\frac{a + b}{2}\right)$$

$$E^M = \frac{f''(\eta)(b - a)^3}{24}$$

$$\text{some } \eta \in (a,b)$$

(5.25)

the *midpoint rule*.

Next, let $k = 1$. Then

$$f(x) = f(x_0) + f[x_0,x_1](x - x_0) + f[x_0,x_1,x]\psi_1(x)$$

To get $\psi_1(x) = (x - x_0)(x - x_1)$ of one sign on (a,b), we choose $x_0 = a$, $x_1 = b$. Then, by (5.20),

$$I(f) = \int_a^b \{f(a) + f[a,b](x - a)\}\, dx + \tfrac{1}{2}f''(\eta) \int_a^b (x - a)(x - b)\, dx$$

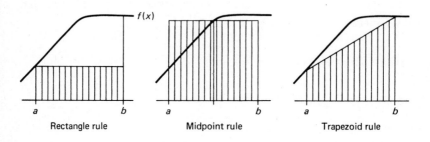

Rectangle rule   Midpoint rule   Trapezoid rule

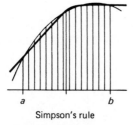   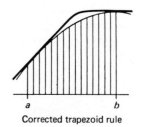

Simpson's rule   Corrected trapezoid rule

Fig. 5.2 Numerical integration.

or

$$I(f) \approx T = \tfrac{1}{2}(b - a)[f(a) + f(b)]$$

$$E^T = -\frac{f''(\eta)(b - a)^3}{12}$$

$$\text{some } \eta \in (a,b)$$

(5.26)

the *trapezoid(al) rule* (see Fig. 5.2).

Now, let $k = 2$.   Then

$$f(x) = p_2(x) + f[x_0, x_1, x_2, x]\psi_2(x)$$

Note that, for distinct x_0, x_1, x_2 in (a,b), $\psi_2(x) = (x - x_0)(x - x_1)(x - x_2)$ is not of one sign on (a,b).   But if we choose $x_0 = a$, $x_1 = (a + b)/2$, $x_2 = b$, then

$$\int_a^b \psi_2(x)\, dx = 0$$

The error is therefore of the form (5.22).   If we choose $x_3 = x_1$, then

$$\psi_3(x) = (x - a)\left(x - \frac{a + b}{2}\right)^2 (x - b)$$

is of one sign on (a,b).   Hence we then have with (5.22) that

$$I(f) = I(p_2) + \frac{1}{4!} f^{iv}(\eta) \int_a^b \psi_3(x)\, dx$$

One calculates directly

$$\int_a^b \psi_3(x)\, dx = \int_a^b (x - a)\left(x - \frac{a + b}{2}\right)^2 (x - b)\, dx = -\frac{4}{15}\left(\frac{b - a}{2}\right)^5$$

so that the error becomes

$$E(f) = -\frac{1}{90}\left(\frac{b - a}{2}\right)^5 f^{iv}(\eta) \qquad \eta \in [a,b]$$

We can calculate $I(p_2)$ directly, but it is instructive to evaluate $I(p_2)$ using a combination of the midpoint and the trapezoid rules.   If we set $f(x) = p_2(x)$ in (5.25) and (5.26), we get that

$$I(p_2) = \begin{cases} (b - a)p_2\left(\dfrac{a + b}{2}\right) + \dfrac{p_2''(\eta_1)(b - a)^3}{24} \\[4mm] \dfrac{b - a}{2}[p_2(a) + p_2(b)] - \dfrac{p_2''(\eta_2)(b - a)^3}{12} \end{cases}$$

(5.27)

respectively. Since $p_2(x)$ is a parabola, we have $p_2''(x) \equiv$ const; hence $p_2''(\eta_1) = p_2''(\eta_2)$, regardless of the points η_1 and η_2. Therefore, by adding $\frac{1}{3}$ of the second equation in (5.27) to $\frac{2}{3}$ of the first, we find

$$I(p_2) = \tfrac{2}{3}(b - a)\left\{ p_2\!\left(\frac{a + b}{2}\right) + \frac{p_2(a) + p_2(b)}{4} \right\}$$

Since $p_2(x)$ interpolates $f(x)$ at $x_0 = a$, $x_1 = (a + b)/2$, $x_2 = b$, this gives

$$I(f) \approx S = \frac{b - a}{6}\left[f(a) + 4f\!\left(\frac{a + b}{2}\right) + f(b) \right]$$

$$(5.28)$$

$$E^S = \frac{-f^{\mathrm{iv}}(\eta)[(b - a)/2]^5}{90}$$

which is the justly famous *Simpson's rule*.

Finally, let $k = 3$. In order to have $\psi_3(x)$ of one sign on (a,b), we choose $x_0 = x_1 = a$, $x_2 = x_3 = b$, and get from (5.20) that

$$E(f) = \frac{1}{4!} f^{\mathrm{iv}}(\eta) \int_a^b (x - a)^2(x - b)^2 \, dx = \frac{f^{\mathrm{iv}}(\eta)(b - a)^5}{720}$$

Since $p_3(x)$ is a cubic polynomial, $p_3^{\mathrm{iv}}(x) \equiv 0$. Hence we can use Simpson's rule (5.28) to evaluate $I(p_3)$ exactly. We get

$$I(p_3) = \frac{b - a}{6}\left[p_3(a) + 4p_3\!\left(\frac{a + b}{2}\right) + p_3(b) \right]$$

Since $p_3(x)$ interpolates $f(x)$ at a, a, b, b, we have $p_3(a) = f(a)$, $p_3(b) = f(b)$, while, for example, from (4.51), (4.53), and (4.55) (see Exercise 4.6-5),

$$p_3\!\left(\frac{a + b}{2}\right) = \tfrac{1}{2}[f(a) + f(b)] + \frac{b - a}{8}[f'(a) - f'(b)]$$

It follows that

$$I(f) \approx CT = \frac{b - a}{2}[f(a) + f(b)] + \frac{(b - a)^2}{12}[f'(a) - f'(b)]$$

$$(5.29)$$

$$E^{CT} = \frac{f^{\mathrm{iv}}(\eta)(b - a)^5}{720}$$

which, for obvious reasons, is known as the *corrected trapezoid rule*.

If the above-mentioned rules for numerical integration do not give a satisfactory approximation to $I(f)$, we could, of course, increase the degree k of the interpolating polynomial used. We discussed the dangers of such an action in Sec. 4.7 and proposed there the use of piecewise-polynomial interpolation as a more reasonable and certain means for achieving high accuracy. Accordingly, we approximate $I(f)$ by $I(g_k)$, where $g_k(x)$ is a piecewise-polynomial function of "low" degree k which interpolates $f(x)$. We discuss the resulting integration rules, usually called *composite rules*, in the next section.

We have derived in this section five basic integration rules. These are the rectangle rule (5.24), the midpoint rule (5.25), the trapezoid rule (5.26), Simpson's rule (5.28), and the corrected trapezoid rule (5.29). The corrected trapezoid rule is the only one of these requiring knowledge of the derivative of $f(x)$, and this is an obvious disadvantage of this particular method. The error terms of these rules suggest that Simpson's rule or the corrected trapezoid rule should be preferred whenever the function $f(x)$ is sufficiently smooth. There are, nevertheless, some functions for which lower-order formulas yield better results than do higher-order formulas [see Exercise 5.2-2].

Example 5.1 Apply each of the five rules given above to find estimates for

$$I = \int_0^1 e^{-x^2}\, dx$$

We set $a = 0$, $b = 1$, $(a + b)/2 = \frac{1}{2}$, and from a table of values find that

$$f(0) = 1 \qquad f(1) = e^{-1} = 0.36788 \qquad f(\tfrac{1}{2}) = e^{-1/4} = 0.77880$$

We will also need

$$f'(0) = 0 \qquad f'(1) = -2e^{-1} = -0.73576$$

We can then calculate from the appropriate formulas

$$R = 1 \cdot e^0 = 1$$
$$M = 1 \cdot e^{-1/4} = 0.77880$$
$$T = \tfrac{1}{2}[e^0 + e^{-1}] = 0.68394$$
$$S = \tfrac{1}{6}[e^0 + 4e^{-1/4} + e^{-1}] = 0.74718$$
$$CT = \tfrac{1}{2}[e^0 + e^{-1}] + 1/12\,[0 + 2e^{-1}] = 0.74525$$

The value of the integral correct to five decimal places is $I = 0.74682$. The corrected trapezoid (CT) rule and Simpson's (S) rule clearly give the best results, as might be expected from a consideration of the error terms and the fact that the first few derivatives of the function e^{-x^2} do not vary much in size.

EXERCISES

5.2-1. Derive Simpson's rule directly by evaluating

$$I(p_2) = \int_a^b p_2(x)\, dx$$

where $p_2(x)$ is the polynomial which interpolates $f(x)$ at the points $x_0 = a$, $x_1 = (a + b)/2$, $x_2 = b$.

5.2-2. The function $f(x)$ is defined on the interval $[0,1]$ as follows:

$$f(x) = \begin{cases} x & 0 \le x \le \frac{1}{2} \\ 1 - x & \frac{1}{2} \le x \le 1 \end{cases}$$

Calculate the results of applying the following rules to find $\int_0^1 f(x)\,dx$:

    (a) The trapezoid rule over the interval $[0,1]$
    (b) The trapezoid rule first over the interval $[0,\frac{1}{2}]$ and then over the interval $[\frac{1}{2},1]$
    (c) Simpson's rule over the interval $[0,1]$
    (d) The corrected trapezoid rule over the interval $[0,1]$

Account for the differences in the results.

5.2-3. Apply each of the five rules given in this section to find an approximation to $I = \int_0^1 e^{-x}\,dx$. Compare the results with the correct value $I = -e^{-x}|_0^1 = -e^{-1} + 1 = 0.63212$. You will need the values $e^0 = 1$, $e^{-1} = 0.36788$, $e^{-1/2} = 0.60653$.

5.3 NUMERICAL INTEGRATION: COMPOSITE RULES

The simple quadrature rules developed in the preceding section to estimate

$$I = \int_a^b f(x)\,dx$$

will usually not produce sufficiently accurate estimates, particularly when the interval $[a,b]$ is reasonably large. It is customary in practice to divide the given interval $[a,b]$ into N smaller intervals and to apply the simple quadrature rules to each of these subintervals. We therefore subdivide the interval $[a,b]$ in such a way that

$$a = x_0 < x_1 < x_2 < \cdots < x_N = b$$

and we denote by $g_k(x)$ a piecewise-polynomial function (see Secs. 4.7 and 4.8) with breakpoints $\{x_i\}$ $(i = 1, \ldots, N - 1)$. Furthermore, let $p_{i,k}(x)$ $(i = 1, \ldots, N)$ denote the polynomial of degree $\le k$ which agrees with $g_k(x)$ on (x_{i-1}, x_i). By the rules of integration we know that

$$I(f) = \int_a^b f(x)\,dx = \sum_{i=1}^N \int_{x_{i-1}}^{x_i} f(x)\,dx$$

and that

$$I(g_k) = \sum_{i=1}^N \int_{x_{i-1}}^{x_i} g_k(x)\,dx = \sum_{i=1}^N \int_{x_{i-1}}^{x_i} p_{i,k}(x)\,dx$$

Hence, approximating $I(f)$ by $I(g_k)$ amounts to approximating

$$\int_{x_{i-1}}^{x_i} f(x)\,dx \quad \text{by} \quad \int_{x_{i-1}}^{x_i} p_{i,k}(x)\,dx \qquad i = 1, \ldots, N$$

and summing the results.   Evidently, on each subinterval (x_{i-1}, x_i), we are proceeding just as in Sec. 5.2.   In particular, we can apply any of the rules derived in Sec. 5.2 by substituting some polynomial for the integrand, on each subinterval, and then summing the results.

In the absence of any reason to do otherwise, we choose the x_i's to be equally spaced,

$$x_i = a + ih \qquad i = 0, \ldots, N, \text{ with } h = \frac{b-a}{N}$$

We also use, as in Sec. 4.5, the abbreviation

$$f_s = f(a + sh)$$

so that $f_i = f(x_i)$, $i = 0, \ldots, N$.

We now consider specific examples.   If we apply the rectangle rule (5.23) on each subinterval, we get

$$\int_{x_{i-1}}^{x_i} f(x)\, dx = (x_i - x_{i-1})f(x_{i-1}) + \frac{f'(\eta_i)(x_i - x_{i-1})^2}{2}$$

$$= hf(x_{i-1}) + \frac{f'(\eta_i)h^2}{2}$$

for the subinterval (x_{i-1}, x_i).   Summing, we obtain

$$I(f) \approx R_N = h \sum_{i=1}^{N} f_{i-1} \tag{5.30a}$$

the composite rectangle rule (on N intervals).   Its error is just the sum of the errors committed in each subinterval,

$$E_N^R = \sum_{i=1}^{N} \frac{f'(\eta_i)h^2}{2}$$

where $\eta_i \in (x_{i-1}, x_i)$.   If $f'(x)$ is continuous (as we assume), this can be simplified, using Theorem 1.2 in Sec. 1.7, as follows:

$$\sum_{i=1}^{N} \frac{f'(\eta_i)h^2}{2} = f'(\eta) \sum_{i=1}^{N} \frac{h^2}{2} = \frac{f'(\eta)Nh^2}{2}$$

so that, with $Nh = b - a$,

$$E_N^R = \frac{f'(\eta)(b - a)h}{2} \qquad \text{some } \eta \in (a,b) \tag{5.30b}$$

We derive next the composite Simpson rule. Letting $a = x_{i-1}$, $b = x_i$, and $x_i - x_{i-1} = h$ in (5.28), we obtain for a single subinterval

$$\int_{x_{i-1}}^{x_i} f(x)\,dx = \frac{h}{6}[f_{i-1} + 4f_{i-1/2} + f_i] - \frac{f^{iv}(\eta_i)(h/2)^5}{90} \qquad x_{i-1} < \eta_i < x_i$$

Summing for $i = 1, \ldots, N$, we obtain

$$I(f) = \sum_{i=1}^{N} \int_{x_{i-1}}^{x_i} f(x)\,dx = \frac{h}{6}\sum_{i=1}^{N}[f_{i-1} + 4f_{i-1/2} + f_i] - \sum_{i=1}^{N}\frac{f^{iv}(\eta_i)(h/2)^5}{90}$$

$$= S_N + E_N^S$$

The composite Simpson approximation S_N can be simplified to yield

$$S_N = \frac{h}{6}\left[f_0 + f_N + 2\sum_{i=1}^{N-1} f_i + 4\sum_{i=1}^{N} f_{i-1/2}\right] \qquad (5.31a)$$

while the error term can be simplified, again using Theorem 1.2 of Sec. 1.7, to

$$E_N^S = -\frac{f^{iv}(\xi)(h/2)^4(b-a)}{180} \qquad a < \xi < b \qquad (5.31b)$$

Note that in Simpson's rule we must be able to evaluate the function at the midpoints $x_{i-1/2}$ ($i = 1, \ldots, N$) as well as at the breakpoints x_i ($i = 0,1, \ldots, N$). This implies in particular that we always need an *odd* number of equally spaced points at which we know the value of the integrand.

In the same manner, one gets the composite midpoint rule

$$I(f) \approx M_N = h\sum_{i=1}^{N} f_{i-1/2} \qquad\qquad E_N^M = \frac{f''(\xi)h^2(b-a)}{24} \qquad (5.32)$$

from the midpoint rule (5.25), and the composite trapezoid rule

$$I(f) \approx T_N = h \sum_{i=1}^{N-1} f_i + \frac{h}{2}(f_0 + f_N)$$

(5.33)

$$E_N{}^T = -\frac{f''(\eta)h^2(b-a)}{12}$$

from (5.26).

Finally, from the corrected trapezoid rule (5.29), one obtains

$$I(f) \approx CT_N = h \sum_{i=1}^{N-1} f_i + \frac{h}{2}(f_0 + f_N) + \frac{h^2}{12}[f'(a) - f'(b)] \quad (5.34)$$

$$E_N{}^{CT} = \frac{f^{iv}(\eta)h^4(b-a)}{720}$$

Note that all the interior derivatives $f'(x_i)$, $i = 1, \ldots, N-1$, cancel each other when the results of applying the corrected trapezoid rule on each subinterval are summed. Hence the composite corrected trapezoid rule is, in fact, a corrected composite trapezoid rule, i.e.,

$$CT_N = T_N + \frac{h^2[f'(a) - f'(b)]}{12}$$

(5.35)

The corrected trapezoid rule has, of course, the disadvantage that the derivative of $f(x)$ must be known or calculable.

If any of these composite rules are to be applied, one has to determine first an appropriate N, or equivalently, an appropriate $h = (b-a)/N$. If some information about the size of the derivative appearing in the error term is available, one simply determines h or N so as to guarantee an error less than a prescribed tolerance.

Example 5.2 Determine N so that the composite trapezoid rule (5.33) gives the value of

$$\int_0^1 e^{-x^2} \, dx$$

correct to six digits after the decimal point, assuming that e^{-x^2} can be calculated accurately, and compute the approximation.

In this example, $f(x) = e^{-x^2}$, $a = 0$, $b = 1$, $h = 1/N$; hence the error in the composite trapezoid rule is $-f''(\eta)N^{-2}/12$, for some $\eta \in (a,b)$. Since we do not know η, the best statement we can make is that the error is in absolute value no bigger than

$$\max_{0 \le \eta \le 1} \frac{|f''(\eta)|N^{-2}}{12}$$

We compute

$$f''(x) = e^{-x^2}(4x^2 - 2)$$

Further, $f'''(x) = e^{-x^2}4x(3 - 2x^2)$, which vanishes at $x = 0$ and $x = \pm\sqrt{1.5}$. Hence $\max |f''(x)|$ on $[0,1]$ must occur at $x = 0$ or at the end points $x = 0, 1$; thus

$$\max_{0 \le \eta \le 1} |f''(\eta)| = \max\{|f''(0)|, |f''(1)|\} = \max\{2, 2e^{-1}\} = 2$$

We are therefore guaranteed six-place accuracy (after the decimal point) if we choose N such that

$$\frac{2N^{-2}}{12} < 5 \cdot 10^{-7}$$

or

$$N^2 > \frac{10^6}{3} = \frac{10^7}{6 \cdot 5}$$

or

$$N > \frac{10^3}{\sqrt{3}} \approx 578$$

The computer output below shows this to be a slight overestimate for N.

As computed by the IBM 7094 in both single precision (SP) and double precision (DP), the results for various values of N are:

N	$I\,(SP)$	$I\,(DP)$
50	7.4679947E-01	7.4679961D-01
100	7.4681776E-01	7.4681800D-01
200	7.4682212E-01	7.4682260D-01
400	7.4682275E-01	7.4682375D-01
800	7.4682207E-01	7.4682404D-01

The value of I correct to eight significant figures is $I = 0.74682413$. It thus appears that in single-precision arithmetic we cannot obtain six-place accuracy, no matter how many subdivisions we take. Indeed, for $N = 800$, the results are worse than those for $N = 400$. This shows that round-off error has affected the last three figures. The double-precision results show that for $N = 500$ we would almost certainly have six-decimal-place accuracy, as predicted above.

The FORTRAN program is:

FORTRAN PROGRAM FOR EXAMPLE 5.2 (SINGLE PRECISION)

```
C        EXAMPLE 5.2, TRAPEZOIDAL INTEGRATION
         F(X) = EXP(-X**2)
```

```
  1 WRITE(6,3)
    READ(5,4)A,B,N
    T = F(A)/2.
    N1 = N - 1
    H = (B - A)/FLOAT(N)
    DO 2 I = 1, N1
  2 T = F(A + FLOAT(I)*H) + T
    T = (F(B)/2. + T)*H
    WRITE(6,5)A,B,N,T
    GO TO 1
  3 FORMAT(36H EXAMPLE 5.2 TRAPEZOIDAL INTEGRATION)
  4 FORMAT(2E20.0,I5)
  5 FORMAT(18H0 INTEGRAL FROM A = 1PE14.7,7H TO B = 1PE14.7,
    19H FOR N = I5,4H IS 1PE14.7)
    END
```

If we use the corrected trapezoid rule (5.34) instead, the required N drops dramatically. We now have the error bounded by

$$\max_{0 \le \eta \le 1} \frac{|f^{\text{iv}}(\eta)| N^{-4}}{720}$$

One calculates $f^{\text{iv}}(x) = 4e^{-x^2}(3 - 12x^2 + 4x^4)$; hence

$$\max_{0 \le \eta \le 1} |f^{\text{iv}}(\eta)| = |f^{\text{iv}}(0)| = 12$$

For six-place accuracy, it is therefore sufficient that

$$\frac{12N^{-4}}{720} < 5 . 10^{-7}$$

or

$$N^4 > (10/3)10^4 = \frac{10^7}{300}$$

or

$$N > 13.5 \approx \sqrt[4]{(10/3) \cdot 10}$$

so that only 14 subintervals are required as compared with 578 for the composite trapezoid rule without the differential end correction.

As this example illustrates, higher-order formulas can reduce the necessary number of function evaluations tremendously over lower-order rules *if* the higher-order derivatives of the integrand are approximately the same size as the lower-order derivatives. Because of their potential, we look at some higher-order formulas in more detail later on (see Secs. 5.4 and 5.5).

In the absence of information about the size of the appropriate derivative of $f(x)$, it is possible only to apply the composite rules for various values of N, thus producing a sequence I_N of approximations to $I(f)$ which, theoretically, converges to $I(f)$ as $N \to \infty$, if $f(x)$ is sufficiently smooth. One terminates this process when the difference between successive estimates becomes "sufficiently small." The dangers of such a procedure have been discussed in Sec. 1.6. An added difficulty arises in this case from round-off effects, which increase with increasing N. The computer results in Example 5.2 show this very clearly.

Example 5.3 Write a program for the corrected trapezoid rule and solve the problem of Example 5.2 using this program.

FORTRAN PROGRAM

```
C       EXAMPLE 5.3 . CORRECTED TRAPEZOID RULE
        F(X) = EXP(-X*X)
        FPRIME(X) = -2.*X*F(X)
        A = 0.
        B = 1.
        WRITE (6,600)
    600 FORMAT(9X1HN7X13HTRAPEZOID SUM7X13HCORR.TRAP.SUM)
        DO 10 N = 10,15
        H = (B - A)/FLOAT(N)
        NM1 = N - 1
        TRAP = (F(A) + F(B))/2.
        DO 1 I = 1,NM1
      1 TRAP = TRAP + F(A + FLOAT(I)*H)
        TRAP = H*TRAP
        CORTRP = TRAP + H*H*(FPRIME(A) - FPRIME(B))/12.
     10 WRITE (6,610) N,TRAP,CORTRP
    610 FORMAT(I10,2E20.7)
        STOP
        END
```

Single precision

N	TRAPEZOID SUM	CORR.TRAP.SUM
10	0.7462108E 00	0.7468239E 00
11	0.7463173E 00	0.7468240E 00
12	0.7463983E 00	0.7468240E 00
13	0.7464612E 00	0.7468240E 00
14	0.7465112E 00	0.7468240E 00
15	0.7465516E 00	0.7468241E 00

Double precision

N	TRAPEZOID SUM	CORR.TRAP.SUM
10	7.4621080E-01	7.4682393E-01
11	7.4631727E-01	7.4682399E-01
12	7.4639825E-01	7.4682403E-01
13	7.4646126E-01	7.4682406E-01
14	7.4651126E-01	7.4682408E-01
15	7.4655159E-01	7.4682409E-01

Example 5.4 Write a program for Simpson's rule and solve the problem of Example 5.2 using this program in both single precision and double precision.

The FORTRAN program and the results obtained on an IBM 7094 are given below for $N = 25$, 50, and 100 subdivisions. Note that the results in single precision are again worse for $N = 50$, 100 than for $N = 25$, indicating round-off-error effects. The double-precision results are all correct to the number of figures given. On comparing these results with those of Examples 5.2 and 5.3, we see that both Simpson's rule and the corrected trapezoid rule are much more efficient than the trapezoid rule.

COMPUTER RESULTS FOR EXAMPLE 5.4

N	$I(SP)$	$I(DP)$
25	7.4682406E-01	7.4682413D-01
50	7.4682400E-01	7.4682413D-01
100	7.4682392E-01	7.4682413D-01

FORTRAN PROGRAM FOR EXAMPLE 5.4 (SINGLE PRECISION)

```
C       EXAMPLE 5.4 SIMPSON'S RULE
        F(X) = EXP(-X**2)
        WRITE (6,3)
      1 READ(5,4)A,B,N
        H = (B - A)/FLOAT(N)
        HOV2 = H/2.
        S = 0.
        HALF = F(A + HOV2)
        NM1 = N - 1
        DO 2 I = 1,NM1
        X = A + FLOAT(I)*H
        S = S + F(X)
      2 HALF = HALF + F(X + HOV2)
        S = (H/6.)*(F(A) + 4.*HALF + 2.*S + F(B))
        WRITE(6,5)A,B,N,S
        GO TO 1
      3 FORMAT(28H EXAMPLE 5.4 SIMPSON'S RULE)
      4 FORMAT(2E20.0,I5)
      5 FORMAT(18H0 INTEGRAL FROM A = 1PE14.7,7H TO B = 1PE14.7,
       19H FOR  N = I5,4H IS 1PE14.7)
        END
```

The composite rules discussed so far are all based on N subintervals of *equal* size. Such a choice of subintervals is quite natural, and at times even necessary, if the integrand is known only at a sequence of equally spaced points, e.g., if $f(x)$ is given only in the form of a table of function values. But if $f(x)$ can be evaluated with equal ease for every point in the interval of integration, it is usually more economical to use subintervals whose length is determined by the local behavior of the integrand. In other words, it is usually possible to calculate $I(f)$ to within a prescribed accuracy with fewer function evaluations if the subintervals are of properly chosen unequal size than if one insists on equal-length subintervals.

Consider, for example, the general composite trapezoid rule

$$I(f) = \sum_{i=1}^{N} \frac{x_i - x_{i-1}}{2} [f(x_{i-1}) + f(x_i)] - \sum_{i=1}^{N} \frac{f''(\eta_i)(x_i - x_{i-1})^3}{12}$$

where the breakpoints $a = x_0 < x_1 < \cdots < x_N = b$ are not necessarily equally spaced. The contribution

$$-\frac{f''(\eta_i)(x_i - x_{i-1})^3}{12} \qquad \text{some } \eta_i \in (x_{i-1}, x_i)$$

from the interval (x_{i-1}, x_i) to the overall error depends on both the size of $f''(x)$ on the interval (x_{i-1}, x_i) and the size $|x_i - x_{i-1}|$ of the subinterval. Hence, in those parts of the interval of integration (a,b) where $|f''(x)|$ is "small," we can take subintervals of "large" size, while in regions where $|f''(x)|$ is "large," we have to take "small" subintervals, if we want the contribution to the overall error from each subinterval to be about equal. It can be shown that such a policy is best if the goal is to minimize the number of subintervals, and hence the number of function evaluations, necessary to calculate $I(f)$ to a given accuracy.

Integration schemes which adapt the length of subintervals to the local behavior of the integrand are called *adaptive*. Although such adaptive schemes are of great importance for general-purpose quadrature programs, their description is too complicated to be included in this book. The major difficulty such schemes have to face is lack of knowledge about the derivative appearing in the error term. This means that such schemes have to *guess* the local behavior of the integrand from its values at a few points.

EXERCISES

5.3-1. Derive the composite trapezoid rule T_N (5.33) and the composite midpoint rule M_N (5.32).

5.3-2. Derive the composite corrected trapezoid rule CT_N (5.34) and verify that the interior derivatives $f'(x_i)$ $(i = 1, \ldots, N-1)$ cancel out in the sum.

5.3-3. Write programs for the trapezoid rule, Simpson's rule, and the corrected trapezoid rule, and use these to calculate the following integrals:

(a) $I = \int_0^1 xe^{-x} \, dx$

(b) $I = \int_0^1 x \sin x \, dx$

(c) $I = \int_0^1 (1 + x^2)^{3/2} \, dx$

Use a sequence of subdivisions and try to estimate the accuracy of the results.

5.4 NUMERICAL INTEGRATION: GAUSSIAN RULES

We have so far discussed the approximate evaluation of $\int_a^b f(x)\,dx$ in case (a,b) is finite and $f(x)$ is sufficiently often differentiable. Not infrequently, one is confronted with calculating $\int_a^b f(x)\,dx$ when these conditions are not satisfied. For instance, $f(x)$ may behave like $(x - a)^\alpha$ near a, for some $\alpha > -1$, or a and/or b may be infinite. In such situations, it is often possible to rewrite the integral as

$$\int_a^b f(x)\,dx = \int_a^b g(x)w(x)\,dx$$

where $w(x)$ is a nonnegative integrable function, and

$$g(x) = \frac{f(x)}{w(x)}$$

is smooth. In the above example, this is the case with $w(x) = (x - a)^\alpha$. Other choices for $w(x)$ are discussed below.

In this section, we use the material on orthogonal polynomials in Sec. 4.10 to derive efficient methods for the approximate evaluation of

$$I(g) = \int_a^b g(x)w(x)\,dx \tag{5.36}$$

when $w(x)$ is a positive integrable function on (a,b), the so-called gaussian rules. All the rules derived in Sec. 5.2, except for the corrected trapezoid rule, can be written in the form

$$I(g) \approx A_0 g(x_0) + A_1 g(x_1) + \cdots + A_k g(x_k) \tag{5.37}$$

where the *weights* $A_0, \ldots , A_k$ do not depend on the particular function $g(x)$. Aside from the use of a function $w(x)$, gaussian rules are different from the quadrature rules discussed so far in that they are exact for polynomials of as high a degree as is possible for a given fixed k.

We say that *the rule (5.37) is exact for the particular function $p(x)$* if substitution of $p(x)$ for $g(x)$ into (5.37) makes (5.37) an identity. The trapezoid rule

$$\int_a^b g(x)\,dx \approx \frac{b - a}{2}\,g(a) + \frac{b - a}{2}\,g(b)$$

for instance, is exact for all polynomials of degree ≤ 1. To check this, we only have to look at the error term for this rule,

$$E^T = \frac{g''(\eta)(b - a)^3}{12}$$

Since this error term involves the second derivative of $g(x)$, and the second derivative of any polynomial of degree ≤ 1 is identically zero, it follows that the error is zero whenever $g(x)$ is a polynomial of degree ≤ 1. More generally, if the error term of (5.37) is of the form

$$E = \text{const } g^{(r+1)}(\eta) \cdot (\text{some function of } x_0, \ldots, x_k) \qquad (5.38)$$

then the rule (5.37) must be exact for all polynomials of degree $\leq r$.

Hence, if we wish to construct a rule of the form (5.37) which, for fixed k, is exact for polynomials of as high a degree as possible, we should construct the rule in such a way that it has an error term of the form (5.38), with r as large an integer as possible. This we can do, using a trick already employed in Sec. 5.2.

As in Sec. 5.2, we use analytic substitution, picking points $x_0, \ldots, x_k$ in (a,b) and writing

$$g(x) = p_k(x) + g[x_0, \ldots, x_k, x]\psi_k(x)$$

where $p_k(x)$ is the polynomial of degree $\leq k$ which interpolates $g(x)$ at $x_0, \ldots, x_k$, and

$$\psi_k(x) = (x - x_0) \cdots (x - x_k)$$

This gives

$$I(g) = I(p_k) + \int_a^b g[x_0, \ldots, x_k, x]\psi_k(x)w(x)\,dx$$

The approximation $I(p_k)$ to $I(g)$ is clearly of the form (5.37). For if we write $p_k(x)$ in Lagrange form (see Sec. 4.1),

$$p_k(x) = g(x_0)l_0(x) + g(x_1)l_1(x) + \cdots + g(x_k)l_k(x)$$

with

$$l_i(x) = \prod_{\substack{j=0 \\ j \neq i}}^{k} \frac{x - x_j}{x_i - x_j} \qquad i = 0, \ldots, k$$

then

$$I(p_k) = \int_a^b p_k(x)w(x)\,dx$$

$$= g(x_0)\int_a^b l_0(x)w(x)\,dx + \cdots + g(x_k)\int_a^b l_k(x)w(x)\,dx$$

Hence

$$I(p_k) = A_0 g(x_0) + A_1 g(x_1) + \cdots + A_k g(x_k) \qquad (5.39a)$$

where

$$A_i = \int_a^b l_i(x)w(x)\,dx \qquad i = 0,\ \ldots,\ k \tag{5.39b}$$

Next, consider the error

$$I(g) - I(p_k) = \int_a^b g[x_0,\ \ldots\ ,x_k,x]\psi_k(x)w(x)\,dx$$

Suppose that

$$\int_a^b \psi_k(x)w(x)\,dx = 0$$

Then, as argued in Sec. 5.2,

$$I(g) - I(p_k) = \int_a^b g[x_0,\ \ldots\ ,x_k,x_{k+1},x]\psi_{k+1}(x)w(x)\,dx$$

for *any choice* of x_{k+1}. If now also

$$\int_a^b \psi_{k+1}(x)w(x)\,dx = 0$$

then, by the same reasoning,

$$I(g) - I(p_k) = \int_a^b g[x_0,\ \ldots\ ,x_{k+2},x]\psi_{k+2}(x)w(x)\,dx$$

Hence, in general, if for certain $x_0,\ \ldots\ ,\ x_{k+m}$,

$$\int_a^b \psi_k(x)(x - x_{k+1})\ \cdots\ (x - x_{k+1+i})w(x)\,dx = 0$$

$$i = 0,\ \ldots\ ,\ m-1 \quad (5.40)$$

then

$$I(g) - I(p_k) = \int_a^b g[x_0,\ \ldots\ ,x_{k+m},x]\psi_{k+m}(x)w(x)\,dx \tag{5.41}$$

Now recall from Sec. 4.10 that we can find, for many $w(x)$, a polynomial $P_{k+1}(x)$ such that

$$\int_a^b P_{k+1}(x)q(x)w(x)\,dx = 0 \tag{5.42}$$

for all polynomials $q(x)$ of degree $\leq k$ (see Property 3 of orthogonal polynomials in Sec. 4.10). Further, by Property 2 of orthogonal polynomials, we can write

$$P_{k+1}(x) = \alpha_{k+1}(x - \xi_0)(x - \xi_1)\ \cdots\ (x - \xi_k)$$

where $\xi_0, \ldots, \xi_k$ are the $k + 1$ distinct points in the interval (a,b) at which P_{k+1} vanishes. Hence, if we set

$$x_j = \xi_j \qquad j = 0, \ldots, k \qquad\qquad (5.43)$$

and let x_{k+j} be arbitrary points in (a,b), $j = 1, \ldots, k + 1$, then (5.40), and therefore (5.41), is satisfied for $m = k + 1$. For then (5.40) is of the form (5.42), with

$$q(x) = \frac{(x - x_{k+1}) \cdots (x - x_{k+1+i})}{\alpha_{k+1}} \qquad i = 0, \ldots, m - 1$$

which, for $m \le k + 1$, are all polynomials of degree $\le k$. Therefore

$$I(g) - I(p_k) = \int_a^b g[x_0, \ldots, x_{2k+1}, x]\psi_{2k+1}(x)w(x)\, dx \qquad (5.44)$$

To get this error into the form (5.38), we pick the x_{k+j}'s as

$$x_{k+j} = \xi_{j-1} \qquad j = 1, \ldots, k + 1$$

Then

$$\begin{aligned}
\psi_{2k+1}(x) &= (x - x_0) \cdots (x - x_{2k+1}) \\
&= (x - \xi_0) \cdots (x - \xi_k)(x - \xi_0) \cdots (x - \xi_k) \\
&= \left[\frac{P_{k+1}(x)}{\alpha_{k+1}}\right]^2
\end{aligned}$$

so that $\psi_{2k+1}(x)w(x)$ is of one sign, i.e., nonnegative, on (a,b). Hence we can apply the mean-value theorem for integrals (see Sec. 1.7) to get

$$I(g) - I(p_k) = g[x_0, \ldots, x_{2k+1}, \eta]\int_a^b \left[\frac{1}{\alpha_{k+1}} P_{k+1}(x)\right]^2 w(x)\, dx$$

Finally, if $g(x)$ is $2k + 2$ times continuously differentiable, we can make use of Theorem 4.5 to express the error in the form

$$I(g) - I(p_k) = \frac{1}{(2k + 2)!} g^{(2k+2)}(\xi)\frac{S_{k+1}}{\alpha_{k+1}^2} \qquad (5.45)$$

where

$$S_{k+1} = \int_a^b [P_{k+1}(x)]^2 w(x)\, dx$$

To summarize, we have shown that if we choose the points $x_0, \ldots, x_k$ in (5.39a) as the zeros of the polynomial $P_{k+1}(x)$ of degree $k + 1$ which is orthogonal with respect to the weight function $w(x)$ over the interval (a,b) to any polynomial of degree $\le k$, and if the coefficients A_i ($i = 0, \ldots, k$) in (5.39a) are chosen according to (5.39b), the resulting gaussian formula

(5.39a) will then be exact for all polynomials of degree $\leq 2k + 1$. Quadrature rules of this type are said to be "best possible" in the sense defined, and under the conditions given above.

We now give some simple examples. First, let $w(x) = 1$. If (a,b) is a finite interval, then the linear change of variables $y = [2x - (a + b)]/(b - a)$ can be used to change the limits of integration from (a,b) to $(-1,1)$. Assuming that this transformation has already been made, we consider the integral (5.36) to be in the form

$$I(g) = \int_{-1}^{1} g(x)w(x)\, dx \tag{5.46}$$

Since $w(x) = 1$, the appropriate orthogonal polynomials are the Legendre polynomials (see Example 4.14). In this case

$$P_1(x) = x \qquad\qquad \xi_0 = 0$$

$$P_2(x) = \tfrac{3}{2}(x^2 - \tfrac{1}{3}) \qquad \xi_0 = -\frac{1}{\sqrt{3}},\ \xi_1 = \frac{1}{\sqrt{3}}$$

$$P_3(x) = \tfrac{5}{2}(x^3 - \tfrac{3}{5}x) \qquad \xi_0 = -\sqrt{\tfrac{3}{5}},\ \xi_1 = 0,\ \xi_2 = \sqrt{\tfrac{3}{5}}$$

etc. If we choose $k = 1$, then $x_0 = \xi_0 = -1/\sqrt{3}$, $x_1 = \xi_1 = 1/\sqrt{3}$, and substituting into (5.39) and (5.45), we obtain

$$\int_{-1}^{1} g(x)\, dx \approx A_0 g\!\left(\frac{-1}{\sqrt{3}}\right) + A_1 g\!\left(\frac{1}{\sqrt{3}}\right) \tag{5.47}$$

$$E = Cg^{iv}(\eta)$$

where

$$A_0 = \int_{-1}^{1} \frac{x - (-1/\sqrt{3})}{1/\sqrt{3} - (-1/\sqrt{3})}\, dx = 1$$

$$A_1 = \int_{-1}^{1} \frac{x - 1/\sqrt{3}}{(-1/\sqrt{3}) - 1/\sqrt{3}}\, dx = 1$$

$$C = \frac{1}{4!}\frac{S_2}{\alpha_2^{\,2}} = \frac{1}{24}\cdot\frac{2}{5}\cdot\frac{4}{9} = \frac{1}{135}$$

since

$$S_2 = \int_{-1}^{1} [P_2(x)]^2\, dx = \tfrac{2}{5} \qquad \alpha_2 = \tfrac{3}{2}$$

Substituting these constants into (5.47), we obtain the gaussian two-point quadrature formula

$$\int_{-1}^{1} g(x)\, dx \approx g\!\left(\frac{-1}{\sqrt{3}}\right) + g\!\left(\frac{1}{\sqrt{3}}\right) \tag{5.47a}$$

Gaussian weights and points for $k = 1, 2, 3, 4$

k	ξ_i	A_i
1	$\xi_1 = -\xi_0 = 0.57735027$	$A_1 = A_0 = 1.0000000$
2	$\xi_1 = 0$	$A_1 = 0.88888889$
	$\xi_2 = -\xi_0 = 0.77459667$	$A_2 = A_0 = 0.55555556$
3	$\xi_2 = -\xi_1 = 0.33998104$	$A_2 = A_1 = 0.65214515$
	$\xi_3 = -\xi_0 = 0.86113631$	$A_3 = A_0 = 0.34785485$
4	$\xi_2 = 0$	$A_2 = 0.56888889$
	$\xi_4 = -\xi_0 = 0.90617985$	$A_4 = A_0 = 0.23692689$
	$\xi_3 = -\xi_1 = 0.53846931$	$A_3 = A_1 = 0.47862867$

with the error

$$E = \frac{1}{135} g^{\text{iv}}(\eta) \tag{5.47b}$$

For $k > 1$, both the points ξ_i and the weights A_i become irrational. Their calculation is, however, straightforward. The results for $k = 1, 2, 3, 4$ are given in the above table. Note that the points ξ_i are symmetrically placed with respect to the origin, that the weights are all positive, and that the weights of symmetrically placed points are the same.

While the irrationality of the gaussian points and weights is a hindrance to hand calculation, it is no hindrance to computer calculations. Moreover, because of their great accuracy, these formulas should be more widely used, at least in those cases when the function to be integrated is sufficiently smooth.

Example 5.5 For comparison purposes, we again wish to evaluate $I = \int_0^1 e^{-x^2}\, dx$, using the gaussian five-point formula ($k = 4$).

First we make the transformation $x = (t + 1)/2$ to obtain

$$I = \int_0^1 e^{-x^2}\, dx = \tfrac{1}{2} \int_{-1}^1 e^{-(t+1)^2/4}\, dt = \tfrac{1}{2} \int_{-1}^1 g(t)\, dt \approx \tfrac{1}{2} \sum_{k=0}^4 A_k g(\xi_k)$$

Taking the weights and points from the table above, we obtain

$$\begin{aligned} I \approx \tfrac{1}{2}\{ &0.23692689 g(-0.90617985) + 0.47862867 g(-0.53846931) \\ &+ 0.56888889 g(0) + 0.47862867 g(0.53846931) + 0.23692689 g(0.90617985)\} \\ = \ &0.74682413 \end{aligned}$$

To achieve comparable accuracy with the trapezoidal rule would require some 2,800 subdivisions, whereas Simpson's rule would require about 20 subdivisions.

Example 5.6 Find an approximation to

$$I = \int_1^3 \frac{\sin^2 x}{x}\, dx$$

using gaussian quadrature with $k = 3$. (The correct value is $I = 0.79482518 \ldots$.)

We again transform to the interval $[-1,1]$ by the change of variable $x = t + 2$. This yields

$$I = \int_{-1}^{1} \frac{\sin^2(t + 2)}{t + 2} \, dt = \int_{-1}^{1} g(t) \, dt$$

Applying the points and weights from the table, we obtain

$$I \approx 0.34735485[g(\xi_0) + g(\xi_3)] + 0.65214515[g(\xi_1) + g(\xi_2)]$$

The FORTRAN program and the results are as follows.

FORTRAN PROGRAM FOR EXAMPLE 5.6

```
C       EXAMPLE 5.6 GAUSSIAN INTEGRATION
        REAL I
        F(T) = SIN (T + 2.)**2/(T + 2.)
        T0 = -.86113631
        T2 =   .33998104
        T3 = -T0
        T1 = -T2
        I  = .34785485*(F(T0) + F(T3)) + .65214515*(F(T1) + F(T2))
        WRITE (6,1) I
        STOP
    1 FORMAT (34H  EXAMPLE 5.6 GAUSSIAN INTEGRATION /
        15H0I = 1PE14.7)
        END

        I = 7.9482833-01
```

Gaussian-type formulas are especially useful when dealing with singular integrals. If, for example, $\int_a^b f(x) \, dx$ is to be calculated, where $f(x)$ has an algebraic singularity at a and/or b, then one transforms the integral into

$$\int_{-1}^{1} g(x)w(x) \, dx$$

where

$$w(x) = (x - 1)^{\alpha}(x + 1)^{\beta}$$

for appropriate exponents α and β. In this case, the ξ_i's are the zeros of the appropriate *Jacobi* polynomial. In the special case $\alpha = \beta = -\frac{1}{2}$, these are just the Chebyshev polynomials introduced in Example 4.15 and discussed in Sec. 4.12. For this special case, one gets the very attractive rule

$$\int_{-1}^{1} \frac{g(x)}{(1 - x^2)^{1/2}} \, dx \approx \frac{\pi}{k + 1} \sum_{i=0}^{k} g(\xi_i) \tag{5.48a}$$

for which all the weights A_i coincide, and for which the ξ_i's are the Chebyshev points [see (4.91) and (4.92)],

$$\xi_i = \cos\left(\frac{2i + 1}{k + 1}\frac{\pi}{2}\right) \qquad i = 0, \ldots, k \tag{5.48b}$$

If the interval of integration is semi-infinite, it is at times of help to transform the integral into

$$\int_0^\infty g(x)w(x)\,dx$$

with

$$w(x) = x^\alpha e^{-x}$$

In this case, the ξ_i's are the zeros of the appropriate *Laguerre* polynomial; see Example 4.17. Finally, integrals of the form

$$\int_{-\infty}^\infty g(x)e^{-x^2}\,dx$$

can often be successfully estimated using the zeros of the appropriate *Hermite* polynomial (see Example 4.16).

For all these examples (and others), tables are available both for the ξ_i's and the weights A_i, the most recent, and probably most extensive, being Stroud and Secrest's "Gaussian Quadrature Formulas" [20].

EXERCISES

5.4-1. For which polynomials is Simpson's rule exact?

5.4-2. Construct a rule of the form

$$I(f) = \int_{-1}^1 f(x)dx \approx A_0 f(-\tfrac{1}{2}) + A_1 f(0) + A_2 f(\tfrac{1}{2})$$

which is exact for all polynomials of degree ≤ 2.

5.4-3. Calculate

$$\int_0^1 \frac{\sin \pi x}{[x(1 - x)]^{3/2}}\,dx$$

correct to four significant digits. [*Hint:* Transform the integral appropriately and use (5.48).]

5.4-4. Find an estimate for $\int_0^\infty e^{-x^2}\,dx$

5.4-5. Derive the weights A_i for the gaussian formula with $k = 3$, using the zeros ξ_i given in the table in the text.

5.4-6. Write a program for the gaussian five-point formula and use it to obtain estimates for the integrals given in Exercise 5.3-3.

5.4-7. Use Exercise 4.10-7 to show that (5.39b) can also be written $A_i = \int_a^b [l_i(x)]^2 w(x)\,dx$, $i = 0, \ldots, k$. Conclude that gaussian weights are always positive.

5.5 EXTRAPOLATION TO THE LIMIT; ROMBERG INTEGRATION

In the preceding sections, we spent considerable effort in deriving expressions for the error of the various rules for approximate integration and differentiation. To summarize: With $L(f)$ the integral of $f(x)$ over some interval $[a,b]$, or the value of some derivative of $f(x)$ at some point a, we constructed an approximation $L_h(f)$ to $L(f)$, which depends on a parameter h and which satisfies

$$\lim_{h \to 0} L_h(f) = L(f)$$

More explicitly, we usually proved that

$$L(f) = L_h(f) + ch^r f^{(s)}(\xi)$$

where $c =$ some constant
r and $s =$ positive integers
$\xi = \xi(h) =$ an unknown point in some interval
We pointed out that a direct bound for the size of the error term requires knowledge of the size of $|f^{(s)}(\xi)|$, which very often cannot be obtained accurately enough (if at all) to be of any use.

Nevertheless, such an error term tells us at what rate $L_h(f)$ approaches $L(f)$ (as $h \to 0$). This knowledge can be used at times to estimate the error from successive values of $L_h(f)$. The possibility of such estimates was briefly mentioned in Sec. 1.6; in Sec. 2.4, we discussed a specific example, the Aitken Δ^2 process.

As a simple example, consider the approximation

$$D_h(f) = \frac{f(a + h) - f(a - h)}{2h}$$

to the value

$$D(f) = f'(a)$$

of the first derivative of $f(x)$ at $x = a$. If $f(x)$ has three continuous derivatives, then, according to (5.8) or (5.11),

$$D(f) = D_h(f) - \tfrac{1}{6}h^2 f'''(\xi) \qquad \text{some } \xi \text{ with } |\xi - a| < |h|$$

Since $\xi(h) \to a$ as $h \to 0$, and $f'''(x)$ is continuous, we have

$$f'''(\xi) \to f'''(a) \qquad \text{as } h \to 0$$

Hence

$$\frac{[f'''(\xi) - f'''(a)]h^2}{6}$$

goes to zero faster than h^2. Using the order notation introduced in Sec. 1.6, we therefore get that

$$D(f) = D_h(f) + C_1 h^2 + o(h^2) \tag{5.49}$$

where the constant $C_1 = -f'''(a)/6$ does not depend on h.

A numerical example might help to bring out the significance of Eq. (5.49). With $f(x) = \sin x$ and $a = 1$, we get

$$D(f) = 0.540302$$
$$C_1 = 0.090050$$

In Table 5.2, we have listed $D_h(f)$, the error $E_h(f) = -h^2 f'''(\xi)/6$, and its two components, $C_1 h^2$ and $o(h^2)$, for various values of h. (To avoid round-off-error noise interference, all entries in this table were computed in double-precision arithmetic, then rounded.) As this table shows, $C_1 h^2$ becomes quickly the *dominant* component in the error since, although $C_1 h^2$ goes to zero (with h), the $o(h^2)$ component goes to zero faster. But this implies that we can get a good estimate for the dominant error component $C_1 h^2$ as follows: Substitute $2h$ for h in (5.49) to get

$$D(f) = D_{2h}(f) + 4C_1 h^2 + o(h^2)$$

On subtracting this equation from (5.49), we obtain

$$0 = D_h(f) - D_{2h}(f) - 3C_1 h^2 + o(h^2)$$

or

$$C_1 h^2 = \frac{D_h(f) - D_{2h}(f)}{3} + o(h^2) \tag{5.50}$$

This last equation states that, for sufficiently small h, the *computable* number

$$\frac{D_h(f) - D_{2h}(f)}{3} \tag{5.51}$$

is a good estimate for the usually *unknown* dominant error component $C_1 h^2$. This is nicely illustrated in Table 5.2, where we have also listed the numbers (5.51).

Table 5.2

h	$D_h(f)$	$E_h(f)$	$C_1 h^2$	$o(h^2)$	$(D_h - D_{2h})/3$	R_h
6.4	0.009839	0.530463	3.688464	−3.158001		
3.2	−0.009856	0.550158	0.922116	−0.371957	−0.065652	−0.57
1.6	0.337545	0.202757	0.230529	−0.027772	0.115800	2.37
0.8	0.484486	0.055816	0.057632	−0.001816	0.048980	3.54
0.4	0.526009	0.014293	0.014408	−0.000115	0.013841	3.88
0.2	0.536707	0.003594	0.003602	−0.000007	0.003566	3.97
0.1	0.539402	0.000900	0.000901	−0.0000005	0.000898	

The catch in these considerations is, of course, the phrase "for sufficiently small h." Indeed, we see from Table 5.2 that, in our numerical example, $(D_h - D_{2h})/3$ is good only as an order-of-magnitude estimate when $h = 3.2$, while for $h = 6.4$, $(D_h - D_{2h})/3$ is not even in the ball park. Hence the number (5.51) should not be accepted indiscriminately as an estimate for the error. Rather, one should protect oneself against drastic mistakes by a simple check, based on the following argument: If $C_1 h^2$ is indeed the dominant error component, i.e., if the $o(h^2)$ is "small" compared with $C_1 h^2$, then, from (5.50),

$$C_1 h^2 \approx \frac{D_h(f) - D_{2h}(f)}{3}$$

Hence also

$$C_1 \left(\frac{h}{2}\right)^2 \approx \frac{D_{h/2}(f) - D_h(f)}{3}$$

Therefore

$$\frac{D_h(f) - D_{2h}(f)}{D_{h/2}(f) - D_h(f)} \approx \frac{C_1 h^2}{C_1 h^2/4} = 4$$

In words, if $C_1 h^2$ is the dominant error component, then the *computable* ratio of differences

$$R_h = \frac{D_h(f) - D_{2h}(f)}{D_{h/2}(f) - D_h(f)} \tag{5.52}$$

should be about 4. This is quite evident, for our numerical example, in Table 5.2, where we have also listed the ratios R_h.

Once one *believes* that (5.51) is a good estimate for the error in $D_h(f)$, having reassured oneself by checking that $R_h \approx 4$, then one can expect

$$D_h^1(f) = D_h(f) + \frac{D_h(f) - D_{2h}(f)}{3} \tag{5.53}$$

to be a much better approximation to $D(f)$ than is $D_h(f)$. In particular, one then believes that

$$|D(f) - D_h^1(f)| < \frac{|D_h(f) - D_{2h}(f)|}{3} \tag{5.54}$$

In order to see how much better an approximation $D_h^1(f)$ might be, we now obtain a more detailed description of the error term

$$E_h(f) = -\tfrac{1}{6} h^2 f'''(\xi)$$

for $D_h(f)$. For the sake of variety, we use Taylor series rather than divided differences for this. If $f(x)$ has five continuous derivatives, then, on expanding both $f(a + h)$ and $f(a - h)$ in a partial Taylor series around $x = a$, we get

$$f(a + h) = f(a) + f'(a)h + \frac{f''(a)h^2}{2} + \frac{f'''(a)h^3}{6} + \frac{f^{iv}(a)h^4}{24}$$

$$+ \frac{f^{v}(a)h^5}{120} + o(h^5)$$

$$f(a - h) = f(a) - f'(a)h + \frac{f''(a)h^2}{2} - \frac{f'''(a)h^3}{6} + \frac{f^{iv}(a)h^4}{24}$$

$$- \frac{f^{v}(a)h^5}{120} + o(h^5)$$

Subtract the second equation from the first; then divide by $2h$ to get

$$D_h(f) = f'(a) + \frac{f'''(a)h^2}{6} + \frac{f^{v}(a)h^4}{120} + o(h^4)$$

Hence

$$D(f) = D_h(f) + C_1 h^2 + C_2 h^4 + o(h^4) \tag{5.55}$$

where the constants

$$C_1 = \frac{-f'''(a)}{6} \qquad C_2 = \frac{-f^{v}(a)}{120}$$

do not depend on h. Therefore, on substituting $2h$ for h in (5.55), we get

$$D(f) = D_{2h}(f) + 4C_1 h^2 + 16C_2 h^4 + o(h^4) \tag{5.56}$$

Subtracting $\frac{1}{3}$ of (5.56) from $\frac{4}{3}$ of (5.55) now gives

$$D(f) = D_h{}^1(f) + C_2{}^1 h^4 + o(h^4) \tag{5.57}$$

with

$$C_2{}^1 = -4C_2 = \frac{f^{v}(a)}{30}$$

since, by (5.53),

$$D_h{}^1(f) = \frac{4D_h(f) - D_{2h}(f)}{3}$$

A comparison of (5.57) with (5.55) shows that $D_h{}^1(f)$ is a *higher-order* approximation to $D(f)$ than is $D_h(f)$: If $C_1 \neq 0$, then $D(f) - D_h(f)$ goes to zero (with h) only as fast as h^2, while $D(f) - D_h{}^1(f)$ goes to zero at least as fast as h^4.

This process of obtaining from two lower-order approximations a higher-order approximation is usually called *extrapolation to the limit*, or *to zero-grid size*. (See Exercise 5.5-4 for an explanation of this terminology.)

Extrapolation to the limit is in no way limited to approximations with $O(h^2)$ error. We get, for example, from (5.57), by setting $h = 2h$, that

$$D(f) = D_{2h}^{1}(f) + 16C_2^{1}h^4 + o(h^4)$$

Hence, on subtracting this from (5.57) and rearranging, we obtain

$$C_2^{1}h^4 = \frac{D_h^{1}(f) - D_{2h}^{1}(f)}{15} + o(h^4)$$

Therefore, setting

$$D_h^{2}(f) = D_h^{1}(f) + \frac{D_h^{1}(f) - D_{2h}^{1}(f)}{15}$$

we get that

$$D(f) = D_h^{2}(f) + o(h^4)$$

showing $D_h^{2}(f)$ to be an even higher order approximation to $D(f)$ than is $D_h^{1}(f)$. More explicitly, it can be shown that

$$D(f) = D_h^{2}(f) + C_3^{2}h^6 + o(h^6) \tag{5.58}$$

if $f(x)$ is sufficiently smooth. But note that, for any particular value of h, $D_h^{2}(f)$ cannot be expected to be a better approximation to $D(f)$ than is $D_h^{1}(f)$ unless

$$\frac{D_h^{1}(f) - D_{2h}^{1}(f)}{15}$$

is a good estimate for the error in $D_h^{1}(f)$, that is, unless $C_2^{1}h^4$ is the dominant part of the error in $D_h(f)$. This will be the case only if

$$R_h^{1} = \frac{D_h^{1}(f) - D_{2h}^{1}(f)}{D_{h/2}^{1}(f) - D_h^{1}(f)} \approx \frac{C_2^{1}h^4}{C_2^{1}(h/2)^4} = 16$$

Hence this condition should be checked before believing that

$$|D(f) - D_h^{2}(f)| < \frac{|D_h^{1}(f) - D_{2h}^{1}(f)|}{15}$$

We have listed in Table 5.3 the results of applying extrapolation to the limit twice to the sequence of $D_h^{1}(f)$ calculated for Table 5.2. We have also listed the various values of R_h^{1}. All calculations were carried out with rounding to six places after the decimal point.

Finally, there is nothing sacred about the number 2 used above for all extrapolations. Indeed, if q is any fixed number, then we get, for example, from (5.55) that

$$D(f) = D_{qh}(f) + q^2C_1h^2 + q^4C_2h^4 + o(h^4)$$

Table 5.3

h	$D_h(f)$	R_h	$D_h{}^1(f)$	$R_h{}^1$	$D_h{}^2(f)$
6.4	0.009839				
3.2	-0.009856	-0.57	-0.075508		
1.6	0.337545	2.37	0.453345	6.1	0.488602
0.8	0.484486	3.54	0.533466	12.5	0.538807
0.4	0.526009	3.88	0.539850	15.1	0.540276
0.2	0.536707	3.97	0.540273	15.7	0.540301
0.1	0.539402		0.540300		0.540302

Subtracting this from (5.55) and rearranging then gives

$$C_1 h^2 = \frac{D_h(f) - D_{qh}(f)}{q^2 - 1} - (1 + q^2)C_2 h^4 + o(h^4)$$

Hence, with

$$D_{h,q}(f) = D_h(f) + \frac{D_h(f) - D_{qh}(f)}{q^2 - 1}$$

we find that

$$D(f) = D_{h,q}(f) - q^2 C_2 h^4 + o(h^4)$$

showing $D_{h,q}(f)$ to be an $O(h^4)$ approximation to $D(f)$. For example, we calculate from Table 5.2 that

$$D_{0.1,4}(f) = 0.539402 + \frac{0.539402 - 0.526009}{16 - 1} = 0.540295$$

which is in error by only seven units in the last place.

We have collected the salient points of the preceding discussion in the following algorithm.

Algorithm 5.1 Extrapolation to the limit Given the means of calculating an approximation $L_h(f)$ to the number $L(f)$ for every $h > 0$, where $L_h(f)$ is known to satisfy

$$L(f) = L_h(f) + Ch^r + o(h^r) \qquad \text{all } h > 0$$

with C a constant independent of h, and r a positive number.

Pick an h, and a number $q > 1$ (for example, $q = 2$) and calculate

$$L_{h,q}(f) = L_h(f) + \frac{L_h(f) - L_{qh}(f)}{q^r - 1}$$

from the two numbers $L_h(f)$ and $L_{qh}(f)$. Then

$$L(f) = L_{h,q}(f) + o(h^r)$$

so that, for sufficiently small h,

$$|L(f) - L_{h,q}(f)| < |L_{h,q}(f) - L_h(f)| \tag{5.59}$$

Before putting any faith in (5.59), ascertain that, at least,

$$\frac{L_h(f) - L_{qh}(f)}{L_{h/p}(f) - L_h(f)} \approx \frac{Ch^r(q^r - 1)}{Ch^r(1 - p^{-r})} = p^r \frac{q^r - 1}{p^r - 1}$$

for some $p > 1$ (for example, $p = q$).

As a further illustration of extrapolation to the limit, we now discuss its best-known application in numerical integration, namely, *Romberg integration*. We start out with the composite trapezoid rule approximation (see Sec. 5.3)

$$T_N = T_N(f) = h \sum_{i=1}^{N-1} f_i + \frac{h(f_0 + f_N)}{2} \tag{5.60}$$

to the number

$$I = I(f) = \int_a^b f(x)\, dx$$

Here N is a positive integer related to h by

$$h = \frac{b - a}{N}$$

and

$$f_i = f_{i,N} = f(a + ih) \qquad i = 0, \ldots, N$$

If $f(x)$ is three times continuously differentiable, we infer from (5.34) and (5.35) that

$$I(f) = T_N(f) + C_1 h^2 + O(h^4) \tag{5.61}$$

where the constant $C_1 = [f'(a) - f'(b)]/12$ is independent of h. Hence extrapolation to the limit is applicable. We get that

$$T_{N,q}(f) = T_N(f) + \frac{T_N(f) - T_{N/q}(f)}{q^2 - 1}$$

is an $O(h^4)$ approximation to $I(f)$, while in general, $T_N(f)$ has only an error of $O(h^2)$.

Note that the choice of q or N is restricted by the condition that N/q be an integer. One usually chooses $q = 2$ (so that N must be even). This choice for q has the computationally important advantage that all function values used for the calculation of $T_{N/q}$ can also be used for the calculation of T_N. Specifically, we prove that for even N,

$$T_N(f) = \frac{T_{N/2}(f)}{2} + h \sum_{i=1}^{N/2} f(a + (2i - 1)h) \qquad (5.62)$$

For by (5.60),

$$T_N(f) = h \sum_{i=1}^{N-1} f(a + ih) + \frac{h(f(a) + f(b))}{2}$$

$$= h \sum_{i=1}^{N/2} f(a + (2i - 1)h) + h \sum_{i=1}^{N/2-1} f(a + 2ih) + \frac{h(f(a) + f(b))}{2}$$

Here the first sum extends over the "odd" points and the second sum over the "even" points. The last two terms can be written

$$\left[2h \sum_{j=1}^{N/2-1} f(a + j(2h)) + \frac{2h(f(a) + f(b))}{2} \right]/2$$

Hence, since

$$2h = \frac{2(b - a)}{N} = \frac{b - a}{N/2}$$

these last two terms add up to $T_{N/2}(f)/2$. This proves (5.62). Note that (5.62) can be written more simply

$$T_N(f) = \frac{T_{N/2}(f) + M_{N/2}(f)}{2}$$

with M denoting the composite midpoint rule (5.32).

If the integrand has $2k + 2$ continuous derivatives, it can be shown that, more explicitly than (5.61),

$$I(f) = T_N(f) + C_1 h^2 + C_2 h^4 + C_3 h^6 + \cdots + C_k h^{2k} + O(h^{2k+2})$$

where the constants $C_1, \ldots, C_k$ do not depend on h. Hence, with

$$T_N^1(f) = T_N(f) + \frac{T_N(f) - T_{N/2}(f)}{3}$$

we get that

$$I(f) = T_N^1(f) + C_2^1 h^4 + C_3^1 h^6 + \cdots + C_k^1 h^{2k} + O(h^{2k+2})$$

with the constants $C_2^1, \ldots, C_k^1$ independent of h. Further extrapolation is therefore meaningful. Setting

$$T_N^2(f) = T_N^1(f) + \frac{T_N^1(f) - T_{N/2}^1(f)}{15}$$

we get that

$$I(f) = T_N^2(f) + C_3^2 h^6 + \cdots + C_k^2 h^{2k} + O(h^{2k+2})$$

More generally, it is seen that, for $m = 1, \ldots, k$,

$$T_N^m(f) = T_N^{m-1}(f) + \frac{T_N^{m-1}(f) - T_{N/2}^{m-1}(f)}{4^m - 1}$$

is an $O(h^{2m+2})$ approximation to $I(f)$.

Note that the calculation of T_N^m involves $T_{N/2}^{m-1}$ and T_N^{m-1}; hence $T_{N/4}^{m-2}$, $T_{N/2}^{m-2}$, and T_N^{m-2}; $\ldots$, and finally, $T_{N/2^m}$, $\ldots$, $T_{N/2}$, and T_N. $N/2^m$ must therefore be an integer,

$$\frac{N}{2^m} = M$$

say, for $T_N{}^m$ to be defined. It is convenient to visualize these various approximations to $I(f)$ as entries of a triangular array, the so-called T table:

$$\begin{array}{llllll}
T_M^0 & & & & \\
T_{2M}^0 & T_{2M}^1 & & & \\
T_{4M}^0 & T_{4M}^1 & T_{4M}^2 & & \\
\cdot & \cdot \quad \cdot \quad \cdot \quad \cdot & \cdot \quad \cdot \quad \cdot & \\
T_{2^mM}^0 & T_{2^mM}^1 & T_{2^mM}^2 & \cdots & T_{2^mM}^m
\end{array}$$

Here we have written $T_N{}^0$ for T_N.

Algorithm 5.2 Romberg integration Given a function $f(x)$ defined on $[a,b]$ and a positive integer M (usually, $M = 1$).

> Set $h = (b - a)/M$
> Calculate $T_M^0 = h \sum_{i=1}^{M-1} f(a + ih) + h(f(a) + f(b))/2$
> For $k = 1, 2, 3, \ldots$, do:
>> Set $h = h/2$
>> Calculate $T_{2^kM}^0 = \frac{1}{2} T_{2^{k-1}M}^0 + h/2^k \sum_{i=1}^{2^{k-1}M} f(a + (2i - 1)h)$
>> For $m = 1, \ldots, k$, do:
>>> Calculate $T_{2^kM}^m = T_{2^kM}^{m-1} + (T_{2^kM}^{m-1} - T_{2^{k-1}M}^{m-1})/(4^m - 1)$

If $f(x)$ has $2m + 2$ continuous derivatives, then

$$I(f) = \int_a^b f(x)\,dx = T_{2^kM}^m + O\left(\left[\frac{b-a}{2^kM}\right]^{2m+2}\right) \qquad k = m, m+1, \cdots$$

Also, if k is sufficiently large, then

$$|I(f) - T_{2^kM}^m| < |T_{2^kM}^m - T_{2^kM}^{m-1}|$$

But before putting any faith in this inequality, check that at least

$$R_k^{m-1} = \frac{T_{2^{k-1}M}^{m-1} - T_{2^{k-2}M}^{m-1}}{T_{2^kM}^{m-1} - T_{2^{k-1}M}^{m-1}} \approx 4^m$$

Example 5.7 Use Romberg integration for Example 5.1.
The integral in question is

$$I(f) = \int_0^1 e^{-x^2}\, dx$$

The FORTRAN program below has been set up to produce the first six rows of the T table and the corresponding table of ratios R_k^m, as follows:

Romberg T table

0.7313700E 00				
0.7429838E 00	0.7468551E 00			
0.7458653E 00	0.7468258E 00	0.7468238E 00		
0.7465842E 00	0.7468238E 00	0.7468237E 00	0.7468237E 00	
0.7467639E 00	0.7468237E 00	0.7468237E 00	0.7468237E 00	0.7468237E 00
0.7468069E 00	0.7468212E 00	0.7468210E 00	0.7468210E 00	0.7468209E 00

Table of ratios

4.03			
4.01	14.88		
4.00	16.50	0.0	
4.17	0.05	0.0	0.0

M was chosen to be 2, so that the first entry in the T table is $T_2(f)$. Note that the first column of ratios converges very nicely to 4, but then begins to move away from 4. This effect is even more pronounced in the second column of ratios, which approach 16 (as they should), and then, as the last entry shows, become erratic. Conclusion: The error in the entries of the last row of the T table is mainly due to round-off (rather than discretization). Hence

0.7468237

seems to be the best estimate for $I(f)$ to be gotten with the particular arithmetic used. Since

$$R_4^1 = 16.5 \approx 16 = 4^2$$

and

$$T_{2^4M}^1 = T_{2^4M}^2 = 0.7468237$$

to the number of places shown, we conclude that this estimate is accurate to the number of places shown. Actually,

$$\int_0^1 e^{-x^2}\, dx = 0.7468241 \cdots$$

The discrepancy between this number and our "accurate" estimate is due to the fact that we are not dealing with the integrand

$$f(x) = e^{-x^2}$$

in our calculations, but rather with a rounded version of $f(x)$, that is, with the function

$$F(X) = EXP(-X*X)$$

All calculations were carried out in single precision on an IBM 360, which has particularly poor rounding characteristics.

FORTRAN PROGRAM FOR EXAMPLE 5.7

```
        DIMENSION T(10,10)
        M = 2
        KMAX = 6
        A = 0.
        B = 1.
        H = (B − A)/FLOAT(M)
        SUM = (F(A) + F(B))/2.
        MM1 = M − 1
        IF (MM1)                          40,10,8
      8 DO 9 I = 1,MM1
      9 SUM = SUM + F(A + FLOAT(I)*H)
     10 T(1,1) = SUM*H
        WRITE (6,600)
    600 FORMAT(1H110X15HROMBERG T−TABLE//)
        WRITE (6,601) T(1,1)
    601 FORMAT(7E15.7)
C
        DO 20 K = 2,KMAX
        H = H/2.
        M = M*2
        SUM = 0.
        DO 11 I = 1,M,2
     11 SUM = SUM + F(A + FLOAT(I)*H)
        T(K,1) = T(K − 1,1)/2. + SUM*H
        FOURJ = 1.
        DO 12 J = 2,K
        FOURJ = FOURJ*4.
C    SAVE DIFFERENCES FOR LATER CALC. OF RATIOS
        T(K − 1,J − 1) = T(K,J − 1) − T(K − 1,J − 1)
     12 T(K,J) = T(K,J − 1) + T(K − 1,J − 1)/(FOURJ − 1.)
     20 WRITE (6,601) (T(K,J),J = 1,K)
        KMAXM2 = KMAX − 2
        IF (KMAXM2)                        40,40,29
CALCULATE RATIOS
     29 WRITE (6,602)
    602 FORMAT(///11X15HTABLE OF RATIOS//)
        DO 35 K = 1,KMAXM2
        DO 30 J = 1,K
        RATIO = 0.
        IF (ABS(T(K + 1,J)) .GT. 0.) RATIO = T(K,J)/T(K + 1,J)
```

```
   30 T(K,J) = RATIO
   35 WRITE (6,603) (T(K,J),J = 1,K)
  603 FORMAT(8F10.2)
   40                                    STOP
      END
      FUNCTION F(X)
      F = EXP(-X*X)
      RETURN
      END
```

EXERCISES

5.5-1. With $f(x) = x + x^2 + x^5$ and $a = 0$, calculate $D_h(f)$ and $D_h^1(f)$ for various values of h. Why is $D_h^1(f)$ *always* a worse approximation to $D(f) = f'(0)$ than is $D_h(f)$? (Use high enough precision arithmetic to rule out round-off as the culprit or get an explicit expression for D_h and D_h^1 in terms of h.)

5.5-2. Show how to obtain Simpson's rule for $\int_{-h}^{h} f(x)\, dx$ by extrapolating from the midpoint rule and the trapezoid rule.

5.5-3. Using extrapolation to the limit, find $f'(0.4)$ for the data given.

x	$\sinh x = f(x)$
0.398	0.408591
0.399	0.409671
0.400	0.410752
0.401	0.411834
0.402	0.412915

In this case the extrapolated value is a poorer approximation. Explain why this is so. [*Note:* The correct value of $f'(0.4) = 1.081072$.]

5.5-4. Show that extrapolation to the limit can be based on analytic substitution. Specifically, with the notation of Algorithm 5.1, show that

$$L_{h,q}(f) = \lim_{x \to 0} p(x) \approx \lim_{x \to 0} L_x(f) = L(f)$$

where the approximation $p(x)$ to $g(x) = L_x(f)$ is obtained by finding A and B such that

$$p(x) = A + Bx^r$$

agrees with $g(x)$ at $x = h$ and $x = qh$. How does this explain the name "extrapolation to the limit"?

5.5-5. Prove that, in Romberg integration, $T_{2M}^1 = S_M$, where S_M is the composite Simpson's rule; see (5.31).

5.5-6. Try to estimate $I(f) = \int_a^b f(x)\, dx$ to within 10^{-6}, using Romberg integration, for each of the following cases:

(a) $f(x) = x^2$ $a = 0, b = 1$, M arbitrary
(b) $f(x) = \sin 101\pi x$ $a = 0, b = 1$, $M = 1$
(c) $f(x) = 1 + \sin 10\pi x$ $a = 0, b = 1$, $M = 1$
(d) $f(x) = |x - \tfrac{1}{3}|$ $a = 0, b = 1$, $M = 1$ and $M = 3$
(e) $f(x) = \sqrt{x}$ $a = 0, b = 1$, M arbitrary

$$(f)\quad f(x) = \begin{cases} \dfrac{\sin x}{x} & x \neq 0 \\ 1 & x = 0 \end{cases} \qquad a = 0, b = 1$$

6

The Solution of Differential Equations

Many problems in engineering and science can be formulated in terms of differential equations. A large part of the motivation for building the early computers came from the need to compute ballistic trajectories accurately and quickly. Today computers are used extensively to solve the equations of ballistic-missile and artificial-satellite theory, as well as those of electrical networks, bending of beams, stability of aircraft, vibration theory, and others.

It is assumed that the student is familiar with the elementary theory of differential equations. In a first course one learns various techniques for solving in closed form some selected classes of differential equations. The vast majority of equations encountered in practice cannot, however, be solved analytically, and recourse must necessarily be made to numerical methods. Fortunately, there are many good methods available for solving differential equations on computers. In this chapter we shall derive several classes of methods, and we shall evaluate them for computational efficiency.

6.1 MATHEMATICAL PRELIMINARIES

It will be useful to review some elementary definitions and concepts from the theory of differential equations. An equation involving a relation between an unknown function and one or more of its derivatives is called a *differential equation*. We shall always assume that the equation can be solved explicitly for the derivative of highest order. An ordinary differential equation of order n will then have the form

$$y^{(n)} = f(x,y,y',y'', \cdots ,y^{(n-1)}) \tag{6.1}$$

By a solution of (6.1) we mean a function $\phi(x)$ which is n times continuously differentiable on a prescribed interval and which satisfies (6.1); that is $\phi(x)$ must satisfy

$$\phi^{(n)}(x) = f(x,\phi,\phi',\phi'', \cdots ,\phi^{(n-1)})$$

The general solution of (6.1) will normally contain n arbitrary constants, and hence there exists an n-parameter family of solutions. If $y(x_0)$, $y'(x_0)$, $\cdots$, $y^{(n-1)}(x_0)$ are prescribed at one point $x = x_0$, we have an *initial-value problem*. We shall always assume that the function f satisfies conditions sufficient to guarantee a unique solution to this initial-value problem. A simple example of a first-order equation is $y' = y$. Its general solution is $y(x) = Ce^x$, where C is an arbitrary constant. If the initial condition $y(x_0) = y_0$ is prescribed, the solution can be written $y(x) = y_0 e^{(x-x_0)}$.

Differential equations are further classified as *linear* and *nonlinear*. An equation is said to be linear if the function f in (6.1) involves y and its derivatives linearly. Linear differential equations possess the important property that if $y_1(x), y_2(x), \cdots , y_n(x)$ are any solution of (6.1), then so is $C_1 y_1(x) + C_2 y_2(x) + \cdots + C_n y_n(x)$ for arbitrary constants C_i. A simple second-order equation is $y'' = y$. It is easily verified that e^x and e^{-x} are solutions of this equation, and hence by linearity the following sum is also a solution:

$$y(x) = C_1 e^x + C_2 e^{-x} \tag{6.2}$$

Two solutions y_1, y_2 of a second-order linear differential equation are said to be linearly independent if the Wronskian of the solution does not vanish, the *Wronskian* being defined by

$$W(y_1,y_2) = y_1 y_2' - y_2 y_1' = \begin{vmatrix} y_1 & y_1' \\ y_2 & y_2' \end{vmatrix} \tag{6.3}$$

The concept of linear independence can be extended to the solutions of equations of higher order. If $y_1(x), y_2(x), \cdots , y_n(x)$ are n linearly independent solutions of a homogeneous differential equation of order n, then

$$y(x) = C_1 y_1(x) + C_2 y_2(x) + \cdots + C_n y_n(x)$$

is called the *general solution*.

Among linear equations, those with constant coefficients are particularly useful and lend themselves to a simple treatment. We write the nth-order linear differential equation with constant coefficients in the form

$$Ly = y^{(n)} + a_{n-1}y^{(n-1)} + \cdots + a_0 y^{(0)} = 0 \qquad (6.4)$$

where the a_i are assumed to be real. If we seek solutions of (6.4) in the form $e^{\beta x}$, then direct substitution shows that β must satisfy the polynomial equation

$$\beta^n + a_{n-1}\beta^{n-1} + \cdots + a_0 = 0 \qquad (6.5)$$

This is called the *characteristic equation* of the nth-order differential equation (6.4). If the equation (6.5) has n distinct roots β_i ($i = 1, \ldots, n$), then it can be shown that

$$y(x) = C_1 e^{\beta_1 x} + C_2 e^{\beta_2 x} + \cdots + C_n e^{\beta_n x} \qquad (6.6)$$

where the C_i are arbitrary constants, is the general solution of (6.4). If $\beta_1 = \alpha + i\beta$ is a complex root of (6.5), so is its conjugate, $\beta_2 = \alpha - i\beta$. Corresponding to such a pair of conjugate-complex roots are two solutions $y_1 = e^{\alpha x} \cos \beta x$ and $y_2 = e^{\alpha x} \sin \beta x$, which are linearly independent. When (6.5) has multiple roots, special techniques are available for obtaining linearly independent solutions. In particular, if β_1 is a double root of (6.5), then $y_1 = e^{\beta_1 x}$ and $y_2 = xe^{\beta_1 x}$ are linearly independent solutions of (6.4). For the special equation $y'' + a^2 y = 0$, the characteristic equation is $\beta^2 = -a^2$; its roots are $\beta_{1,2} = \pm ia$, and its general solution is $y(x) = C_1 \cos ax + C_2 \sin ax$.

Finally, if Eq. (6.1) is nonhomogeneous, i.e., if

$$Ly = g(x) \qquad (6.7)$$

and if $\zeta(x)$ is a particular solution of (6.7), i.e., if

$$L\zeta = g(x)$$

then the general solution of (6.7), assuming that the roots of (6.5) are distinct, is

$$y = \zeta(x) + C_1 e^{\beta_1 x} + C_2 e^{\beta_2 x} + \cdots + C_n e^{\beta_n x} \qquad (6.8)$$

Example Find the solution of the equation

(a) $\quad y'' - 4y' + 3y = x$

satisfying the initial conditions

(b) $\quad y(0) = \frac{4}{9} \qquad y'(0) = \frac{7}{3}$

1. To find a particular solution $y^P(x)$ of (a), we try $y^P(x) = ax + b$, since the right side is a polynomial of degree ≤ 1 and the left side is such a polynomial whenever $y = y(x)$ is. Substituting into (a), we find that $a = \frac{1}{3}$, $b = \frac{4}{9}$. Hence

$$y^P(x) = \tfrac{1}{3}x + \tfrac{4}{9}$$

2. To find solutions of the homogeneous equation

$$y'' - 4y' + 3y = 0$$

we examine the characteristic equation

$$\beta^2 - 4\beta + 3 = 0$$

Its roots are $\beta_1 = 3$, $\beta_2 = 1$. Hence the two linearly independent solutions of the homogeneous system are

$$y^{(1)}(x) = e^{3x} \qquad y^{(2)}(x) = e^x$$

3. The general solution of equation (a) is

$$y(x) = \frac{x}{3} + \frac{4}{9} + C_1 e^{3x} + C_2 e^x$$

4. To find the solution satisfying conditions (b), we must have

$$y(0) = \tfrac{4}{9} + C_1 + C_2 = \tfrac{4}{9}$$
$$y'(0) = \tfrac{1}{3} + 3C_1 + C_2 = \tfrac{7}{3}$$

The solution of this system is $C_1 = 1$, $C_2 = -1$. Hence the desired solution is

$$y(x) = \frac{x}{3} + \frac{4}{9} + e^{3x} - e^x$$

EXERCISES

6.1-1. Find the general solution of the equations

(a) $y' = -2y$ (b) $y'' - 4y' + 4y = 0$
(c) $y''' - 2y'' - y' + 2y = 0$ (d) $y' - ay = x$
(e) $y' - xy = e^x$ (f) $y'' - 2y' + 2y = 0$

6.1-2. Find the solution of the following initial-value problems:

(a) $y' + 2y = 1$ $y(0) = 1$
(b) $y'' - a^2 y = 0$ $y(0) = 0$ $y'(0) = 1$
(c) $y'' - 4y' + 4y = x$ $y(0) = 0$ $y'(0) = 1$

6.2 SIMPLE DIFFERENCE EQUATIONS

To analyze numerical methods for the solution of differential equations, it is necessary to understand some simple theory of difference equations. A difference equation of order N is a relation between the differences $y_n = \Delta^0 y_n$, $\Delta^1 y_n, \Delta^2 y_n, \ldots, \Delta^N y_n$ of a number sequence

$$\Delta^N y_n = f(n, y_n, \Delta y_n, \ldots, \Delta^{N-1} y_n) \tag{6.9}$$

A solution of such a difference equation is a sequence $y_m, y_{m+1}, y_{m+2}, \cdots$ of numbers such that (6.9) holds for $n = m, m + 1, m + 2, \ldots$. Hence, whereas a differential equation involves functions, defined on some interval of real numbers, and their derivatives, a difference equation involves functions, defined on some "interval" of integers, and their differences.

If (6.9) is a *linear* difference equation, so that the right side of (6.9) depends linearly on $y_n, \ldots, \Delta^{N-1}y_n$, then it is possible and customary to write (6.9) explicitly in terms of the y_j's as

$$y_{n+N} + a_{n,N-1}y_{n+N-1} + a_{n,N-2}y_{n+N-2} + \cdots + a_{n,0}y_n = b_n$$

Evidently, a linear difference equation of order N can be viewed as a (finite or infinite) system of linear equations whose coefficient matrix is a banded matrix of bandwidth $N + 1$.

Simple examples of linear difference equations are

$$y_{n+1} - y_n = 1 \quad\quad \text{all } n \tag{6.10a}$$

$$y_{n+1} - y_n = n \quad\quad \text{all } n \geq 0 \tag{6.10b}$$

$$y_{n+1} - (n + 1)y_n = 0 \quad\quad \text{all } n \geq 0 \tag{6.10c}$$

$$y_{n+2} - (2 \cos \gamma)y_{n+1} + y_n = 0 \quad\quad \text{all } n \tag{6.10d}$$

By direct substitution, these equations can be shown to have the solutions

$$y_n = n + c \quad\quad \text{all } n \tag{6.11a}$$

$$y_n = c \frac{n(n-1)}{2} \quad\quad \text{all } n \geq 0 \tag{6.11b}$$

$$y_n = cn! \quad\quad \text{all } n \geq 0 \tag{6.11c}$$

$$y_n = c \cos \gamma n \quad\quad \text{all } n \tag{6.11d}$$

with c an arbitrary constant.

We consider in detail a homogeneous linear difference equation of order N with constant coefficients

$$y_{n+N} + a_{N-1}y_{n+N-1} + \cdots + a_0 y_n = 0 \tag{6.12}$$

As with homogeneous linear differential equations with constant coefficients, we seek solutions of the form $y_n = \beta^n$, all n. Substituting into (6.12) yields

$$\beta^{n+N} + a_{N-1}\beta^{n+N-1} + \cdots + a_0\beta^n = 0$$

Dividing by β^n, we obtain the characteristic equation

$$p(\beta) = \beta^N + a_{N-1}\beta^{N-1} + \cdots + a_0 = 0 \tag{6.13}$$

This is a polynomial of degree N. We assume, first, that its roots $\beta_1, \beta_2, \ldots, \beta_N$ are distinct. Then $\beta_1^n, \beta_2^n, \ldots, \beta_N^n$ are all solutions of (6.12), and by linearity it follows that

$$y_n = c_1\beta_1^n + c_2\beta_2^n + \cdots + c_N\beta_N^n \quad\quad \text{all } n \tag{6.14}$$

for arbitrary constants c_i is also a solution of (6.12). Moreover, in this case it can be shown that (6.14) is the general solution of (6.12).

As an example, the difference equation

$$y_{n+3} - 2y_{n+2} - y_{n+1} + 2y_n = 0 \tag{6.15}$$

is of third order, and its characteristic equation is

$$\beta^3 - 2\beta^2 - \beta + 2 = 0$$

The roots of this polynomial are $+1, -1, 2$, and the general solution of (6.15) is

$$\begin{aligned} y_n &= c_1(1)^n + c_2(-1)^n + c_3(2)^n \\ &= c_1 + (-1)^n c_2 + 2^n c_3 \end{aligned} \tag{6.16}$$

If the first $N - 1$ values of y_n are given, the resulting *initial-value* difference equation can be solved explicitly for all succeeding values of n. Thus in (6.15), if $y_0 = 0$, $y_1 = 1$, $y_2 = 1$, then y_3 as computed from (6.14) is

$$y_3 = 2(1) + 1 - 0 = 3$$

Continuing to use (6.15), we find that $y_4 = 5$, $y_5 = 11$, etc. This does not yield a closed formula for y_n. However, using (6.16) and imposing the initial conditions for $n = 0, 1, 2$, we obtain the following system of equations for c_1, c_2, c_3:

$$\begin{aligned} 0 &= c_1 + c_2 + c_3 \\ 1 &= c_1 - c_2 + 2c_3 \\ 1 &= c_1 + c_2 + 4c_3 \end{aligned}$$

Its solution is $c_1 = 0$, $c_2 = -\tfrac{1}{3}$, $c_3 = \tfrac{1}{3}$, so that the closed-form solution of the initial-value problem is

$$y_n = -\tfrac{1}{3}(-1)^n + \frac{2^n}{3}$$

If the characteristic polynomial (6.13) has a pair of conjugate-complex roots, the solution can still be expressed in real form. Thus, if $\beta_1 = \alpha + i\beta$ and $\beta_2 = \alpha - i\beta$, we first express $\beta_{1,2}$ in polar form,

$$\begin{aligned} \beta_1 &= re^{i\theta} \\ \beta_2 &= re^{-i\theta} \end{aligned}$$

where $r = \sqrt{\alpha^2 + \beta^2}$, and $\theta = \arctan(\beta/\alpha)$. Then the solution of (6.12) corresponding to this pair of roots is

$$\begin{aligned} c_1\beta_1{}^n + c_2\beta_2{}^n &= c_1 r^n e^{in\theta} + c_2 r^n e^{-in\theta} \\ &= r^n[c_1(\cos n\theta + i \sin n\theta) + c_2(\cos n\theta - i \sin n\theta)] \\ &= r^n(C_1 \cos n\theta + C_2 \sin n\theta) \end{aligned}$$

where $C_1 = c_1 + c_2$ and $C_2 = i(c_1 - c_2)$. As a simple example, we consider the difference equation

$$y_{n+2} - 2y_{n+1} + 2y_n = 0 \qquad (6.17)$$

Its characteristic equation is $\beta^2 - 2\beta + 2 = 0$, and the roots of this equation are $\beta_{1,2} = 1 \pm i$. Hence $r = \sqrt{2}$ and $\theta = \pi/4$, so that the general solution of (6.17) is

$$y_n = (\sqrt{2})^n \left(c_1 \cos \frac{n\pi}{4} + c_2 \sin \frac{n\pi}{4} \right)$$

If β_1 is a double root of the characteristic equation (6.13), then a second solution of (6.13) is $n\beta_1{}^n$. To verify this, we note first that if β_1 is a double root of $p(\beta)$, then $p(\beta_1) = 0$ and also $p'(\beta_1) = 0$. Now on substituting $y_n = n\beta_1{}^n$ in (6.12) and rearranging, we find that

$$(n + N)\beta_1^{n+N} + a_{n-1}(n + N - 1)\beta_1^{n+N-1} + \cdots + a_0 n\beta_1{}^n$$
$$= \beta_1{}^n \{ n(\beta_1{}^n + a_{N-1}\beta_1^{N-1} + \cdots + a_0)$$
$$+ \beta_1[N\beta_1^{N-1} + a_{N-1}(N - 1)\beta_1^{N-2} + \cdots + a_1] \}$$
$$= \beta_1{}^n [np(\beta_1) + \beta_1 p'(\beta_1)] = 0$$

since $p(\beta_1) = p'(\beta_1) = 0$. It can, moreover, be shown that these two solutions $\beta_1{}^n$ and $n\beta_1{}^n$ are linearly independent.

As an illustration, for the difference equation

$$y_{n+3} - 5y_{n+2} + 8y_{n+1} - 4y_n = 0$$

the roots of the characteristic equation are 2, 2, 1, and the general solution is

$$y_n = 2^n(c_1 + nc_2) + c_3$$

We consider, finally, the solution of the nonhomogeneous linear difference equation with constant coefficients. The general solution of the equation

$$y_{n+N} + a_{N-1}y_{n+N-1} + \cdots + a_0 y_n = b_n \qquad (6.18)$$

can be written in the form

$$y_n = y_n{}^G + y_n{}^P$$

where $y_n{}^G$ is the general solution of the homogeneous system (6.12), and $y_n{}^P$ is a particular solution of (6.18). In the special case when $b_n = b$ is a constant, a particular solution can easily be obtained by setting $y_n{}^P = A$ (a constant) in (6.18). Substitution of $y_n = A$ in (6.18) leads to the determination

$$A = \frac{b}{1 + a_{N-1} + \cdots + a_0}$$

provided that the sum of the coefficients does not vanish.

The general solution of the nonhomogeneous equation

$$y_{n+2} - 2y_{n+1} + 2y_n = 1$$

is

$$y_n = 2^{n/2}\left(c_1 \cos\frac{n\pi}{4} + c_2 \sin\frac{n\pi}{4}\right) + 1$$

The simple properties of difference equations considered here will be sufficient for the applications in the remainder of this chapter.

Example Show that the general solution of the difference equation

$$(a) \quad y_{n+2} - (2 + h^2)y_{n+1} + y_n = h^2 \qquad h > 0$$

can be expressed in the form

$$(b) \quad y_n = c_1\left[1 + h + \frac{h^2}{2} + O(h^3)\right]^n + c_2\left[1 - h + \frac{h^2}{2} + O(h^3)\right]^n - 1$$

Solution

1. A particular solution of (a), obtained by trying $y_n^P = C$ in (a), is found to be

$$y_n^P = -1$$

2. The characteristic equation of the homogeneous equation of (a) is

$$\beta^2 - (2 + h^2)\beta + 1 = 0$$

By the quadratic formula the roots are

$$\beta_{1,2} = \frac{2 + h^2 \pm \sqrt{4h^2 + h^4}}{2}$$

$$= \frac{2 + h^2 \pm 2h\sqrt{1 + h^2/4}}{2}$$

$$= 1 + \frac{h^2}{2} \pm h\left(1 + \frac{h^2}{4}\right)^{1/2}$$

On expanding $(1 + t)^{1/2}$ around $t = 0$ into a Taylor series and substituting $h^2/4$ for t, we obtain

$$\beta_{1,2} = 1 + \frac{h^2}{2} \pm h\left[1 + \frac{h^2}{8} + O(h^4)\right]$$

$$\beta_1 = 1 + h + \frac{h^2}{2} + O(h^3)$$

$$\beta_2 = 1 - h + \frac{h^2}{2} + O(h^3)$$

Hence the general solution of the homogeneous system is

$$y_n^G = c_1\beta_1^n + c_2\beta_2^n$$

3. The solution of (a) is therefore

$$y_n = y_n^P + y_n^G$$

which establishes the solution in the form (b).

EXERCISES

6.2-1. Find the general solution of the difference equations

(a) $y_{n+1} - 3y_n = 5$
(b) $y_{n+2} - 4y_{n+1} + 4y_n = n$

(*Hint:* To find a particular solution, try $y_n{}^P = an + b$.)

(c) $y_{n+2} + 2y_{n+1} + 2y_n = 0$
(d) $y_{n+3} - y_{n+2} + 2y_{n+1} - 2y_n = 0$
(e) $y_{n+2} - y_{n+1} - y_n = 0$

6.2-2. Find the solution of the initial-value difference equations

(a) $y_{n+2} - 4y_{n+1} + 3y_n = 2^n$ $y_0 = 0$ $y_1 = 1$
(b) $y_{n+2} - y_{n+1} - y_n = 0$ $y_0 = 0$ $y_1 = 1$

[*Hint:* To find a particular solution of (a), try $y_n{}^P = A2^n$.]

6.2-3. Show that the general solution of the difference equation

$$y_{n+2} + 4hy_{n+1} - y_n = 2h$$

where h is a positive constant, can be expressed in the form

$$y_n = c_1[1 - 2h + O(h^2)]^n + c_2(-1)^n[1 + 2h + O(h^2)]^n + \tfrac{1}{2}$$

6.2-4. Show that if $y_0 = 1$, $y_1 = x$, then the nth term, $y_n = y_n(x)$, of the solution of

$$y_{n+2} - 2xy_{n+1} + y_n = 0$$

is a polynomial of degree n in x with leading coefficient 2^{n-1}. [*Note:* The $y_n(x)$ are the Chebyshev polynomials considered in Sec. 4.12.]

6.3 NUMERICAL INTEGRATION BY TAYLOR SERIES

We are now prepared to consider numerical methods for integrating differential equations. We shall first consider a first-order initial-value differential equation of the form

$$y' = f(x,y) \qquad y(x_0) = y_0 \tag{6.19}$$

The function f may be linear or nonlinear, but we assume that f is sufficiently differentiable with respect to both x and y. It is known that (6.19) possesses a unique solution if $\partial f/\partial y$ is continuous on the interval of interest. If $y(x)$ is the exact solution of (6.19), we can expand $y(x)$ into a Taylor series about the point $x = x_0$:

$$y(x) = y_0 + (x - x_0)y'(x_0) + \frac{(x - x_0)^2}{2!} y''(x_0) + \cdots \tag{6.20}$$

The derivatives in this expansion are not known explicitly since the solution is not known. However, if f is sufficiently differentiable, they can be obtained by taking the total derivative of (6.19) with respect to x, keeping in mind that y is itself a function of x (see Sec. 1.7). Thus we obtain for the first few derivatives:

$$
\begin{aligned}
y' &= f(x,y) \\
y'' &= f' = f_x + f_y y' = f_x + f_y f \\
y''' &= f'' = f_{xx} + f_{xy}f + f_{yx}f + f_{yy}f^2 + f_y f_x + f_y^2 f \\
&= f_{xx} + 2f_{xy}f + f_{yy}f^2 + f_x f_y + f_y^2 f
\end{aligned}
\qquad (6.21)
$$

Continuing in this manner, we can express any derivative of y in terms of $f(x,y)$ and its partial derivatives. It is already clear, however, that unless $f(x,y)$ is a very simple function, the higher total derivatives become increasingly complex. For practical reasons then, one must limit the number of terms in the expansion (6.20) to a reasonable number, and this restriction leads to a restriction on the value of x for which (6.20) is a reasonable approximation. If we assume that the truncated series (6.20) yields a good approximation for a step of length h, that is, for $x - x_0 = h$, we can then evaluate y at $x_0 + h$; reevaluate the derivatives y', y'', etc., at $x = x_0 + h$; and then use (6.20) to proceed to the next step. If we continue in this manner, we will obtain a discrete set of values y_n which are approximations to the true solution at the points $x_n = x_0 + nh$ ($n = 0, 1, 2, \ldots$). In this chapter we shall always denote the value of the exact solution at a point x_n by $y(x_n)$ and of an approximate solution by y_n.

In order to formalize this procedure, we first introduce the operator

$$
T_k(x,y) = f(x,y) + \frac{h}{2!}f'(x,y) + \cdots + \frac{h^{k-1}}{k!}f^{(k-1)}(x,y)
$$

$$
k = 1, 2, \ldots \quad (6.22)
$$

where we assume that a fixed step size h is being used, and where $f^{(j)}$ denotes the jth total derivative of the function $f(x,y(x))$ with respect to x. We can then state Algorithm 6.1

Algorithm 6.1 Taylor's algorithm of order k. To find an approximate solution of the differential equation

$$
\begin{aligned}
y' &= f(x,y) \\
y(a) &= y_0
\end{aligned}
$$

over an interval $[a,b]$:

1. Choose a step $h = (b - a)/N$. Set

$$
x_0 = a \qquad x_n = a + nh \qquad y(x_n) = y(a + nh) \qquad x_N = b
$$

2. Generate approximations y_n to $y(x_n)$ from the recursion

$$
y_{n+1} = y_n + hT_k(x_n,y_n) \qquad n = 0, 1, \ldots, N - 1
$$

where $T_k(x,y)$ is defined by (6.22).

Taylor's theorem with remainder shows that the local error of Taylor's algorithm of order k is

$$E = \frac{h^{k+1}f^{(k)}(\xi, y(\xi))}{(k+1)!} \qquad x_n < \xi < x_n + h$$

$$= \frac{h^{k+1}}{(k+1)!} y^{(k+1)}(\xi)$$

On setting $k = 1$ in Algorithm 6.1 we obtain *Euler's method* and its local error,

$$\boxed{y_{n+1} = y_n + hf(x_n, y_n)} \qquad \boxed{E = \frac{h^2}{2} y''(\xi)} \qquad (6.23)$$

To illustrate Euler's method, consider the initial-value problem

$$y' = y \qquad y(0) = 1$$

On applying (6.23) with $h = 0.01$ and retaining six decimal places, we obtain

$$y(0.01) \approx y_1 = 1 + 0.01 = 1.01$$
$$y(0.02) \approx y_2 = 1.01 + 0.01(1.01) = 1.0201$$
$$y(0.03) \approx y_3 = 1.0201 + 0.01(1.0201) = 1.030301$$
$$y(0.04) \approx y_4 = 1.030301 + 0.01(1.030301) = 1.040606$$

Since the exact solution of this equation is $y = e^x$, the correct value at $x = 0.04$ is 1.0408. It is clear that, to obtain more accuracy with Euler's method, we must take a considerably smaller value for h.

If we take $h = 0.005$, we obtain the values

$$y(0.005) \approx y_1 = 1.0050$$
$$y(0.010) \approx y_2 = 1.0100$$
$$y(0.015) \approx y_3 = 1.0151$$
$$y(0.020) \approx y_4 = 1.0202$$
$$y(0.025) \approx y_5 = 1.0253$$
$$y(0.030) \approx y_6 = 1.0304$$
$$y(0.035) \approx y_7 = 1.0356$$
$$y(0.040) \approx y_8 = 1.0408$$

These results are correct to four decimal places.

Because of the relatively small step size required, Euler's method is not commonly used for integrating differential equations.

We could, of course, apply Taylor's algorithm of higher order to obtain better accuracy, and in general, we would expect that the higher the order of the algorithm, the greater the accuracy for a given step size. If $f(x,y)$ is a relatively simple function of x and y, then it is often possible to generate the required derivatives relatively cheaply on a computer by employing symbolic differentiation, or else by taking advantage of any particular properties the function $f(x,y)$ may have (see Exercise 6.3-4). However, the necessity of calculating the higher derivatives makes Taylor's algorithm completely unsuitable on high-speed computers for general integration purposes. Nevertheless, it is of great theoretical interest because most of the practical methods attempt to achieve the same accuracy as a Taylor algorithm of a given order without the disadvantage of having to calculate the higher derivatives. Although the general Taylor algorithm is hardly ever used for practical purposes, the special case of Euler's method will be considered in more detail for its theoretical implications.

Example 6.1   Using Taylor's series, find the solution of the differential equation

$$xy' = x - y \qquad y(2) = 2$$

at $x = 2.1$ correct to five decimal places.

The first few derivatives and their values at $x = 2$, $y = 2$ are

$$y' = 1 - \frac{y}{x} \qquad\qquad y_0' = 0$$

$$y'' = \frac{-y'}{x} + \frac{y}{x^2} \qquad\qquad y_0'' = \tfrac{1}{2}$$

$$y''' = \frac{-y''}{x} + \frac{2y'}{x^2} - \frac{2y}{x^3} \qquad\qquad y_0''' = -\tfrac{3}{4}$$

$$y^{\text{iv}} = \frac{-y'''}{x} + \frac{3y''}{x^2} - \frac{6y'}{x^3} + \frac{6y}{x^4} \qquad y_0^{\text{iv}} = \tfrac{3}{2}$$

The Taylor series expansion about $x_0 = 2$ is

$$y(x) = y_0 + (x - 2)y_0' + \tfrac{1}{2}(x - 2)^2 y_0'' + \tfrac{1}{6}(x - 2)^3 y_0''' + \tfrac{1}{24}(x - 2)^4 y_0^{\text{iv}} + \cdots$$
$$= 2 + (x - 2)0 + \tfrac{1}{4}(x - 2)^2 - \tfrac{1}{8}(x - 2)^3 + \tfrac{1}{16}(x - 2)^4 + \cdots$$

At $x = 2.1$ we obtain

$$y(2.1) = 2 + 0.0025 - 0.000125 + 0.0000062 - \cdots$$
$$\approx 2.00238$$

Since the terms in this Taylor series decrease in magnitude and alternate (see Exercise 6.3-4) in sign, this result is correct to five decimal places. If we now wished to find $y(2.2)$ to the same accuracy, we would have to carry the series through two additional terms. Alternatively, we could now make a new expansion about $x = 2.1$, reevaluate the first four derivatives at $x = 2.1$, and then compute $y(2.2)$.

Example 6.2   Solve the equation

$$y' = \frac{1}{x^2} - \frac{y}{x} - y^2$$
$$y(1) = -1$$

from $x = 1$ to $x = 2$. Use Taylor's algorithm of order 2. Solve the problem with $h = \tfrac{1}{16}, \tfrac{1}{32}, \tfrac{1}{64}, \tfrac{1}{128}$, and estimate the accuracy of the results.

Solution Since

$$f(x,y) = \frac{1}{x^2} - \frac{y}{x} - y^2$$

$$f'(x,y) = \frac{-2}{x^3} - \frac{y'}{x} + \frac{y}{x^2} - 2yy'$$

then

$$T_2(x,y) = f + \frac{h}{2}f'$$

and

$$y_{n+1} = y_n + h\left[f(x_n,y_n) + \frac{h}{2}f'(x_n,y_n)\right]$$

The results as computed on the IBM 7090 are given below. The step size h is given in the first column, and the values of $y(1.5)$, $y'(1.5)$, $y(2.0)$, $y'(2.0)$, respectively, are given in the next four columns. The exact solution of this equation is $y = -1/x$, so that the exact value of $y(1.5)$ is $-\frac{2}{3}$, and the exact value of $y(2.0)$ is $-\frac{1}{2}$. We may estimate the total discretization error as follows: The local error of Taylor's algorithm of order 2 is $(h^3/6)y'''$. Since

COMPUTER RESULTS FOR EXAMPLE 6.2

Method 1—Taylor expansion method of order 2

H	Y(1.5)	YPRM(1.5)	Y(2.)	YPRM(2.)
0.62500000E-01	-0.66787238E 00	0.44363917E-00	-0.50187737E 00	0.24905779E-00
0.31250000E-01	-0.66696430E 00	0.44424593E-00	-0.50046334E 00	0.24976812E-00
0.15625000E-01	-0.66674034E 00	0.44439532E-00	-0.50011456E 00	0.24994271E-00
0.78125000E-02	-0.66668454E 00	0.44443253E-00	-0.50002744E 00	0.24998628E-00

Method 2—Simplified Runge-Kutta order 2

H	Y(1.5)	YPRM(1.5)	Y(2.)	YPRM(2.)
0.62500000E-01	-0.66552725E 00	0.44520275E-00	-0.49822412E-00	0.25088478E-00
0.31250000E-01	-0.66637699E 00	0.44463748E-00	-0.49954852E-00	0.25022554E-00
0.15625000E-01	-0.66659356E 00	0.44449317E-00	-0.49988601E-00	0.25005698E-00
0.78125000E-02	-0.66664808E 00	0.44445683E-00	-0.49997083E-00	0.25001458E-00

Method 3—Classical Runge-Kutta order 4

H	Y(1.5)	YPRM(1.5)	Y(2.)	YPRM(2.)
0.62500000E-01	-0.66666625E 00	0.44444472E-00	-0.49999941E-00	0.25000029E-00
0.31250000E-01	-0.66666664E 00	0.44444446E-00	-0.49999997E-00	0.25000001E-00
0.15625000E-01	-0.66666666E 00	0.44444444E-00	-0.50000000E 00	0.25000000E-00
0.78125000E-02	-0.66666667E 00	0.44444444E-00	-0.50000001E 00	0.24999999E-00

$y''' = 6/x^4$, its maximum value on the interval [1,2] is 6, and hence the local error is for each step, at most, h^3. With $h = \frac{1}{128}$, we will take 128 integration steps so that the accumulated error will be, at most, $128h^3 = (\frac{1}{128})^2 \approx 0.00006$. The actual error at $x = 2.0$ appears to be 0.00003, in close agreement with this estimate. In general, we will not know the solution to check against. Even without knowing the solution, however, we can estimate from the number of places of agreement as $h \to 0$, the accuracy of the solution. Since each halving of h appears to produce almost one additional digit of accuracy, it appears that in the absence of round-off error, a step of $1/1,024$ should produce at least seven places of accuracy. Because of round-off error, however, it would be very difficult, using this method, to obtain full eight-place accuracy on the IBM 7090. This same problem will be solved later by two other methods. For comparison purposes, the results for all three methods are included here.

EXERCISES

6.3-1. For the equation

$$y' = -xy + \frac{1}{y^2} \qquad y(1) = 1$$

derive the difference equation corresponding to Taylor's algorithm of order 3. Carry out by hand one step of the integration with $h = 0.01$. Write a program for solving this problem, and carry out the integration from $x = 1$ to $x = 2$, using $h = \frac{1}{64}$ and $h = \frac{1}{128}$.

6.3-2. For the equation

$$y' = 2y \qquad y(0) = 1$$

obtain the exact solution of the difference equation obtained from Euler's method. Estimate a value of h small enough to guarantee four-place accuracy in the solution over the interval [0,1]. Carry out the solution with an appropriate value of h for 10 steps.

6.3-3. From the Taylor series for $y(x)$, find $y(0.1)$ correct to six decimal places if $y(x)$ satisfies

$$y' = xy + 1 \qquad y(0) = 1$$

6.3-4. Prove that, for the function $f(x,y) = 1 - y/x$ of Example 6.1, $y'' = (1 - 2y')/x$, $y^{(k)} = -ky^{(k-1)}/x$, $k = 3, 4, \ldots$. Based on this, write a FORTRAN program which finds the value $y(3)$ of the solution $y(x)$ of the problem in Example 6.1 to within 10^{-6}, using Algorithm 6.1.

6.4 ERROR ESTIMATES AND CONVERGENCE OF EULER'S METHOD

To solve the differential equation $y' = f(x,y)$, $y(x_0) = y_0$ by Euler's method, we choose a constant step size h, and we apply the formula

$$y_{n+1} = y_n + hf(x_n,y_n) \qquad n = 0, 1, \ldots \qquad (6.23)$$

where $x_n = x_0 + nh$. We denote the true solution of the differential equation at $x = x_n$ by $y(x_n)$, and the appropriate solution obtained by applying (6.23) as y_n. We wish to estimate the magnitude of the *discretization* or *truncation* error e_n defined by

$$e_n = y(x_n) - y_n \qquad (6.24)$$

We note that, if y_0 is exact, as we shall assume, then $e_0 = 0$. Assuming that the appropriate derivatives exist, we can expand $y(x_{n+1})$ about $x = x_n$, using Taylor's theorem with remainder:

$$y(x_{n+1}) = y(x_n) + hy'(x_n) + \frac{h^2}{2} y''(\xi_n) \qquad x_n \le \xi_n \le x_{n+1} \qquad (6.25)$$

The quantity $(h^2/2)y''(\xi_n)$ is called the *local discretization* error, i.e., the error committed in the single step from x_n to x_{n+1}, assuming that y and y' were known exactly at $x = x_n$. On a computer there will also be an error in computing y_{n+1} using (6.23), due to round-off. Round-off errors will be neglected in this section.

On subtracting (6.23) from (6.25) and using (6.24), we obtain

$$e_{n+1} = e_n + h[f(x_n, y(x_n)) - f(x_n, y_n)] + \frac{h^2}{2} y''(\xi_n) \qquad (6.26)$$

By the mean-value theorem of differential calculus, we have

$$f(x_n, y(x_n)) - f(x_n, y_n) = f_y(x_n, \bar{y}_n)(y(x_n) - y_n)$$
$$= f_y(x_n, \bar{y}_n)e_n$$

where $\bar{y}_n$ is between y_n and $y(x_n)$. Hence (6.26) becomes

$$e_{n+1} = e_n + hf_y(x_n, \bar{y}_n)e_n + \frac{h^2}{2} y''(\xi_n) \qquad (6.27)$$

We now assume that over the interval of interest,

$$|f_y(x,y)| < L \qquad |y''(x)| < Y$$

where L and Y are fixed positive constants. On taking absolute values in (6.27), we obtain

$$|e_{n+1}| \le |e_n| + hL|e_n| + \frac{h^2}{2} Y = (1 + hL)|e_n| + \frac{h^2}{2} Y \qquad (6.28)$$

We will now show by induction that the solution of the difference equation

$$\xi_{n+1} = (1 + hL)\xi_n + \frac{h^2}{2} Y \qquad (6.29)$$

with $\xi_0 = 0$ dominates the solution of (6.27); i.e., we will show that

$$\xi_n \ge |e_n| \qquad n = 0, 1, \ldots \qquad (6.30)$$

Since $e_0 = \xi_0 = 0$, (6.30) is certainly true for $n = 0$. Assuming the truth of (6.30) for an integer n, it then follows from (6.29), since $\xi_n \geq |e_n|$ and $(1 + hL) > 1$, that

$$\xi_{n+1} \geq |e_{n+1}|$$

completing the induction.

The solution ξ_n of the nonhomogeneous difference equation (6.29) therefore provides an upper bound for the discretization error e_n. From the theory of difference equations given in Sec. 6.2, the solution of (6.29) is

$$\xi_n = c(1 + hL)^n - B \tag{6.31}$$

where c is an arbitrary constant, and

$$B = \frac{hY}{2L}$$

To satisfy the condition $\xi_0 = 0$, we see that we must choose $c = +B$, so that (6.31) becomes

$$\xi_n = B(1 + hL)^n - B$$

We infer from Sec. 1.7 that $e^x = 1 + x + e^\xi x^2/2$; hence $e^x \geq 1 + x$, for all x. It follows that $1 + hL \leq e^{hL}$ and therefore also that $(1 + hL)^n \leq e^{nhL}$. Using this in (6.31), we can therefore assert that

$$\xi_n \leq B(e^{nhL} - 1)$$

$$= \frac{hY}{2L}(e^{nhL} - 1)$$

$$= \frac{hY}{2L}(e^{(x_n - x_0)L} - 1)$$

where we have used the fact that $nh = x_n - x_0$. Since $|e_n| \leq \xi_n$, we have proved the following theorem.

Theorem 6.1 Let y_n be the approximate solution of (6.19) generated by Euler's method (6.23). If the exact solution $y(x)$ of (6.19) has a continuous second derivative on the interval $[x_0, b]$, and if on this interval the inequalities

$$|f_y(x,y)| < L \qquad |y''(x)| < Y$$

are satisfied for fixed positive constants L and Y, the error $e_n = y(x_n) - y_n$ of Euler's method at a point $x_n = x_0 + nh$ is bounded as follows:

$$|e_n| \leq \frac{hY}{2L}(e^{(x_n - x_0)L} - 1) \tag{6.32}$$

This theorem shows that the error is $O(h)$; that is, the error tends to zero as $h \to 0$, like ch for some constant c if $x = x_n$ is kept fixed. It must be emphasized that the estimate (6.32) provides an upper bound rather than a realistic bound. Its primary importance is to establish convergence of the method rather than to provide us with a realistic a priori error estimate.

Example 6.3   Determine an upper bound for the discretization error of Euler's method in solving the equation $y' = y$, $y(0) = 1$ from $x = 0$ to $x = 1$.

Solution   Here $f(x,y) = y$, $\partial f/\partial y = 1$; hence we can take $L = 1$. Also, since $y = e^x$, then $y'' = e^x$ and $|y''(x)| \le e$ for $0 \le x \le 1$. To find a bound for the error at $x = 1$, we have $x_n - x_0 = 1$, $y = e^1$, and from (6.32)

$$|e(1)| \le \frac{he}{2}(e - 1)$$
$$< 2.4h$$

Thus the error $e(1)$ at $x = 1$ is bounded by $2.4h$. To see how realistic this bound is, we shall obtain the exact solution of Euler's method for this problem. Thus

$$y_{n+1} = y_n + hf(x_n,y_n)$$
$$= (1 + h)y_n$$

The solution of this difference equation satisfying $y(0) = 1$ is

$$y_n = (1 + h)^n$$

Now if $h = 0.1$, $n = 10$, we find on expanding $(1.1)^{10}$ that Euler's method gives $y_{10} \approx y(1) = 2.5937$. On subtracting this from the exact solution $y(1) = e = 2.71828$, we find the error to be 0.1246, compared with the bound of 0.24 obtained by using (6.32).

EXERCISES

6.4-1. For the equation $y' = -2y$, $y(0) = 1$, $0 \le x \le 1$:
   (a) Find an upper bound on the error at $x = 1$ in terms of the step size h, using (6.32).
   (b) Solve the difference equation which results from Euler's method.
   (c) Compare the bound obtained from (a) with the actual error as obtained from (b) at $x = 1$ for $h = 0.1$, $h = 0.01$.
   (d) How small a step size h would have to be taken to produce six significant figures of accuracy at $x = 1$, using Euler's method (assuming no round-off error)?
6.4-2. The error e_n of an integration method is known to satisfy a difference inequality

$$|e_{n+2}| \le a_1|e_{n+1}| + a_2|e_n| + A$$

where a_1, a_2, A are positive constants with $e_1 = e_0 = 0$. Let ξ_n be a solution of the difference equation

$$\xi_{n+2} = a_1\xi_{n+1} + a_2\xi_n + A$$

with $\xi_1 = \xi_0 = 0$. Show by induction that

$$|e_n| \le \xi_n \qquad \text{for all } n$$

6.5 RUNGE-KUTTA METHODS

As mentioned previously, Euler's method is not very useful in practical problems because it requires a very small step size for reasonable accuracy. Taylor's algorithm of higher order is unacceptable as a general-purpose procedure because of the need to obtain higher total derivatives of $y(x)$.   The Runge-Kutta methods attempt to obtain greater accuracy, and at the same time avoid the need for higher derivatives, by evaluating the function $f(x,y)$ at selected points on each subinterval.   We shall derive here the simplest of the Runge-Kutta methods.   A formula of the following form is sought:

$$y_{n+1} = y_n + ak_1 + bk_2 \tag{6.33}$$

where

$$k_1 = hf(x_n,y_n)$$
$$k_2 = hf(x_n + \alpha h, y_n + \beta k_1)$$

and a, b, α, β are constants to be determined so that (6.33) will agree with the Taylor algorithm of as high an order as possible.   On expanding $y(x_{n+1})$ in a Taylor series through terms of order h^3, we obtain

$$y(x_{n+1}) = y(x_n) + hy'(x_n) + \frac{h^2}{2} y''(x_n) + \frac{h^3}{6} y'''(x_n) + \cdots$$

$$= y(x_n) + hf(x_n,y_n) + \frac{h^2}{2} (f_x + ff_y)_n$$

$$+ \frac{h^3}{6} (f_{xx} + 2ff_{xy} + f_{yy}f^2 + f_xf_y + f_y^2f)_n + O(h^4) \tag{6.34}$$

where we have used the expansions (6.21), and the subscript n means that all functions involved are to be evaluated at $\{x_n,y_n\}$.

On the other hand, using Taylor's expansion for functions of two variables (see Sec. 1.7), we find that

$$\frac{k_2}{h} = f(x_n + \alpha h, y_n + \beta k_1) = f(x_n,y_n) + \alpha h f_x + \beta k_1 f_y$$

$$+ \frac{\alpha^2 h^2}{2} f_{xx} + \alpha h \beta k_1 f_{xy} + \frac{\beta^2 k_1^2}{2} f_{yy} + O(h^3)$$

where all derivatives are evaluated at $\{x_n,y_n\}$.

If we now substitute this expression for k_2 into (6.33) and note that $k_1 = hf(x_n,y_n)$, we find upon rearrangement in powers of h that

$$y_{n+1} = y_n + (a + b)hf + bh^2(\alpha f_x + \beta ff_y)$$

$$+ bh^3\left(\frac{\alpha^2}{2} f_{xx} + \alpha\beta ff_{xy} + \frac{\beta^2}{2} f^2 f_{yy}\right) + O(h^4) \tag{6.34a}$$

On comparing this with (6.34), we see that to make the corresponding powers of h and h^2 agree we must have

$$a + b = 1$$
$$b\alpha = b\beta = \tfrac{1}{2} \qquad\qquad (6.35)$$

Although we have four unknowns, we have only three equations, and hence we still have one degree of freedom in the solution of (6.35).   We might hope to use this additional degree of freedom to obtain agreement of the coefficients in the h^3 terms.   It is obvious, however, that this is impossible for all functions $f(x,y)$.

There are many solutions to (6.35), the simplest perhaps being

$$a = b = \tfrac{1}{2} \qquad \alpha = \beta = 1$$

This choice leads to the formula

$$
\begin{aligned}
y_{n+1} &= y_n + \tfrac{1}{2}(k_1 + k_2) \\
&= y_n + \frac{h}{2}\left[f(x_n,y_n) + f(x_n + h,\, y_n + hf(x_n,y_n))\right]
\end{aligned}
\qquad (6.36)
$$

which we designate as Algorithm 6.2.

Algorithm 6.2   Runge-Kutta method of order 2   For the equation

$$y' = f(x,y) \qquad y(x_0) = y_0$$

generate approximations y_n to $y(x_0 + nh)$, for h fixed and $n = 0, 1, \ldots,$ using the recursion formula (6.36).

Algorithm 6.2 may be pictured geometrically as in Fig. 6.1.   Euler's method yields an increment $P_1P_0 = hf(x_n,y_n)$ to y_n; $P_2P_0 = hf(x_n + h,$

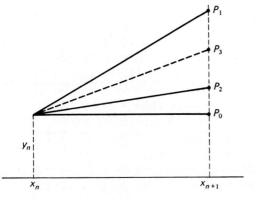

Fig 6.1

$y_n + hf(x_n, y_n))$ is another increment based on the slope obtained at x_{n+1}. Taking the average of these increments leads to formula (6.36).

The local error of (6.36) is of the form

$$y(x_{n+1}) - y_{n+1} = \frac{h^3}{12}(f_{xx} + 2ff_{xy} + f^2 f_{yy} - 2f_x f_y - 2ff_y^2) + O(h^4)$$

The complexity of the coefficient in this error term is characteristic of all Runge-Kutta methods and constitutes one of the least desirable features of such methods since local error estimates are very difficult to obtain. The local error of (6.36) is, however, of order h^3, whereas that of Euler's method is h^2. We can therefore expect to be able to use a larger step size with (6.36). The price we pay for this is that we must evaluate the function $f(x,y)$ twice for each step of the integration. Formulas of the Runge-Kutta type for any order can be derived by the method used above. However, the derivations become exceedingly complicated. The most popular and most commonly used formula of this type is contained in Algorithm 6.3.

Algorithm 6.3 Runge-Kutta method of order 4 For the equation $y' = f(x,y)$, $y(x_0) = y_0$, generate approximations y_n to $y(x_0 + nh)$ for h fixed and for $n = 0, 1, 2, \ldots$, using the recursion formula

$$\boxed{y_{n+1} = y_n + \tfrac{1}{6}(k_1 + 2k_2 + 2k_3 + k_4)} \qquad (6.37)$$

where

$$k_1 = hf(x_n, y_n)$$

$$k_2 = hf\left(x_n + \frac{h}{2}, y_n + \frac{1}{2}k_1\right)$$

$$k_3 = hf\left(x_n + \frac{h}{2}, y_n + \frac{1}{2}k_2\right)$$

$$k_4 = hf(x_n + h, y_n + k_3)$$

The local truncation error of Algorithm 6.3 is $O(h^5)$. Again the price we pay for the favorable discretization error is that four function evaluations are required per step. This price may be considerable in computer time for those problems in which the function $f(x,y)$ is complicated. The Runge-Kutta methods have additional disadvantages, which will be discussed later. Formula (6.37) is widely used in practice with considerable success. It has the important advantage that it is self-starting; i.e., it requires only the value of y at a point $x = x_n$ to find y and y' at $x = x_{n+1}$.

A general-purpose FORTRAN program based on Algorithm 6.2 for a single differential equation is given below. To use this program, the user must include a subroutine for evaluating the function $f(x,y)$, and he must specify the step h, the total number of steps N, and the initial value $y(x_0) = y_0$.

FORTRAN PROGRAM FOR ALGORITHM 6.2

```
C       FORTRAN IV PROGRAM TO SOLVE THE FIRST
C       ORDER DIFFERENTIAL EQUATION
C
C       Y'(X) = F(X,Y)
C       WITH INITIAL CONDITION OF
C       Y(X0) = Y0.
C       SECOND ORDER RUNGE-KUTTA METHOD USED.
C       A FUNCTION SUBPROGRAM CALLED 'F' MUST BE
C       SUPPLIED.
        REAL K1,K2
        READ (5,100) H,X,Y,N
        DERIV = F(X,Y)
        NSTEP = 0
        WRITE (6,101) NSTEP, X, Y, DERIV
        N = N - 1
        DO 10 NSTEP = 1,N
        K1 = H*F(X,Y)
        K2 = H*F(X + H,Y + K1)
        Y = Y + .5*(K1 + K2)
        X = X + H
        DERIV = F(X,Y)
     10 WRITE (6,101) NSTEP,X,Y,DERIV
    100 FORMAT (3F10.5,I3)
    101 FORMAT (1X,I3,3E21.9)
        STOP
        END
```

Example 6.4 Solve the problem of Example 6.2 by the second-order Runge-Kutta method (6.36) and by the fourth-order Runge-Kutta method (6.37).

In the machine results given in Sec. 6.3, (6.36) is called method 2 and (6.37) method 3. We see that the second-order Runge-Kutta method gives results which are entirely comparable with the Taylor algorithm of order 2 (method 1). The fourth-order Runge-Kutta method, however, yields remarkably improved results correct to six decimal places for $h = \frac{1}{16}$ and to seven or eight places for other values of h. The computational efficiency of methods 2 and 3 may be compared by considering the number of function evaluations required for each. Method 2 requires two function evaluations per step and for $h = \frac{1}{128}$ requires in all 256 evaluations. Method 3 requires four function evaluations and for $h = \frac{1}{16}$ a total of only 64 function evaluations and yet produces considerably more accurate results. The fourth-order Runge-Kutta method is clearly a more efficient method to use for this problem, and this is generally true.

EXERCISES

6.5-1. For the equation $y' = x + y$, $y(0) = 1$, calculate the local error of method (6.36). Compare this with the error of Taylor's algorithm of order 2. Which would you expect to give better results over the interval $[0,1]$?

6.5-2. Carry out a few steps of the integration of $y' = x + y$, $y(0) = 1$, using (6.36) and a step size of $h = 0.01$; then write a program to solve this problem on a computer from $x = 0$ to $x = 1$.

6.5-3. To Eqs. (6.35) add the additional condition that the coefficients of f_{xx} in (6.34) and (6.34a) must agree. Solve the resulting system of equations for a, b, α, β. Determine the error term of the second-order Runge-Kutta method obtained from this choice of a, b, α, β.

6.5-4. It can be shown that the error of the fourth-order Runge-Kutta method satisfies for a step size h a relation of the form

$$y_n(h) - y_n = A(b)h^4 + O(h^5)$$

as h goes to zero, where $b = x_0 + nh$, and the constant $A(b)$ does not depend on h. Use an extrapolation procedure as in the case of Romberg integration to obtain an approximation to $y(b)$ for which the error is $O(h^5)$.

6.6 MULTISTEP FORMULAS

The Taylor algorithm of order k and the Runge-Kutta methods require information about the solution at a single point $x = x_n$, from which the methods proceed to obtain y at the next point $x = x_{n+1}$. *Multistep methods* make use of information about the solution at more than one point. Let us assume that we have already obtained approximations to y' and y at a number of equally spaced points, say $x_0, x_1, \ldots, x_n$. One class of multistep methods is based on the principle of numerical integration. If we integrate the differential equation $y' = f(x,y)$ from x_n to x_{n+1}, we will have

$$\int_{x_n}^{x_{n+1}} y' \, dx = \int_{x_n}^{x_{n+1}} f(x,y(x)) \, dx$$

or

$$y_{n+1} = y_n + \int_{x_n}^{x_{n+1}} f(x,y(x)) \, dx \tag{6.38}$$

To carry out the integration in (6.38) we now approximate $f(x,y(x))$ by a polynomial which interpolates $f(x,y(x))$ at the $(m + 1)$ points $x_n, x_{n-1}, x_{n-2}, \ldots, x_{n-m}$. If we use the notation

$$f(x_k, y(x_k)) = f_k$$

we can use the Newton backward formula (4.31a) of degree m for this purpose:

$$p_m(x) = \sum_{k=0}^{m} (-1)^k \binom{-s}{k} \Delta^k f_{n-k} \qquad s = \frac{x - x_n}{h}$$

Inserting this into (6.38) and noting that $dx = h\,ds$, we obtain

$$y_{n+1} = y_n + h \int_0^1 \sum_{k=0}^m (-1)^k \binom{-s}{k} \Delta^k f_{n-k}\, ds$$

$$= y_n + h\{\gamma_0 f_n + \gamma_1 \Delta f_{n-1} + \cdots + \gamma_m \Delta^m f_{n-m}\} \qquad (6.39)$$

where

$$\gamma_k = (-1)^k \int_0^1 \binom{-s}{k} ds \qquad (6.40)$$

From the definition of the binomial function given in Chap. 4 we can easily compute the γ_k, the first few of which are

$$\gamma_0 = 1 \qquad \gamma_1 = \tfrac{1}{2} \qquad \gamma_2 = \tfrac{5}{12} \qquad \gamma_3 = \tfrac{3}{8} \qquad \gamma_4 = \tfrac{251}{720}$$

Formula (6.39) is known as the *Adams-Bashforth method*. The simplest case, obtained by setting $m = 0$ in (6.39), again leads to Euler's method. In general, the use of (6.39) requires the value of $y' = f$ at the $m + 1$ points x_n, $x_{n-1}, \ldots, x_{n-m}$. From these we can form the differences $\Delta f_{n-1}, \Delta^2 f_{n-2}$, $\ldots, \Delta^m f_{n-m}$; from (6.39) we can compute y_{n+1}; from the differential equation we can compute $f_{n+1} = f(x_{n+1}, y_{n+1})$. We now relabel the point x_{n+1} as x_n, form a new line of differences, and repeat the process. For $m = 3$, which is commonly used in practice, the difference table is

$$
\begin{array}{llllll}
x_{n-3} & y_{n-3} & f_{n-3} \\
& & & \Delta f_{n-3} \\
x_{n-2} & y_{n-2} & f_{n-2} & & \Delta^2 f_{n-3} \\
& & & \Delta f_{n-2} & & \Delta^3 f_{n-3} \\
x_{n-1} & y_{n-1} & f_{n-1} & & \Delta^2 f_{n-2} \\
& & & \Delta f_{n-1} \\
x_n & y_n & f_n
\end{array}
$$

and (6.39) specializes to

$$\boxed{y_{n+1} = y_n + h(f_n + \tfrac{1}{2}\Delta f_{n-1} + \tfrac{5}{12}\Delta^2 f_{n-2} + \tfrac{3}{8}\Delta^3 f_{n-3})} \qquad (6.41)$$

In practice, it is more convenient computationally to work with ordinates instead of differences. From the definition of the forward-difference operator Δ we find that

$$\Delta f_{n-1} = f_n - f_{n-1}$$
$$\Delta^2 f_{n-2} = f_n - 2f_{n-1} + f_{n-2}$$
$$\Delta^3 f_{n-3} = f_n - 3f_{n-1} + 3f_{n-2} - f_{n-3}$$

Substituting in (6.41) and regrouping, we obtain

$$y_{n+1} = y_n + \frac{h}{24}(55f_n - 59f_{n-1} + 37f_{n-2} - 9f_{n-3}) \qquad (6.42)$$

The local error of (6.41) may be derived as follows: From (4.32) we know that the error of Newton's backward formula with $n = 3$ and $k = 0$ is

$$h^4 f^{(4)}\binom{-s}{4} ds$$

The error of (6.41) is then given by

$$E_{AB} = h \int_0^1 h^4 f^{(4)}(\eta)\binom{-s}{4}$$

Since $\binom{-s}{4}$ does not change sign on the interval [0,1], there exists a point ξ between x_{n-3} and x_{n+1} such that

$$E_{AB} = h^5 f^{(4)}(\eta)(\xi)\int_0^1 \binom{-s}{4} ds$$

$$\qquad (6.43)$$

$$E_{AB} = h^5 y^v(\xi)\tfrac{251}{720}$$

To use (6.42) we must have four starting values. These starting values must be obtained from some independent source. To illustrate how (6.42) is used, we carry out a few steps of the integration of the equation

$$y' = -y^2$$
$$y(1) = 1$$

with $h = 0.1$. The exact solution of this problem is $y = 1/x$. In the table below, the first four starting values are obtained from the exact solution, and the remaining entries by (6.42).

x_n	y_n	$f_n = -y_n{}^2$	$y(x_n) = 1/x_n$
1.0	1.00000000	−1.00000000	
1.1	0.90909091	−0.82644628	0.90909091
1.2	0.83333333	−0.69444444	0.83333333
1.3	0.76923077	−0.59171598	0.76923077
1.4	0.71443632	−0.51041926	0.71428571
1.5	0.66686030	−0.44470266	0.66666667
1.6	0.62524613	−0.39093272	0.62500000

The values y_n computed by formula (6.42) are seen to be in error by about two units in the fourth decimal place. Using the local error estimate (6.43) and the fact that

$$|y^v(x)| = \left|\frac{5!}{x^6}\right| \leq 120 \qquad 1 < x < 2$$

we obtain the error bound

$$|E_{AB}| \leq \tfrac{251}{720}(120)(10^{-5}) \approx 0.0004$$

This bound is about twice as large as the errors encountered in going from one step to the next.

A number of other formulas of the multistep type can be derived similarly, using numerical integration. Instead of integrating $f(x,y)$ in (6.38) from x_n to x_{n-1}, we could, for example, integrate from x_{n-p} to x_{n+1} for some integer $p \geq 0$. If we again interpolate at the $m + 1$ points x_n, $x_{n-1}, \ldots, x_{n-m}$ with Newton's backward formula, we obtain

$$y_{n+1} = y_{n-p} + h \int_{-p}^{1} \sum_{k=0}^{m} (-1)^k \binom{-s}{k} \Delta^k f_{n-k}\, ds \qquad (6.44)$$

The case $p = 0$ yields the Adams-Bashforth formula (6.39). Some especially interesting formulas of this type are those corresponding to $m = 1$, $p = 1$ and to $m = 3$, $p = 3$. These formulas together with their local-error terms are

$$\boxed{y_{n+1} = y_{n-1} + 2hf_n} \qquad \boxed{E = \frac{h^3}{3} y'''(\xi)} \qquad (6.45)$$

$$\boxed{y_{n+1} = y_{n-3} + \frac{4h}{3}(2f_n - f_{n-1} + 2f_{n-2})} \qquad \boxed{E = \tfrac{14}{45}h^5 y^v(\xi)}$$
$$(6.46)$$

Formula (6.45), which is comparable in simplicity to Euler's method, has a more favorable discretization error. Similarly (6.46), which requires knowledge of $f(x,y)$ at only three points, has a discretization error comparable with that of the Adams-Bashforth method (6.42). It can be shown that all formulas of the type (6.44) with m odd and $m = p$ have the property that the coefficient of the mth difference vanishes, thus yielding a formula of greater accuracy than might be expected. On the other hand, these formulas are subject to greater instability, a concept which will be developed later.

A major disadvantage of multistep formulas is that they are not self-starting. Thus, in the Adams-Bashforth method (6.42), we must have four successive values of $f(x,y)$ at equally spaced points before this formula can be used. These starting values must be obtained by some independent method. We might, for example, use Taylor's algorithm or one of the Runge-Kutta methods to obtain these starting values. We must also be assured that these starting values are as accurate as necessary for the overall required accuracy. A second disadvantage of the Adams-Bashforth method is that, although the local discretization error is $O(h^5)$, the coefficient in the error term is somewhat larger than for formulas of the Runge-Kutta type of the same order. Runge-Kutta methods are generally, although not always, more accurate for this reason. On the other hand, the multistep formulas require only one derivative evaluation per step, compared with four evaluations per step with Runge-Kutta methods, and are therefore considerably faster and require less computational work.

Example 6.5   Solve the equation

$$y' = x + y \qquad y(0) = 0$$

from $x = 0$ to $x = 1$, using the Adams-Bashforth method.

An IBM 7090 FORTRAN program and the results for this problem are given below. The exact solution of this problem is $y = e^x - 1 - x$. The first four starting values are computed, using this solution. The first column of the results gives the values of x_n with $h = \frac{1}{32}$, the second column gives y_n as computed by formula (6.42), the third column gives the value $y(x_n)$ as computed from the solution, and the fourth column gives the absolute error $e_n = y_n - y(x_n)$.

The results are correct to about six significant figures, which is approximately what would be expected from the error formula (6.43). Since the accumulated discretization error is $O(h^4)$, we would expect to reduce the error by $\frac{1}{16}$ if the step size h were halved.

FORTRAN PROGRAM FOR EXAMPLE 6.5

```
C        ADAMS-BASHFORTH METHOD
         DIMENSION F(4)
C
         SOLN(X) = EXP(X) - 1.0 - X
C
C        ** INITIALIZE
         WRITE (6,500)
         N = 4
         H = 1./32.
         NSTEP = 32
         Y0 = 0.0
         X0 = 0.0
         EN = 0.0
         NZ = 0
```

```
C
C          ** COMPUTE FIRST FOUR POINTS USING EXACT SOLUTION
           F(1) = X0 + Y0
           WRITE (6,510) NZ,X0,Y0,Y0,EN
           XN = X0
           DO 20 I = 2,4
           K = I - 1
           XN = XN + H
           YN = SOLN(XN)
           F(I) = XN + YN
           WRITE (6,510) K,XN,YN,YN,EN
        20 CONTINUE
C
C          ** BEGIN ITERATION
           DO 50 K = 4,NSTEP
           YN = YN + (H/24.)*(55.*F(N) - 59.*F(N - 1) + 37.*F(N - 2) -
           X9.*F(N - 3))
           XN = XN + H
           F(N - 3) = F(N - 2)
           F(N - 2) = F(N - 1)
           F(N - 1) = F(N)
           F(N) = XN + YN
           YXN = SOLN(XN)
           EN = YN - YXN
           WRITE (6,510) K,XN,YN,YXN,EN
        50 CONTINUE
           STOP
       500 FORMAT (23H1ADAMS-BASHFORTH METHOD/
           X1H04X1HN6X2HXN18X2HYN18X5HY(XN)15X15HEN = YN - Y(XN))
       510 FORMAT (1H 2XI3,4X 4(E16.8,4X))
           END
```

COMPUTER RESULTS FOR EXAMPLE 6.5

N	XN	YN	Y(XN)	EN = YN − Y(XN)
0	0.	0.	0.	0.
1	0.31250000E-01	0.49340725E-03	0.49340725E-03	0.
2	0.62500000E-01	0.19944459E-02	0.19944459E-02	0.
3	0.93750000E-01	0.45351386E-02	0.45351386E-02	0.
4	0.12500000E-00	0.81484411E-02	0.81484467E-02	−0.55879354E-08
5	0.15625000E-00	0.12868421E-01	0.12868434E-01	−0.12922101E-07
6	0.18750000E-00	0.18730211E-01	0.18730238E-01	−0.26309863E-07
7	0.21875000E-00	0.25770056E-01	0.25770098E-01	−0.41676685E-07
8	0.25000000E-00	0.34025350E-01	0.34025416E-01	−0.65192580E-07
9	0.28125000E-00	0.43534677E-01	0.43534756E-01	−0.78696758E-07
10	0.31250000E-00	0.54337843E-01	0.54337934E-01	−0.90803951E-07
11	0.34375000E-00	0.66475919E-01	0.66476032E-01	−0.11269003E-06
12	0.37500000E-00	0.79991280E-01	0.79991400E-01	−0.12014061E-06
13	0.40625000E-00	0.94927646E-01	0.94927788E-01	−0.14156103E-06

COMPUTER RESULTS FOR EXAMPLE 6.5 (*continued*)

N	XN	YN	Y(XN)	EN = YN − Y(XN)
14	0.43750000E-00	0.11133012E-00	0.11133029E-00	−0.16111881E-06
15	0.46875000E-00	0.12924525E-00	0.12924545E-00	−0.19185245E-06
16	0.50000000E 00	0.14872105E-00	0.14872126E-00	−0.21234155E-06
17	0.53125000E 00	0.16980705E-00	0.16980730E-00	−0.24400651E-06
18	0.56250000E 00	0.19255438E-00	0.19255465E-00	−0.26822090E-06
19	0.59375000E 00	0.21701577E-00	0.21701607E-00	−0.29988587E-06
20	0.62500000E 00	0.24324562E-00	0.24324594E-00	−0.31664968E-06
21	0.65625000E 00	0.27130008E-00	0.27130044E-00	−0.34645200E-06
22	0.68750000E 00	0.30123707E-00	0.30123746E-00	−0.39115548E-06
23	0.71875000E 00	0.33311634E-00	0.33311677E-00	−0.42840838E-06
24	0.75000000E 00	0.36699954E-00	0.36700001E-00	−0.46566129E-06
25	0.78125000E 00	0.40295030E-00	0.40295079E-00	−0.49173832E-06
26	0.81250000E 00	0.44103424E-00	0.44103476E-00	−0.52526593E-06
27	0.84375000E 00	0.48131907E-00	0.48131964E-00	−0.56624413E-06
28	0.87500000E 00	0.52387466E 00	0.52387527E 00	−0.61094761E-06
29	0.90625000E 00	0.56877308E 00	0.56877375E 00	−0.66310167E-06
30	0.93750000E 00	0.61608872E 00	0.61608934E 00	−0.71525574E-06
31	0.96875000E 00	0.66589829E 00	0.66589907E 00	−0.77486038E-06
32	0.09999999E 01	0.71828098E 00	0.71828181E 00	−0.82701445E-06

EXERCISES

6.6-1. Derive the formulas in (6.46), using (6.44) and the error (4.32) in polynomial interpolation.

6.6-2. Verify (6.45) by expanding y_{n+1} and y_{n-1} about $x = x_n$ through third-order terms, assuming that the starting values are exact.

6.6-3. Solve the equation $xy' = x - y$, $y(2) = 2$ from $x = 2$ to $x = 2.5$ with $h = 0.05$. Obtain the starting values $y(2.05) - y(2.15)$ by Taylor's series, retaining enough terms to assure accuracy to five decimal places. Then continue the solution by (*a*) the Adams-Bashforth method (6.42) and (*b*) Milne's method (6.46). Compare the answers with those of the exact solution $y(x) = x/2 + 2/x$ (see Example 6.1).

6.6-4. Write a computer program to solve the equation

$$y' = \frac{x}{y} + \frac{y}{x} \qquad y(1) = 0.5$$

from $x = 1$ to $x = 2$, using the Adams-Bashforth method (6.42). Take $h = \frac{1}{64}$, $h = \frac{1}{128}$, and estimate the value of h which will yield seven decimal places of accuracy.

6.7 PREDICTOR-CORRECTOR METHODS

The multistep methods of Sec. 6.6 were derived using polynomials which interpolated at the point x_n and at points backward from x_n. These are sometimes known as formulas of *open* type. Formulas of *closed* type can also be derived by basing the interpolating polynomial on the point x_{n+1}, as well as on x_n and points backward from x_n. The simplest formula of this type is obtained if we approximate the integral in (6.38) by the trapezoidal formula (5.26). This leads to the formula

$$
y_{n+1} = y_n + \frac{h}{2}[f(x_n,y_n) + f(x_{n+1},y_{n+1})] \qquad n = 0, 1, \ldots \quad (6.47)
$$

The error of this formula is $-(h^3/12)y'''$ and thus represents an improvement over Euler's method. However, (6.47) is an implicit equation for y_{n+1} since y_{n+1} appears as an argument on the right-hand side.

If $f(x,y)$ is a nonlinear function, we will, in general, not be able to solve (6.47) for y_{n+1} exactly. We can, however, attempt to obtain y_{n+1} by means of iteration. Thus, keeping x_n fixed, we obtain a first approximation $y_{n+1}^{(0)}$ to y_{n+1} by means of Euler's formula

$$
y_{n+1}^{(0)} = y_n + hf(x_n,y_n) \tag{6.48}
$$

We then evaluate $f(x_{n+1},y_{n+1}^{(0)})$ and substitute in the right-hand side of (6.47) to obtain the approximation

$$
y_{n+1}^{(1)} = y_n + \frac{h}{2}[f(x_n,y_n) + f(x_{n+1},y_{n+1}^{(0)})]
$$

Next we evaluate $f(x_{n+1},y_{n+1}^{(1)})$ and again use (6.47) to obtain a next approximation. In general, the iteration is defined by

$$
y_{n+1}^{(k)} = y_n + \frac{h}{2}[f(x_n,y_n) + f(x_{n+1},y_{n+1}^{(k-1)})] \qquad k = 1, 2, \ldots \quad (6.49)
$$

The iteration is terminated when two successive iterates agree to the desired accuracy. This iteration for obtaining improved values of y_{n+1} at a fixed point x_{n+1} is sometimes called an *inner iteration* to distinguish it from (6.47), which is used to generate values of y_n at $n = 0, 1, \ldots$. We shall summarize this procedure in Algorithm 6.4.

Algorithm 6.4 A second-order predictor-corrector method For the differential equation $y' = f(x,y)$, $y(x_0) = y_0$ with h given and $x_n = x_0 + nh$, for each fixed $n = 0, 1, \ldots$:

1. Compute $y_{n+1}^{(0)}$, using (6.48).
2. Compute $y_{n+1}^{(k)}$ ($k = 1, 2, \ldots$), using (6.49), iterating on k until

$$
\frac{|y_{n+1}^{(k)} - y_{n+1}^{(k-1)}|}{|y_{n+1}^{(k)}|} < \epsilon \qquad \text{for a prescribed } \epsilon
$$

In specifying ϵ in Algorithm 6.4, we must keep in mind that the accuracy that can be expected on each step is limited by the error of the basic formula (6.47) and by the step size h.

To adapt this algorithm to the solution of a specific problem, we would have to specify (*a*) the number N of steps desired; (*b*) a maximum number K of inner iterations; (*c*) what to do in case k exceeds K.

It is customary to call an explicit formula such as Euler's formula an open-type formula, while an implicit formula such as (6.47) is said to be of closed type. When they are used as a pair of formulas, the open-type formula is also called a *predictor*, while the closed-type formula is called a *corrector*. A corrector formula is generally more accurate than a predictor formula, even when both have a discretization error of the same order, primarily because the coefficient in the error term is smaller. Two questions arise naturally in connection with corrector formulas. The first is, "Under what conditions will the inner iteration on k converge?," and the second, "How many iterations will be needed to produce the required accuracy?" The answer to the latter question will depend on many factors. However, if the predictor and corrector formulas are of the same order, experience has shown that only one or two applications of the corrector are sufficient, provided that the step size h has been properly selected. If we find that one or two corrections are not sufficient, it is better to reduce the step size h than to continue to iterate. The answer to the first question is contained in Theorem 6.2.

Theorem 6.2 If $f(x,y)$ and $\partial f/\partial y$ are continuous in x and y on the closed interval $[a,b]$ the inner iteration defined by (6.49) will converge, provided h is chosen small enough so that, for $x = x_n$, and all y with $|y - y_{n+1}| \le |y_{n+1}^{(0)} - y_{n+1}|$,

$$\left|\frac{\partial f}{\partial y}\right| h < 2 \tag{6.50}$$

To prove this, we first observe that in the iteration (6.49) x_n is fixed. Hence, if we set $y_{n+1}^{(k)} = Y^{(k)}$, we can write (6.49) in the form

$$Y^{(k)} = F(Y^{(k-1)})$$

where

$$F(Y) = \frac{h}{2}f(x_{n+1},Y) + C$$

and where C depends on n but not on Y. This can be viewed as an instance of fixed-point iteration considered in Sec. 2.3. In a corollary to Theorem 2.1 we proved that such an iteration will converge provided that $F'(Y)$ is continuous and satisfies

$$|F'(Y)| < 1$$

for all Y with $|Y - y_{n+1}| \leq |Y^{(0)} - y_{n+1}|$, where y_{n+1} is the fixed point of $F(Y)$. Since $F'(Y) = (h/2)\, \partial f/\partial y$, and since $\partial f/\partial y$ is bounded and non-vanishing by assumption, the iteration (6.49) will converge if

$$|F'(Y)| = \left| \frac{h}{2} \frac{\partial f}{\partial y} \right| < 1$$

i.e., if

$$h < \frac{2}{|\partial f/\partial y|}$$

Since $F'(Y) = (h/2)\, \partial f/\partial y$, this proves the theorem.

Example 6.6 Solve the equation

$$y' = x - \frac{1}{y} \qquad y(0) = 1$$

from $x = 0$ to $x = 0.2$, using Algorithm 6.4 with $h = 0.1$.

Since the error of (6.49) is $-(h^3/12)y'''$, and since by differentiating above we find that $y''(0) \approx -2$, the error will be approximately 0.0002. We cannot therefore expect much more than three decimal places of accuracy in the results.

Step 1

$$
\begin{array}{ll}
\text{By Euler's method:} & y_1^{(0)} = 0.9 \\
\text{By (6.49):} & y_1^{(1)} = 0.8994 \\
& y_1^{(2)} = 0.8994
\end{array}
$$

Since $y_1^{(1)}$ and $y_1^{(2)}$ agree to four places, we accept this answer, and we compute $y_1' = f(x_1, y_1) = -1.0118$.

Step 2   By Euler's method,

$$y_2^{(0)} = 0.8994 + 0.1(-1.0118) = 0.7982$$

By (6.49),

$$y_2^{(1)} = 0.8994 + 0.05\left[-1.0118 + \left(0.2 - \frac{1}{0.7982} \right) \right] = 0.7962$$

$$y_2^{(2)} = 0.8994 + 0.05\left[-1.0118 + \left(0.2 - \frac{1}{0.7962} \right) \right] = 0.7960$$

$$y_2^{(3)} = 0.7960$$

Again we accept $y_2 = 0.7960$, compute y_2', and proceed to the next step.

As the computation proceeds, we can expect a gradual loss of accuracy. It appears here that for $h = 0.1$ we need two or three applications of the corrector. This is primarily due to the fact that we are using a predictor which is of lower order than the corrector.

To verify that the inner iterations for this example will converge for $h = 0.1$, we compute $\partial f/\partial y = 1/y^2$, and hence, from Theorem 6.2, we want

h to be less than $2y^2$. We do not know the solution y, but it is clear from the above steps that $y > 0.7$ on the interval $[0,0.2]$. Hence the inner iterations will converge if $h < 2(0.7)^2 = 0.98$.

EXERCISES

6.7-1. For the special equation $y' = Ay$, $y(0) = 1$, show that the trapezoidal corrector formula (6.47) leads to a difference equation whose solution is

$$y_n = \left[\frac{(1 + Ah/2)}{(1 - Ah/2)}\right]^n$$

provided that $|Ah/2| < 1$.

6.7-2. For the solution obtained in Exercise 6.7-1 show that

$$\lim_{h \to 0} y_n = e^{Ax_n}$$

for a fixed value of $x = x_n = nh$.

6.7-3. Solve the equation $y' = x^2 + y$, $y(0) = 1$, from $x = 0$ to $x = 0.5$, using Euler's method as a predictor and (6.49) as a corrector. Determine the step h so that four decimal places of accuracy are obtained at $x = 0.5$.

6.8 THE ADAMS-MOULTON METHOD

Corrector formulas of higher order can be obtained by using a polynomial which interpolates at $x_{n+1}, x_n, \ldots, x_{n-m}$ for an integer $m > 0$. The Newton backward formula which interpolates at these $m + 2$ points in terms of $s = (x - x_n)/h$ is

$$P_{m+1}(s) = \sum_{k=0}^{m+1} (-1)^k \binom{1-s}{k} \Delta^k f_{n+1-k} \tag{6.51}$$

These differences are based on the values $f_{n+1}, f_n, \ldots, f_{n-m}$. If we integrate (6.51) from x_n to x_{n+1} and use (6.38), we obtain

$$y_{n+1} = y_n + h(\gamma_0' f_{n+1} + \gamma_1' \Delta f_n + \cdots + \gamma_{m+1}' \Delta^{m+1} f_{n-m}) \tag{6.52}$$

where

$$\gamma_k' = (-1)^k \int_0^1 \binom{1-s}{k} ds \qquad k = 0, 1, \ldots, m+1$$

The first few values of γ_k' are

$$\gamma_0' = 1 \qquad \gamma_1' = -\tfrac{1}{2} \qquad \gamma_2' = -\tfrac{1}{12} \qquad \gamma_3' = -\tfrac{1}{24} \qquad \gamma_4' = -\tfrac{19}{720}$$

The error of (6.52), based on the error of the interpolating polynomial, is

$$E = \gamma_{m+2}' h^{m+3} y^{(m+3)}(\xi) \tag{6.53}$$

The case $m = 2$ is frequently used. If the differences in (6.52) are expressed in terms of ordinates for $m = 2$, we obtain

$$y_{n+1} = y_n + \frac{h}{24} (9f_{n+1} + 19f_n - 5f_{n-1} + f_{n-2}) \tag{6.54}$$

with the error

$$E_{AM} = -\tfrac{19}{720}h^5 y^v(\xi) \tag{6.55}$$

The formula (6.52) is known as the Adams-Moulton formula. The fourth-order Adams-Moulton formula (6.54) is clearly a corrector formula of closed type since $f_{n+1} = f(x_{n+1}, y_{n+1})$ involves the unknown quantity y_{n+1}. It must therefore be solved by iteration. It can be shown that the iteration based on (6.54) will converge, provided that h is small enough so that the condition $9h/24|\partial f/\partial y| < 1$ is satisfied. A convenient predictor to use with this corrector is the Adams-Bashforth fourth-order formula (6.42). In this case the predictor is of the same order as the corrector. If h is properly chosen, then one application of the corrector will yield a significant improvement in accuracy.

Specifications for a fourth-order predictor-corrector method are given in Algorithm 6.5.

Algorithm 6.5 The Adams-Moulton predictor-corrector method

For the differential equation $y' = f(x,y)$ with h fixed and $x_n = x_0 + nh$ and with (y_0, f_0), (y_1, f_1), (y_2, f_2), (y_3, f_3) given, for each fixed $n = 3, 4, \ldots$:

1. Compute $y_{n+1}^{(0)}$, using the formula

$$y_{n+1}^{(0)} = y_n + \frac{h}{24} (55f_n - 59f_{n-1} + 37f_{n-2} - 9f_{n-3})$$

2. Compute $f_{n+1}^{(0)} = f(x_{n+1}, y_{n+1}^{(0)})$.
3. Compute

$$y_{n+1}^{(k)} = y_n + \frac{h}{24} [9f(x_{n+1}, y_{n+1}^{(k-1)}) + 19f_n - 5f_{n-1} + f_{n-2}]$$

$$k = 1, 2, \ldots$$

4. Iterate on k until

$$\frac{|y_{n+1}^{(k)} - y_{n+1}^{(k-1)}|}{|y_{n+1}^{(k)}|} < \epsilon \qquad \text{for } \epsilon \text{ prescribed}$$

Again this algorithm is not complete unless we specify what to do in case of nonconvergence in step 4. We shall consider later a more complete specification for a general-purpose subroutine to solve differential equations.

Besides yielding improved accuracy, the corrector formula serves another useful function. It provides an estimate of the local discretization error, which can then be used to decide whether the step h is adequate for the required accuracy. To examine this error estimation procedure for the predictor-corrector pair consisting of the Adams-Bashforth and Adams-Moulton fourth-order formulas, we write the local-error estimate for each:

$$\begin{aligned} E_{AB} &= \tfrac{251}{720}h^5 y^v(\xi_1) \\ E_{AM} &= -\tfrac{19}{720}h^5 y^v(\xi_2) \end{aligned} \tag{6.56}$$

Let $y_{n+1}^{(0)}$ represent the value of y_{n+1} obtained from (6.42), and $y_{n+1}^{(1)}$ the result obtained with one application of Algorithm 6.5. If the values of f are assumed to be exact at all points up to and including x_n, and if $y(x_{n+1})$ represents the exact value of y at x_{n+1}, then from (6.56) we obtain the error estimates

$$\begin{aligned} y(x_{n+1}) - y_{n+1}^{(0)} &= \tfrac{251}{720}h^5 y^v(\xi_1) \tag{6.57a} \\ y(x_{n+1}) - y_{n+1}^{(1)} &= -\tfrac{19}{720}h^5 y^v(\xi_2) \tag{6.57b} \end{aligned}$$

In general, $\xi_1 \neq \xi_2$. However, if we assume that over the interval of interest $y^v(x)$ is approximately constant, then on subtracting (6.57b) from (6.57a), we obtain the following estimate for y^v:

$$h^5 y^v = \tfrac{720}{270}(y_{n+1}^{(1)} - y_{n+1}^{(0)})$$

Substituting this into (6.57b), we find that

$$\begin{aligned} y(x_{n+1}) - y_{n+1}^{(1)} &= -\tfrac{19}{270}(y_{n+1}^{(0)} - y_{n+1}^{(0)}) \\ &\approx -\tfrac{1}{14}(y_{n+1}^{(1)} - y_{n+1}^{(0)}) = D_{n+1} \end{aligned} \tag{6.58}$$

Thus the error of the corrected value is approximately $-\tfrac{1}{14}$ of the difference between the corrected and predicted values.

As mentioned before, it is advisable to use the corrector only once. If the accuracy as determined by (6.58) is not sufficient, it is better to reduce the step size than to correct more than once.

In a general-purpose routine for solving differential equations, the error estimate is used in the following manner: let us assume that we wish to keep the local error bounded so that

$$E_1 \leq |D_{n+1}| \leq E_2$$

and that starting values have been provided. We proceed as follows:

1. Use (6.42) to obtain $y_{n+1}^{(0)}$. Compute $f_{n+1}^{(0)}$.
2. Use (6.54) to obtain $y_{n+1}^{(1)}$. Compute $f_{n+1}^{(1)}$.

3. Compute $|D_{n+1}|$ from (6.58).
4. If $E_1 \leq |D_{n+1}| \leq E_2$, proceed to the next integration step, using the same value of h.
5. If $|D_{n+1}| > E_2$, the step size h is too large and should be reduced. It is customary to replace h by $h/2$, recompute four starting values, and then return to step 1.
6. If $|D_{n+1}| < E_1$, more accuracy is being obtained than is necessary. Hence we can save computer time by replacing h by $2h$, recomputing four new starting values at intervals of length $2h$, and returning to step 1.

In using predictor-corrector methods with variable step size as outlined above, it is necessary to (a) have a method for obtaining the necessary starting values initially; (b) have a method for obtaining the necessary values of y at half steps when the interval is halved; and (c) have a method for obtaining the necessary values of y when the interval is doubled. Special formulas can be worked out for each of these three situations. These formulas add considerably to the complexity of a program. However, a fairly ideal combination is to use the fourth-order Runge-Kutta method (6.37), together with a fourth-order predictor-corrector pair such as (6.42) and (6.54). The Runge-Kutta method can then be used for starting the solution initially, for halving, and for doubling, while the predictor-corrector pair can be used for normal continuation when the step size is kept fixed.

Before leaving this section, it should be pointed out that there are many other predictor-corrector formulas, and in particular that the following formulas due to Milne are often used:

$$y_{n+1}^{(0)} = y_{n-3} + \frac{4h}{3}(2f_n - f_{n-1} + 2f_{n-2}) + \tfrac{28}{90}h^5 y^v(\xi_1) \qquad (6.59a)$$

$$y_{n+1}^{(1)} = y_{n-1} + \frac{h}{3}(f_{n+1}^{(0)} + 4f_n + f_{n-1}) - \tfrac{1}{90}h^5 y^v(\xi_2) \qquad (6.59b)$$

Equation (6.59a) was derived in Sec. 6.6, and (6.59b) is based on Simpson's rule for numerical integration. Proceeding as in the Adams-Moulton formulas, we can show that a local-error estimate is provided by

$$D_{n+1} = -\tfrac{1}{29}(y_{n+1}^{(1)} - y_{n+1}^{(0)}) \qquad (6.60)$$

The error estimate for the Milne method appears to be somewhat more favorable than for the Adams-Moulton method, but as we shall see, (6.59b) is subject to numerical instability in some cases.

While the literature is abundant with methods for integrating differential equations, the most popular in the United States are the fourth-order Runge-Kutta method and predictor-corrector methods such as those of

Adams-Moulton or Milne (6.59). Although no one method will perform uniformly better than another method on all problems, it is appropriate to point out the advantages and disadvantages of each of these types for general-purpose work.

Runge-Kutta methods have the important advantage that they are self-starting. In addition, they are stable, provide good accuracy, and, as a computer program, occupy a relatively small amount of core storage. However, they provide no estimate of the accuracy being achieved, so that the user has no way of knowing whether the step h being used is adequate. One can, of course, run the same problem with several values of h and estimate the accuracy by comparing the results, but this is expensive in machine time. The second major disadvantage of the fourth-order Runge-Kutta method is that it requires four function evaluations per integration step, compared with only two using the fourth-order predictor-corrector methods. On some problems Runge-Kutta methods will require almost twice as much computing time.

Predictor-corrector methods provide an automatic error estimate at each step, thus allowing the program to select an optimum value of h for a required accuracy. They are also fast since they require only two function evaluations per step. On the other hand, predictor-corrector subroutines are very complicated to write, they require special techniques for starting and for doubling and halving the step size, and they may be subject to numerical instability (see Sec. 6.10).

For many years Runge-Kutta methods were used almost exclusively in the United States for general-purpose work, but recently predictor-corrector methods have been gaining in popularity.

Example 6.7 Solve the problem of Example 6.5 with $h = \frac{1}{32}$, using the Adams-Moulton predictor-corrector formulas. Compare the results with those of Example 6.5.

The program and the machine results are given below. In this case we list x_n, y_n (corrected value); the local-error estimate D_n; and the actual error e_n. On comparing these results with those of Example 6.5, we notice a decided improvement in accuracy, particularly as x approaches 1, where the results are correct to seven or eight significant figures. The local-error estimate D_n appears to be relatively constant and in general somewhat smaller than the actual error e_n. On closer examination, however, we find that in steps 5 to 13 the results are correct to only six significant figures. The explanation for this is that the values of y_n for these steps are an order of magnitude smaller than they are as $x \to 1$. Since D_n is an absolute error test, it does not indicate the number of significant digits of accuracy in the result. This is a typical situation when working in floating-point arithmetic. When working with numbers which are either very large or very small compared with 1, a better indicator of the number of significant digits of accuracy is provided by a relative test than by an absolute test. A relative error test for the Adams-Moulton formula, for instance, would be

$$\bar{D}_{n+1} = \frac{1}{14} \frac{|y_{n+1}^{(0)} - y_{n+1}^{(1)}|}{|y_{n+1}^{(1)}|}$$

in place of (6.58).

FORTRAN PROGRAM FOR EXAMPLE 6.7

```
C       ADAMS-MOULTON METHOD
        DIMENSION F(4)
C
        SOLN(X) = EXP(X) - 1.0 - X
C
C       ** INITIALIZE
        WRITE (6,500)
        N = 4
        H = 1./32.
        NSTEP = 32
        Y0 = 0.0
        X0 = 0.0
        DN = 0.0
        EN = 0.0
        NZ = 0
C
C       ** COMPUTE FIRST FOUR POINTS USING EXACT SOLUTION
        F(1) = X0 + Y0
        WRITE (6,510) NZ,X0,Y0,DN,EN
        XN = X0
        DO 20 I = 2,4
        K = I - 1
        XN = XN + H
        YN = SOLN(XN)
        F(I) = XN + YN
        WRITE (6,510) K,XN,YN,DN,EN
     20 CONTINUE
C
C       ** BEGIN ITERATION
        DO 50 K = 4,NSTEP
C       ** PREDICT USING ADAMS-BASHFORTH FORMULA
        YNP = YN + (H/24.)*(55.*F(N) - 59.*F(N - 1) + 37.*F(N - 2) -
       X9.*F(N - 3))
        XN = XN + H
        FNP = XN + YNP
C       ** CORRECT USING ADAMS-MOULTON FORMULA
        YN = YN + (H/24.)*(9.*FNP + 19.*F(N) - 5.*F(N - 1) + F(N - 2))
        DN = (YN - YNP)/14.
        F(N - 3) = F(N - 2)
        F(N - 2) = F(N - 1)
        F(N - 1) = F(N)
        F(N) = XN + YN
        YXN = SOLN(XN)
        EN = YN - YXN
        WRITE (6,510) K,XN,YN,DN,EN
     50 CONTINUE
        STOP
    500 FORMAT (21H1ADAMS - MOULTON METHOD/
       XH04X1HN6X2HXN18X2HYN23X2HDN16X15HEN = YN - Y(XN))
    510 FORMAT (1H 2XI3,4X 4(E16.8,4X))
        END
```

COMPUTER RESULTS FOR EXAMPLE 6.7

N	XN	YN	DN	EN = YN − Y(XN)
0	0.	0.	0.	0.
1	0.31250000E-01	0.49340725E-03	0.	0.
2	0.62500000E-01	0.19944459E-02	0.	0.
3	0.93750000E-01	0.45351386E-02	0.	0.
4	0.12500000E-00	0.81484520E-02	0.78164571E-09	0.53551048E-08
5	0.15625000E-00	0.12868445E-01	0.90637643E-09	0.11408702E-07
6	0.18750000E-00	0.18730249E-01	0.88143028E-09	0.11175871E-07
7	0.21875000E-00	0.25770108E-01	0.91469178E-09	0.10011718E-07
8	0.25000000E-00	0.34025417E-01	0.93132257E-09	0.13969839E-08
9	0.28125000E-00	0.43534759E-01	0.96458407E-09	0.37252903E-08
10	0.31250000E-00	0.54337942E-01	0.99784564E-09	0.83819032E-08
11	0.34375000E-00	0.66476036E-01	0.99784564E-09	0.37252903E-08
12	0.37500000E-00	0.79991416E-01	0.10643686E-08	0.15832484E-07
13	0.40625000E-00	0.94927801E-01	0.11308917E-08	0.13969839E-07
14	0.43750000E-00	0.11133030E-00	0.11308917E-08	0.14901161E-07
15	0.46875000E-00	0.12924545E-00	0.10643686E-08	0.55879354E-08
16	0.50000000E 00	0.14872127E-00	0.11974147E-08	0.74505806E-08
17	0.53125000E 00	0.16980730E-00	0.13304609E-08	0.18626451E-08
18	0.56250000E 00	0.19255465E-00	0.13304609E-08	0.37252903E-08
19	0.59375000E 00	0.21701607E-00	0.13304609E-08	0.
20	0.62500000E 00	0.24324595E-00	0.13304609E-08	0.11175871E-07
21	0.65625000E 00	0.27130044E-00	0.13304609E-08	0.11175871E-07
22	0.68750000E 00	0.30123746E-00	0.13304609E-08	0.
23	0.71875000E 00	0.33311676E-00	0.13304609E-08	−0.37252903E-08
24	0.75000000E 00	0.36700001E-00	0.15965530E-08	−0.74505806E-08
25	0.78125000E 00	0.40295079E-00	0.15965530E-08	0.37252903E-08
26	0.81250000E 00	0.44103477E-00	0.15965530E-08	0.74505806E-08
27	0.84375000E 00	0.48131964E-00	0.18626451E-08	0.74505806E-08
28	0.87500000E 00	0.52387527E 00	0.15965530E-08	0.74505806E-08
29	0.90625000E 00	0.56877375E 00	0.21287372E-08	0.
30	0.93750000E 00	0.61608943E 00	0.21287372E-08	0.
31	0.96875000E 00	0.66589906E 00	0.21287372E-08	−0.74505806E-08
32	0.09999999E 01	0.71828180E 00	0.21287372E-08	−0.74505806E-08

EXERCISES

6.8-1. Show that the iteration defined by

$$y_{n+1}^{(k)} = y_n + \frac{h}{24} [9f(x_{n+1}, y_{n+1}^{(k-1)}) + 19f_n - 5f_{n-1} + f_{n-2}] \qquad \begin{array}{l} k = 1, 2, \ldots \\ x_n \text{ fixed} \end{array}$$

will converge, provided that $|(9h/24)(\partial f/\partial y)| < 1$ (see Sec. 6.7).

6.8-2. Derive the error (6.55) for the Adams-Moulton method, using (6.52) and (6.53).

6.8-3. Derive the local-error estimate (6.60) for the Milne predictor-corrector formulas (6.59).

6.8-4. Solve the equation $y' = y + x^2$, $y(0) = 1$, from $x = 0$ to $x = 2$ with $h = 0.1$, using the Adams-Moulton predictor-corrector formulas. The starting values correct to six decimal places are

$$y(0) = 1.000000$$
$$y(0.1) = 1.105513$$
$$y(0.2) = 1.224208$$
$$y(0.3) = 1.359576$$

Compute D_{n+1}, and estimate the error at $x = 2$.

6.9 STABILITY OF NUMERICAL METHODS

When computers first became widely used for solving differential equations, it was observed that some of the commonly used integration formulas, such as Milne's formulas (6.59), led to errors in the solution much larger than would be expected from the discretization error alone. Moreover, as the step size was made smaller, these errors for a fixed value of x actually became larger rather than smaller. To illustrate this behavior, let us consider the method derived in Sec. 6.6,

$$y_{n+1} = y_{n-1} + 2hf_n \tag{6.61}$$

for which the discretization error is $\frac{1}{6}h^3 y'''(\xi)$. We would expect this method to give more accurate results for h fixed than Euler's method, whose error is $O(h^2)$. Consider, however, the following simple problem,

$$y' = -2y + 1 \qquad y(0) = 1 \tag{6.62}$$

whose exact solution is $y = \frac{1}{2}e^{-2x} + \frac{1}{2}$.

The results given in Table 6.1 were obtained by the computer, using a step size of $h = \frac{1}{32}$. The first column gives selected values of x at which the solution is printed, Y(N) denotes the exact solution, Y1(N) denotes the solution obtained by Euler's method, Y2(N) the solution obtained by (6.61), and E1(N), E2(N) their respective errors. Method (6.61) requires two starting values y_0 and y_1. For y_1 we take the exact value as computed from the exact solution.

The error columns show that E2(N) is considerably smaller than E1(N) for the first few steps but grows rapidly, so that at $x = 2.25$, E2(N) is greater than E1(N). As $x \to 4$, the solution approaches the steady-state value $y = \frac{1}{2}$. Euler's method actually approaches this steady-state solution with monotonically decreasing error, whereas for method (6.61) the error is growing exponentially. Moreover, as the last few steps (where the results are printed at every integration step) show, the errors E2(N) oscillate in sign. Beyond $x = 4$, Y2(N) would have no significant digits of accuracy. The phenomenon exhibited in this example is known as *numerical instability*.

Table 6.I

X(N)	Y(N)	Y1(N)	Y2(N)	E1(N)	E2(N)
0.	1.0000000	1.0000000	1.0000000	0.	0.
0.0312500	0.9697065	0.9687500	0.9697065	−0.0009565	−0.0000000
0.5000000	0.6839397	0.6780370	0.6840817	−0.0059027	0.0001420
1.0000000	0.5676676	0.5633943	0.5678247	−0.0042733	0.0001571
1.5000000	0.5248935	0.5225730	0.5251328	−0.0023205	0.0002392
2.0000000	0.5091578	0.5080376	0.5097007	−0.0011202	0.0005429
2.2500000	0.5055545	0.5047962	0.5064264	−0.0007583	0.0008719
2.5000000	0.5033690	0.5028620	0.5047904	−0.0005070	0.0014214
3.0000000	0.5012394	0.5010190	0.5050759	−0.0002203	0.0038365
3.5000000	0.5004559	0.5003628	0.5108669	−0.0000931	0.0104110
3.7500000	0.5002765	0.5002165	0.5174337	−0.0000601	0.0171571
3.7812500	0.5002598	0.5002029	0.4819995	−0.0000568	−0.0182603
3.8125000	0.5002440	0.5001903	0.5196837	−0.0000538	0.0194397
3.8437500	0.5002293	0.5001784	0.4795391	−0.0000509	−0.0206902
3.8750000	0.5002154	0.5001672	0.5222413	−0.0000482	0.0220260
3.9062500	0.5002023	0.5001568	0.4767589	−0.0000456	−0.0234434
3.9375000	0.5001901	0.5001470	0.5251465	−0.0000431	0.0249564
3.9687500	0.5001785	0.5001378	0.4736156	−0.0000408	−0.0265630
4.0000000	0.5001677	0.5001292	0.5284445	−0.0000386	0.0282768

To help us understand this behavior, let us examine the difference equation (6.61) more closely. For the example being considered, $f_n = -2y_n + 1$, and hence (6.61) becomes

$$y_{n+1} + 4hy_n - y_{n-1} = 2h \qquad y_0 = 1 \tag{6.63}$$

We can solve this difference equation explicitly, using the methods of Sec. 6.2. The general solution of (6.63) is

$$y_n = C_1 \beta_1{}^n + C_2 \beta_2{}^n + \tfrac{1}{2} \tag{6.64}$$

where β_1, β_2 are the roots of the characteristic equation

$$\beta^2 + 4h\beta - 1 = 0$$

These roots are

$$\beta_{1,2} = -2h \pm \sqrt{1 + 4h^2}$$

If we expand $\sqrt{1 + 4h^2}$ in a Taylor's series through linear terms, these roots can be expressed in the form

$$\beta_1 = 1 - 2h + O(h^2)$$
$$\beta_2 = -(1 + 2h) + O(h^2)$$

Substituting into (6.64), we have

$$y_n = C_1(1 - 2h + O(h^2))^n + C_2(-1)^n(1 + 2h + O(h^2))^n + \tfrac{1}{2} \quad (6.65)$$

In the calculus it is shown that

$$\lim_{\epsilon \to 0} (1 + \epsilon)^{1/\epsilon} = e$$

Using this limit and the fact that $n = x_n/h$, it follows for x_n fixed that

$$\lim_{h \to 0} (1 + 2h)^n = \lim_{h \to 0} (1 + 2h)^{(1/2h)(2x_n)} = e^{2x_n}$$

and similarly that

$$\lim_{h \to 0} (1 - 2h)^n = e^{-2x_n}$$

Hence, as $h \to 0$, the solution (6.65) approaches

$$y_n = (C_1 e^{-2x_n} + \tfrac{1}{2}) + C_2(-1)^n e^{2x_n} \quad (6.66)$$

Thus the first term tends to the true solution of the differential equation. The second term is extraneous and arises only because we have replaced a first-order differential equation by a second-order difference equation. Imposing the initial conditions will, if all arithmetic operations are exact, result in choosing $C_2 = 0$ so that the correct solution will be selected from (6.66). In practice, however, some errors will be introduced, primarily due to round-off or to inexact starting values, and hence C_2 will not be exactly zero. A small error will therefore be introduced at each step of the integration, and this error will subsequently be magnified because it is being multiplied by the exponentially increasing factor $(-1)^n e^{2x_n}$. Because the major part of the true solution is exponentially decreasing, the error introduced from the extraneous solution will eventually dominate the true solution and lead to completely incorrect results.

Loosely speaking, we can say that a method is unstable if errors introduced into the calculations grow at an exponential rate as the computation proceeds.

One-step methods like those of the Runge-Kutta type do not exhibit any numerical instability for h sufficiently small. Multistep methods may, in some cases, be unstable for all values of h, and in other cases for a range of values of h. To determine whether a given multistep method is stable, we can proceed as follows: If the multistep method leads to a difference equation of order k, find the roots of the characteristic equation corresponding to the homogeneous difference equation. Call these β_i $(i = 1, \ldots, k)$. The general solution of the homogeneous difference equation is then

$$y_n = c_1\beta_1{}^n + c_2\beta_2{}^n + \cdots + c_k\beta_k{}^n \quad (6.67)$$

One of these solutions, say $\beta_1{}^n$, will tend to the exact solution of the differential equation as $h \to 0$. All the other solutions are extraneous. A multistep method is defined to be *strongly stable* if the extraneous roots satisfy as $h \to 0$ the condition

$$|\beta_i| < 1 \qquad i = 2, 3, \ldots, k$$

Under these conditions any errors introduced into the computation will decay as n increases, whereas if any of the extraneous β_i are greater than one in magnitude, the errors will grow exponentially.

For the general differential equation $y' = f(x,y)$, it will be impossible to obtain the roots β_i of the characteristic equation. A consideration of the special equation $y' = Ay$, A constant, is usually sufficient, however, to give an indication of the stability of a method.

For the Adams-Moulton method (6.54), for example, if we set

$$f(x,y) = Ay$$

and rearrange, we obtain the following difference equation of order 3:

$$\left(1 - \frac{9hA}{24}\right)y_{n+1} - \left(1 + \frac{19Ah}{24}\right)y_n + \frac{5Ah}{24}y_{n-1} - \frac{Ah}{24}y_{n-2} = 0 \quad (6.68)$$

The characteristic equation for this difference equation is

$$(1 - 9\gamma)\beta^3 - (1 + 19\gamma)\beta^2 + 5\gamma\beta - \gamma = 0$$

where $\gamma = Ah/24$. The roots of this equation are, of course, functions of h. However, as $h \to 0$, we note that this equation reduces to

$$\beta^3 - \beta^2 = 0$$

whose roots are $\beta_1 = 1$, $\beta_2 = \beta_3 = 0$.

For h small it can be shown that $\beta_1{}^n$ approximates the desired solution of the differential equation while $\beta_2{}^n$ and $\beta_3{}^n$ represent extraneous solutions whose magnitudes are less than one. It follows, therefore, that the Adams-Moulton method is strongly stable for h sufficiently small.

For Milne's method (6.59b) we have

$$y_{n+1} = y_{n-1} + \frac{h}{3}\left(y'_{n+1} + 4y'_n + y'_{n-1}\right)$$

If we set $y' = Ay$ and rearrange, we obtain the difference equation

$$(1 - \gamma)y_{n+1} - 4\gamma y_n - (1 + \gamma)y_{n-1} = 0 \tag{6.69}$$

where $\gamma = Ah/3$. The characteristic equation now is

$$(1 - \gamma)\beta^2 - 4\gamma\beta - (1 + \gamma) = 0 \tag{6.70}$$

If we set $h = 0$, the characteristic equation becomes $\beta^2 - 1 = 0$. Its roots, $\beta_1 = 1, \beta_2 = -1$, are both of magnitude one. Making use of the quadratic formula and by Taylor's series, the roots of (6.70) for small h are of the form

$$\begin{aligned} \beta_1 &= 1 + Ah + O(h^2) \\ \beta_2 &= -(1 - Ah/3) + O(h^2) \end{aligned} \qquad (6.71)$$

Hence the general solution of (6.69) is

$$y_n = C_1(1 + Ah + O(h^2))^n + C_2(-1)^n(1 - Ah/3 + O(h^2))^n$$

Since $n = x_n/h$, then as $h \to 0$, this solution approaches

$$y_n = C_1 e^{Ax_n} + C_2(-1)^n e^{-Ax_n/3} \qquad (6.72)$$

In this case the question of stability rests upon the sign of A. If $A > 0$, so that the desired solution is exponentially increasing, it is clear the extraneous solution will be exponentially decreasing. Milne's method in this case will be stable. On the other hand, if $A < 0$, the extraneous solution is exponentially increasing and the method will be unstable. Methods of this type, whose stability depends upon the sign of A, are sometimes called weakly unstable. For the more general equation $y' = f(x,y)$ we can expect weak instability from Milne's method whenever $\partial f/\partial y < 0$ on the interval of integration. Several schemes have been proposed for eliminating the instability in Milne's method [16].

Almost all predictor-corrector methods, as they are commonly used in practice, are subject to instability for some range of values of the step size h.

EXERCISES

6.9-1. Show that the corrector formula based on the trapezoidal rule (6.47) is stable for equations of the form $y' = Ay$ (see Exercise 6.7-1).

6.9-2. Show that the roots of the characteristic equation (6.70) can be expressed in the form (6.71) as $h \to 0$, and that the solution of the difference equation (6.69) approaches (6.72) as $h \to 0$.

6.9-3. Write a computer program to find the roots of the characteristic equation (6.68) for the Adams-Moulton formula. Take $A = -1$ and $h = 0(0.1)\bar{h}$. Determine an approximate value of $\bar{h}$ beyond which one or more roots of this equation will be greater than one in magnitude. Thus establish an upper bound on h, beyond which the Adams-Moulton method will be unstable.

6.9-4. Solve Eq. (6.62) by Milne's method (6.59) from $x = 0$ to $x = 6$ with $h = \frac{1}{4}$. Take the starting values from Table 6.1. Note the effect of instability on the solution.

6.10 ROUND-OFF-ERROR PROPAGATION

In Sec. 6.4 we defined the discretization error e_n as

$$e_n = y(x_n) - y_n$$

where $y(x_n)$ is the true solution of the differential equation, and y_n is the exact solution of the difference equation which approximates the differential equation. In practice, because computers deal with finite word lengths, we will obtain a value $\tilde{y}_n$ which will differ from y_n because of round-off errors. We shall denote by

$$r_n = y_n - \tilde{y}_n$$

the *accumulated round-off error*, i.e., the difference between the exact solution of the difference equation and the value produced by the computer at $x = x_n$. At each step of an integration, a round-off error will be produced which we call the *local round-off error* and which we denote by ϵ_n. In Euler's method, for example, ϵ_n is defined by

$$\tilde{y}_{n+1} = \tilde{y}_n + hf(x_n, \tilde{y}_n) + \epsilon_n$$

The accumulated round-off error is not simply the sum of the local round-off errors, because each local error is propagated and may either grow or decay as the computation proceeds. In general, the subject of round-off-error propagation is poorly understood, and very few theoretical results are available. The accumulated round-off depends upon many factors, including (1) the kind of arithmetic used in the computer, i.e., fixed point or floating point; (2) the way in which the machine rounds; (3) the order in which the arithmetic operations are performed; (4) the numerical procedure being used.

As shown in Sec. 6.9, where numerical instability was considered, the effect of round-off propagation can be disastrous. Even with stable methods, however, there will be some inevitable loss of accuracy due to rounding errors. This was illustrated in Chap. 5, where the trapezoidal rule was used to evaluate an integral. Over an extended interval the loss of accuracy may be so serious as to invalidate the results completely.

It is possible to obtain estimates of the accumulated rounding error by making some statistical assumptions about the distribution of local round-off errors. These possibilities will not be pursued here. We wish to consider here a simple but effective procedure for reducing the loss of accuracy due to round-off errors when solving differential equations.

Most of the formulas discussed in this chapter for solving differential equations can be written in the form

$$y_{n+1} = y_n + h\,\Delta y_n$$

where $h\,\Delta y_n$ represents an increment involving combinations of $f(x,y)$ at selected points. The increment is usually small compared with y_n itself. In forming the sum $y_n + h\,\Delta y_n$ in floating-point arithmetic, the IBM 7090 computer will therefore shift $h\,\Delta y_n$ to the right until the exponent of $h\,\Delta y_n$ agrees with that of y_n, dropping bits at the right end as it does so. The addition is then performed, but because of the bits which were dropped, there will be a rounding error. To see this more clearly, let us attempt to add the two floating-point numbers $(0.5472)(10^4)$ and $(0.3856)(10^2)$, assuming a word length of four decimal places. If we shift the second number two places to the right, drop the last two digits, and add to the first number, we will obtain $(0.5510)(10^4)$, whereas with proper rounding the result should be $(0.5511)(10^4)$. This is, of course, an exaggerated example, since the computer will be working with binary bits and longer word lengths, but even then the cumulative effects can be serious.

We shall now describe a simple procedure which will significantly reduce errors of this type. First, each computed value of y_n is stored in double-precision form; next $h \Delta y_n$ is computed in single precision, and only the single-precision part of any value of y_n needed in forming $h \Delta y_n$ is used; the sum $y_n + h \Delta y_n$ is formed in *double precision*; and $y_{n+1} = y_n + h \Delta y_n$ is stored in double precision. This procedure may be called *partial double-precision accumulation*. On some computers double-precision arithmetic is available as an instruction, but even when it is not, only one double-precision sum must be formed per integration step. The major part of the computation is determining $h \Delta y_n$, and this is performed in single precision. The extra amount of work as well as the extra storage is quite minor. On the other hand, the possible gain in accuracy can be very significant, especially when great accuracy over an extended interval is required. Indeed, this procedure is so effective in reducing round-off-error accumulation that no general-purpose library routine for solving differential equations should ever be written which does not provide for some form of partial double-precision accumulation.

A final word of caution is apropos at this point. The accuracy of a numerical integration will depend upon the discretization error and the accumulated rounding error. To keep the discretization error small, we will normally choose the step size h small. On the other hand, the smaller h is taken, the more integration steps we shall have to perform, and the greater the rounding error is likely to be. There is, therefore, an optimum value of the step size h which for a given machine and a given problem will result in the best accuracy. This optimum is in practice very difficult to find without the use of extensive amounts of computer time. The existence of such an optimum does show, however, that there is some danger in taking too small a step size.

A realistic practical example illustrating round-off-error accumulation is presented in Sec. 6.11.

Example 6.8 Solve the equation

$$y' = \frac{1}{x^2} - \frac{y}{x} - y^2 \qquad y(1) = -1$$

from $x = 1$ to $x = 3$, using the Adams-Bashforth method, with and without partial double-precision accumulation, for $h = \frac{1}{256}$.

The machine results are given below. The step size is purposely chosen small enough so that the discretization error is negligible. The results are printed every 16 steps. The exact solution of this problem is $y = -1/x$. The accuracy can therefore be easily checked. At $x = 3$ the partial double-precision results are correct to three units in the eighth decimal place; the single-precision results are correct to 253 units in the eighth decimal place. Since all this error is due to round-off, this example clearly demonstrates the effectiveness of partial double precision in reducing round-off-error accumulation.

COMPUTER RESULTS FOR EXAMPLE 6.8

X	SINGLE PRECISION	PARTIAL DOUBLE PRECISION
0.99999999	−0.99999999	−0.99999999
1.06250000	−0.94117642	−0.94117647
1.12500000	−0.88888878	−0.88888889
1.18750000	−0.84210509	−0.84210526
1.24999990	−0.79999977	−0.80000000
1.31249990	−0.76190444	−0.76190476
1.37500000	−0.72727232	−0.72727273
1.43750000	−0.69565168	−0.69565218
1.50000000	−0.66666608	−0.66666667
1.56249990	−0.63999934	−0.64000001
1.62499990	−0.61538386	−0.61538462
1.68750000	−0.59259175	−0.59259260
1.75000000	−0.57142763	−0.57142858
1.81250000	−0.55172310	−0.55172415
1.87499990	−0.53333220	−0.53333335
1.93749990	−0.51612781	−0.51612905
2.00000000	−0.49999869	−0.50000001
2.06250000	−0.48484711	−0.48484850
2.12500000	−0.47058678	−0.47058825
2.18749990	−0.45714134	−0.45714287
2.24999990	−0.44444284	−0.44444446
2.31250000	−0.43243076	−0.43243245
2.37500000	−0.42105088	−0.42105265
2.43750000	−0.41025458	−0.41024643
2.49999990	−0.39999810	−0.40000002
2.56249990	−0.39024193	−0.39024393
2.62500000	−0.38095033	−0.38095240
2.68750000	−0.37209089	−0.37209304
2.75000000	−0.36363416	−0.36363639
2.81249990	−0.35555328	−0.35555558
2.87499990	−0.34782372	−0.34782612
2.92750000	−0.34042308	−0.34042556
3.00000000	−0.33333080	−0.33333336

6.11 SYSTEMS OF DIFFERENTIAL EQUATIONS

Most general-purpose differential-equation subroutines assume that a pth-order differential has been expressed as a system of p first-order equations. For a pth-order equation given in the form

$$y^{(p)} = f(x,y,y',y'', \ldots ,y^{(p-1)}) \tag{6.73}$$

this reduction can always be accomplished as follows: With $y_1 = y$, we set

$$
\begin{aligned}
y_1' &= y_2 \\
y_2' &= y_3 \\
y_3' &= y_4 \\
&\cdot\ \cdot\ \cdot\ \cdot \\
y_{p-1}' &= y_p \\
y_p' &= f(x,y_1,y_2, \ldots ,y_p)
\end{aligned} \tag{6.74}
$$

The system (6.74) is equivalent to (6.73). Not every system of equations will be expressible in the simple form of (6.74). More generally, a system of p first-order equations will have the form

$$
\begin{aligned}
y_1' &= f_1(x,y_1,y_2, \ldots ,y_p) \\
y_2' &= f_2(x,y_1,y_2, \ldots ,y_p) \\
&\cdot\ \cdot\ \cdot\ \cdot\ \cdot\ \cdot\ \cdot\ \cdot\ \cdot\ \cdot\ \cdot\ \cdot \\
y_p' &= f_p(x,y_1,y_2, \ldots ,y_p)
\end{aligned} \tag{6.75}
$$

All the numerical methods considered in this chapter can be adapted to the system (6.75). The system (6.75) can be expressed more compactly in vector form,

$$\mathbf{y}' = \mathbf{f}(x,\mathbf{y})$$

where $\mathbf{y}'$, $\mathbf{f}$, and $\mathbf{y}$ are vectors with p components.

We illustrate the procedure for the Runge-Kutta method for two equations, which we write in the form

$$
\begin{aligned}
y' &= f(x,y,z) \\
z' &= g(x,y,z)
\end{aligned} \tag{6.76}
$$

The improvement formulas corresponding to (6.37) will now be

$$
\begin{aligned}
y_{n+1} &= y_n + \tfrac{1}{6}(k_1 + 2k_2 + 2k_3 + k_4) \\
z_{n+1} &= z_n + \tfrac{1}{6}(l_1 + 2l_2 + 2l_3 + l_4)
\end{aligned} \tag{6.77}
$$

where

$$
\begin{aligned}
k_1 &= hf(x_n,y_n,z_n) \\
l_1 &= hg(x_n,y_n,z_n) \\
k_2 &= hf\left(x_n + \frac{h}{2},\, y_n + \frac{k_1}{2},\, z_n + \frac{l_1}{2}\right)
\end{aligned}
$$

$$l_2 = hg\left(x_n + \frac{h}{2}, y_n + \frac{k_1}{2}, z_n + \frac{l_1}{2}\right)$$

$$k_3 = hf\left(x_n + \frac{h}{2}, y_n + \frac{k_2}{2}, z_n + \frac{l_2}{2}\right)$$

$$l_3 = hg\left(x_n + \frac{h}{2}, y_n + \frac{k_2}{2}, z_n + \frac{l_2}{2}\right)$$

$$k_4 = hf(x_n + h, y_n + k_3, z_n + l_3)$$
$$l_4 = hg(x_n + h, y_n + k_3, z_n + l_3)$$

Extension to a system of equations is obvious. Note that all the increments with lower subscript must be computed before proceeding to those of next higher subscript.

The Adams-Moulton formulas adapted to the pair of equations (6.76) proceed as follows:

$$y_{n+1}^{(0)} = y_n + \frac{h}{24} [55f(x_n,y_n,z_n) - 59f(x_{n-1},y_{n-1},z_{n-1})$$

$$+ 37f(x_{n-2},y_{n-2},z_{n-2}) - 9f(x_{n-3},y_{n-3},z_{n-3})]$$

$$z_{n+1}^{(0)} = z_n + \frac{h}{24} [55g(x_n,y_n,z_n) - 59g(x_{n-1},y_{n-1},z_{n-1})$$

$$+ 37g(x_{n-2},y_{n-2},z_{n-2}) - 9g(x_{n-3},y_{n-3},z_{n-3})] \quad (6.78)$$

$$y_{n+1}^{(1)} = y_n + \frac{h}{24} [9f(x_{n+1},y_{n+1}^{(0)},z_{n+1}^{(0)}) + 19f(x_n,y_n,z_n)$$

$$- 5f(x_{n-1},y_{n-1},z_{n-1}) + f(x_{n-2},y_{n-2},z_{n-2})]$$

$$z_{n+1}^{(1)} = z_n + \frac{h}{24} [9g(x_{n+1},y_{n+1}^{(0)},z_{n+1}^{(0)}) + 19g(x_n,y_n,z_n)$$

$$- 5g(x_{n-1},y_{n-1},z_{n-1}) + g(x_{n-2},y_{n-2},z_{n-2})]$$

A flow chart of a general-purpose subroutine for solving a system of first-order differential equations is given. In this program the system is expressed in the form $\mathbf{y}' = \mathbf{f}(x,\mathbf{y})$, where $\mathbf{y}$ and $\mathbf{f}$ are to be interpreted as vectors with N components. The subroutine is called AMRK. It uses the Runge-Kutta method to compute the first four starting values (starting with box A and ending with box B) and the Adams-Moulton method to continue (starting with box C and ending with box B). No provision is made for changing the step size. The subroutine requires a block of N storage registers for y, a block of N registers for $y' = f(x,y)$, and seven additional blocks of N registers, each labeled $b_x, b_1, b_2, \ldots, b_6$, for past function and derivative values. Input to the subroutine consists of the initial point x_0, the step h, the final point x_s, the initial vector $\mathbf{y}_0$, and the vector of functions $\mathbf{y}' = \mathbf{f}(x,\mathbf{y})$.

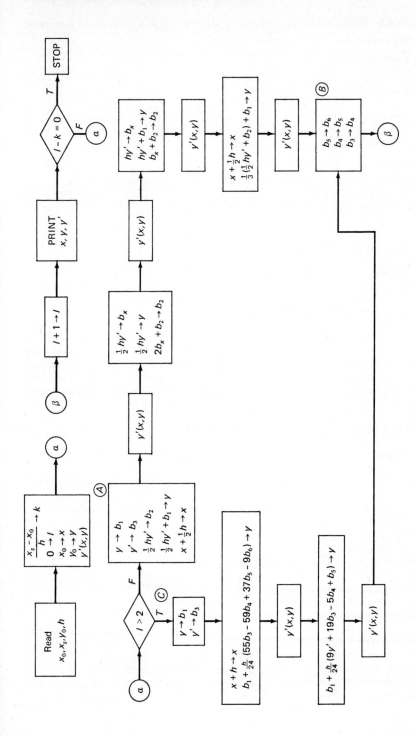

Example 6.9 The equations of motion of a body moving in a plane about a spherical earth are

$$\ddot{x} = -G\frac{x}{r^3}$$
$$\ddot{y} = -G\frac{y}{r^3}$$
(6.79)

where dots signify differentiation with respect to time t; x and y are rectangular planar coordinates of the body, $r = \sqrt{x^2 + y^2}$; and G is the gravitational constant. If we take $G = 1$ and prescribe the initial conditions

$$x(0) = 1 \quad\quad \dot{x}(0) = 0 \quad\quad y(0) = 0 \quad\quad \dot{y}(0) = 1$$
(6.80)

the trajectory of the motion described by (6.79) will be a circle with period 2π.

As a first step in solving this problem, we rewrite (6.79) as a system of first-order equations. Thus, with $x_1 = x$ and $y_1 = y$, (6.79) becomes

$$\dot{x}_1 = x_2$$
$$\dot{x}_2 = -G\frac{x_1}{r^3}$$
$$\dot{y}_1 = y_2$$
$$\dot{y}_2 = -G\frac{y_1}{r^3}$$
$$r = \sqrt{x_1{}^2 + y_1{}^2}$$
(6.79a)

We shall solve this problem twice, once with a standard subroutine AMRK which incorporates partial double precision as explained in Sec. 6.10, and again with the subroutine SAMRK in which no partial double precision is used. Both routines use the Runge-Kutta method to obtain the first four starting values and then the Adams-Moulton method to continue. The CALL statement for AMRK and SAMRK has the form

CALL AMRKS (VAR,DER,DAUX,N,TEMPS)

where the parameters have the following meanings:

VAR: VAR(1) = time t; VAR(2) = x_1; VAR(3) = y_1; VAR(4) = $x_2 = \dot{x}$; VAR(5) = $y_2 = \dot{y}$.
DER: DER(1) = the step size h (fixed); DER(2) = $\dot{x}_1$; DER(3) = $\dot{y}_1$; DER(4) = $\dot{x}_2$; DER(5) = $\dot{y}_2$.
DAUX: The subroutine package for the derivatives appearing in (6.79a). This is to be supplied by the programmer.
N: The number of equations (four in this case).
TEMPS: Location of $9N + 11$ cells of temporary storage available to AMRK and to be used to contain the less significant parts of t, y_1, y_2, y_3, y_4. In addition, a subroutine HSET is used to set up the limits of integration and the number of integration steps per revolution.

The program and results are given below. The integration was carried out with 200 steps per revolution, i.e., with a fixed step size $h = 2\pi/200 = 0.031415962$. For this step size the local discretization error is negligible to the number of places printed. Hence all the error is due to round-off. Below are given the time T at intervals of 10 steps, the single-precision value of $r = \sqrt{x^2 + y^2}$, and the partial double-precision results.

Since the trajectory is a circle of radius 1, the exact solution is $r = 1$ for all values of T.   At the end of 400 steps there is a loss due to round-off of three places of accuracy in the single-precision results, compared with a loss of one place in the double-precision results.   By extrapolating these results, it is clear that at the end of six revolutions the single-precision results would be completely in error.

FORTRAN PROGRAM FOR EXAMPLE 6.9

```
C       ** 2 BODY INTEGRATION
C       COMMON VAR(5),DER(5),TEMPS(50),G,R

        EXTERNAL DAUX

C       ** PRESET
        IFLAG ≡ 0
      5 IFLAG = IFLAG + 1
        GO TO (6,7),IFLAG
      6 WRITE (6,900)
        GO TO 8
      7 WRITE (6,905)
      8 NSTEP = 400
        STEPS = 200.
        PIX2 = 6.2831853
        G = 1.0
        RO = 1.0
        VC = 1.0
        PER = PIX2

C       ** INITIALIZE VARIABLES AND DERIVATIVES
        VAR(1) = 0.0
        VAR(2) = RO
        VAR(3) = 0.0
        VAR(4) = 0.0
        VAR(5) = VC
        DER(1) = PIX2/STEPS
        CALL DAUX
C       WRITE (6,910) VAR(1),R

C       ** SET UP PARAMETERS AND AMRK
        DO 20 I = 1,50
     20 TEMPS(I) = 0.0
        CALL HSET (PER,STEPS,DER(1),TEMPS(2))
        GO TO (31,32),IFLAG
     31 CALL AMRKS(VAR,DER,DAUX,4,TEMPS)
        GO TO 40
     32 CALL SAMRKS(VAR,DER,DAUX,4,TEMPS)
C
C       ** MAIN ITERATION
     40 DO 100 N = 1,NSTEP
        GO TO (51,52),IFLAG
```

```
      51 CALL AMRK
         GO TO 60
      52 CALL SAMRK
      60 IF (MOD(N,10)) 100,70,100
      70 WRITE (6,920) N,VAR(1),R
     100 CONTINUE
         WRITE (6,910) VAR(1),R
C
         GO TO (5,200),IFLAG
     200 STOP
     900 FORMAT (1H124  HPARTIAL DOUBLE PRECISION)
     905 FORMAT (1H1  16HSINGLE PRECISION)
     910 FORMAT (1H   2HT = E16.8,4X2HR = E16.8)
     920 FORMAT (1H   2HN = I3,4X2HT = E16.8,4X2HR = E16.8)
         END
C        ** DERIVATIVE PACKAGE FOR 2 BODY
         SUBROUTINE DAUX
         COMMON VAR(5),DER(5),TEMPS(50),G,R
C
         RSQ = VAR(2)**2 + VAR(3)**2
         R = SQRT(RSQ)
         R3 = RSQ*R
         DER(2) = VAR(4)
         DER(3) = VAR(5)
         DER(4) = -G*(VAR(2)/R3)
         DER(5) = -G*(VAR(3)/R3)
      50 RETURN
         END
```

COMPUTER RESULTS FOR EXAMPLE 6.9

N	T	R-SINGLE PRECISION	R-PARTIAL DOUBLE PRECISION
N = 0	0.	0.09999999E 01	0.09999999E-01
N = 10	0.31415926E-00	0.99999996E 00	0.99999999E-00
N = 20	0.62831853E 00	0.99999991E 00	0.99999999E 00
N = 30	0.94247766E 00	0.99999982E 00	0.99999999E 00
N = 40	0.12566370E 01	0.99999971E 00	0.99999999E 00
N = 50	0.15707963E 01	0.99999958E 00	0.99999999E 00
N = 60	0.18849555E 01	0.99999940E 00	0.99999999E 00
N = 70	0.21991148E 01	0.99999918E 00	0.99999999E 00
N = 80	0.25132740E 01	0.99999893E 00	0.99999999E 00
N = 90	0.28274333E 01	0.99999866E 00	0.99999999E 00
N = 100	0.31415926E 01	0.99999838E 00	0.09999999E 01
N = 110	0.34557518E 01	0.99999809E 00	0.09999999E 01
N = 120	0.37699112E 01	0.99999780E 00	0.10000000E 01
N = 130	0.40840704E 01	0.99999753E 00	0.10000000E 01
N = 140	0.43982296E 01	0.99999729E 00	0.10000000E 01
N = 150	0.47123889E 01	0.99999708E 00	0.10000000E 01
N = 160	0.50265481E 01	0.99999692E 00	0.10000000E 01

COMPUTER RESULTS FOR EXAMPLE 6.9 (*continued*)

N	T	R-SINGLE PRECISION	R-PARTIAL DOUBLE PRECISION
N = 170	0.53407075E 01	0.99999678E 00	0.10000001E 01
N = 180	0.56548667E 01	0.99999666E 00	0.10000001E 01
N = 190	0.59690259E 01	0.99999658E 00	0.10000001E 01
N = 200	0.62831852E 01	0.99999652E 00	0.10000001E 01
N = 210	0.65973444E 01	0.99999646E 00	0.10000001E 01
N = 220	0.69115037E 01	0.99999639E 00	0.10000001E 01
N = 230	0.72256630E 01	0.99999631E 00	0.10000001E 01
N = 240	0.75398223E 01	0.99999620E 00	0.10000001E 01
N = 250	0.78539816E 01	0.99999607E 00	0.10000001E 01
N = 260	0.81681408E 01	0.99999590E 00	0.10000001E 01
N = 270	0.84823000E 01	0.99999569E 00	0.10000001E 01
N = 280	0.87964592E 01	0.99999545E 00	0.10000001E 01
N = 290	0.91106185E 01	0.99999520E 00	0.10000001E 01
N = 300	0.94247778E 01	0.99999493E 00	0.10000001E 01
N = 310	0.97389371E 01	0.99999467E 00	0.10000001E 01
N = 320	0.10053096E 02	0.99999438E 00	0.10000001E 01
N = 330	0.10367256E 02	0.99999412E 00	0.10000002E 01
N = 340	0.10681415E 02	0.99999389E 00	0.10000002E 01
N = 350	0.10995574E 02	0.99999371E 00	0.10000002E 01
N = 360	0.11309733E 02	0.99999355E 00	0.10000002E 01
N = 370	0.11623893E 02	0.99999342E 00	0.10000002E 01
N = 380	0.11938052E 02	0.99999331E 00	0.10000002E 01
N = 390	0.12252211E 02	0.99999323E 00	0.10000002E 01
N = 400	0.12566370E 02	0.99999317E 00	0.10000002E 01

EXERCISES

6.11-1. Write the second-order equation

$$y'' = 2\sqrt{e^{2x} - y^2}$$
$$y(0) = 0$$
$$y'(0) = 1$$

as a system of first-order equations.

Solve it from $x = 0$ to $x = 1$, using a fourth-order Runge-Kutta method with $h = \frac{1}{64}$ and $h = \frac{1}{128}$.

6.11-2. Express the following pair of equations as a system of first-order equations:

$$\frac{d^2x}{dt^2} = x^2 - y + e^t$$

$$\frac{d^2y}{dt^2} = x - y^2 - e^t$$

$$x(0) = \frac{dx(0)}{dt} = 0 \qquad y(0) = 1 \qquad \frac{dy(0)}{dt} = -2$$

Obtain the solution of this system correct to six significant figures from $t = 0$ to $t = 1$.

6.11-3. Solve the following second-order equation from $x = 1$ to $x = 2$,

$$y'' = 2y^3$$
$$y(1) = 1 \qquad y'(1) = -1$$

using the Adams-Moulton formulas (6.78) with $h = 0.1$. Starting values correct to eight figures are

n	x_n	y_n	f_n
0	1.0	1.00000000	2.00000000
1	1.1	0.90909090	1.50262960
2	1.2	0.83333333	1.15740240
3	1.3	0.76923077	0.91033228

(*Exact solution:* $y = 1/x$.)

7

Boundary-value Problems in Ordinary Differential Equations

In Chap. 6 we considered numerical methods for solving initial-value problems. In such problems all the initial conditions are given at a single point. In this chapter we consider problems in which the conditions are specified at more than one point. A simple example of a second-order boundary-value problem is

$$y''(x) = y(x) \qquad y(0) = 0 \qquad y(1) = 1 \tag{7.1}$$

An example of a fourth-order boundary-value problem is

$$y^{iv}(x) + ky(x) = q \tag{7.2a}$$
$$y(0) = y'(0) = 0 \tag{7.2b}$$
$$y(L) = y''(L) = 0 \tag{7.2c}$$

Here y may represent the deflection of a beam of length L which is subjected to a uniform load q. Condition (7.2b) states that the end $x = 0$ is built in, while (7.2c) states that the end $x = L$ is simply supported. We shall consider two methods for solving such problems: the method of finite differences

373

and an adaptation of the methods of Chap. 6, which we shall call "shooting" methods.

7.1 FINITE-DIFFERENCE METHODS: SECOND-ORDER EQUATIONS

We assume that we have a linear differential equation of order greater than one, with conditions specified at the end points of an interval $[a,b]$. We divide the interval $[a,b]$ into N equal parts of width h. We set $x_0 = a$, $x_N = b$, and we define

$$x_n = x_0 + nh \qquad n = 1, 2, \ldots , N - 1$$

as the *interior mesh points*. The corresponding values of y at these mesh points are denoted by

$$y_n = y(x_0 + nh) \qquad n = 0, 1, \ldots , N$$

We shall sometimes have to deal with points outside the interval $[a,b]$. These will be called *exterior mesh points*, those to the left of x_0 being denoted by $x_{-1} = x_0 - h$, $x_{-2} = x_0 - 2h$, etc., and those to the right of x_N being denoted by $x_{N+1} = x_N + h$, $x_{N+2} = x_N + 2h$, etc. The corresponding values of y at the exterior mesh points are denoted in the obvious way as $y_{-1}, y_{-2}, y_{N+1}, y_{N+2}$, etc.

To solve a boundary-value problem by the method of finite differences, every derivative appearing in the equation, as well as in the boundary conditions, is replaced by an appropriate difference approximation. Central differences are usually preferred because they lead to greater accuracy. Some typical central-difference approximations are the following (see Chap. 5):

$$y'(x_n) \approx \frac{y_{n+1} - y_{n-1}}{2h}$$

$$y''(x_n) \approx \frac{y_{n+1} - 2y_n + y_{n-1}}{h^2} \tag{7.3}$$

$$y^{iv}(x_n) \approx \frac{y_{n+2} - 4y_{n+1} + 6y_n - 4y_{n-1} + y_{n-2}}{h^4}$$

In each case the finite-difference representation is an $O(h^2)$ approximation to the respective derivative. To illustrate the procedure, we consider the linear second-order differential equation

$$y''(x) + f(x)y' + g(x)y = q(x) \tag{7.4}$$

under the boundary conditions

$$y(x_0) = \alpha \tag{7.5}$$
$$y(x_N) = \beta \tag{7.6}$$

The finite-difference approximation to (7.4) is

$$\frac{y_{n-1} - 2y_n + y_{n+1}}{h^2} + \frac{f(x_n)(y_{n+1} - y_{n-1})}{2h} + g(x_n)y_n = q(x_n)$$

$$n = 1, 2, \ldots, N - 1$$

Multiplying through by h^2, setting $f(x_n) = f_n$, etc., and grouping terms, we have

$$\left(1 - \frac{h}{2}f_n\right)y_{n-1} + (-2 + h^2 g_n)y_n + \left(1 + \frac{h}{2}f_n\right)y_{n+1} = h^2 q_n$$

$$n = 1, 2, \ldots, N - 1 \quad (7.7)$$

Since y_0 and y_N are specified by the conditions (7.5) and (7.6), (7.7) is a linear system of $N - 1$ equations in the $N - 1$ unknowns y_n ($n = 1, \ldots, N - 1$). Writing out (7.7) and replacing y_0 by α and y_N by β, the system takes the form

$$(-2 + h^2 g_1)y_1 + \left(1 + \frac{h}{2}f_1\right)y_2 = h^2 q_1 - \left(1 - \frac{h}{2}f_1\right)\alpha$$

$$\left(1 - \frac{h}{2}f_2\right)y_1 + (-2 + h^2 g_2)y_2 + \left(1 + \frac{h}{2}f_2\right)y_3 = h^2 q_2$$

$$\left(1 - \frac{h}{2}f_3\right)y_2 + (-2 + h^2 g_3)y_3 + \left(1 + \frac{h}{2}f_3\right)y_4 = h^2 q_3 \tag{7.8}$$

$$\cdots \cdots \cdots \cdots \cdots \cdots \cdots \cdots \cdots \cdots \cdots$$

$$\left(1 - \frac{h}{2}f_{N-2}\right)y_{N-3} + (-2 + h^2 g_{N-2})y_{N-2} + \left(1 + \frac{h}{2}f_{N-2}\right)y_{N-1} = h^2 q_{N-2}$$

$$\left(1 - \frac{h}{2}f_{N-1}\right)y_{N-2} + (-2 + h^2 g_{N-1})y_{N-1} = h^2 q_{N-1} - \left(1 + \frac{h}{2}f_{N-1}\right)\beta$$

The coefficients in (7.8) can, of course, be computed since $f(x)$, $g(x)$, and $q(x)$ are known functions of x. This linear system can now be solved by any of the methods discussed in Chap. 3. In matrix form we have $A\mathbf{y} = \mathbf{b}$ [$\mathbf{y} = (y_1, y_2, \ldots, y_{N-1})$], representing the vector of unknowns; $\mathbf{b}$, representing the vector of known quantities on the right-hand side of (7.8); and

A, the matrix of coefficients. The matrix A in this case is tridiagonal and of order $N - 1$. It has the special form

$$A = \begin{bmatrix} B_1 & C_1 & & & & \\ A_2 & B_2 & C_2 & & & \\ & A_3 & B_3 & C_3 & & \\ & \cdots & \cdots & \cdots & \cdots & \\ & & A_{N-2} & B_{N-2} & C_{N-2} & \\ & & & A_{N-1} & B_{N-1} \end{bmatrix}$$

The system $A\mathbf{y} = \mathbf{b}$ can be solved directly using Algorithm 3.3 of Sec. 3.2. We need only replace n by $N - 1$, identify $\mathbf{x}$ and $\mathbf{y}$, and apply the recursion formulas of Algorithm 3.3.

Returning to the boundary conditions, let us see how the system (7.8) is affected if in place of (7.5) we prescribe the following condition at $x = x_0$:

$$y'(x_0) + \gamma y(x_0) = 0 \tag{7.9}$$

If we replace $y'(x_0)$ by a forward difference, we will have

$$\frac{y(x_0 + h) - y(x_0)}{h} + \gamma y(x_0) = 0$$

or on rearranging,

$$y_1 + (-1 + \gamma h)y_0 = 0 \tag{7.9a}$$

If we now write out (7.7) for $n = 1$ and then replace y_0 by $y_1/(1 - \gamma h)$, we will have

$$\left[(-2 + h^2 g_1) + \frac{1 - (h/2) f_1}{1 - \gamma h}\right] y_1 + \left(1 + \frac{h}{2} f_1\right) y_2 = h^2 q_1 \tag{7.10}$$

The first equation of (7.8) can now be replaced by (7.10). All other equations of (7.8) will remain unchanged, and the resulting system can again be solved, using Algorithm 3.3. We note, however, that (7.9a) is only an $O(h)$ approximation to the boundary condition (7.9) (see Sec. 5.1).

The accuracy of the solution will also then be of order h. To obtain a solution which is everywhere of order h^2, we replace (7.9) by the approximation

$$\frac{y(x_0 + h) - y(x_0 - h)}{2h} + \gamma y(x_0) = 0$$

or on rearranging,

$$y_1 - y_{-1} + 2h\gamma y_0 = 0 \tag{7.9b}$$

Since we have introduced an exterior point y_{-1}, we must now consider y_0 as well as $y_1, y_2, \ldots, y_{N-1}$ as unknowns. Since we now have N unknowns, we must have N equations. We can obtain an additional equation by taking

$n = 0$ in (7.7). If we then eliminate y_{-1} using (7.9b), we will have for the first two equations

$$\left[2h\gamma\left(1 - \frac{h}{2}f_0\right) + (-2 + h^2g_0)\right]y_0 + 2y_1 = h^2q_0 \qquad n = 0$$

$$\left(1 - \frac{h}{2}f_1\right)y_0 + (-2 + h^2g_1)y_1 + \left(1 + \frac{h}{2}f_1\right)y_2 = h^2q_1 \qquad n = 1$$

The remaining equations will be the same as those appearing in (7.8). The system is still tridiagonal but now of order N. It can again be solved explicitly with the aid of Algorithm 3.3.

The accuracy attainable with finite-difference methods will clearly depend upon the fineness of the mesh and upon the order of the finite-difference approximation. As the mesh is refined, the number of equations to be solved increases. As a result, the amount of computer time required may become excessive, and good accuracy may be difficult to achieve. The use of higher-order approximations will yield greater accuracy for the same mesh size but results in considerable complication, especially near the end points of the interval where the exterior values will not be known.

In practice, it is advisable to solve the linear system for several different values of h. A comparison of the solutions at the same mesh points will then indicate the accuracy being obtained. In addition, the extrapolation process, described in Sec. 5.5, can usually be applied to yield further improvement. As adapted to the solution of finite-difference systems, extrapolation to the limit proceeds as follows. Let $y_n(h)$ ($n = 1, \ldots, N - 1$) denote the approximate solution of the boundary-value problem based on N subdivisions of the interval $[a,b]$. Let $y_m(h/2)$ ($m = 1, 2, \ldots, 2N - 1$) be the approximate solution of the same problem based on $2N$ subdivisions of the interval $[a,b]$. At the $N - 1$ points $x_1 = a + h$, $x_2 = a + 2h$, $\ldots$, $x_{N-1} = a + (N - 1)h$, we now have two approximations, $y_n(h)$ and $y_n(h/2)$. Applying extrapolation to these, we obtain

$$y_n^{(1)} = \frac{4y_n(h/2) - y_n(h)}{3} \qquad n = 1, 2, \ldots, N - 1$$

This extrapolation will usually produce a significant improvement in the approximation.

Example 7.1 Solve the boundary-value problem (7.1), using finite-difference methods.
Taking $f(x) = 0$, $g(x) = -1$, $q(x) = 0$, and setting $y_0 = 0$, $y_N = 1$ in (7.8), we obtain the system

$$\begin{aligned}(-2 + h^2)y_1 + y_2 &= 0 \\ y_{n-1} + (-2 + h^2)y_n + y_{n+1} &= 0 \qquad n = 2, 3, \ldots, N - 2 \\ y_{N-2} + (-2 + h^2)y_{N-1} &= -1\end{aligned}$$

COMPUTER RESULTS FOR EXAMPLE 7.1

XN	YN(H = 0.05)	YN(H = 0.10)	YN(1)	Y(XN)
0	0	0	0	0
0.05	.04256502			.04256363
0.10	.08523646	.08524469	.08523372	.08533369
0.15	.12812098			.12811689
0.20	.17132582	.17134184	.17132048	.17132045
0.25	.21495896			.21495239
0.30	.25912950	.25915240	.25912187	.25912183
0.35	.30394787			.30393920
0.40	.34952610	.34955449	.34951663	.34951659
0.45	.39597815			.39596794
0.50	.44342014	.44345213	.44340946	.44340942
0.55	.49197068			.49195965
0.60	.54175115	.54178427	.54174010	.54174004
0.65	.59288599			.59287506
0.70	.64550304	.64553425	.64549263	.64549258
0.75	.69973386			.69972418
0.80	.75571401	.75573958	.75570550	.75570543
0.85	.81358345			.81357635
0.90	.87348684	.87350228	.87348166	.87348163
0.95	.93557395			.93557107
1.00	1	1	1	1

This is a system of $N - 1$ equations in the $N - 1$ unknowns: $y_1, y_2, \ldots, y_{N-1}$. This system was solved on the IBM 7090 with $h = 0.1$ and $h = 0.05$, using a subroutine based on Algorithm 3.3. The results are given below. The fourth column gives the extrapolated values at intervals of 0.1 obtained from the formula

$$y_n^{(1)} = \frac{4y_n(0.05) - y_n(0.1)}{3}$$

The values in the last column are obtained from the exact solution to the problem,

$$y(x) = \frac{\sinh x}{\sinh 1}$$

These results show that for $h = 0.1$ the solution is correct to three to four significant figures and for $h = 0.05$ to four to five significant figures, while the extrapolated solution is correct to about seven significant figures. To obtain seven significant figures of accuracy without extrapolation would require a subdivision of the interval [0,1] into approximately 100 mesh points ($h = 0.01$).

EXERCISES

7.1-1. Solve by difference methods the boundary-value problem

$$\frac{d^2y}{dx^2} + y = 0$$

$$y(0) = 0$$
$$y(1) = 1$$

Take $h = \frac{1}{4}$, and solve the resulting system, using a desk calculator.

Ans.: $y_1 = 0.2943$, $y_2 = 0.5702$, $y_3 = 0.8104$

Compare this solution with the exact solution $y = (\sin x)/(\sin 1)$.

7.1-2. Solve the boundary-value problem (7.1) with the condition $y(0) = 0$ replaced by the condition $y'(0) + y(0) = 0$, using a mesh $h = 0.1$.

7.1-3. Write an $O(h^2)$ finite-difference system for approximating the solution of the boundary-value problem

$$y'' + xy' + y = 2x$$
$$y(0) = 1$$
$$y(1) = 0$$

Let $h = 0.1$, and write the system in matrix form. Then solve this system, using a computer program based on Algorithm 3.3.

7.1-4. Show that the Gauss-Seidel iterative method can also be used to solve the system of Example 7.1, and obtain this solution by iteration to four significant figures of accuracy. For this problem, is the direct method more efficient than the iterative method?

7.1-5. Solve by difference methods the boundary-value problem

$$y'' + 2y' + y = x \qquad y(0) = 0 \qquad y(1) = 0$$

using $h = \frac{1}{8}$, $h = \frac{1}{16}$, and improve the results by extrapolation.

7.2 FINITE-DIFFERENCE METHODS: FOURTH-ORDER EQUATIONS

We now solve the boundary-value problem (7.2) by difference methods. Using the difference approximations in (7.3) with $x_0 = 0$, $x_N = L$, and $Nh = L$, we will have

$$y_{n-2} - 4y_{n-1} + (6 + kh^4)y_n - 4y_{n+1} + y_{n+2} = h^4q$$
$$n = 1, 2, \ldots, N - 1 \quad (7.11a)$$
$$y_0 = 0 \qquad y_{-1} = y_1 \qquad\qquad\qquad\qquad\quad (7.11b)$$
$$y_N = 0 \qquad y_{N+1} = -y_{N-1} \qquad\qquad\quad (7.11c)$$

Writing out (7.11a) for $n = 1, 2, \ldots, N - 1$, and using the boundary conditions (7.11b) and (7.11c), we obtain

$$
\begin{aligned}
(7 + kh^4)y_1 - 4y_2 + y_3 &= h^4q \\
-4y_1 + (6 + kh^4)y_2 - 4y_3 + y_4 &= h^4q \\
y_{n-2} - 4y_{n-1} + (6 + kh^4)y_n - 4y_{n-1} + y_{n-2} &= h^4q \qquad (7.12) \\
n = 3, 4, \ldots, N - 3 & \\
y_{N-4} - 4y_{N-3} + (6 + kh^4)y_{N-2} - 4y_{N-1} &= h^4q \\
y_{N-3} - 4y_{N-2} + (5 + kh^4)y_{N-1} &= h^4q
\end{aligned}
$$

In this case the matrix is again bandtype, the nonzero elements appearing only along the principal five diagonals. An algorithm is again available for solving directly such systems. To describe this algorithm, we write (7.12) in matrix form $Ay = b$

$$Ay = \begin{bmatrix} C_1 & D_1 & E_1 \\ B_2 & C_2 & D_2 & E_2 \\ A_3 & B_3 & C_3 & D_3 & E_3 \\ & A_4 & B_4 & C_4 & D_4 & E_4 \\ & & & \cdots \cdots \cdots \cdots \cdots \cdots \cdots \cdots \\ & & & A_{N-2} & B_{N-2} & C_{N-2} & D_{N-2} \\ & & & & A_{N-1} & B_{N-1} & C_{N-1} \end{bmatrix} \begin{bmatrix} y_1 \\ y_2 \\ \cdot \\ \cdot \\ \cdot \\ y_{N-2} \\ y_{N-1} \end{bmatrix} = \begin{bmatrix} b_1 \\ b_2 \\ \cdot \\ \cdot \\ \cdot \\ b_{N-2} \\ b_{N-1} \end{bmatrix}$$

(7.13)

Algorithm 7.1   Direct solution of five-diagonal systems   The algorithm

consists in applying the following steps:

1. Compute the initial values

$$\omega_1 = C_1$$
$$\beta_1 = D_1\omega_1 \qquad \beta_0 = 0 \qquad \beta_{N-1} = 0$$
$$\gamma_1 = E_1\omega_1 \qquad \gamma_0 = 0 \qquad \gamma_{N-1} = \gamma_{N-2} = 0$$

2. Compute recursively

$$\delta_n = B_n - A_n\beta_{n-2}$$
$$\omega_n = C_n - A_n\gamma_{n-2} - \delta_n\beta_{n-1} \qquad n = 2, 3, \ldots, N-1$$

$$\beta_n = \frac{D_n - \delta_n\gamma_{n-1}}{\omega_n}$$

$$\gamma_n = \frac{E_n}{\omega_n}$$

3. Compute

$$h_0 = 0$$

$$h_1 = \frac{b_1}{\omega_1}$$

$$h_n = \frac{b_n - A_nh_{n-2} - \delta_nh_{n-1}}{\omega_n} \qquad n = 2, 3, \ldots, N-1$$

4. Compute the values of y backward, using

$$y_{N-1} = h_{N-1}$$
$$y_n = h_n - \beta_ny_{n+1} - \gamma_ny_{n+2} \qquad n = N-2, N-3, \ldots, 1$$

Example 7.2   Solve the boundary-value problem (7.2), using finite-difference methods. Take $k = 1, L = 1, q = 16 \cdot 10^4$.

COMPUTER RESULTS FOR EXAMPLE 7.2

N	YN(H = 0.05)	YN(H = 0.025)	YN(1)
0	0	0	
1	24.812481	23.362666	22.879394
2	87.296463	84.603290	83.705566
3	176.498330	172.758530	171.511623
4	282.463930	277.864600	276.331490
5	396.237960	390.956600	389.196146
6	509.863350	504.067960	502.213616
7	616.380620	610.229860	
8	709.827130	703.470540	
9	785.236390	778.814480	
10	838.637520	832.282220	
11	867.054840	860.890000	
12	868.507460	862.649340	
13	842.009190	836.566950	
14	787.568410	782.644590	
15	706.188280	701.879050	
16	599.867140	596.262590	
17	471.598860	468.783160	
18	325.373700	323.425320	
19	166.178990	165.170940	
20	0	0	

In matrix form the system (7.12) then becomes

$$
\begin{bmatrix}
7 + h^4 & -4 & 1 \\
-4 & 6 + h^4 & -4 & 1 \\
1 & -4 & 6 + h^4 & -4 & 1 \\
& 1 & -4 & 6 + h^4 & -4 & 1 \\
& & \cdots & \cdots & \cdots & \cdots \\
& & & 1 & -4 & 6 + h^4 & -4 \\
& & & & 1 & -4 & 5 + h^4
\end{bmatrix}
\begin{bmatrix}
y_1 \\ y_2 \\ \cdot \\ \cdot \\ \cdot \\ \cdot \\ y_{N-1}
\end{bmatrix}
= h^4 q
\begin{bmatrix}
1 \\ 1 \\ \cdot \\ \cdot \\ \cdot \\ \cdot \\ 1
\end{bmatrix}
$$

$$(7.14)$$

On identifying the elements of this coefficient matrix with those of (7.13), we can now apply Algorithm 7.1 to obtain the solution. The second column gives the results for $h = 0.05$ ($N = 20$ subdivisions), and the third column the results for $h = 0.025$ at the points corresponding to $n = 20$ subdivisions. There are at most two significant figures of agreement between the two solutions, indicating that the results for $h = 0.025$ are probably correct to at most two or three significant figures. More accurate results can be obtained by increasing the number of subdivisions or by applying h^2 extrapolation. The first few extrapolated values are given under the column headed YN(1).

EXERCISES

7.2-1. The deflection y of an elastic beam under a transverse load $q(x)$ is governed by the equation

$$EIy^{iv} = q(x)$$

If the beam is simply supported at the end $x = 0$ and rigidly supported at the end $x = L$, the boundary conditions are

$$y(0) = 0 \qquad y''(0) = 0$$
$$y(L) = 0 \qquad y'(L) = 0$$

    (a) Write a finite-difference approximation to this boundary-value problem.

    (b) Let $E = I = 1$, and let $q(x) = 1$. Solve the system for $h = 0.1$, using Algorithm 7.1.

    (c) Compare this with the exact solution $y = (q/48)(2x^4 - 3x^3 + x)$.

7.2-2. Use extrapolation to the limit to complete the fourth column of Table 7.2.

7.2-3. Write an $O(h^2)$ difference approximation to the boundary-value problem

$$y^{\text{iv}} + 25x^2 y = 25x$$
$$y(0) = y'(0) = 0$$
$$y(1) = y''(1) = 0$$

Solve the system of equations using $h = \frac{1}{16}$, $h = \frac{1}{32}$, and then improve the results by extrapolation.

7.3 SHOOTING METHODS

For linear boundary-value problems, a number of methods can be used. The method of differences described above works reasonably well in such cases. Other methods attempt to obtain linearly independent solutions of the differential equation and to combine them in such a way as to satisfy the boundary conditions. For nonlinear equations, the latter method cannot be used. Difference methods can be adapted to nonlinear problems, but they require guessing at a tentative solution and then improving this by an iterative process. In addition to the complexity of the programming required, there is no guarantee of convergence of the iterations. The shooting method to be described in this section applies equally well to linear and nonlinear problems. Again, there is no guarantee of convergence, but the method is easy to apply, and when it does converge, it is usually more efficient than other methods.

    Consider again the problem given in (7.1).

    We wish to apply the initial-value methods discussed in Chap. 6, but to do so, we must know both $y(0)$ and $y'(0)$. Since $y'(0)$ is not prescribed, we consider it as an unknown parameter, say α, which must be determined so that the resulting solution yields the prescribed value $y(1)$ to some desired accuracy. We therefore guess at the initial slope and set up an iterative procedure for converging to the correct slope. Let α_0, α_1 be two guesses at the initial slope $y'(0)$, and let $y(\alpha_0;1)$, $y(\alpha_1;1)$ be the values of y at $x = 1$ obtained from integrating the differential equation. Graphically, the situation may be presented as in Figs. 7.1 and 7.2.

    In Fig. 7.1 the solutions of the initial-value problems are drawn, while in Fig. 7.2, $y(\alpha;1)$ is plotted as a function of α. A normally better approximation to α can now be obtained by linear interpolation. The intersection of

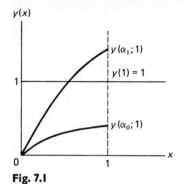

Fig. 7.1

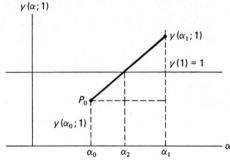

Fig. 7.2

the line joining P_0 to P_1 with the line $y(1) = 1$ has its α coordinate given by

$$\alpha_2 = \alpha_0 + (\alpha_1 - \alpha_0) \frac{y(1) - y(\alpha_0;1)}{y(\alpha_1;1) - y(\alpha_0;1)} \qquad (7.15)$$

We now integrate the differential equation, using the initial values $y(0) = 0$, $y'(0) = \alpha_2$, to obtain $y(\alpha_2;1)$. Again, using linear interpolation based on α_1, α_2, we can obtain a next approximation α_3. The process is repeated until convergence has been obtained, i.e., until $y(\alpha_i;1)$ agrees with $y(1) = 1$ to the desired number of places. There is no guarantee that this iterative procedure will converge. The rapidity of convergence will clearly depend upon how good the initial guesses are. Estimates are sometimes available from physical considerations, and sometimes from simple graphical representations of the solution.

For a general second-order boundary-value problem

$$y'' = f(x,y,y') \qquad y(0) = y_0 \qquad y(b) = y_b \qquad (7.16)$$

the procedure is summarized in Algorithm 7.2.

Algorithm 7.2 The shooting method for second-order boundary-value problems

1. Let α_k be an approximation to the unknown initial slope $y'(0) = \alpha$. (Choose the first two α_0, α_1, using physical intuition.)
2. Solve the initial-value problem

$$y'' = f(x,y,y') \qquad y(0) = y_0 \qquad y'(0) = \alpha_k$$

from $x = 0$ to $x = b$, using any of the methods of Chap. 6. Call the solution $y(\alpha_k;b)$ at $x = b$.

3. Obtain the next approximation from the linear interpolation

$$\alpha_{k+1} = \alpha_{k-1} + (\alpha_k - \alpha_{k-1}) \frac{y_b - y(\alpha_{k-1};b)}{y(\alpha_k;b) - y(\alpha_{k-1};b)} \qquad k = 1, 2, \ldots$$

4. Repeat steps 2 and 3 until $|y(\alpha_k;b) - y_b| < \epsilon$ for a prescribed ϵ.

The iteration used in Algorithm 7.2 is an application of the secant method described in Chap. 2.

For systems of equations of higher order, this procedure becomes considerably more complicated, and convergence more difficult to obtain. The general situation for a nonlinear system may be represented as follows. We consider a system of four equations in four unknowns:

$$\begin{aligned}
x' &= f(x,y,z,w,t) \\
y' &= g(x,y,z,w,t) \\
z' &= h(x,y,z,w,t) \\
w' &= l(x,y,z,w,t)
\end{aligned} \qquad (7.17)$$

where now t represents the independent variable. We are given two conditions at $t = 0$, say

$$\begin{aligned}
x(0) &= x_0 \\
y(0) &= y_0
\end{aligned}$$

and two conditions at $t = T$, say

$$\begin{aligned}
z(T) &= z_T \\
w(T) &= w_T
\end{aligned}$$

Let $z(0) = \alpha$, $w(0) = \beta$ be the correct initial values of $z(0)$, $w(0)$, and let α_0, β_0 be guesses for these initial values. Now integrate the system (7.17), and denote the values of z and w obtained at $t = T$ by $z(\alpha_0,\beta_0;T)$ and $w(\alpha_0,\beta_0;T)$.

Since z and w at $t = T$ are clearly functions of α and β, we may expand $z(\alpha,\beta;T)$ and $w(\alpha,\beta;T)$ into a Taylor series for two variables through linear terms:

$$\begin{aligned}
z(\alpha,\beta;T) = z(\alpha_0,\beta_0;T) &+ (\alpha - \alpha_0) \frac{\partial z}{\partial \alpha}(\alpha_0,\beta_0;T) \\
&+ (\beta - \beta_0) \frac{\partial z}{\partial \beta}(\alpha_0,\beta_0;T) \\
w(\alpha,\beta;T) = w(\alpha_0,\beta_0;T) &+ (\alpha - \alpha_0) \frac{\partial w}{\partial \alpha}(\alpha_0,\beta_0;T) \\
&+ (\beta - \beta_0) \frac{\partial w}{\partial \beta}(\alpha_0,\beta_0;T)
\end{aligned} \qquad (7.18)$$

We may set $z(\alpha,\beta;T)$ and $w(\alpha,\beta;T)$ to their desired values z_T and w_T, but before we can solve (7.18) for the corrections $\alpha - \alpha_0$ and $\beta - \beta_0$, we must obtain the partial derivatives in (7.18). We do not know the solutions z and

w and therefore cannot find these derivatives analytically.   However, we can find approximate numerical values for them.   To do so, we solve (7.17) once with the initial conditions x_0, y_0, α_0, β_0, once with the conditions x_0, y_0, $\alpha_0 + \Delta\alpha_0$, β_0, and then with the conditions x_0, y_0, α_0, $\beta_0 + \Delta\beta_0$, where $\Delta\alpha_0$ and $\Delta\beta_0$ are small increments.   Omitting the variables x_0, y_0 which remain fixed, we then form the difference quotients:

$$\frac{z(\alpha_0,\beta_0 + \Delta\beta_0;T) - z(\alpha_0,\beta_0;T)}{\Delta\beta_0} \approx \frac{\partial z}{\partial\beta}(\alpha_0,\beta_0;T)$$

$$\frac{w(\alpha_0,\beta_0 + \Delta\beta_0;T) - w(\alpha_0,\beta_0;T)}{\Delta\beta_0} \approx \frac{\partial w}{\partial\beta}(\alpha_0,\beta_0;T)$$

$$\frac{z(\alpha_0 + \Delta\alpha_0,\beta_0;T) - z(\alpha_0,\beta_0;T)}{\Delta\alpha_0} \approx \frac{\partial z}{\partial\alpha}(\alpha_0,\beta_0;T)$$

$$\frac{w(\alpha_0 + \Delta\alpha_0,\beta_0;T) - w(\alpha_0,\beta_0;T)}{\Delta\alpha_0} \approx \frac{\partial w}{\partial\alpha}(\alpha_0,\beta_0;T)$$

After replacing $z(\alpha,\beta;T)$ by z_T and $w(\alpha,\beta;T)$ by w_T, we can then solve (7.18) for the corrections $\delta\alpha_0 = \alpha - \alpha_0$ and $\delta\beta_0 = \beta - \beta_0$, to obtain new estimates $\alpha_1 = \alpha_0 + \delta\alpha_0$, $\beta_1 = \beta_0 + \delta\alpha_0$ for the parameters α and β.   The entire process is now repeated, starting with x_0, y_0, α_1, β_1 as the initial conditions.

Each iteration thus consists in solving the system (7.17) three times. In general, if there are n unknown initial parameters, each iteration will require $n + 1$ solutions of the original system.   The method used here is equivalent to a modified Newton's method for finding the roots of equations in several variables.

Boundary-value problems constitute one of the most difficult classes of problems to solve on a computer.   Convergence is by no means assured, good initial guesses must be available, and considerable trial and error, as well as large amounts of machine time, are usually required.

Example 7.3 Solve the problem (7.1), using the shooting method.   Start with the initial approximations $\alpha_0 = 0.3$ and $\alpha_1 = 0.4$ to $y'(0)$ and $h = 0.1$.

The solution given below was obtained using the AMRK differential equation solver described in Chap. 6, combined with linear interpolation based on (7.15).   The iteration was stopped by the condition $|\alpha_{k+1} - \alpha_k| < 1 \cdot 10^{-6}$.

Iteration no.	α_k	$y(\alpha_k;1)$
1	0.30000000	0.35256077
2	0.40000000	0.47008103
3	0.85091712	0.99999999
4	0.85091712	0.99999999

The correct value of y' at $x = 0$ is $\sinh^{-1} 1 = 0.85091813$. Convergence for this problem is very rapid. Moreover, the indicated accuracy is exceptionally good, considering the coarse step size used. To obtain comparable accuracy using the finite-difference methods of Sec. 7.1 would require a step size $h = 0.01$. Nevertheless, the finite-difference method might still be computationally more efficient.

Example 7.4 Solve the nonlinear boundary-value problem

$$yy'' + 1 + y'^2 = 0$$
$$y(0) = 1$$
$$y(1) = 2$$

(7.19)

by the shooting method.

Solution Let $\alpha_0 = 0.5$, $\alpha_1 = 1.0$ be two approximations to the unknown slope $y'(0)$. Using again the AMRK package and linear interpolation with a step size $h = \frac{1}{64}$, the following results were obtained:

α_i	$y(\alpha_i;1)$
0.5000000	0.9999999
0.9999999	1.4142133
1.7071071	1.8477582
1.9554118	1.9775786
1.9982968	1.9991463
1.9999940	1.9999952
2.0000035	2.0000000

The correct slope at $x = 0$ is $y'(0) = 2$. After seven iterations, the initial slope is seen to be correct to six significant figures, while the value of y at $x = 1$ is correct to at least seven significant figures. After the first three iterations, convergence could have been speeded up by using quadratic interpolation.

The required number of iterations will clearly depend upon the choice of the initial approximations α_0 and α_1. These approximations can sometimes be obtained from graphical or physical considerations.

EXERCISES

7.3-1. Find a numerical solution of the equation

$$2yy'' - y'^2 + 4y^2 = 0$$

satisfying the conditions

$$y\left(\frac{\pi}{6}\right) = \frac{1}{4}$$

$$y\left(\frac{\pi}{2}\right) = 1$$

Take $\alpha_0 = 0.5$, $\alpha_1 = 0.8$ as initial approximations to $y'(\pi/6)$, and iterate until the condition at $x = \pi/2$ is satisfied to five places. [*Solution:* $y = \sin^2 x$; and the initial slope is $y'(\pi/6) = \sqrt{3}/2$.]

7.3-2. In Example 7.4 use quadratic interpolation based on α_0, α_1, α_2 to obtain the next approximation.   How many iterations would have been saved?

7.3-3. Solve the following problems, using the shooting method:

(a) $y'' = 2y^3$, $y(1) = 1$, $y(2) = \frac{1}{2}$, taking $y'(1) = 0$ as a first guess. (*Exact solution:* $y = 1/x$.)

(b) $y'' = e^y$, $y(0) = y(1) = 0$, taking $y'(0) = 0$ as a first guess.

References

1. Hamming, R. W.: "Numerical Methods for Scientists and Engineers," McGraw-Hill Book Company, New York, 1962.
2. Henrici, P. K.: "Elements of Numerical Analysis," John Wiley & Sons, Inc., New York, 1964.
3. Traub, J. F.: "Iterative Methods for the Solution of Equations," Prentice-Hall, Inc., Englewood Cliffs, N.J., 1963.
4. Scarborough, J. B.: "Numerical Mathematical Analysis," The Johns Hopkins Press, Baltimore, 1958.
5. Hildebrand, F. B.: "Introduction to Numerical Analysis," McGraw-Hill Book Company, New York, 1956.
6. Muller, D. E.: A method of solving algebraic equations using an automatic computer, *Mathematical Tables and Other Aids to Computation (MTAC)*, **10**:208–215 (1956).
7. Hastings, C., Jr.: "Approximations for Digital Computers," Princeton University Press, Princeton, N.J., 1955.
8. Milne, W. E.: "Numerical Calculus," Princeton University Press, Princeton, N.J., 1949.

9. Lanczos, C.: "Applied Analysis," Prentice-Hall, Inc., Englewood Cliffs, N.J., 1956.

10. Householder, A. S.: "Principles of Numerical Analysis," McGraw-Hill Book Company, New York, 1953.

11. Faddeev, D. K., and V. H. Faddeeva: "Computational Methods of Linear Algebra," W. H. Freeman and Company, San Francisco, 1963.

12. Carnahan, B., et al.: "Applied Numerical Methods," John Wiley & Sons, Inc., New York, 1964.

13. "Modern Computing Methods," Philosophical Library, Inc., New York, 1961.

14. McCracken, D., and W. S. Dorn: "Numerical Methods and Fortran Programming," John Wiley & Sons, Inc., New York, 1964.

15. Henrici, P. K.: "Discrete Variable Methods for Ordinary Differential Equations," John Wiley & Sons, Inc., New York, 1962.

16. Hamming, R. W.: Stable predictor-corrector methods for ordinary differential equations, *Journal of the Association for Computing Machinery (JACM)*, **6**(1):37–47 (1959).

17. Rice, J. R.: "The Approximation of Functions," vols. 1 and 2, Addison-Wesley Publishing Company, Inc., Reading, Mass., 1964.

18. Forsythe, G., and C. B. Moler: "Computer Solution of Linear Algebraic Systems," Prentice-Hall, Inc., Englewood Cliffs, N.J., 1967.

19. Isaacson, E., and H. Keller: "Analysis of Numerical Methods," John Wiley & Sons, Inc., New York, 1966.

20. Stroud, A. H., and D. Secrest: "Gaussian Quadrature Formulas," Prentice-Hall, Inc., Englewood Cliffs, N.J., 1966.

Index

Acceleration (*see* Convergence
  acceleration)
Adams-Bashforth method, 341–346,
  364
  predictor form, 351
  program, 344–345
Adams-Moulton method, 350ff., 360
  error of, 352
  program, 355
  for systems, 366–371
Adaptive quadrature, 298
Aitken's Δ^2-process, 53–54, 56, 307
  algorithm, 53
AMRK subroutine for differential
  equations, 366–368
Analytic substitution, 274ff., 318
Approximation:
  Chebyshev, 265
  least-squares (*see* Least-squares
    approximation)

Back-substitution, 111, 123, 128
  algorithm, 111, 128
  program, 129–130
Backward error analysis, 16, 152
Base of a number system, 1
Basis for n-vectors, 104, 174
Bessel interpolation, 237
Bessel's function, zeros of, 80
Binary search, 43
Binary system, 2
Binomial coefficient, 215
Binomial function, 215, 341
Bisection method, 28–29, 35–37
  algorithm, 28
  program, 35–37
Boundary-value problems, 373–387
  finite difference methods for, 374–
    381
  fourth-order equation, 379ff.

Boundary-value problems:
  second-order equation, 374ff.
  shooting methods for, 382–387
Breakpoints of a piecewise-polynomial
  function, 233, 290
Broken-line interpolation, 232–233

Characteristic equation:
  of a difference equation, 323
  of a differential equation, 321
  of a matrix, 185
Characteristic polynomial of a matrix,
  185
Chebyshev approximation, 265
Chebyshev economization, 265ff.
Chebyshev points, 232, 269, 306
Chebyshev polynomials, 252, 267–
  271, 305, 327
  nested multiplication for, 254
Choleski's method, 142
Chopping, 8
Compact schemes, 137ff.
  algorithm, 141
Composite rules for numerical
  integration, 290ff.
Computational efficiency, 61, 129
Condition number, 149, 150ff.
Convergence:
  geometric, 18
  linear, 50, 54
  quadratic, 57ff.
  of a sequence, 17ff.
  of a vector sequence, 158, 159
Convergence acceleration, 50ff.
  (*See also* Extrapolation to the limit)
Conversion:
  binary to decimal, 2, 7, 67
  decimal to binary, 3, 7
Corrected trapezoid rule, 288, 293,
  295

Corrected trapezoid rule:
program, 296
Corrector formulas, 347–356
Adams-Moulton, 351
Milne's, 353
Cramer's rule, 85, 183
Cubic spline, 237, 283
interpolation, 237–240

Data fitting, 241ff.
Decimal system, 1
Deflation, 68, 79, 80, 187
for the power method, 190
Degree of a polynomial, 25, 66
Determinants, 180ff.
Diagonally dominant (see Matrix)
Difference equations, 322ff., 333, 335,
358, 360
initial value, 324
linear, 323
Differential equations, 320ff.
basic notions, 320–322
boundary-value problems, 373–387
Euler's method, 329ff.
initial-value problems, 320, 327-
372
linear with constant coefficients,
321–322
multistep methods, 340ff.
Runge-Kutta methods, 336ff.
systems of, 365ff.
Taylor's algorithm, 327ff.
Differential remainder for Taylor's
formula, 24
Differentiation, numerical, 275ff.
Direct methods for solving linear
systems, 107, 110–154
Discretization error, 280, 333, 335,
357, 368
Divided difference, 60, 195, 201ff.,
221
table, 202, 203, 209
Double precision, 8, 15
accumulation, 363
partial, 363
of scalar products, 139, 155

Economization of power series, 265ff.
Eigenvalues, 170ff., 184ff.
Eigenvectors, 171
complete set of, 174, 190
Equivalence of linear systems, 112,
158
Euler's method, 329, 332–335
Exactness of a rule, 299
Exponent of a floating-point number, 7
Exponential growth, 14, 359, 360
Extrapolation to the limit, 50ff., 307ff.,
340, 377, 381
algorithm, 312

Factorization of a matrix, 130–133,
183
False position method (see Regula
falsi)
Finite-difference methods:
fourth-order equations, 379ff.
second-order equations, 374ff.
Five-diagonal (see Matrix)
Fixed point, 44
Fixed-point iteration, 33, 44ff., 157ff.,
170ff., 348
algorithm, 44
for linear systems, 163
for systems, 84
Floating-point arithmetic, 7ff.
Forward difference:
operator $\triangle$, 53, 214ff., 341
table, 215–216
Fraction:
binary, 5
decimal, 4
Fundamental theorem of algebra, 25,
186

Gauss elimination, 108, 112ff.
algorithm, 119
for five-diagonal systems, 380
for tridiagonal systems, 121
program, 122
program, 132–133

Gauss-Seidel iteration, 166–169, 379
  algorithm, 166
  program for tridiagonal systems,
    168
Gaussian rules for numerical integration, 299ff.
Geometric series, 18
Gershgorin's circle theorem, 189

Hermite:
  interpolation, 236
  polynomials, 252, 306
Hessenberg matrix, 189
Homogeneous difference equations,
  323–325
Homogeneous differential equations,
  321–322
Homogeneous linear systems, 99–101,
  160
Horner's scheme (see Nested multiplication)

Ill-conditioned, 153, 244
Initial-value problem, 320
  numerical solution of, 327–372
Instability, 13–14, 72, 357, 360
Integral remainder for Taylor's formula, 23
Integration, 284–318
  corrected trapezoid rule, 288
  Gaussian rules, 299ff.
  midpoint rule, 286
  rectangle rule, 285
  Romberg rule, 313–317
  Simpson's rule, 288, 353
  trapezoid rule, 287
Intermediate-value theorem for continuous functions, 22, 28, 45
Interpolating polynomial, 191–230,
  275
  difference forms, 214–219
  error, 210ff.
  Lagrange form, 191ff.
  Newton form, 195ff.
  uniqueness of, 193

Interpolation:
  at equally spaced points, 213ff.
  in a function table, 205–209
Interval arithmetic, 16
Inverse of a matrix, 96, 127
  calculation of, 133–136
  program, 135–136
Inverse interpolation, 210
Iteration function for fixed-point
  iteration, 44, 157
Iterative improvement, 154–156, 165
  algorithm, 155
Iterative methods for solving linear
  systems, 107, 157ff.

Jacobi iteration, 158, 161, 165
  algorithm, 165
Jacobi polynomials, 305
Jacobian, 86

Lagrange form of the interpolating
  polynomial, 191ff., 275, 300
Lagrange polynomials, 193, 255, 275
Laguerre polynomials, 252, 306
Least-squares approximation, 134,
  243–265
  by polynomials, 255ff., 282
  program, 260–261
Legendre polynomials, 250, 256, 303
Linear convergence, 50, 54
Linear independence, 103, 320
Linear operation, 275
Linear system, 91
Local discretization error, 333, 368
Loss of significance, 10–12, 32, 71,
  76, 262, 280
Lower-triangular, 94

Mantissa of a floating-point number,
  7
Matrix, 91
  bandtype or banded, 379
  dense, 108
  diagonal, 94

Matrix:
   diagonally dominant, 156, 161, 166,
      167, 170, 189, 238, 246
   equality, 92
   five-diagonal, 379
   general properties, 91–107
   Hessenberg, 189
   identity, 95, 171
   inverse, 96, 127
   invertible, 95, 117, 165, 181
   multiplication, 93
   null, 97
   permutation, 106, 181
   positive definite, 125, 142, 167
   sparse, 108, 157
   square, 92
   symmetric, 105
   trace, 109
   transpose, 104
   triangular, 94, 110, 136, 151, 170, 181
   triangular factorization, 130–133
   tridiagonal, 119–123, 166, 167, 180,
      188, 238, 376
Mean-value theorem:
   for derivatives, 23, 32, 47, 51, 60,
      211, 278, 333
   for integrals, 22, 284, 291, 302
Midpoint rule, 286
   composite, 292, 314
Milne's method, 353
Minimax approximation (*see* Chebyshev approximation)
Minor of a matrix, 183
Modified regula falsi, 31, 37–40
   algorithm, 31
   program, 37–40
Muller's method, 74ff., 186–188
   algorithm, 77
   program, 78–79
Multistep methods, 340ff.

Nested form of a polynomial, 66
Nested multiplication, 67
   for Chebyshev polynomials, 254
   for the Newton form, 199
   for orthogonal polynomials, 253

Newton backward-difference form,
   218, 340, 350
Newton form:
   of the interpolating polynomial,
      195ff., 197
   algorithm for the calculation of
      coefficients, 204
      program, 204–205, 227–228
   of a polynomial, 198
Newton forward-difference form, 215
Newton's method, 33, 40–42, 57ff.,
   68ff.
   algorithm, 33
      for finding real zeros of poly-
         nomials, 68
         program, 70, 89
   program, 41–42
   for systems, 86
Norm, 142ff.
   Euclidean, 145
   matrix, 145
   max, 145
   vector, 144
Normal equations for the least-squares
   problem, 243, 256
Normalized floating-point number, 7
Numerical differentiation (*see* Differentiation)
Numerical instability (*see* Instability)
Numerical integration
   (*see* Integration)
Numerical quadrature
   (*see* Integration)

Octal system, 3
Optimum step size:
   in differentiation, 282
   in solving differential equations,
      353, 363
Order:
   of convergence, 18–20
   of a root, 19, 65
   symbol O (·), 18–20, 129, 189,
      312ff., 326ff., 335–338, 340,
      358–359, 361
   symbol o (·), 18–20, 53, 308ff.

Orthogonal functions, 245, 247
Orthogonal polynomials, 246ff., 248, 301
  generation of, 257
Osculatory interpolation, 221ff.
  program, 227–228
Overflow, 8

Partial double-precision accumulation, 363, 368, 370–371
Partial pivoting, 125
Permutation, 106
Piecewise-cubic interpolation, 233ff.
  programs, 234–238
Piecewise-polynomial functions, 232ff., 290
Piecewise-polynomial interpolation, 232ff.
Pivotal equation in elimination, 114
Pivoting strategy in elimination, 123ff.
Polynomial equations, 66ff.
  complex roots, 74ff.
  real roots, 66ff.
Polynomial interpolation (*see* Interpolating polynomial)
Power method, 175–179
Predictor-corrector methods, 346ff.
Propagation of errors, 13

Quadratic convergence, 57ff.
Quadratic formula, 12
Quotient polynomial, 67

Rectangle rule, 285
  composite, 291
Reduced or deflated polynomial, 68
Regula falsi, 30
  modified (*see* Modified regula falsi)
Residual, 143
Rolle's theorem, 23, 28, 211
Romberg integration, 313–317
  program, 317–318
Rounding, 8
Round-off error, 9

Round-off error:
  in differentiation, 281
  in integration, 294
  propagation of, 13, 361ff.
  in solving differential equations, 361–364
  in solving equations, 37, 42, 43, 71–72
  in solving linear systems, 124, 137, 139, 142, 151, 164, 167
Rule, 275
Runge-Kutta methods, 336ff.
  order 2, 337
  order 4, 338

Scalar product, 106, 139
  of functions, 247
Secant method, 32, 40–42, 384
  algorithm, 32
  program, 40–41
Self-starting, 338
Sequence, 17
Shooting methods, 382ff.
Significant-digit arithmetic, 16
Significant digits, 10
Similarity transformation, 188
Simpson's rule, 288, 304, 353
  composite, 292
  program, 297
Simultaneous displacement (*see* Jacobi iteration)
Simultaneous nonlinear equations, 84ff.
Single precision, 8
Spline, 237
Stability (*see* Instability)
Steffensen iteration, 54, 56, 61
  algorithm, 54
  program, 55
Successive displacement (*see* Gauss-Seidel iteration)
Synthetic division, 67

Tabulated function, 214
Taylor polynomial, 223

Taylor series, truncated, 23, 57, 222, 226, 266, 271, 309, 326, 327, 330, 358
   for functions of two variables, 25, 85, 336, 384
Taylor's algorithm, 327ff., 336, 339
Taylor's formula with (integral) remainder, 23
   (*See also* Taylor series, truncated)
Telescoping of power series, 267
Termination criterion, 35, 40, 42, 163, 169
Three-term recurrence relation, 250
Total pivoting, 126
Trace of a matrix, 109
Trapezoid rule, 287, 304, 313
   composite, 293
   corrected (*see* Corrected trapezoid rule)
   program, 294–295

Triangle inequality, 144, 149
Triangular factorization, 127ff.
   program, 132–133
Tridiagonal (*see* Matrix)
Truncation error (*see* Discretization error)
Two-point boundary-value problems, 373ff.

Underflow, 8
Unit vector, 98
Unstable, 14
Upper-triangular, 94

Weakly unstable, 361
Wronskian, 320

Zeitgeist, 396